D1291675

THE PARIETAL LOBES

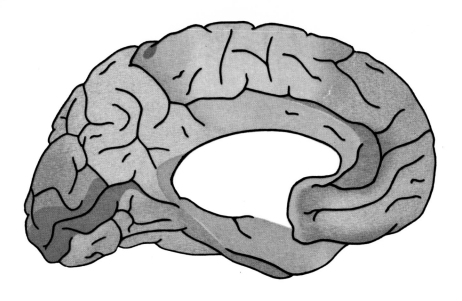

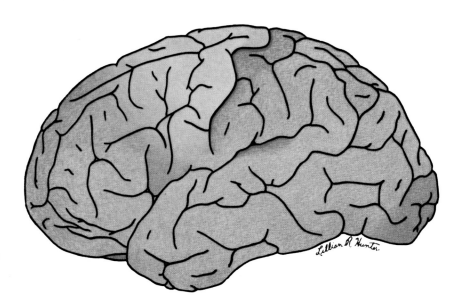

Regions of the cerebral cortex, according to Bailey.

Blue	= allocortex	Brown	= parakoniocortex
Pink	= eulaminate isocortex	Green	= mesocortex
Dark red	= koniocortex	Orange	= dysgranular cortex
Grey	= areas with large cells within the third layer		
Yellow	= agranular regions		
Mauve	= transition zones between the allocortex and the eulaminate isocortex		

(Reproduced by courtesy of Dr. Percival Bailey,
Rev. Neurol., 1950, **82**, 3–20.)

THE
PARIETAL LOBES

BY

MACDONALD CRITCHLEY
M.D., F.R.C.P.

Neurologist, King's College Hospital.
Physician, National Hospital for Nervous Diseases,
Queen Square, London.
Dean, Institute of Neurology.

QP
385
C7
1966

(*facsimile of 1953 edition*)

19 66

HAFNER PUBLISHING COMPANY
NEW YORK   LONDON

Originally Published 1953
Reprinted 1966

Printed and Published by
HAFNER PUBLISHING COMPANY, INC.
31 East 10th Street
New York, N.Y. 10003

Library of Congress Card Catalogue Number 66-18174

INTRODUCTION

" There is sometimes a compulsion in the selection of a subject, against which it is not wise to strive. That which I now submit to your consideration has, for some time, pressed on my thought too persistently to permit me to use this opportunity in any other way." These arresting sentences of Sir William Gowers would not be inappropriate today as an introduction to a survey of parietal symptomatology. The subject is topical, and has become of wide appeal. There was a time, however, when the theme had a purely regional allure, and we recall an American comment to the effect that a visitor to the pre-war neurological centres in Europe might be tempted to remember the Psychiatric Clinic of Vienna as a " Posterior Parietal Lobe Institute ". Today, something very similar has even been said of the National Hospital, Queen Square. It is largely to the efficient co-operation of a large number of House Officers, Registrars and Clinical Clerks (too numerous to name) that this present monograph owes its origin, and also to the courteous interest of my colleagues who have generously invited me to see and examine some of their cases and to quote them, if desired.

The present wide interest in the parietal lobes mainly results from a happy conjunction of numerous and diversified researches in the spheres of neurology and psychology. It will soon pass, no doubt, but the problem of cerebral localization will have gained a good deal from this world-wide focusing of attention. Perhaps it is not sufficiently realized that the parietal lobes are empirical conceptions rather than autonomous entities in the anatomical or physiological sense. Consequently, there is something essentially artificial about a full-dress discussion limited to a sector of the cerebral hemisphere. For this reason, it is tempting to predict that this present monograph, though one of the first to be devoted to the subject of parietal symptomatology, may well be the last. Subsequent writers will probably approach the problem of cerebral function from a wider angle.

A fairly comprehensive list of references is given at the end of the book, arranged according to chapter-headings. Although by nature sceptical of bibliographies—being annoyed by the inadequate ones, and suspicious of the elaborate ones—the author believes that many neurologists will find useful at any rate this section of the book. Great care has been taken to record all references accurately, for it has been found only too often that medical literature is on the whole deplorably weak in this respect. After these strictures, one is conscious of having taken up a vulnerable position, but the stern necessity for preparing always a bibliography without blemish should never be forgotten.

Many grateful acknowledgments are due to gracious help received at many hands. To Professor John Kirk and to my friend and colleague, Dr. Samuel Nevin, in particular, whose criticisms and factual aid have been generously given, but who are in no way responsible for any distortions which I may have perpetrated. To Dr. C. Kalanova, G.M., I have been indebted for much assistance in unravelling the continental literature on the subject. Dr. M. Reinhold has been most helpful, both in her clinical investigation of patients upon my service, and in her shrewd and philosophical understanding of the problems entailed. For the forbearance and co-operation of my very efficient Ward Sister, Miss Magnússon, I am indeed grateful. My loyal and assiduous secretaries, Miss Doreen Brown and Mrs. Eileen Smith, have had much to endure, but they have done so willingly and well. Some of the costs entailed in my studies of parietal symptomatology have been defrayed by grants from the Research Advisory Committee of the Institute of Neurology.

CONTENTS

PLATE IN COLOUR

CHAPTER I

ANATOMICAL CONSIDERATIONS

Though it be, of course, meet and right that Anatomy should not be the handmaid of Medicine, it cannot, nevertheless, be denied, on the other hand, that she would do well to present the results of her enquiries—with the increase in value of which she is chiefly concerned—in such shape as will promote their utilization ; but it is specially in the present instance that the egoism of the anatomist is almost greater than his love for his neighbour.

ECKER, 1873.

Comparative anatomy

A parietal region first appears in those lower mammalia where traces of a neopallium can be discovered, as distinct from the predominantly archipallial type of olfactory brain. Even in some of the macrosmatic species, gyrencephaly can be said to show itself in the development of a rhinal fissure. This separates the olfactory from the non-olfactory regions of the brain. In rather more advanced types of mammalia, that part of the brain lying caudal to the rhinal fissure becomes faintly convoluted, and shows evidence of primitive temporal and occipital lobes. This development coincides with the increasing use which the mammal (e.g. rabbit) begins to make of auditory and visual impressions, in addition to its still keenest faculty,

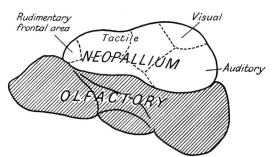

Fig. 1. Left cerebral hemisphere of the jumping shrew (*Macroscelides*).
The anterior part of the tactile area represents the " motor area " (after Elliot Smith).

namely, that of smell. At this same stage, one can also discern the beginnings of a corpus callosum.

The larger mammals are endowed with a greater degree of gyrencephaly. The coronal sulcus—precursor of the central sulcus —separates a primitive motor area from a coronal gyrus, which is mainly concerned with the reception of deep sensory impulses. A

I   B

rapidly increasing complexity of structure is built up around a sylvian
sulcus in association with a developing temporal lobe. This merges
behind into a laterally placed visual cortex. At this stage in the
mammalian ascent, therefore, we find a fairly large pyriform lobe, a
motor area, a small sensory area and fairly large auditory and visual
areas. The cerebrum of the dog, though pre-eminently macrosmatic,
is well convoluted. A frontal lobe can be identified, made up of the

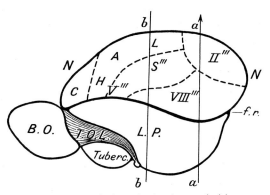

Fig. 2. A map of the cortical territories in a primitive mammal (left
lateral aspect of hemisphere).

II''', The visual area. *VIII'''*, The auditory area. *S'''*, Tactile area. *V'''*, The
trigeminal tactile area. *H*, *A*, *L*, The motor area ; *H*, head ; *A*, arm ; *L*, leg. *L.P.*,
Lobus pyriformis. *T.O.L.*, Tractus olfactorius lateralis. *Tuberc.*, Tuberculum olfactorium.
B.O., Bulbous olfactorius. (After Elliot Smith.)

crucial, sigmoid, coronal, presylvian and frontal formations, the coronal
gyrus being concerned with the reception of deep sensory impulses.
A temporal lobe can be recognized (in a complex made up of sylvian,
posterior ectosylvian, polar and posterior suprasylvian formations),
while an auditory area is identifiable within the posterior sylvian
gyrus. In carnivora, the parietal lobe comprises the coronal, anterior
sylvian, ectosylvian, middle ectosylvian, suprasylvian and lateral gyri
(Papez).

Associated with the occasional use of the forelimbs for purposes
other than pure locomotion (as, for example, in the bear), and with
a trend towards arboreal habits, the cortex expands particularly in
the regions immediately caudal to the coronal sulcus, where the presylvian and anterior ectosylvian gyri become more and more buried.
Thus we see the beginnings of opercularization of an insula. But it
is in the arboreal mammals (tree-shrews, lemurs and especially the
lower primates) that the parietal area shows its most conspicuous
advancement. This rather sudden parietal elaboration concerns
mainly the upper and anterior region of the sensory cortex, for the
postero-inferior development is delayed until a later stage. The

expansion is, however, sufficient to crowd the purely visual cortex backwards and the auditory area downwards.

Parietal expansion is not the only feature of the arboreal brain, for frontal lobe development is also conspicuous. A rapid increase, moreover, takes place in fibre-structure, particularly in respect of the complex intercommunications between one part of the brain and another, as well as between identical parts of the two hemispheres. This last-named is readily discerned in the growth of the commissures. Whereas there are three main commissural tracts in the lower mammals, approximately equal in size, the middle commissure begins to attain relative preponderance in structure and function, and so forms the conspicuous mass of the corpus callosum. Even here, there is an uneven degree of development. The most forward portion, or genu, for long remains far bulkier than the middle and hindmost thirds (the body and splenium respectively). With the increasing complexity of the parietal regions, however, the body of the corpus callosum becomes larger, although never—not even in man—attaining the thickness of the genu and the splenium.

We may summarize the expansion of the parietal region of the brain during the ascent from macrosmatic to arboreal animals, and

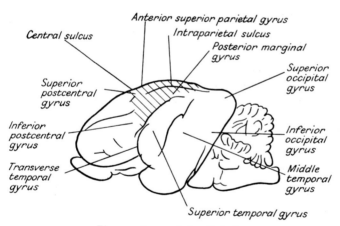

Fig. 3. Lemur (after Papez).

thence to primates, as follows : (1) a retrocoronal area for the reception of deep sensibility (which may become incorporated later within the frontal lobe) ; (2) a cortical expansion of the trigeminal sensory zone ; (3) a sensory expansion in the cortical projection of the manual or fore-paw region ; (4) later, the beginnings of inferior postcentral gyrus ; (5) later, a superior parietal lobule ; (6) still later, a marginal gyrus ; then (7) a more posteriorly situated angular gyrus, and finally, and in man alone, (8) a postparietal gyrus.   These last three, namely, the marginal, angular, and postparietal gyri, constitute in man the inferior parietal lobule.

In primates, the parietal lobe is roughly speaking made up of the cortex which lies behind the central sulcus (earlier called the coronal sulcus) and dorsal to the sylvian fissure (made up of a fusion of the middle suprasylvian, anterior ectosylvian and circular sulci).   The

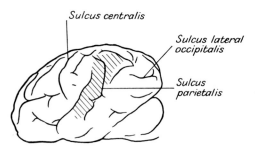

Fig. 4.   Gibbon (after Elliot Smith).

posterior limit is the paroccipital sulcus within the depths of the *Affenspalte*.   The primate parietal lobe thus comprises postcentral, superior and middle parietal, marginal and angular gyri.   On the medial aspect of the hemisphere, the parietal lobe of the primate is made up of the precuneal gyrus, the posterior part of the paracentral gyrus, and the splenial gyrus.

The simian brain can be studied in its simplest form in the *cebida*

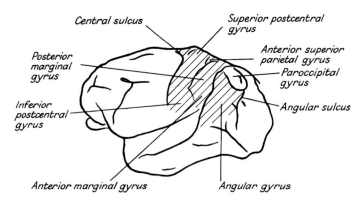

Fig. 5.   *Cebus capucinus.*

or *New World monkey* (see Fig. 5).   The superior parietal and precuneal regions are poorly developed.   The *Affenspalte* is superficially placed, having no operculum.   The superior parietal gyrus is fused with the superior postcentral gyrus. There is an inferior postcentral sulcus only, except in the *lagothrix* where a superior post-central sulcus is also to be found. The anterior limb of the marginal

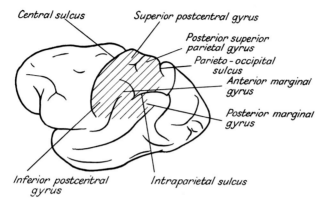

Fig. 6. *Lagothrix* (after Papez).

gyrus joins in the ventral half of the postcentral gyrus (as well as with part of the precentral gyrus) to form an operculum over the insula. The inferior parietal gyrus is made up of a large marginal gyrus and a narrower angular gyrus. It is possible that the detailed

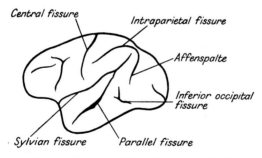

Fig. 7. *Macacus sinicus* (Bonnet monkey).

conformation of the angular and marginal gyri, so variable from one species to another within the *cebidae*, is to be associated with the varying degree of development of the thumb. All the *cebidae*, be it noted, possess prehensile tails.

In the *baboon*, the parietal area is relatively small, especially as regards the superior parietal gyrus. There is a well-marked intra-parietal sulcus which is confluent in front with the inferior postcentral sulcus (as in man). Little or no superior postcentral sulcus can be seen. The marginal and angular gyri join to form a T-shaped pattern which is typical of the primate brain.

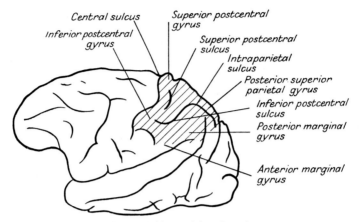

Fig. 8.   Baboon (after Papez).

The brain of the *anthropoid* apes (*orang, chimpanzee, gorilla*) shows important developments. The postcentral gyrus here forms a curved vertical structure, the upper third of which is believed to relate to the lower limbs, the middle third to the upper limbs and the lower third

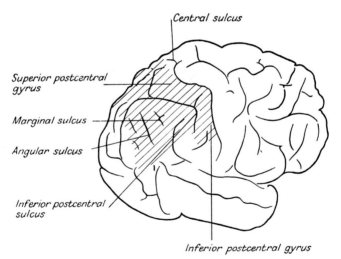

Fig. 9.   Orang (after Papez).

to the head. At the lower extremity, the pre- and postcentral gyri are connected by the transverse postcentral sulcus in the opercular margin. Though this conformation is the rule in apes, it is unstable in man, especially in the right hemisphere. The superior postcentral sulcus is now a well-marked structure, as in man. The superior parietal gyrus

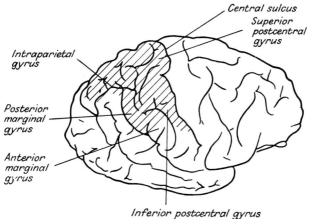

Fig. 10.   Chimpanzee (after Papez).

is divisible into a superior and a middle region, by a superior parietal sulcus, which may even join the angular sulcus. Thus, a conspicuous middle (or oblique) parietal gyrus is often present. The posterior end of the intraparietal sulcus ends in the anterior occipital gyrus. The

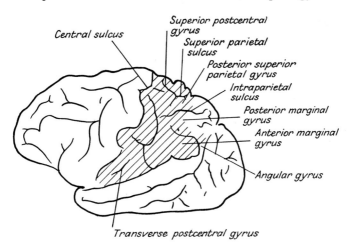

Fig. 11.   Gorilla (after Papez).

marginal and angular gyri present a characteristic T-shaped formation, but posteriorly and inferiorly the angular gyrus shows a good deal of variability, especially in its relationship with the *Affenspalte* and the upturned temporal gyri.

The anatomy of the cerebral hemispheres has been studied recently in very great detail by Bonin and Bailey as regards the *macaca mulatta* and in

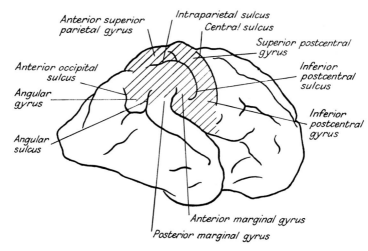

Fig. 12.　Human foetus (7-month).

the chimpanzee by Bailey, Bonin and McCulloch. These various observers have investigated with great thoroughness the fissural pattern, the architectonics and the fibre-connections of the various cortical regions.

The parietal lobe in man

The arbitrary limits of the human parietal lobe are nowadays generally agreed as follows :

Anteriorly, the central sulcus (fissure [1] of Rolando) forms a well-marked anatomical frontier. In 80–90 per cent of cases, the fissure does not intersect the lateral sulcus (or sylvian fissure), but ends in the white matter of the frontal operculum. Therefore, in order to complete the anterior boundary of the parietal lobe, it is necessary to

[1] A word becomes necessary concerning terminology, and the use of the words " sulcus " and " fissure ". In 1888, Broca spoke of those furrows which divide the various cerebral lobes from each other as " fissures ", while " sulci " were applied to the furrows occurring within a lobe. He defined fissures as *Totalfurchen*, or folds within the pallium as a whole, and sulci as *Rindenfurchen*, that is to say, folds within the cortex itself. Elliot Smith (1902) desired that " fissures " should be used to distinguish the neopallium from other pallial areas. Herrick used the terms differently, but the general usage is nowadays to employ both terms almost interchangeably. Moreover, when sulcus is used, gyrus is the appropriate Latin term, while convolution is associated with the English term fissure. In this account of the parietal lobes, the B.N.A. terminology will be used as consistently as possible throughout.

Table 1

THE GYRI AND SULCI OF THE PARIETAL REGION IN MAMMALIA

	Carnivora	Primates	Man
1. *Gyri :*	Coronal	Inferior postcentral	Postcentral
	Anterior ectosylvian	Superior postcentral	
	Lateral	Anterior superior parietal	Superior parietal lobule
		Posterior superior parietal	
	Middle suprasylvian	Anterior marginal	Supramarginal
		Posterior marginal	
	Posterior suprasylvian	Angular	Angular
	Ectolateral	Parieto-occipital	
2. *Sulci :*	Ansate	Superior postcentral ⎫	
	Lateral	Intraparietal ⎪	Interparietal
	Parietal	Superior parietal ⎬	(or intraparietal)
	Diagonal	Transverse postcentral ⎭	
		Marginal	Sylvian (lateral)
	Ectolateral	Angular	First temporal
	Posterior lateral	Anterior occipital	
	Supracalcarine	Transverse occipital	
		Paroccipital	

draw a short imaginary line vertically downwards. In Asiatics, however, it is usual for the central sulcus to terminate within the depths of the lateral sulcus.

The upper limit of the parietal lobe is naturally marked by the supero-medial border between the convex outer surface and the flat medial surface. Posteriorly, one again hypothecates a vertical line descending from the external parieto-occipital sulcus as it cuts the convex surface. This imaginary line is drawn vertically downwards as far as the edge separating the convex outer surface and the basal surface of the temporal and occipital lobes. At the lower end, it terminates in a blunt indentation, more easily seen in children's brains—the *preoccipital notch,* a point which corresponds with the bend of the sigmoid sinus.

Most indeterminate of all is the lower margin of the parietal lobe for which no natural frontier can be identified. One usually imagines a horizontal line drawn forwards from this point until it reaches the central sulcus (or its downward extension), or until it meets the posterior horizontal limb of the lateral sulcus, or more precisely, till it meets the lateral sulcus at its final point of angulation. This imaginary horizontal line separates the lower parietal from the upper temporal regions.

Lastly, on the medial aspect of the brain, the parietal lobe is generally regarded as ending below in the postlimbic sulcus, below which lies the *cingulate (or pericallosal) gyrus*. More accurately perhaps, the medial surface of the parietal lobe can, with its most inferior

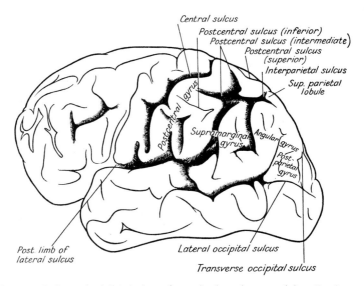

Fig. 13. Left cerebral hemisphere from the lateral aspect (after Symington).

part, be regarded as a component of the limbic area (archipallial rhinencephalon). The medial surface of the parietal lobe, therefore, comprises anteriorly the narrow posterior part of the paracentral lobule and, behind that, the *precuneus*, or *quadrate lobule of Foville*. The boundaries of this latter are the superomedial border, the upturned end of the cingulate sulcus in front, the internal parieto-occipital sulcus behind and the subparietal (i.e. postlimbic) sulcus below.

It must be admitted, therefore, that the boundaries of the parietal lobe are not altogether satisfactory and that the exact surface-area is often a matter of conjecture.

The underlying white matter of the parietal lobe is delimited within the depths of the hemisphere by the thalamus. This observation leads us to the difference in conception held by the pure anatomist and by the neurological clinician respectively when discussing the parietal lobe. To the former, the parietal lobe is mainly a cortical quadrilateral with established boundaries, albeit rather artificial. Such a conception is really an areal, or two-dimensional one. The clinician, on the other hand, brings in the notion of depth as made up of the white matter below the cortex. Thus, the parietal lobe becomes a three-dimensional structure, irregularly wedge-shaped. Its base is formed by the convex surface of the parietal region, and its blunted apex abuts upon the superior border of the thalamus.

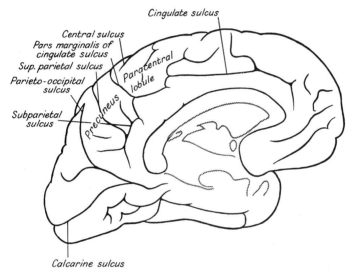

Fig. 14. Left cerebral hemisphere from the mesial aspect (after Symington).

Between these boundaries lies the white matter, with its complicated fibre-structure. This three-dimensional conception is an attractive one, for it readily fits into the modern clinical and physiological views upon cerebral localization " in depth ". It leaves a number of anatomical points still in the air, however, as, for example, the relationship between the parietal lobe and the internal, external and extreme capsules, the corpus striatum, the insula and the claustrum. Questions as to exactly where these structures belong in reference to the parietal lobe need to be answered authoritatively.

Subdivision of the parietal lobe according to gyri and sulci

The closer one examines the convolutional pattern of a large series of brains, and especially when one takes into consideration secondary and tertiary gyri, the more difficult is the task of identifying one's landmarks.

The central sulcus (fissure of Rolando) is usually described as made up of two flexures, the *superior genu*, with its concavity forwards, and the *inferior genu*, with its convexity forwards. The former comprises the upper two-thirds of the sulcus, and it is separated from the latter by a well-marked annectant gyrus (the inferior frontoparietal gyrus) which occasionally is visible on the surface. (Such a separation

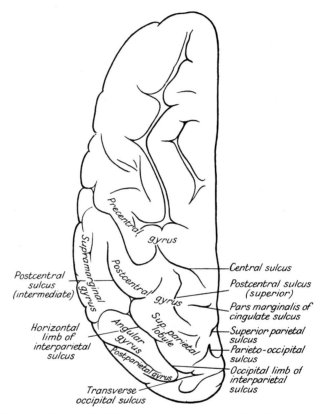

Fig. 15.   Left cerebral hemisphere from above (after Symington).

of upper from lower parts is the rule in the brain of the five months' foetus.)

Immediately posterior to this sulcus, and between it and the vertical limit of the interparietal (or intraparietal) sulcus (to be described later) lies the postcentral gyrus (or ascending parietal convolution). This region is also at times spoken of in physiological terms as the " somestheto-sensory area ", or " primary sensory area ". Above, the gyrus is narrower than the corresponding part of the precentral gyrus. Medially, the postcentral gyrus constitutes the posterior and smaller part of the paracentral lobule. Below, this convolution helps to form the parietal operculum of the insula. Two small annectant gyri (*plis de passage transversaux*) bridge the gap between the pre- and postcentral gyri. One of these has already been mentioned, namely, the inferior frontoparietal gyrus (or Rolandic operculum). The other consists in the superior frontoparietal gyrus (or paracentral lobule). Occasionally, a small horizontal sulcus is found running transversely across the postcentral gyrus. Lowrey (1920) described this as a not infrequent occurrence in the brains of

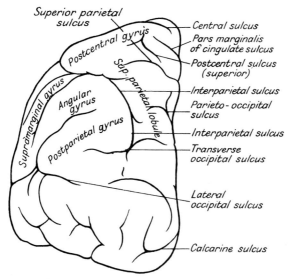

Fig. 16. Left cerebral hemisphere from behind (after Symington).

psychotics and he regarded this anomaly as the evidence of a loosely organized nervous system.

That region of the parietal lobe behind the postcentral gyrus is broken up by two sulci which are generally in contiguity. There is a vertical sulcus lying more anteriorly, and a horizontal sulcus. These may be spoken of as the " postcentral sulcus " and the " inter-parietal sulcus " respectively.

The interparietal sulcus (B.N.A.) (or *sillon parietal*) was originally described by Turner (1866), who termed it the *sulcus intraparietalis*. Some authors still prefer this term, but " interparietal " is now a more generally adopted expression. (" Intraparietal " is the term adopted nevertheless in the latest edition of Gray's *Anatomy*, and also in Bonin and Bailey's monograph.) The sulcus was originally described as a sort of arch, with its convexity upwards, traversing the parietal lobe in a sagittal direction. Following the descriptions made by Jefferson (1913) and by Rosett (1933), it is now customary to associate this horizontal sulcus with the postcentral sulcus, and to isolate a more complex fissural pattern, comprising roughly the following :

(1) A horizontal ramus (the interparietal sulcus proper) ; also called the sulcus interparietalis of Ecker ;

(2) A vertical limb situated anteriorly and comprising actually the superior and inferior rami postcentralis (of Retzius), or the inferior retrocentral sulcus (of Kukenthal and Ziehen), and

(3) Posteriorly, a short vertical sulcus, the ramus occipitalis (sulcus paroccipitalis of Wilder), to which may be added the sulcus occipitalis transversus of Ecker (1869). (In apes, the interparietal sulcus ends quite differently, for it is abruptly terminated by the external perpendicular sulcus.)

Some anatomists affirm that the interparietal sulcus extends backwards beyond the limits of the parietal lobe, and ends as a *sulcus interoccipitalis*.

Cunningham, Retzius and Jefferson have each separately studied the variations in relationship of the first and second elements of this complex. That is to say, (2) may be interrupted into two limbs, an upper and a lower, either (or neither) of which may be in contact with the horizontal limb. Or the horizontal ramus (1) may not actually reach the vertical ramus (of the postcentral sulcus). Very rarely, the horizontal ramus may extend unduly forwards and intersect the postcentral gyrus (Fig. 17).

From an embryological point of view, the sulcus is late in development and in attaining a definitive morphological pattern. A short descending sulcus may be present extending downwards from the horizontal limb of the interparietal sulcus, cutting into the upper part of the grey matter of the supramarginal gyrus. This is spoken of as the " intermediate sulcus of Jensen ". At the age of six months of foetal life, the interparietal sulcus is in two parts—an anterior and a posterior (Cunningham). Turner (1948) has shown that the postcentral region, though surprisingly simple at the time of birth, becomes complex later in life. He also stated that, in early postuterine life, the brain pattern in the parietal region has shown considerable change. The interparietal sulcus has now " practically divided into three, so that it caps individually the sylvian, the superior temporal and the occipital anterior sulcus : . . . the superior postcentral sulcus has now joined the inferior postcentral and interparietal sulci ". Turner went on to state that between birth and the age of two years (and thereafter more slowly up to about ten years), there is a period of rapid expansion in the parietal lobe. The greater part of this development is attained by the age of six years. Jefferson set out the order of appearance of the various portions of the interparietal complex in embryological development, as (1) the sulcus postcentralis inferior; (2) the sulcus paroccipitalis ; (3) the ramus horizontalis of the interparietal fissure ; and (4) lastly, the sulcus postcentralis superior. The interparietal fissure is often interrupted by small transecting clefts, either superficial or deep, which are called the

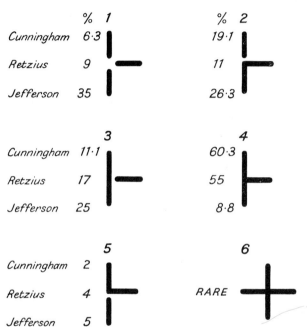

	% 1		% 2
Cunningham	6·3		19·1
Retzius	9		11
Jefferson	35		26·3

	3		4
Cunningham	11·1		60·3
Retzius	17		55
Jefferson	25		8·8

	5		6
Cunningham	2		
Retzius	4	RARE	
Jefferson	5		

Fig. 17. Modifications in the morphology of the sulcus interparietalis (or intra-parietalis), based upon the findings of Cunningham, Retzius and Jefferson.

" vertical fissures of Gromier ". One in particular ascends just in front of the parieto-occipital sulcus ; this is the " transverse parietal fissure " of Brissaud.

The interparietal sulcus divides the parietal lobe into a *superior parietal lobule* and an *inferior parietal lobule*. This fissure is relatively late in phylogenetic development, and this region of the brain, and more especially the lower portion, is a relatively " new " structure, liable to a considerable amount of morphological variation from one brain to another. As Ingalls (1914) suggested, such convolutional variability means, either that the structure has not yet attained full development, or else it is on the wane. Extraneous evidence favours the former idea.

Broca, Huxley and Turner have all spoken of the superior parietal lobule as the *postparietal lobule*. Small annectant gyri connect this region with the postcentral gyrus anteriorly, and the occipital lobe posteriorly. The superior parietal lobule is continued over on to the medial surface of the hemisphere, as the precuneus. Sometimes, a small fissure—the sulcus parietalis superior—runs vertically across the superior margin so as to appear on the outer or convex surface, and it may even reach the horizontal limb of the interparietal fissure.

Below the horizontal ramus of the interparietal fissure are a group of convolutions of great variability and no little complexity. Reduced to the simplest terminology, they can be said to constitute those convolutional regions which surround the terminations of (1) the lateral sulcus and (2) the superior temporal sulcus. Together (1) and (2) constitute the *inferior parietal lobule* of Ecker (also called the second parietal convolution), but individually they comprise the *supramarginal* and the *angular* gyri respectively. This differentiation within the inferior parietal lobule again is essentially a primate, if not human, characteristic and finds no counterpart below the lower apes. These gyri are ill-developed even in the higher apes.

According to Jefferson, the *sulcus gyri angularis* described by Zuckerkandl is none other than the *sulcus occipitalis anterior* and this latter term should be used in preference to the former. This anterior occipital sulcus is the boundary line between the parietal lobule and Brodmann's " peristriate area "—or what Elliot Smith termed, rather indefinitely, the *area parieto-occipitalis*.

Small annectant gyri are said to connect the supramarginal gyrus with the first temporal gyrus (the first parietotemporal gyrus of Broca), and the angular gyrus is said to be bridged across to the second temporal gyrus by the second parietotemporal gyrus of Broca, and to the occipital lobe by the parieto-occipital gyrus of Gratiolet.

The status of these two gyri, i.e. supramarginal and angular, was for a time a matter of dispute. Although nowadays there is agreement in allocating them to the parietal region, early in the century Campbell maintained that they were really a part of the *regio temporalis*.

According to Jefferson, a small fissure may also lie between the supramarginal and the angular gyri, the *sulcus parietalis inferior*.

In the dominant hemisphere, the inferior parietal lobule (supramarginal and angular gyri) together with the posterior third of T.1, make up what is often termed by continental neuro-anatomists, " Wernicke's area ".

Buried within the depths of the lateral sulcus, there is a certain amount of concealed parietal cortex which constitutes the upper lip of the fissure, or the opercular surface. This region may be divided into anterior and posterior portions, the former of which lies opposed to the hinderpart of the insula. The inferior surface lies against the temporal lobe, with a ridge well marked in front. It comprises two or three small convolutions running transversely outwards. The posterior part of the operculum is variable and is made up of a few small gyri (see Fig. 18).

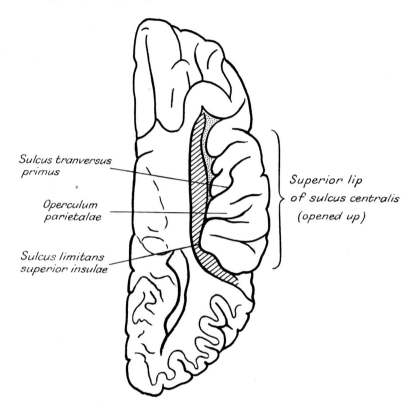

Sulcus tranversus primus

Operculum parietalae

Sulcus limitans superior insulae

Superior lip of sulcus centralis (opened up)

Fig. 18. The under aspect of the frontal and parietal lobes, showing the opercular surfaces of the superior frontal and the parietal opercula (after Symington).

The external parieto-occipital sulcus of Retzius—which forms the posterior limiting landmark of the parietal lobe—is surrounded by a U-shaped convolution (*arcus intercuneatus*—Elliot Smith) ; *lobulus parieto-occipitalis* (Retzius) ; *cuneolus* (Wilder) ; the *postparietal convolution* (Cunningham). The morphology is apt to be complicated. Originally a depression, or fossa, it deepens, and in this way the arcus intercuneatus becomes buried in the great majority of cases. This region undergoes considerable expansion in the transition from lower apes to man. Cunningham spoke of a " growth antagonism "

c

between the parietal and occipital regions, causing an opercularization of this area, where gradually, in the process of development, the anterior part expands more than the posterior.

Between the ramus marginalis of the cingulate sulcus and the medial portion of the parieto-occipital sulcus is the *precuneus* or *quadrate lobule*. This is bounded ventrally by the subparietal sulcus (or postlimbic fissure) which is really not a well-defined structure, but suggests a continuation backwards of the sulcus cinguli, beyond the point where it turns sharply upwards behind the paracentral lobule.

The complicated nature of the boundary zone between the parietal and occipital lobes is further enhanced by the problem of the *Affenspalte* or *sulcus lunatus* of Elliot Smith. In apes, this is a well-defined fissure which can also be easily identified in the human foetal brain as a deep infolding of the cortex—the *fissura perpendicularis externa*. Late in development, this becomes smoothed out, and in the adult human cerebrum it is sometimes affirmed that no trace of this simian (and foetal) sulcus can be identified. This is not invariably so, however, and Cunningham (1892) did not deny the possibility of its persisting in the adult brain, but at the same time he contended that it was not represented by Ecker's sulcus occipitalis transversus. This latter statement arose out of a belief expressed earlier by Wernicke (1875) that occasionally an operculum could be observed on the posterior lip of the sulcus transversus, and that this was the homologue of the sulcus lunatus. Using the argument of cyto-architectonics, however, von Economo asserted that Ecker's sulcus represented the adult human pattern of the *Affenspalte*.

Elliot Smith, who had coined the term sulcus lunatus because of its arc-like configuration, believed that it could at times be identified in the human brain and especially in the cerebra of prehistoric and primitive specimens (Kooy). He made the interesting observation that when present it was usually asymmetrical and that it was more commonly present in the left hemisphere than the right. This fact indicated, in his opinion, the beginnings of cerebral dominance.

Zuckerkandl (1904) discussed in even greater detail the problem of this simian sulcus. This writer distinguished an *Affenspalte* (or *sulcus simiarum*) from an *Affenspaltgrube* (or *fossa simiarum*). He believed that the sulcus lunatus was merely a component of the base of the fossa simiarum. Kappers apparently supported Zuckerkandl in this view, and he quoted many anatomists who had been able to identify the sulcus lunatus in human brains—not only in primitives or defectives—but also in normals, but particularly in those possessing an ateloid type of brain. However, because of the great development in man of the hinder part of the parietal lobe, pushing the occipital area more and more back, the sulcus lunatus usually becomes lost. When present, the sulcus lunatus really belongs to the territory of the occipital lobe and not to the " parietal lobe " area anatomically considered.

Connolly's recent study of the external configuration of the brain in man and primates has brought out some interesting points concerning the parietal lobes (1950). The human lateral fissure was usually longer in the left hemisphere than in the right, as first noted by Eberstaller : this leads to a certain asymmetry in the fissural patterns. Thus, the lower end of the postcentral sulcus is generally larger on the left side. The components of the inferior parietal lobule are more crowded together in the left hemisphere. The intraparietal (interparietal) sulcus proper bears a closer relationship to the inferior than to the superior postcentral sulcus. The anterior medial branch of the paroccipital sulcus is an important furrow which constitutes the forward limit of the arcus parieto-occipitalis ; it represents the processus acuminis of other primates. The anterior lateral branch seems to be of lesser importance and in many specimens it constitutes a continuation of the intraparietal sulcus proper. Into the inferior parietal lobule there ascend three rami which he designates A1, A2 and A3 (representing respectively the superior parallel sulcus, derived from the superior temporal sulcus ; the sulcus angularis and the anterior occipital (preoccipital) sulcus). Wang and Kappers had named these three small sulci " ascending ramus I, II and III " respectively. Much variability in morphology was found to exist in this region of the brain.

The parietal lobe as the cortical expansion of the thalamus

It is impossible to avoid the important conclusion that the cerebral cortex, as the representative of the neopallium, is in close connection with deeper structures, and in particular with the thalamus. Although much of our knowledge of this matter derives from animal extirpation experiments, some of our facts are garnered, as far as the human brain goes, by the surgical procedure of prefrontal leucotomy. According to Bonin, the human cerebral hemisphere can be equated with the thalamus in the following manner :

Thalamic nucleus	Cerebral cortex
Nucleus dorsalis medius	regio frontalis
Nucleus ventralis	regio centralis
Nucleus pulvinar ⎱ Nucleus lateralis posterior⎰	REGIO PARIETALIS
Nucleus geniculatis lateralis	regio occipitalis
Nucleus geniculatis medialis	regio supratemporalis

Bailey pointed out that the regio temporalis of the cerebral cortex has no thalamic connection, and that the hippocampus and pyriform lobe possess olfactory connections. Moreover, the perifalciform region has important respiratory functions and the operculum is associated with gustatory representations. Hence, to isolate the regio parietalis and to associate it with the pulvinar and the postero-lateral region of the thalamus (the geniculate bodies excepted), is a logical method of demarcation, so long as the regio parietalis of the histologist can be shown to correspond adequately with the current anatomical convention as to the confines of the parietal lobe. More-over, a delimitation of corticothalamic sectors promises to offer a logical method of parcellating the parietal lobe (or region) according to groupings of thalamic cells—or actual subnuclei. Such a method of point-to-point representation would offer a preferable system to that of isolating individual gyri or subgyri.

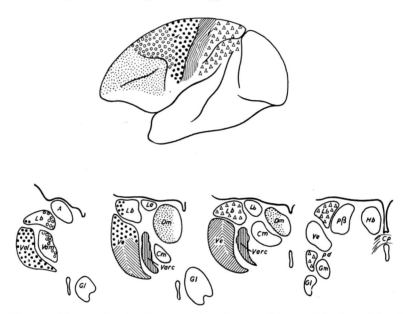

Fig. 19.   Diagram showing the connections between different thalamic nuclei and
different cortical areas.

Fine dots = area frontalis granularis (areas 8 and 9); coarse dots = motor area (area 4); circles = area frontalis agranularis (area 6); hatching = area post centralis (areas 1, 2 and 3); triangles = post sensory areas of the parietal cortex (areas 5, 7, 18 and 19). (Courtesy of Le Gros Clark and Boggon.)

In the case of the monkey, such a method of parcellation would seem to be possible. This study really dates from the work of Monakow (1882) and of the Dejerines (1901). Le Gros Clark and Boggon (1935) found that the postsensory regions of the parietal lobe (i.e. areas 5, 7, 18 and 19) receive fibres from the caudal half of the lateral nucleus (*Lb*), mainly from its posterior extremity and also from the nucleus *pd* (area intergeniculata) of the pulvinar. It would appear that *Lb* is related to areas 5 and 7, while *pd* projects on the area 18 or area 19 or both. The area postcentralis of the parietal

Plate I

GRAFTON ELLIOT SMITH

lobe receives fibres entirely from the pars externa of the ventral nucleus (see Fig. 19). Earl Walker (1938) also studied the cells of origin and areas of destination of the thalamocortical tracts. His findings correlate well with those subsequently made by Peele (1942).

Unfortunately, we must admit that the so-called regio parietalis may not be absolutely identical with the arbitrary " parietal lobe " of the anatomist, though the points of difference are not very great. More serious objection to any conception of the " parietal lobe " as coterminous with the regio parietalis (or caudal expansion of certain parts of the thalamic complex) is that in man there is probably an intermingling of fibres, which would cause point-to-point correspondence difficult to identify. Particularly is this the case when we realize that in juxtaposition with the thalamoparietal fibres there must lie a complex of corticofugal fibres, as well as corticocortical associational and commissural tracts.

The composition of these parietofugal fibres should be studied more closely. Their nature in man is relatively unknown, but we have a series of comparative studies available which deal with efferent fibres from the parietal lobe in monkeys. Monakow (1915) had suggested that a small component of the pyramidal tract in man and lower animals had its origin in the parietal lobe. Minkowski (1924) found parietofugal fibres in the macacque : some were commissural, passing via the corpus callosum to corresponding contralateral parietal areas : some passed as short associational fibres to contiguous parts of the ipsilateral cortex. But many were projectional in type, and traversed the internal capsule to the thalamus, the lateral half of the cerebral peduncle, the locus niger, the grey matter of the pons, and descending alongside the pyramidal tract, even extended as far as the lumbar region of the spinal cord.

By tracing the course of degenerating fibres, Biemond (1930) confirmed the presence of projectional components in one macacque, passing from the parietal region to the pons, pulvinar and superior colliculus. (It may be objected, however, that this monkey did not sustain a clear-cut parietal lesion.) Mettler (1935) traced parietofugal fibres into the subcortical nuclei in *macaca mulatta*. Le Gros Clark and Boggon (1935) found something similar in the *macacus rhesus*, though here again the parietal injury was not strictly an isolated one. Sakuma (1937) found that area 7 projected fibres, in macacques, into the lateral parts of the thalamus, peduncle and locus niger ; and into the pontine grey matter and the pyramidal. Uesugi (1937) traced fibres from areas 1 and 2, in various types of macacques, through the internal and external capsules, into the ventral and lateral thalamic nuclei, locus niger, peduncle, pons, and also into the corticospinal tracts on both sides. Sunderland (1940) identified in macacques a large parietal constituent within the lateral half of the cerebral peduncle running to the pontine grey substance—a few fibres passing further caudally into the medulla.

The most searching study upon this problem has been made by Peele, who performed parietal topectomies, or cortical ablations, in nine monkeys (*macaca mulatta*). Brodmann's cytoarchitectonic map of *cercopithecus* was followed and his five areas were found to apply adequately in these macacques. By concentrating upon small parietal areas or areal combinations, Peele found that each parietal area sent associational fibres to other parietal areas. The more anterior parietal areas (3, 1, 2) sent fibres to the precentral gyrus of the frontal lobe. Areas 5, 7 and possibly 3 sent fibres to the anterior occipital gyri. Area 5 connected with the adjacent part of the callosomarginal gyrus. Some fibres from areas 3, 1, 2 and 7 passed to the rostral part of the superior temporal gyrus (via the external and extreme capsules). Part of the posterior part of area 7 communicated with the posterior half of the superior temporal gyrus. Commissural fibres connected homologous parietal areas. But in addition, area 3 of one side connected with areas 3, 1, 2 and 4 ; areas 1 and 2 connected with areas 1, 2, 3 and 4 ; area 5 connected with areas 5, 3, 2, 1 and 4 ; and area 7 connected with areas 7, 5, 2 and 1.

Parietal projectional fibres proved to be both complex and important. Peele described them thus :

Table 2

DISTRIBUTION OF PARIETOFUGAL PATHWAYS

Pathways	Destination
Parietothalamic	dorsal thalamic nuclei
Parietotectal ⎫ Parietopretectal ⎬ Parietonigral ⎭	midbrain
Parietopontine	medulla
Parietospinal	cord

Speaking about the parietothalamic connections, Peele specified that all parietal areas connect with the thalamic nuclei lateralis posterior, ventralis posterolateralis, and ventralis posteromedialis. Fibres from rostral parietal areas terminate rostrally in the nuclei. Area 5 sends a few fibres to the nucleus medialis dorsalis. (These thalamic nuclei are the same as those which, according to Walker, give origin to thalamoparietal connections.)   The parietospinal fibres traverse the pyramids ; most of them decussate, though not all. Area 3, areas 1–2, and, to a lesser extent, area 5 project to lumbar cord levels of the opposite side ; area 7 sends fibres to cervical levels only ; area 3 sends a few fibres to ipsilateral lumbar cord levels. Peele suggested that the parietospinal fibres arise from cells of the external and internal pyramidal laminae ; that the parietothalamic fibres arise from the fusiform lamina (while the cells of the internal granular lamina receive thalamocortical and intraregional association fibres).

According to Minkowski (1949) ablation of the parietal convolutions (Brodmann's areas 5 and 7) in the macacque, produced retrograde degeneration in the posterior extremity of the ventrolateral nucleus.   Extirpation of the ascending parietal cortex (Brodmann's areas 1 and 3) was followed by degeneration of an extensive part of

Table 3

MACACA MULATTA

LATERAL PULVINAR	
Anterior dorsal part	⎧ medial surface of parietal lobe ⎨ posterior part of superior parietal lobule ⎩ depth of the interparietal sulcus
Anterior ventral part	⎰ posteromedial part of superior parietal lobule ⎱ depth of interparietal sulcus
Posterior dorsal part	⎰ depth of sylvian fissure ⎱ ventral prestriate cortex
Posterior ventral part	temporo-occipital region
MEDIAL PULVINAR	
Anterior part	(not known)
Posterior part	lateral surface of temporal lobe
INFERIOR PULVINAR	
Dorsal part	prestriate region
Ventral part	temporo-occipital region

(After Kao Liang Chow.)

the ventrolateral nucleus, and of the posterior segment of the ventromedian nucleus.   Ablation of the superior and inferior parietal lobules (Brodmann's areas 5 and 7) and of the postparietal region (areas 18 and 19) produced degeneration in the pulvinar.

Kao Liang Chow (1950) has also studied the parietothalamic

connections in the monkey (*macaca mulatta*). According to him the anterior dorsal part of the nucleus pulvinaris lateralis projects to the medial surface of the parietal lobe, the hind part of the superior parietal lobule and the deepest parts of the interparietal sulcus. The anterior ventral part is linked up to the posteromedial part of the parietal lobule and the depths of the interparietal sulcus also ; the posterior ventral part projects, however, to the deepest regions of the sylvian fissure and the ventral prestriate cortex ; while the posterior ventral part is associated with the temporo-occipital region.

The problem is less involved in the case of the lower mammals. Gerebtzoff (1937), basing his conclusions upon the anatomy of the nervous system in the rabbit, laid down his " three principles of thalamocortical projection " as follows : (1) each thalamic nucleus has a field limited to one of Brodmann's architectonic areas ; (2) antero-posterior systematization of the cortex corresponds to anteroposterior systematization of the nucleus ; and (3) inferosuperior systematization of the cortex corresponds to mediolateral systematization of the nucleus. On this foundation, he constructed a schematic diagram of the rabbit's brain. Lashley believed that the problem was not so simple in the case of the rodent brain. In 1939, Stoffels added a fourth principle, or the " principle of lamellation ", to the effect that the fibres retain their relative positions in the path from the nucleus to the cortical field, without crossing or intermingling. Waller (1934) had already affirmed that the thalamic nuclei which are contiguous are also represented in cortical areas which are contiguous. Lashley (1941) studied the problem in rats, and found an accurate correspondence of the sensory nuclei of the thalamus with the cortical area, except in the case of the medial geniculate body. The cortical distribution corresponded roughly with the cytoarchitectonic fields.

Thickness of the parietal cortex

One of the first attempts at analysing the structure of the cerebral cortex was founded upon the basis of the varying degrees of thickness. Economo's chart (see Fig. 20) demonstrates that the grey matter is thinnest over the poles of the hemispheres, and thickest just in front of and behind the central sulcus. In addition, there are other differences, in that the cortex tends universally to be broader over the summits of the gyri and narrower in the depths of the fissures. According to Economo, this convolutional difference may be as great as 50 per cent.

The parietal area is found to be variable in regard to its thickness.

Most anteriorly, the postcentral gyrus attains a thickness of only 2 mm. or less, while the remaining portions of the parietal lobe are broader.

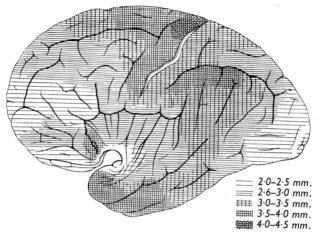

2·0–2·5 mm.
2·6–3·0 mm.
3·0–3·5 mm.
3·5–4·0 mm.
4·0–4·5 mm.

Fig. 20. Thickness of the cortex according to Economo.

Table 4

		mm.
Parietal lobe	Paracentral lobuli	3·6–4·0
	Posterior lip of the central sulcus	2·0–2·5
	Postcentral gyrus	3·0–3·5
	Superior parietal lobule	2·6–3·0
	Precuneus	2·6–3·0
	Upper part of inferior parietal lobule	3·6–4·0
	Lower part of angular and supramarginal gyri	3·0–2·5
Frontal lobe	Precentral convolution, upper	4·0–4·5
	lower	3·6–4·0
	Frontal lobe, posterior	3·0–3·5
	anterior	2·6–3·0
	Frontal pole	2·0–2·5
Temporal lobe	Temporal pole	4·0–4·5
	Superior temporal convolution, middle	2·6–3·0
	inferior	3·0–3·5
Occipital lobe	Occipital pole	2·0
	Parieto-occipital area, posterior	2·0–2·5
	anterior	2·6–3·0

Economo has also set out in the following table his findings as to thickness of cortex in various regions of the brain :

Thickness of the Cortex in mm. over the
Convolutions of the Principal Areas

Area	Thickness in mm.	Area	Thickness in mm.	Area	Thickness in mm.
F𝒜	4,5−3.5	F𝒟L	2,8−2,6	T𝒜	3,0−2,8
F𝐵	4,0−3.2	F𝒟ₚ	2,5−2,4	T𝐵	3,0−2.9
F𝒞	3,4−2.6	P𝒜₁	2,2−2,0	T𝒞	2,9−2,7
F𝒟	3,0−2,4	P𝒜₂	2,8−2,5	T𝒟	2,8−2,7
F𝒢	2,6−2,3	P𝐵₁, P𝐵₂	2,2−1,9	T𝒢	3,6−3,2
F𝑓	3,2−2,7	P𝒞	3,3−3,0	T𝑓	3,1−2,9
F𝒮	2,4−2,0	P𝒟	2,4−2,2	T𝒮	3,8−3,2
F𝓗	2,8−2,5	P𝒢	3,0−2,8	L𝒜	2,9−2,6
F𝒥	3,5−3,1	P𝑓	3,6−3,1	L𝒞	3,0−2,7
F𝒥̇	2,5−0,5	P𝒮	3,4−3,0	L𝒟	2,4−2,2
F𝓛	2,5−1,8	P𝓗	3,0−2,5	L𝒞	2,3−2,0−0,4
F𝓜	1.8−0.4	I𝒜	3,1−2,9	H𝒜	3.0−2.8
F𝓝	1,0−0.3	I𝐵	3,0−2,8	H𝐵	2,9−2,6
F𝐵𝒞ₘ	3,2−3,0	O𝒜	2,6−2,3	H𝒞	2,7−2,4
F𝒟I'	2,6−2,4	O𝐵	2.2−1.8	H𝒟	2,4−2,2
F I	2,9−2,7	O𝒞	2,3−1,8	H𝒞	3,0−1,2

Fig. 21.

Area of the parietal cortex

The total surface of the cerebral cortex has been computed as somewhere between 170,000 sq. mm. (Baillarger ; Paulier) and 200,000 sq. mm. (Wagner). Of this, there is twice as much buried cortex as exposed. The parietal cortex constitutes about one-fifth of the total cortical area. This proportion is well shown in the following table, which gives the actual figures found by Wagner in four specimens :

Table 5

Specimen	Nature	Parietal	Free and deep surface	Proportion
A	Mathematician aet. 78 years	45,493	219,638	1 : 4·82
B	Physician aet. 52 years	44,783	221,005	1 : 4·93
C	Female	41,838	204,115	1 : 4·87
D	Artisan	40,142	187,652	1 : 4·67

While still concerned with this matter of the relative thickness of the different parts of the cortex, we have to consider not only the cellular components (which will be dealt with in more detail later) but also the system of nerve fibres as they exist within the cortex itself. These constitute the so-called *intracortical fibres*, made up of axons of Golgi type II cells, and collaterals of Golgi type I cells. They make up the tangential fibres and the ground fibres in the parietal lobe. As regards the comparative weights of the different lobes of the brain, Meynert estimated the percentages as, frontal 41·5 ; temporo-occipital 35·1 ; and parietal 23·4.

The white matter of the parietal lobe

This highly important subject is one which has not attracted sufficient attention in discussions upon parietal anatomy and sympto-matology. Cortex, it is true, occupies a relatively great proportion of the mass of parietal tissue, but nevertheless, the fibre-tracts forming the white matter are of considerable significance. Some of these

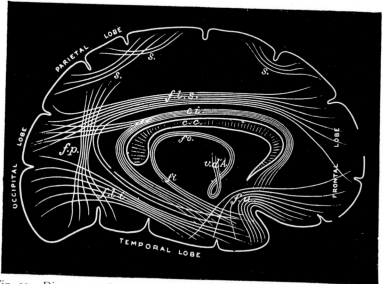

Fig. 22. Diagram to show the general course of the association fibres of the cerebral hemisphere (Meynert).

s.—short association fibres, connecting adjacent gyri ; f.l.s.—fasciculus longitudinalis superior ; ci.—cingulum ; f.p.—fasciculus perpendicularis ; f.l.i.—fasciculus longitudinalis inferior ; f.u.—fasciculus uncinatus ; fo.—fornix ; fi.—fimbria ; v.d'A—bundle of Vicq d'Azyr ; c.c.—corpus callosum.

fibre-tracts take origin in the parietal cortex : others terminate in the parietal cortex. These constitute the efferent and the afferent con-nections respectively. Some short fibre-tracts loop from one part of the parietal cortex to another. Lastly, certain long associational or projectional pathways take passage through the parietal lobe, arising and ending in more remote portions of the nervous system.

The system of myelinated fibres can be set out much as follows :

(1) *Parietothalamic fibres.* These take origin in the small pyra-midal cells of the cortex and the axons descend and converge mainly upon the lateral and anterior parts of the thalamus.

(2) *Thalamoparietal fibres.* Here we have the final part of the general afferent system of the body. Here, again, the fibres take origin in the cells which constitute the posterolateral thalamic nucleus, and therefrom they stream upwards to end in the parietal cortex and particularly in the postcentral convolution. The more precise areal distribution has already been described. It is perhaps necessary to reiterate, however, that thalamoparietal afferents and parietothalamic efferents course in very close apposition.

U-shaped short associational fibres pass in a complicated fashion so as to link up all neighbouring areas of the homolateral parietal cortex. Such fibre-tracts usually, or mainly, take origin in the

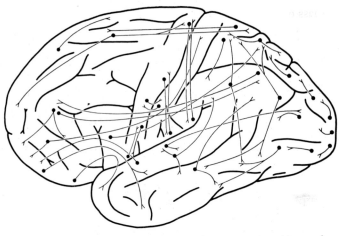

Fig. 23. Corticocortical fibres, based on experimental evidence from the chimpanzee, but drawn into a human brain. The scheme is necessarily tentative (courtesy of von Bonin).

granular cells of the parietal cortex. The exact distribution and conformation of such corticocortical fibres are not known for certain in man, but their complexity can be gauged by way of the newer techniques of physiological neuronography. On the analogy of the simian brain, certain dispositions can be surmised as probably occurring in humans, and have been depicted by Bonin (see Fig. 23).

Commissural fibres also make up a proportion of the parietal white matter. These comprise fibres which, taking origin in one part of the cortex, run transversely across the middle third of the corpus callosum and terminate in a corresponding point in the opposite hemisphere.

Among the longer associational fibres which pass in transit through the parietal lobe must be mentioned the *fronto-occipital fasciculus.* Possibly some fibres take origin in the frontal lobe and come to rest in the parietal lobe, and vice versa. Temporoparietal association pathways also probably exist.

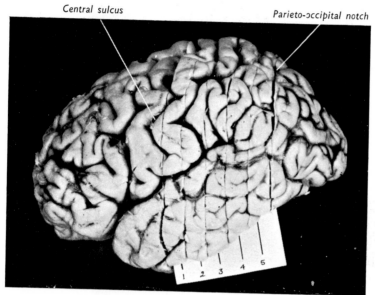

Fig. 24.

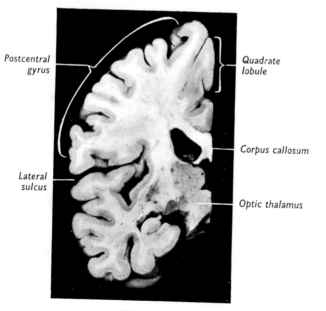

Fig. 25.

Superior parietal
lobule

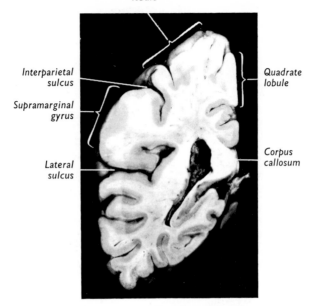

Interparietal
sulcus

Supramarginal
gyrus

Lateral
sulcus

Quadrate
lobule

Corpus
callosum

Fig. 26.

Interparietal
sulcus

Superior parietal
lobule

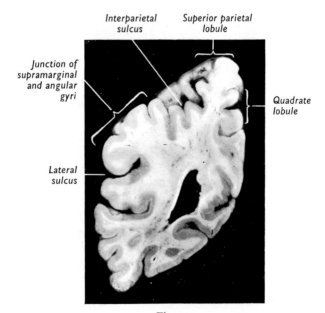

Junction of
supramarginal
and angular
gyri

Lateral
sulcus

Quadrate
lobule

Fig. 27.

Superior parietal
lobule

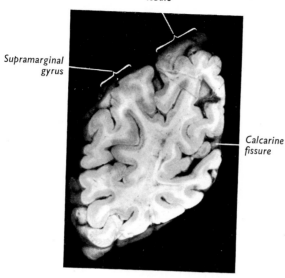

Supramarginal
gyrus

Calcarine
fissure

Fig. 28.

Superior parietal
lobule

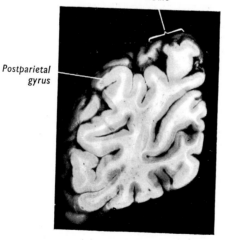

Postparietal
gyrus

Fig. 29.

Figs. 24–29. The white matter of the parietal lobe, as displayed in a series of five obliquely vertical sections. The first cut (Fig. 25) is made through the central fissure, while the last cut takes origin in the parieto-occipital notch

There is an important projectional fibre-system which comes into relationship with the extreme ventral part of the white matter of the parietal lobe, namely, the optic radiation of Gratiolet. Taking origin from the lateral geniculate body, the fibres form a well-defined bundle

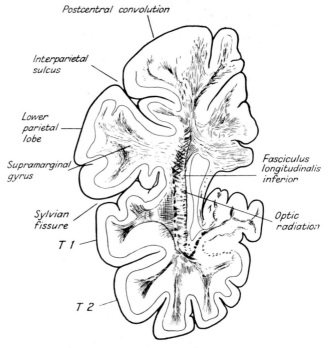

Fig. 30. Coronal section of the human brain to demonstrate the relationship of the optic radiation to the lateral ventricle (after Monakow).

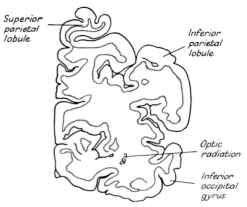

Fig. 31. Coronal section of the hemisphere near the occipital pole, to show the optic radiation (after Tilney and Riley).

which passes backwards ; then loops forward and splays out so as to avoid the descending horn of the lateral ventricle within the substance of the temporal lobe (= the Flechsig-Meyer " loop "). Posteriorly,

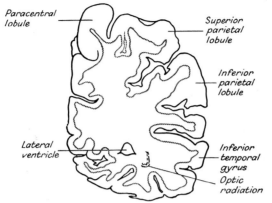

Fig. 32. Coronal section through the occipital horn of the lateral ventricle, to show the relationship of the optic radiation (after Tilney and Riley).

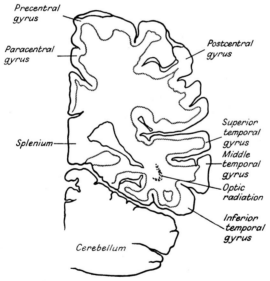

Fig. 33. Coronal section through the position of the optic radiation in relation to the parietal and temporal lobes (after Tilney and Riley).

the bundle becomes a more compact structure which traverses the parietal substance, deep to the supramarginal and angular gyri and between these structures and the main body of the lateral ventricle.

The optic radiation is often regarded as divisible into an upper, middle and lower strip of fibres. Their relationship to the posterior longitudinal fasciculus, and to the white matter of the temporo-parietal region is shown in the Figs. 30 to 33. Obviously, the radiation lies, strictly speaking, just outside the parietal territory, though Monakow's illustration demonstrates that the upper strata approximate to the junction of the white matter belonging to the temporal and parietal lobes. Tilney and Riley's picture shows the relationship to be more remote. Possibly some variability may exist in this relationship.

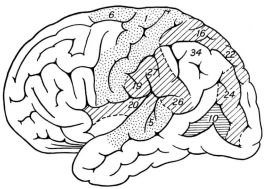

Fig. 34. Flechsig's myelinogenetic areas as they apply to the parietal lobe.
The three types of shading refer to the three types of cortex : primary, intermediate and late. The numerals indicate the order of myelination.

Myelinization of the parietal lobe

That certain regions of the cerebral hemispheres in the human foetus myelinate earlier, while others do so at a later date was first demonstrated by Flechsig. He constructed a map or diagram of the brain, indicating " areas " of early or late myelinogenesis. Of Flechsig's thirty-six myelinogenetic areas, so numbered according to their myelination times, the parietal lobe falls into several groups as shown by the following table :

Table 6

			Numbers
Primary group 1–10	Myelination at or soon after birth	Postcentral gyrus	1
Intermediate group : 11–31	Myelination starts at end of first month	Superior parietal lobule Anterior part of inferior parietal lobule	16 anterior 22 posterior
Late or final group : 32–36	Myelination occurs between 1 and 8 months	Angular gyrus Postparietal gyrus	34

Architectonics of the parietal lobe

Examination of the cerebral cortex under low-power magnification at once reveals a vertical radiation, an appearance which is more conspicuous in the lower parts of the lobe, where they merge into the temporal lobe. The pioneer workers upon the subject of cortical cyto-architectonics were, of course, Brian Lewis and Hammarberg. Our modern ideas date from the first histological chart of the brain which was constructed, at Sherrington's suggestion, by Campbell (1905). This author isolated various areas of specific histological structure—relatively few in number compared with those who were to come later. Thus, he recognized the following : prefrontal, frontal, intermediate precentral, precentral, intermediate postcentral,

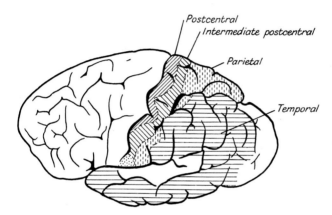

Fig. 35. Campbell's parcellation of the parietal and temporal lobes.

parietal, temporal, visuopsychic, auditosensory, auditopsychic, visuosensory, olfactory and limbic.

What we term today the parietal lobe includes not only Campbell's intermediate postcentral and parietal area but also the upper part of his temporal area, which, in his opinion, embraced the supramarginal and angular gyri.

Two years later, Elliot Smith published the results of his own researches upon the structure of the brain, a study which had been based upon the naked eye scrutiny of the cortex of about a hundred specimens. Contrasts in thickness, texture and coloration were noted, and formed the foundations of a system of parcellation. Elliot Smith noted that his areas of specific structure corresponded in most cases to the more stable convolutional patterns, and furthermore to the myelinogenic areas of Flechsig. By dint of these data, in which the horizontal fibre-strips of Baillarger were important,

Elliot Smith identified twenty-eight or thirty areas in the cortex, which were separated one from another quite abruptly. His cortical map is shown in Fig. 36 in so far as it applies to the parietal lobe. The postcentral gyrus was found to be made up of two parallel areas (area postcentral A and B). The superior parietal lobule was divisible into two areas, separated by the superior parietal sulcus (the area parietalis superior B and A). Below the interparietal fissure were three areas which he named the areae parietalis inferior A, B and C, corresponding fairly closely with the angular and supramarginal gyri, and with the parietal operculum respectively. More posteriorly, there were also the area parieto-occipitalis, and the area peristriata.

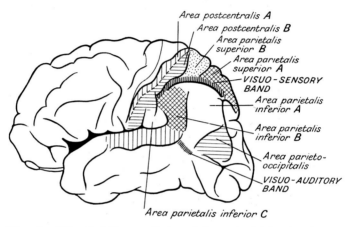

Fig. 36.   Elliot Smith's parcellation of the parietal lobe, showing the visuo-sensory and the visuo-auditory bands.

Special mention should be made of two interesting systems of fibre-bands running anteroposteriorly. The lower of these was found to extend forwards from the sulcus prelunatus, as far as the upper end of the sulcus temporalis superior, in the floor of which it merges into the area temporalis superior. Elliot Smith called the structure the *visuo-auditory band.* The histological pattern of this band resembles that of the peristriate area, or, at times, that of the parieto-occipital area. The other, and better known, of these structures was identified by Elliot Smith in naked eye examination of fresh sections of the adult parietal lobe. When the lobe is incised at right angles to the interparietal fissure, the lines of Baillarger in the superior parietal lobule will be found suddenly to become denser, whiter and more conspicuous, from a point 2 or 3 mm. from the upper lip of the sulcus, downwards to the very depths of the furrow. This was a small region which Flechsig had already noticed as myelinating earlier than the rest of the parietal region. Elliot Smith was able to trace this band backwards into the visual area (i.e. the floor of the par-occipital sulcus) and forwards into the postcentral. The term *visuo-sensory band* was therefore appropriate (later to be called by Pötzl, the interparietal striae).

These two structures, namely, the visuo-auditory band and the visuo-sensory band, represent in all probability the attentuated frag-ments of the extensive direct connections between the visual, sensory and auditory regions of the cortex, which in subhominoid brains are actually contiguous. They constitute, in other words, " adhesions " brought about by the rapid expansion of the inferior parietal lobule in the brains of the highest anthropoids and of man, at a point between the sensory, auditory and visual areas.

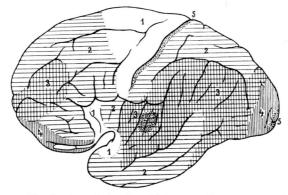

Fig. 37. Distribution of the five chief types of cortex, according to Economo.

Two weeks after the publication of Elliot Smith's paper, there appeared Brodmann's detailed parcellation of the human cortex based upon a minute histological study of one specimen. Other papers upon this topic were to follow, not only by Brodmann, but also by the Vogts and by Economo (in one instance in association with Koskinas). Their findings may be given in so far as they concern the parietal lobe.

For many years, most neuro-anatomists have preferred to make use of the scheme of cellular architectonics introduced by Economo and Koskinas. Economo identified within his " isocortex " five main types of lamination, of which his type 3 was also called by him " the parietal type ". This variant was said to be characterized by a well-defined six-layered structure with broader and denser granular layers than in the frontal type (i.e. type 2). The pyramidal cells of layers III and V were described as being smaller, more slender and numerous than in the frontal type of lamination, and less orderly in arrangement.

The cells in layer V were especially ill formed, resembling small spindle-shaped cells.

Although Economo spoke of his type 3 as the " parietal type "— his charts indicate that this particular morphology applies only to the inferior parietal lobule, the remainder of the lobe (i.e. virtually 50 per cent of it) conforming to the so-called " frontal " type or type 2.

In more detailed fashion, Economo subdivided the cyto-architectonics of the parietal lobe into the following areas :

(1) PA or the area postcentralis gigantopyramidalis,
(2) PB or the area postcentralis oralis (granulosa),
(3) PC or the area postcentralis intermedia,
(4) PD or the area postcentralis caudalis,
(5) PE or the area parietalis superior,
(6) PF or the area supramarginalis,
(7) PG or the area angularis, and
(8) PH or the area basalis.

Economo's description of the outstanding cyto-architectonic features of these areas may be quoted a little more fully :

> The areas PA, PB, PC and PD constitute the postcentral convolution.
>
> PA abruptly changes from the immediately adjacent FAγ, by showing a narrow granular type of pattern. This area occupies the lower third of the postcentral convolutions, deep within the central sulcus. A PA$_1$ can be distinguished from a PA$_2$. Both contain within layer V a number of Betz's giant pyramidal cells.
>
> PB also extends in a strip-like fashion parallel and posterior to PA through the whole length of the fissure of Rolando. This area contains smaller cells, almost granular. It forms part of the system of what he called the *Koniocortex*. It was estimated that this important granular area amounts to about 35–40 sq. cm. when the two hemispheres are computed.
>
> PC extends as a parallel strip behind PA and PB. The architecture is quite unlike that of PB and is more reminiscent of a " frontal " type of cortex. In one region, layer III is rich in giant cells, and this may be described as PCγ (the area postcentralis intermedia gigantopyramidalis).
>
> PD occupies the anterior and posterior lips of the postcentral sulcus and it also occupies the walls of the interparietal sulcus. This latter part shows features intermediate between PD and PE, and is sometimes designated as PDE. Postero-inferiorly, there is a transition zone PFD which approximates to PF.
>
> PE comprises the superior parietal lobule. This contains a pale band in lamina V which is visible to the naked eye, and which is part of the Bechterew-Kaes system. The most caudal part of this area shows slender giant cells, and is sometimes termed the area parietalis superior gigantopyramidalis (or PE).
>
> PF, which shows in clearest fashion the characteristics of the so-called " parietal " type of cortex, occupies the supramarginal gyrus. A number of minor variants can be made out : e.g. the narrow opercular area (PFop) ;

the area supramarginalis corticalis (PFt) ; and the area supra-marginalis columniata (PFc), adjacent to the first temporal convolution.

PG occupies the angular gyrus, being slightly narrower than PF. The typical columnar arrangement of cells is even more conspicuous. Transitions from PG to the occipital lobe, and to the second and third temporal convolutions are, from a cyto-architectonic standpoint, rather gradual.

PH extends over the occipitotemporal intermediate zone. The cortex is narrower, but resembles PF rather than PG. Transition zones posteriorly and inferiorly are easily made out, and are termed PHO and PHT.

So far, the cyto-architectonic plan of the parietal lobe has been discussed as broadly sketched by Campbell and by Elliot Smith, and as set out in detail by Economo. But simultaneous with the first two workers, the Vogts and Brodmann were also devising their own charts of the cortex. According to the classical map of Brodmann (where the cortex is made up of about fifty different areas), the parietal region can be taken as being made up of areas 1, 2, 3, 5, 7, 23, 31, 37, 39, 40 and 43. The Vogts extended Brodmann's system in an even more detailed fashion, breaking down some areas into subareas. In this way, over a hundred different cortical " organs " were claimed as being detectable. This highly complicated—and artificial— system of parcellation is largely favoured by experimentalists, while

Table 7

Campbell	Elliot Smith	Brodmann	Economo	The Vogts
Intermediate postcentral	Area post-centralis A	3	PA	Area postcentralis termigranularis Area postcentralis supragranularis
	Area post-centralis B	1	PB	Area postcentralis eumacropyramid Area postcentralis macropyramid
Parietal	Area parietalis inferior C	43	PDF	Area sulcentralis
	Area parietalis superior B	5	PA₂	Area praeparietalis
	Area parietalis superior A	7	PE	Area parietalis superior
Temporal	Area parietalis inferior B	40	PF	Area supra-marginalis
	Area parietalis inferior A	39	PG	Area angularis
			PH	Area basalis

clinicians have generally preferred to utilize the schemata of either
Brodmann or Economo.   Modifying the tabulation set out by Moffie
(1949), we can set out a comparison of the classification adopted by
these various anatomists (see Table 7).

The Percival Bailey has also joined those who have criticized severely
the over-elaborate systems of parcellation devised by Brodmann,
Economo and more especially by the Vogts.   One of his main arguments concerns the frontiers between adjacent zones : Bailey was not
impressed by any clean-cut demarcation.   Rather did the zones seem
to him to merge one into another by a process of gradual transition.
Consequently, the conventional black and white maps of the cortex
were to Bailey less convincing than a coloured chart in which it was
possible to depict shades of difference in cellular arrangement.   In
his coloured map, Bailey depicted the allocortex blue ; various shades
of pink represented the granular cortices, of which the eulaminate
isocortex was shown as rose and the koniocortex as dark red.   Grey
represented the large cells of the third layer, and yellow the areas
devoid of granules.   Areas intermediate between the allocortex (blue)
and the eulaminate cortex (rose) were printed as mauve-coloured
(see Frontispiece).

Vascular supply of the parietal lobe

The lateral aspect of the parietal lobe receives its blood supply
from the middle cerebral or sylvian artery, while the mesial aspect is
supplied mainly by the anterior cerebral artery, though to a slight
extent by the posterior cerebral also.

According to Duret (and also Charcot), the " sylvian artery "—
the term mainly used by earlier anatomists—supplies the parietal lobe
by way of its third and fourth terminal branches.   Of these, the third
branch, or *midparietal*, ascends in the depth of the central sulcus and
irrigates the pre- and postcentral gyri, and sometimes also the superior
parietal convolution.   The fourth or *postparietal* branch is larger.   It
lies within the horizontal limb of the lateral sulcus, and ascending
branches therefrom supply the inferior parietal lobule (while its
descending branches supply the superior temporal gyrus).

Testut described the sylvian artery as a vessel lying in the depths
of the lateral sulcus, terminating in the *artery of the angular gyrus*,
which irrigates not only that gyrus but also contiguous parts of the
temporal and occipital lobes.

Moutier reported an instance of an unduly early bifurcation of
the sylvian artery, one branch of which supplied the frontoparietal
convolutions, the island of Reil, and the supramarginal gyrus.   Mlle
Tixier also described a precocious bifurcation of this artery in the

region of the insula : the anterior frontoparietal group constituted a
" perirolandic artery ", while the posterior component was a " temporoparieto-occipital vessel ", also called the " artery of Wernicke's
zone ".

Foix and his pupil, Lévy, reopened this anatomical problem.
They found that the middle cerebral artery is a single vessel along its
course up to its termination in 46 out of 50 instances.   It ends as the
artery to the angular gyrus.   They described the cortical branches as
follows : (1) the anterior temporal ; (2) ascending arteries, often
springing from a common trunk (22 times out of 50) which then

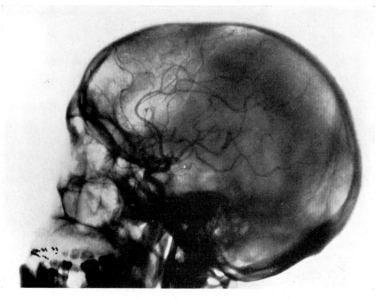

Fig. 38.   Normal arteriogram, showing the distribution of the anterior
and middle cerebral arteries.

divides up so as to form : (*a*) external inferior orbitofrontal ; (*b*) the
artery of the prerolandic fissure ; (*c*) the artery of the rolandic fissure ;
and (*d*) the anterior parietal.   Of these, the *artery of the rolandic fissure*
supplies both the precentral and the postcentral gyri.   The *anterior
parietal artery* (or *artery of the interparietal fissure*) not infrequently
arises directly from the sylvian trunk and not from the common stem
of the ascending vessels.   It follows the interparietal sulcus and
irrigates the posterior part of the postcentral gyrus, part of the inferior
and superior parietal lobules as well as the posterior part of the insula.
Behind the site of origin of the foregoing arise the *posterior parietal
artery* and a posterior temporal artery.   These two, together with the

terminal branch (or artery of the angular gyrus) form a sort of posterior sylvian trunk, which then irrigates the posterior part of the parietal lobe, Wernicke's zone, and part of the optic radiation.

According to Niessl von Mayendorff (1925) there is a special artery, or branch of the main sylvian trunk which passes upwards to the lower part of the postcentral gyrus, to supply a territory which he regards as representing the thumb-mouth area. This vessel, which he termed the *interopercular parietal artery*, he believed to have

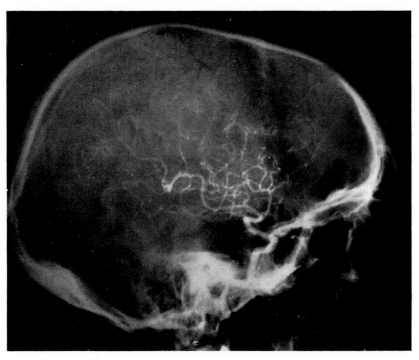

Fig. 39.   Arteriogram : the anterior cerebral artery is not filled, so that the vascular pattern displayed comprises the middle cerebral artery and its branches.

important clinical significance, in that its occlusion might be expected to produce a uniform and clear-cut symptomatological pattern (see Fig. 40).

Foix and Lévy emphasized that the region of supply of these vessels combines white matter as well as areas of cortex, and that the ischaemic zone which follows arterial occlusion is always regarded as " cortico-subcortical " in nature.

The foregoing descriptions probably over-simplify the true picture.   In particular, the arterial system lying within the depths of the lateral sulcus is complex, and is as yet inadequately charted.   The

middle cerebral artery, as it passes over the convexity of the insula,
is very frequently made up of two, three or even four trunks, all of
which lie closely apposed to each other. From these various trunks

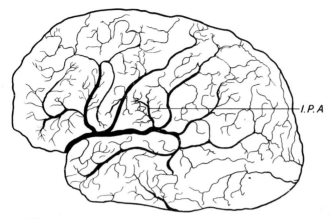

Fig. 40. The interopercular parietal artery (*I.P.A.*) a branch of the middle
cerebral trunk (after Niessl von Mayendorff).

short branches pass outwards to supply the upper surface of the
parietal operculum, and others to supply the transverse temporal gyri
on its inferior surface. Longer branches leave the depths of the
lateral sulcus and either turn upwards to ascend over the parietal

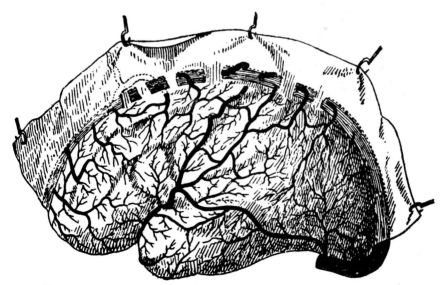

Fig. 41. Veins of the cerebral cortex (by courtesy of Raymond Garcin).

cortex, or downwards and backwards to supply the temporal lobe. In this way, the lateral sulcus and peri-insular region are associated with an unusual profusion of arterial channels, many of which are of no mean calibre.

The *venous drainage* of the parietal lobe has not yet been adequately studied in all its details. The presence of a large vein which runs in close association with the central sulcus is, of course, well

Three cerebral veins, in place of a single well-defined vein of Trolard

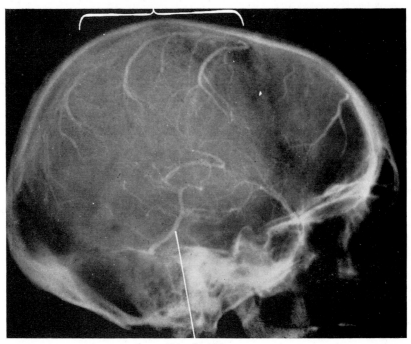

Vein of Labbé

Fig. 42.

known, and it is frequently clearly shown at the later stages of carotid arteriography. This large vessel which runs between the cavernous sinus (or superior petrosal sinus) below and the superior longitudinal sinus above, is commonly spoken of as the *great anastomotic vein of Trolard* (see Fig. 41). The second striking venous landmark on the convex surface of the brain is the *vein of Labbé*, which connects the first part of Trolard's vein with the lateral sinus. This vein crosses the upper part of the temporal lobe from before backwards. The veins of Trolard and of Labbé are sometimes called the *anterior anastomotic* and the *posterior anastomotic veins* respectively. The other veins coursing across the parietal lobe are not named, though there is a large vessel which ascends parallel with Trolard's vein from the point of origin of Labbé's vein from Trolard's vein. This vessel roughly overlies the vertical limb of the interparietal fissural complex, and it may well be spoken of as the *ascending parietal*

Vein of Trolard

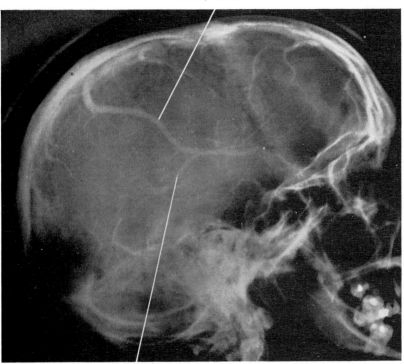

Deep internal
cerebral vein

Fig. 43.

vein. Ordinarily, the cortical veins are merely referred to as being made up of the superior and inferior sets.

Examination of a series of cerebral phlebograms with Dr. James Bull shows clearly that the morphology is far less definitive in the case of the veins than of the arteries of the brain. There are indications that the size of the veins of Trolard and of Labbé are in inverse ratio one with the other (see Fig. 42). At times, Trolard's vein may be replaced by two or three small vessels running parallel to each other (see Fig. 42). A possible error lies in the fact that the phlebogram is actually a " still " taken from a kinetic process, and the timing—and consequently the filling—may vary from one picture to another.

Besides these cortical or superficial veins, with their free anastomoses with each other as well as with the veins of Trolard and of Labbé, there is an important set of deep middle cerebral veins which drain the insular region. These vessels occupy the lateral (sylvian) sulcus, in close apposition to the middle cerebral artery.

The rise of the parietal lobe

The brain of *homo sapiens* is outstanding by reason of its general fissural complexity in the first place, and secondly by the relatively high ratio of brain-weight to body-weight. In addition, certain regional or localized elaborations can be demonstrated in the human brain. Among them, parietal complexities are conspicuous, especially in a postero-inferior direction. An attempt to trace the phylogenetic beginnings of this development would be of interest, especially if it were possible to correlate the anatomical data with such functional considerations, as, for example, the change in habits, modes of life and of feeding, special sense aptitudes, general bodily conformation, and so on. In seeking to draw such parallels, one will cautiously avoid the snares of teleological speculation. Whether changing function precedes and determines changing structure, or *vice versa*, is an exercise in biological philosophy which cannot be discussed here, and no adherence with adaptationism, or any other particular discipline of thought or belief can be allowed.

The cerebral hemispheres of the lowliest vertebrates, including fishes, reptiles and birds, cannot be regarded as homologous with the human cortex ; and in particular, for the purpose of our present discussion, nothing identifiable with the human parietal lobe can be indicated. In the lowest mammals, however, we can realize the importance for survival purposes of the olfactory sense. On the anatomical side, we witness what Wood Jones has picturesquely called " the rise of the smell brain " in the development of a cortical layer of cells superior to the sensorimotor nerve cell-masses which make up the avian, piscine and reptilian brains. This new cell-layer is also superior in anatomical and physiological senses of the word, for it now lies like a mantle covering the older motor and sensory systems. Hence the term " pallium ". The pallial brain of these most primitive mammals is mainly olfactory, and at this stage the hemispheres are lissencephalic or smooth, except for a hippocampal groove. Later, a shallow furrow appears, which constitutes the beginnings of a rhinal fissure, separating the olfactory part of the pallium from a more caudal region of the brain. Therein are contained cell-masses concerned with motility, and with afferent impulses of tactile, visual and auditory sense. This region of the brain, lying behind the rhinal fissure, was called by Elliot Smith " the neo-pallium ". The brain is still macrosmatic, however.

Other fissures appear later, and break up the cerebral hemispheres into various regions. Chief among these are the calcarine fissure, the orbital fissure and the suprasylvian fissure. In this way, there develop specializations within the neopallium, at the expense of both the palaeo- and the archipallium, both of which are essentially olfactory in character.

The mammal at this important stage has developed (or is developing) certain new biological aptitudes. Its olfactory world is enriched by a specialization of tactile impulses, which are elaborated around the most forward positions of its anatomy. The shape of the animal is changing : it is elongating : its skull is adorned by a conspicuous muzzle or snout-formation at the tip of which is a highly sensitive cap of mucous membrane, kept continually moist, and receptive not only to a rich variety of olfactory stimuli—most of which are too subtle for human appreciation—but also sensitive to purely tactile impressions. Behind and alongside this wet-nosed muzzle is a complicated arrangement of feelers, or vibrissae, implanted mainly along the upper lip and jaw, and around the orbits. The mammal thus " noses its way " around, seeking out food and picking up the alarm signals given out by nearby potential foes. A specialization has thus taken place in the trigeminotactile zone, or more accurately, in the maxillary area. No doubt this corresponds with what Edinger used to call the " oral sense ". This specialization can be correlated in the brain with a well-demarcated nucleus rotundus in the thalamus, which in turn, is associated with an adjacent cortical cluster of cells—the beginnings of a somesthetic cortex or parietal lobe. As Brouwer has said, the parietal lobe can be looked upon as the leader in the development of the neopallium.

At this point, it is desirable to pay passing notice to the nervous system of one unusual offshoot from the main vertebrate stream, namely, the *proboscideae*. These animals, by reason of development of ever heavier tusks, require the counterbalance of a shorter and stouter neck. Consequently, it would become impossible for the animal to drink were it not for an elaboration of the snout and upper lip so as to form an elongated, sensitive, prehensile and mobile trunk through which it can suck water, and with which it can pick up food and convey it to its mouth. The elephant's trunk eventually becomes a sensorimotor tool of incredible delicacy and efficiency—which may

E

be likened to an unpaired forelimb, with a dexterity found in no other mammal lower than the higher primates. At the same time the elephant may be said to possess a higher degree of " intelligence " than any other mammal in the wild state—though attempts to define or describe the term " intelligence " in this connection would not be easy. It is not surprising to find that the elephant's brain is endowed with certain peculiar features : size, richness of convolutional pattern, prominence of the temporal lobes, for instance (Fig. 44). The parietal region of the elephant's brain has not been specifically studied, but it can be said that the motor and sensory cortices are conspicuous in so far as they are concerned with the facio-

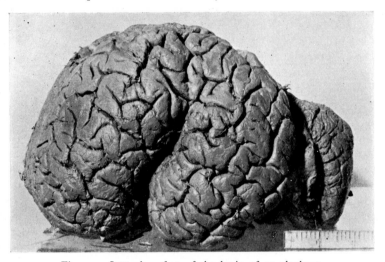

Fig. 44.   Lateral surface of the brain of an elephant.

trigeminal zones which subserve the trunk. The median unpaired position of the trunk presupposes an efficient bicortical system of intercommunication, a system which can be correlated with the comparatively larger size of the corpus callosum. On the other hand, the sensory functions in the elephant as affecting the fore- and hindlimbs, the tail and the body, vision and hearing are less in demand and are probably not correlated with any complex cortical development. Thus, the posterior lobes of the elephant's brain are relatively small and leave the cerebellum uncovered. None the less, the elephant's relative agility in crossing uneven or difficult terrain— despite an inability to guide its steps by vision—presupposes an efficient proprioceptive system which must be related partly to a well-developed parietal lobe.

From the standpoint of phylogenesis of the parietal lobe, the stage of maxillary tactile specialization, challenging olfactory pre-eminence, is the first important step. The second great advance occurs at or about the time of the change of habits from a terrestrial to an arboreal environment.

To scale the branches of trees, there to dwell, seek food and avoid enemies is a revolutionary advance. A macrosmatic creature, with little but its wet nose and whiskers to help it, would be poorly equipped for arboreal survival. Quite a different body-build would be required, together with special sense acuity other than smell and muzzle sensitivity. Again, the manner in which changing function and changing structure are related cannot be asserted dogmatically, and will not be discussed. Suffice it to say that a successful arboreal existence is assisted by limbs which are to some extent prehensile ; which can if necessary be used for activities other than locomotion, e.g. grasping food and conveying it to the mouth as in the case of the fore-limbs. Olfactory stimuli would not be expected to play so much of a role in the arboreal animal's world as auditory and visual messages. The latter would be particularly significant, for not only must food and enemies be perceived at a distance, but the arboreal animal needs to leap accurately from one branch to another. Many, too, are in the habit of seizing an article of food, such as a nut, and picking it up with a paw, or rather holding it between its two fore-paws, and conveying it directly to its mouth. The hand is no longer a unit in a mechanism for locomotion ; it has been released for other work. Moreover, it has taken over from the snout the role of the principal examining organ. The creature no longer puts its nose to a strange object which it sniffs and nuzzles, employing all the arts and devices of olfaction and touch. Now, it is able to seize the object, feel it, and bring it close to the eyes and peer at it curiously. But to do this, the faculty of sight must be brought into full partnership. Vision thus becomes a highly important, perhaps even a paramount, sensory experience. For accuracy of motility, the animal must be able to see and to move with precision within three-dimensional space. This can only be done if the eyeballs are so placed that the two fields of vision largely overlap and form a binocular stereoscopic field. Laterally placed orbits, as in so many terrestrial animals, are relatively inefficient. The globes of the eyes would be best situated if facing directly forwards. In such circumstances, the prominent muzzle of the opossum (or the elaborate snout of the *proboscideae*) would be largely an encumbrance. A flat face, forward-facing eyes, an ability to converge the eyeballs so as to fix upon a near point would be the most efficient morphology for an arboreal creature. Such indeed is largely the case, even though in the simplest representatives, e.g. the shrews and squirrels, these features are not yet well developed. The morphology of the nervous system becomes modified, for the optic nerves at this stage now undergo only a partial decussation at the chiasma. But most relevant from our point of view is the development of a cortical area which subserves the hand or fore-paw, not only from the point of view of motility but also of somaesthesia. The trigeminal sensory zone has now expanded so as to form a well-defined sensory neocortex lying immediately behind the central sulcus, in which the hind-limbs are roughly represented near the upper margin, the facial area lowermost, and the area for the fore-paw intermediate. Behind this sensory zone lies a well-marked visual cortex occupying the postero-external region of the brain. Below is the auditory cortex.

Two other considerations must also be mentioned here. For an arboreal creature to move with speed and safety through the hazardous intricacies of the tree-tops, vision is not the only guide. The creature might be expected to possess in addition a shrewd, though unobtrusive, knowledge as to the position of its limbs in space and the power to regulate exactly the degree of muscular contraction needed to propel itself from one branch to another. In other words, the proprioceptive system of such a creature must be one of extraordinary efficiency, even greater perhaps than in the case of *homo sapiens*.

The second factor which comes into play far up the arboreal scale, but in an ephemeral fashion only, is the development of a prehensile and highly sensitive tail. The spider monkey, for example, possesses what is really a fifth limb, for by means of its tail it can " feel " its way on to a suitable support and by grasping this can swing like a pendulum from one perch to another. The tail itself is unusual in structure for at the appropriate distance from the tip is an area devoid of hair, but endowed with an unusually rich assortment of tactile nerve-endings. This segment of the tail is at least as sensitive and as motile as the fore-paw. It is not surprising to learn that in the cerebrum of the spider-monkey there is an excessively well-developed portion of the motor and sensory cortices on both sides which corresponds with the functional activities of the tail.

The spider-monkey's tail—like the elephant's trunk—is an example of extreme specialization : perhaps even undue specialization, for the development which had been so rapid hitherto, culminated in these two organs, and then dropped out of the scheme of things altogether, like discarded tools. Such, too, was the fate of the sensitive and unwieldy snout of the *platypus*. These three structures all possessed important parietal as well as thalamic correlates, which find little in the way of homologue in the human brain.

Arboreal habits reached their peak in the middle rank of primates, but with the coming of the gorilla and of *homo sapiens*, the phylum reverted to a terrestrial mode of life. The experiences which accrued during this arboreal apprenticeship were of great teleological value, and in so far as they concern the story of the parietal lobe, they were associated with the development of a sinuous post-central gyrus with complicated cellular architectonics ; a well-defined superior parietal lobule ; and the beginnings of an inferior parietal lobule. The sensorimotor area was being encroached upon from behind, while the visual cortex was being crushed in a backward direction to constitute an operculation. Below, the auditory cortex was being forced downwards and inwards so as eventually to become buried beneath a top-weight of parietal overgrowth.

Wood Jones and Porteous have described the benefits of arboreal pupillage in graphic words : " It was life among the branches that liberated the hand from the servile business of supporting the body weight and set it free to grasp strange objects, to feel them, examine them, weigh them and turn them this way and that so that all aspects could be seen and correlated. It was the liberated hand that carried food to the mouth and so permitted that shortening of the muzzle that was the necessary precursor of the changes in the eyes."

Discussion

Parietal lobe in prehistoric man

A study of the markings of the inner surface of the fossil cranial bones is the only practical method of gleaning information as to the morphology of the brain in prehistory. It is obvious that such specimens must have shown a distinct sulcus lunatus (*Affenspalte*). Furthermore, at a very early stage, e.g. in pithecanthropus (or Java man of early Pleistocene age), this sulcus was appearing in an asymmetrical fashion. In the majority of specimens of crania examined, this sulcus has been more conspicuous on the left side. Moreover, the occipital fossae now tend to become of unequal size and depth. It is tempting to look upon these facts as suggestive evidence of unilateral cerebral dominance, and therefore of handedness. Below this stage in the vertebrate scale there is no firm evidence—either clinical or anatomical—of consistent and natural unimanual preference.

At the same time it must be realized that some anatomists are sceptical whether these grooves, noticeable upon the prehistoric cranial bones, really do represent a sulcus lunatus at all (Le Gros Clark *et al.*, 1936–40).

Examination of the fossil cranial bones of certain prehistoric specimens also reveals a well-defined fossa parietalis on both sides. This landmark connotes a special development of the postero-inferior portions of the parietal lobes, a region which is to be looked upon as largely a specific hominid feature. Parietal eminences are demonstrable in the cranial casts of pithecanthropus (as compared with the gorilla's brain), but the development is slight as compared with *homo sapiens*, and in any case, is less conspicuous than in the frontal area. Examination of the cranial casts of eoanthropus (Pilt-down man) shows that the parietal eminence has developed in a striking fashion, and furthermore, in this particular specimen, the left hemisphere was larger than the right. In the case of *homo primigenius* (Neanderthal man) there was a striking advance in the parietal area. It is tempting to associate these two factors (cerebral

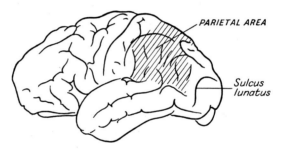

Fig. 45. Pithecanthropus (after Elliot Smith).

dominance and postparietal elaboration) with the acquisition of speech. By " speech " one refers not to systems of communication and interjection which are within the capacity of many creatures below the rank of *homo sapiens*, but to the use of vocal symbols which can indicate abstract ideas. It is unlikely that language of this sort developed sharply out of a system of animal speech, and the idea of a " rubicon " envisaged by the philological philosophers of a century ago probably cannot be defended. Animal speech doubtless merged into human speech by a gradual process of progressive elaboration and use of abstractions. For such reasons it is rash to assign a frontier and to try and separate prehistoric man into those that could speak and those that could not. It is not surprising that anatomists should differ on this topic, although the argument is largely sterile. Elliot Smith was of the opinion that speech was possible to pithe-canthropus ; Keith put the stage much later, however, for he held the view that no specimen lower than Neanderthal man made use of speech. Tilney, taking up a compromise, considered that Piltdown man was capable of some sort of language.

The parietal lobe as an empirical convention

More than once it has been emphasized that the parietal lobe cannot be regarded as an autonomous anatomical entity. Its boundaries cannot be drawn with any precision except by adopting conventional and artificial landmarks and frontiers. Later, it will also be seen that it is not possible to equate the parietal lobe with any narrowly defined physiological function. In other words, the parietal lobe represents a topographical convenience pegged out empirically upon the surface of the brain. The name serves a mere descriptive rôle, as can be borne out by reference to its short etymological history.

Up to 150 years ago, the cerebrum was not divided into lobes or regions by any established fissural patterns. Later, anatomists, following Burdach, began to speak of the cerebrum as being made up of lobes. Burdach (1819–26) actually spoke of anterior, upper and lower lobes, the operculum, and the island of Reil. At a still later date (cf. Quain, 1837), there were three lobes identified, namely, the anterior, posterior and middle lobes, indicating the various positions of the brain as related to the fossae of the base of the skull. This system was adopted and recapitulated in text-books until 1850. Around that time, there developed a tendency to associate regions of the brain with the overlying cranial bones. Thus, the anterior lobe became the frontal lobe, while the cortical territory underlying the os sincipitis (os bregmatis or os parietalis) became known as the parietal lobe. This term is to be found in the monograph by Henle (1868), but it possibly dates from the study made by Arnold in 1838. (". . . das Scheitelbein deckt die von Burdach als Oberlappen bezeichnete Abtheilung und sie kann daher als *lobus parietalis* aufgeführt werden . . .") The term did not reach English anatomical teaching until somewhere between 1873 and 1880 (i.e. the 7th and 9th editions of Gray's *Anatomy*).

There is no inherent reason to doubt but that the term parietal lobe (just as also the terms frontal, temporal, occipital as applied to other cerebral regions) will eventually be replaced by some other nomenclature. The ideal would be a less narrow terminology, and one which would include the whole retro-rolandic complex, or a three-dimensional temporo-parieto-occipital territory, as a functional dominion.

Methods of subdividing the parietal lobe

As our knowledge of this region and its connections increases, the nomenclature of such a territory so intimately correlated, both structurally and functionally, with other parts of the cerebrum may, perhaps, compel the use of a terminology indicating something more than a circumscribed surface area of cortex. Meantime, it does serve the useful purpose of enabling us to map out its contours and to localize in some measure its functional values.

Purely for purposes of description, it is therefore convenient to be able to partition the parietal lobe. This procedure assists the surgeon, the experimental physiologist and the clinician, in locating and earmarking a circumscribed lesion. An ideal system of parcellation should be logical, simple, consistent and scientifically founded. Until such a system is found and adopted, the various available techniques may be enumerated and discussed.

One must rate as objectionable the not uncommon practice often adopted in neurological literature of referring to regions of the brain in a wholly inconsistent fashion. Thus, in one and the same paper, an author may be found speaking at one time of area 40, at another of PG and later still of the angular gyrus or the *G. angularis*. However unsatisfactory each individual system may be, inconsistency of terminology offers a still more serious abuse.

(*A*) *Convolutional morphology.* The most obvious scheme for subdividing the parietal lobe would be one which is founded upon the pattern of gyri and sulci. It is tempting, therefore, to refer to the parietal lobe in terms of the ascending parietal, supramarginal and angular gyri, the superior parietal lobule and the precuneus. Unfortunately, this system in practice proves unhelpful, firstly because of the difficulty in identifying even the chief sulci, and secondly because of the not uncommon variability in their layout. Although it is usually easy to indicate, without dissection, the central sulcus and the lateral sulcus, the units of the interparietal complex, for example, may not be readily traced. The varying manner in which annectant gyri, secondary and tertiary gyri, and *plis de passage* are developed, and lie, maybe buried or maybe exposed, adds considerably to the problem. Jefferson (1914) expressed himself cautiously upon this matter. " I am fully aware that the sulci cannot be taken as the rigid boundaries of specialized areas, as was pointed out long ago by Sherrington. But at the same time, I cannot conceive of sulci as being far removed from such boundaries, seeing that it was specialization of cortex which produced them." There is also a possible relationship between intellectual endowment and convolutional intricacy, which must be considered as a complicating factor, especially in view of the fact that Economo, Riese and Goldstein, Spitzka and others have correlated an undue convolutional development in the inferior parietal lobule with such aptitudes as mathematical or musical ability.

(*B*) *Architectonic areas* are still commonly quoted by neurologists in their attempt to describe small areas of the brain. This practice has been perhaps more often employed in Continental and American clinics than in Great Britain, where the various systems of cyto-architectonics have never been accepted unreservedly. In the first place—if recourse is had to this terminology—it becomes necessary to decide which architectonic system is to be adopted, and not to vacillate from the schema of the Vogts to that of Brodmann or Economo. Even if one system is selected and adhered to strictly, one still has to contend with the grave and innate disadvantages from which each method suffers. These defects have been eloquently discussed by Lashley and Clarke, Walshe, Bailey, Bonin, Le Gros Clark and others.

Some of the major weaknesses can be summarized :

(1) Each cyto-architectonic map merely strikes a compromise between the varying patterning of· six cell-layers which constitute any one section of the cerebral cortex.

(2) The edges of each architectonic area are far from being as sharp as the cortical maps would imply. Often one area merges into another by a transitional zone.

(3) The thickness of the cortex, and with it, the cell-structure, varies considerably according to whether the base or the summit of a gyrus is being examined.

(4) Although alterations in cell-structure have been taken as implying a difference in function, this may actually be true only when grosser types of cellular difference are concerned. While an agranular and a granular cortex may no doubt possess a very different functional significance, the same probably cannot be assumed in the case of say Brodmann's areas 39 and 40. Furthermore, the question of cerebral dominance is quite unanswered in this connection. Thus, no evidence is at present available to show that any marked difference exists between Brodmann's area 40 in the right and in the left hemispheres, and yet all the clinical evidence goes to show that the two contrasting but mirror-opposite areas of cortex are concerned with very different physiological activities.

(5) All the systems of architectonics so far in use take cognizance of nerve-cells alone. The important systems of constituent fibres are not utilized, and are indeed, for technical reasons, too difficult to be incorporated.

(*C*) *Thalamic projectional areas.* Although in the primate brain it would seem possible to identify the cortex as an area upon which subcortical cell-groups project, there is as yet no evidence that this is possible or feasible in the case of man. The parietal region, it is true, is largely made up of areas which subtend cell-groups within the thalamus and the pulvinar. In man, however, the pattern of thalamoparietal projection is complicated in the first place by interlacing and overlapping fibres from one group of cells to another ; and in the second place, by descending parietothalamic pathways.

(D) *Relationship to suppressor strips.* The claim to identify in the primate brain cortical strips of inhibitory cells (or suppressor bands) at one time made it hypothetically possible to map out and enumerate such strips, and to put a numerical seal both upon them and also upon the intervening cell-tissue. Thus, in the gorilla's brain, it might conceivably have been justifiable to number the suppressor bands from before backwards as—for example—I, II, III, IV and V ; and the intervening normal cellular tissue might have been termed 1, 2, 3, 4, 5, 6 . . . Unfortunately, these suppressor bands have not been unequivocally demonstrated in the human subject, despite some tentative essays. Furthermore, the suspicion that the whole doctrine of suppressor bands is unsound and that they may be no more than an artefact throws doubt upon the status of this particular chapter in neuro-anatomy and neurophysiology.

(E) *Cerebro-arterial topography.* The contention has been made that the distribution of the cerebral arteries is by no means haphazard but indeed is rigidly determined. Anomalies, it is suggested, mainly concern the site of origin of an arterial trunk and not its ultimate distribution. If this belief is well founded and can be substantiated, then it follows that it might be possible to divide the brain into vascular territories. One could perhaps speak of the anterior cerebral territory, the middle cerebral territory, and so on. In the case of the parietal lobe, it might even be possible to demarcate sub-areas, according to the distribution of the various branches of the middle cerebral artery. Thus, it might perhaps be justifiable to speak of the anterior, middle and posterior parietal areas, and perhaps even to subdivide these according to the various twigs which emerge from the anterior, middle and posterior parietal branches.

Unfortunately, however, we are not yet sure enough of our grounds in contending that cerebral arteries are rigid as regards their course and ultimate distribution. Furthermore, we do not know sufficient of the normal morphology of the middle cerebral artery to be able confidentially to identify the various ramifications.

There is yet another feature which would complicate any system of cerebral arterial topography. Most of the larger branches lie in the depths of the sulci from which they irrigate the sides of adjacent convolutions. These gyri may happen to be of vastly different histological structure and presumably possess differing functions.

Thus, the rolandic artery courses up the length of the central sulcus and it supplies not only the posterior strip of the precentral gyrus but also the anterior strip of the postcentral gyrus. The area of supply of the rolandic artery would, therefore, actually prove to be frontoparietal in distribution, or motori-sensory in function. This may not in itself be a necessary handicap, but it would at any rate run counter to our accepted ideas of cortical physiology today. It would also offend the doctrine of the physiological significance of the individual cerebral arteries (Hilton ; Shellshear).

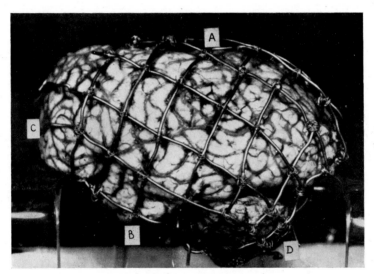

Fig. 46. Geometric encephalometry, using a pliable wire network laid in close apposition to the cortex.

(F) *Geometric encephalometry.* Parcellation of the parietal lobe may be feasible on the basis of another measure, one which virtually constitutes the very opposite of the more natural methods which have so far been mentioned. Failing to achieve a reliable technique for parcellation based upon dependable natural landmarks, a purely artificial method suggests itself whereby hypothetical lines of longitude and latitude are projected upon the curved surface of the hemispheres. To attain precision, it is necessary to determine one or two fixed points to serve as *points de repère.* The first one obviously comprises the site at which the central sulcus loops over the superior border of the hemisphere. Another rigid landmark would be the place where the inferior end of the central sulcus meets the lateral sulcus. (Or if these two do not come into contact, where an imaginary vertical line dropped from the lower extremity of the cerebral sulcus meets the lateral sulcus.) These two determined points may now be joined. This line could then be bisected by a horizontal line placed at a fixed angle (say, one of 60°). In this way, two fixed lines, *AB* and *CD*, are now formed. These can be divided so as to form ordinates and abscissae. These can be made to lie in close apposition to the surface of the brain by employing a wire network wrapped around the hemispheres (see Fig. 46). To identify any given area of cortex, it is only necessary to attach numbers or letters appropriately, and to read off the area as on a map.

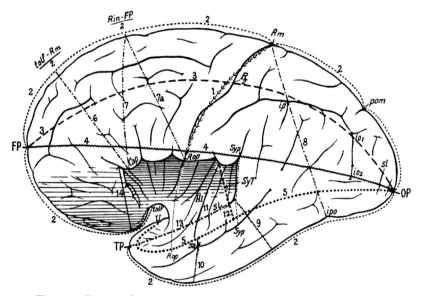

Fig. 47. System of geometric encephalometry, as devised by Economo.

Economo in elaborating a technique for the study of the brains of specially gifted persons has identified a number of other fixed points besides the *A* and *B* mentioned above (see Fig. 47).

Brief mention may be made of the rather unusual method of dividing a cerebral cortex described by Schepers (1948). Progressive telencephalization is regarded by him as taking place by way of a series of cortical buds, arising from the equivalent of the human paradentate gyrus. These buds ultimately form : (1) the auditory sensory gyrus of Heschl ; (2) the circumambient audito-associative component of the superior temporal and marginal gyri ; (3) the temporopolar behaviouristic cortices of more recent origin ; (4) the middle temporal psychomotor cortex ; (5) the inferior temporal visuo-motoric cortex ; (6) the visuosensory striate formation of the occipital lobe ; (7) the somatic sensory field comprising the postcentral gyrus and the submerged gyri of the interparietal and parieto-occipital fissures ; and (8) the stato-equilibratory and stereognosic centres constituting the superior parietal lobule and the precuneus. The foregoing make up the posterior half of the brain, according to the author, and the anterior portion develops from an elaboration of another seven or eight cortical buds.

CHAPTER II

EXPERIMENTAL PHYSIOLOGY

En Science la méthode est tout.

C. F. Ludwig

The very nature of the functional processes with which the parietal lobe is concerned demands for their study the co-operation of a conscious and intelligent subject. It is not surprising, therefore, that animal experimental investigations of this region of the cerebral cortex have been neither extensive nor rewarding in the past ; and that, only with the advance of modern electrophysiological techniques have data of greater significance been obtained.

It is the purpose of this chapter to set forth in descriptive manner the experimental observations on the parietal lobe, as far as they appear well established, in order that their correlation with anatomical knowledge on the one hand, and with clinical studies on the other, may be readily appreciated. Their physiological implications will be touched upon only briefly, as their significance in problems of cortical function will be referred to again in a later chapter.

Evoked cortical potentials

The arrival at the cortex of an afferent volley from any source can be detected by the evoked cortical potentials which it creates. This fact constitutes one of the most interesting developments in electrical neurophysiology. The most significant of such potentials is a surface positive wave having a time course around 10–80 milliseconds and an amplitude which varies greatly, ranging between 50 and 2,000 microvolts, according to the species. Higher ratios are found in smaller animals, such as the rat and rabbit, a fact which Woolsey and Erickson (1950) attributed to the thinness of their cortex. Depending on the region of the cortex, and its state, it may be preceded by briefer potentials and be followed by a surface negative potential or a rhythmical discharge. But in all cases the primary surface positive wave, sharply localized to the area of cortex where the afferent discharge terminates, is the most constant electrical sign of the arrival of a sensory stimulus. Although not more constant than the volleys of action-potentials in the afferent fibres entering the grey matter, it is on the whole more easily detected and recorded. In fact, one explanation of the evoked surface positive wave is that it is a result of a potential gradient set up by these afferent impulses. Another possible explanation is that it is due to the synaptic excitatory action of the afferent impulses on cortical neurones in the third and fourth layers. Even if this latter view is eventually proved correct, clearly the evoked cortical potential which has been described indicates only the focus where cortical neurones are first affected by a sensory stimulus ; subsequent events within the cortex itself have so far been little elucidated by the electrical method.

The technique of evoked potentials has been used a great deal in the exploration of the parietal sensory cortex with interesting results. Adrian (1941) found that touch, pressure and movement were the only stimuli which gave well-marked responses in the cortex. He observed in the cat no responses to pain or thermal stimuli. In the monkey and lower forms, the responses occurred in an area which corresponds closely with the somatic receiving area as delimited by cell structure and by tracing afferent projections from the thalamus. The general arrangement is that responses from the leg and trunk appear most medially and superiorly, and those from the face most laterally and inferiorly. Responses from the arm are projected to an intermediate area. The positions of these various areas correspond closely in different species in the region homologous to the postcentral gyrus in the monkey, but there is considerable variation in the cortical area supplied, so to speak, by different parts of the body surface in different animals depending on their relative importance in relation to the outside world. Thus, in the dog and rabbit, the areas concerned with the mouth and face are most important, whereas in the cat, the dorsal surface of the fore-limbs and trunk supplies a larger cortical area than the face. In the goat and sheep, the chief supply to the cortex comes from the upper and lower lip, while in the pig practically the whole of the cortical receiving area is taken up with the afferent inflow from the snout. (Adrian, 1943 ; Woolsey and Fairman, 1946.)

Other observations of Adrian (1941) on the afferent discharge to the cortex, apart altogether from its location, are of much interest. Pressure on the forefoot in the cat under dial anaesthesia gives a sustained discharge which may gradually rise as the pressure is increased, and may gradually decline with a constant stimulus ; this corresponds closely with the discharge which travels from the receptors in the afferent nerve-fibre. The maximum frequency is, however, considerably lower than in a peripheral nerve-fibre, rarely exceeding 100 a second ; and the discharge may appear at times in brief repetitive bursts—a quality which is imposed on it by the thalamic neurones. Pressure is the only type of stimulus which gives a sustained discharge to the cortex ; stretching of a muscle, which may afford a prolonged discharge along the peripheral nerve, produces only a brief discharge in the cortex. The tactile discharge is quite brief and does not differ greatly from that in the peripheral nerve where the impulses are also spaced at intervals. One afferent unit to the cortex can be activated by touching any cluster of hairs within an area of seven square centimetres on the back of a cat, so that considerable convergence in terms of skin areas exists. *Per contra*, convergence is much less in the case of the forefoot and one unit could only be activated by touching the hairs over an area between the toes, measuring three square millimetres. When the animal is under a suitable anaesthetic, a discharge from the touch receptors to the cortex is often followed by a thalamic after-discharge which consists of a succession of short volleys 10–20 times a second. It is most pronounced if the afferent pathway has been at rest for some time, and it does not appear if the primary discharge has lasted more than a second or so. The discharge, which may sometimes be non-rhythmical, is most probably indicative of repetitive firing of thalamic neurones in the direct pathway from sense-organs to the cortex.

Marshall, Woolsey and Bard (1941) in their experiments on the somatic receiving areas, mainly employed as touch stimulation a small camel-hair brush, or a short section of a cat's vibrissa. The animals, most often monkeys, were under barbiturate anaesthesia so adjusted as to diminish spontaneous electrical activity without affecting significantly the evoked cortical potential. The cortex was explored in detail during sensory stimulation by mounting the pick-up electrode in a Horsley-Clarke instrument. In monkeys, responses were found in Brodmann's areas 3, 1 and 2, but not in areas 4 or 5. Evoked potentials have been found also in area 4 (as well as in 3, 1 and 2) following posterior root stimulation, and may possibly be proprioceptive sensory discharges. (Woolsey, Chang and Bard, 1947.) It was found in several experiments that stimulation at one point on the dorsal surface of the hand or forearm gave maximal responses in two cortical regions, one in or near the posterior lip of the central sulcus and another situated about five millimetres more caudally. In some experiments, the anterior region appeared as two foci about three millimetres apart, possibly situated in Brodmann's architectonic areas 3 and 1 respectively, while the caudal foci were located in area 2. Each focus, it seems, is maximal at one point and is surrounded by a submaximal margin extending asymmetrically up to four millimetres wide. The latency of the responses varies from 12 to 16 milliseconds, the more posterior responses having the longer latency. (Latencies for stimulation of the foot in the monkey are 15–20 milliseconds and for the face 8–11 milliseconds.) Thus, it would appear that a restricted stimulus can activate a number of afferent units to the cortex, and from the slight difference in latency it can be concluded that the spreading of the excitation probably takes place in the thalamic neurones of the ventrolateral nucleus. If the peripheral stimulus is moved a short distance, e.g. from one digit to the next, the groups of responses in the cortex are found in slightly different positions, leaving a certain area of overlap. The convergence of pathways to the cortex, observed also by Adrian, is further revealed in the observation of Marshall *et al.* that one cortical point may be activated maximally and also submaximally from a considerable area of skin, which varies from region to region. Thus, stimulation anywhere on the volar and dorsal surface of the thumb will fire off one point on the cortex, but weaker potentials can also be obtained from the same point by stimulation over the palm of the hand and fingers, and also by stimulation of the radial side of the dorsal surface of the hand. Furthermore, continuous stimulation at one point can mask or abolish the responses from another point and this effect may be observed by stimulating such widely separated regions as the thumb and the face. Finally, the evoked cortical potential from any one point decreases if the stimulation frequency is greater than one a second and disappears at a frequency of 12–15 a second, a fact no doubt linked with the long refractory period of the thalamic neurones under barbiturate anaesthesia, and not likely to obtain in the intact animal.

The work of Adrian and of Marshall, Woolsey and Bard has so far revealed that the receptor discharges resulting from sensory stimuli are passed on to the somatic receiving area in the anterior part of the parietal lobe, probably little altered in their passage through the neurones. The principle of convergence applies and different receptor units in the skin can activate one afferent unit to the cortex and thus, a focal group of cortical neurones, probably in layers 3 and 4. Also, it would appear that different afferent units and different foci of cortical cells can be activated by a single receptor unit. It is of much interest that no response has as yet been observed to thermal and painful stimuli in the experimental animal. Possibly anaesthesia masks some responses ; or, the spontaneous activity of the cortex may, in the unanaesthetized animal, hinder detection of the signals following pain and thermal stimulation. It would be premature therefore to conclude that cortical responses to such stimuli will not eventually be found.

Somatic receiving area in the parietal cortex

Woolsey, Marshall and Bard (1942) studied in great detail the topographical localization of stimuli from the contralateral surface of

F

the body, within the somatic receiving areas (Brodmann's fields 3, 1, 2) in the monkey (*macaca mulatta*).   As conditions in man may prove to be comparable, their conclusions from data obtained in relevant experiments are of considerable importance.   They found the cortical sensory sequence, from the lateral part of the postcentral gyrus to the sulcus calloso-marginalis on the medial surface of the hemisphere to be as follows : pharynx, tongue, lower buccal cavity, lower lip, upper lip and upper buccal cavity, nose and nasal passage, eye, forehead, side of head, chin, thumb, index finger, digits 3, 4 and 5, hand, radial and ulnar surfaces of forearm, pre-axial surface of upper arm, shoulder, neck, side of head and ear, occiput, postaxial surface of arm, trunk, pre-axial surface of leg, thigh, knee and lower leg, anterior surface of ankle and medial side of foot, heel, postaxial surface of leg, i.e. of the thigh, the popliteal fossa and the calf, genitalia, anus, lower sacrum, base of tail and tip of tail.   Everywhere, the arrangement is strictly contralateral, with the exception of an ipsilateral face area located in the anterior part of the face area, and concerned mainly with sensory impulses from the lips, tongue, palate, floor of mouth and, to a slight extent, from the face adjacent to the mouth.   In this sensory arrangement, the authors emphasized the location of evoked potentials from the postaxial surface of the leg on the medial aspect of the hemisphere and from the pre-axial aspect high on the lateral part of the hemisphere.   Another interesting feature is that potentials from the head and neck are located between the pre-axial and postaxial arm locations.   Here, impulses from all parts of the head enter the cortex, but the maximal potentials are from the occipital and lateral surfaces.   A strip of cortex no wider than 2·5 millimetres receives projections from all twelve thoracic segments between the pre-axial leg area and the postaxial arm area. The overlapping fields for the three divisions of the trigeminal nerve in the most lateral part of the postcentral gyrus are considerable, and are separated quite sharply from the field for the lower cervical nerves from the thumb and digits.   There is also a fairly sharp division between the field for the arm and trunk, and that for the leg.   From a detailed analysis of the responses from the surface areas of the different dermatomes, and from the effects of posterior root stimulation in the monkey, Woolsey and his collaborators considered that the spinal segments from T_1 caudally are projected to the cortex in the same serial order as they occur in the cord.   The cervical signals are also projected serially, but are reversed *en bloc* so that C_2 lies adjacent to the trunk area and C_8 to the face area, in the lower and lateral part of the postcentral gyrus.   Another interesting finding is that the spinal segments with the largest number of posterior root-fibres, namely, C8 and L5, send responses to the widest area of cortex.

The numerous careful researches of Woolsey *et al.* have delimited the sensory sequence in the postcentral gyrus in greater detail than was possible before, and their findings in this respect are supported by the observations of Adrian in his more limited experience in the case of the monkey. The relative positions in the cortex for the pre- and postaxial limb surfaces justify Woolsey and his colleagues in drawing attention to the possible dermatomal sequence which can be discerned. Whether this is a useful conception to introduce at the cortical level is doubtful, unless it is assumed that there is a unitary projection from the receptors in the dermatomes to the cortex. This is unjustified, for the twelve thoracic dermatomes project to an area of 2·5 millimetres, great convergence having taken place. Moreover, the cervical segments are completely reversed as a whole, introducing here some principle in organization other than a purely dermatomal one.

Although the electrical method has delimited in detail the areas of the postcentral gyrus related to specific skin regions, it cannot be assumed that these areas represent cortical sensory function for the cutaneous regions concerned. No matter what explanation is eventually accepted for the evoked cortical potential, clearly it indicates only cortical stimulation and is relatively unaffected by the anaesthetics which greatly depress cortical function. Furthermore, it is not possible at present to determine the extent of cortical excitation following stimulation ; it may well be, as Adrian has observed, that under light ether anaesthesia, pressure or touch produces a wide-spread increase of activity in parts of the cortex beyond the somatic receiving area. Indeed, movement of one of the vibrissae of the muzzle may accelerate cortical neurone activity in the foot area of either hemisphere, suggesting that the evoked potential technique, carried out as it usually is under barbiturate anaesthesia, may give but a limited view of the induced cortical activity even of the somatic receiving areas. This point is further emphasized by the few observations which have already been made in man (Woolsey and Erickson), where evoked potentials of lower amplitude than those in animals can be obtained only from the posterior margin of the central sulcus ; that is, a small fraction of the cortex which is known, from clinical evidence, to be concerned with somatic sensation. Thus, in the intact brain, the spontaneous activity of cortical neurones, the origin of which is not yet understood, masks the detection of incoming signals and of their spread. Even in the postcentral gyrus, the cortical effects following stimulation depend a great deal upon the condition of the cortex. The presence of a surface negative wave probably indicates spread of excitation to cortical neurones locally, whereas the appearance of a rhythmical discharge may represent the arrival at the cortex of a thalamic after-discharge, or else the intrinsic activity of cortical neurones. A detailed discussion of these and other electrical effects in the sensory cortex is inappropriate here. Clearly, the organization of cortical sensory function cannot be delimited to the somatic receiving areas as outlined by the evoked potential technique. In this connection, the studies of Gay and Gellhorn (1949) are to be noted. They found cortical excitation, as indicated by the disappearance of dial potentials or an increase in the amplitude and frequency of background potentials in the electrocorticogram, in the sensorimotor areas in the cat and monkey following proprioceptive stimulation. In the monkey, this effect appeared especially in the precentral cortex (area 4), and to a lesser extent in the postcentral sensory cortex. Effects were greatest in the specific sensorimotor field, but they were also present in the remaining contralateral sensory cortex and also in the ipsilateral specific field.

A second sensory area in the parietal cortex

The postcentral gyrus and the homologous region in lower forms is not the only part of the parietal lobe where evoked potentials can be located following sensory stimuli. In his experiments in the cat, Adrian demonstrated an area in the anterior ectosylvian gyrus, behind the face regions of the main somatic receiving area, which was activated by contralateral stimulation of the footpads by touch or pressure. This cortical area gave movements of the claws on direct electrical stimulation, and it therefore appeared probable that it was a cortical area specially concerned with the control of the movement of the claws. Adrian did not find it in other animals, but Woolsey (1947) described an homologous area in all species which he called sensory area II and which, in the monkey, lies along the superior margin of the sylvian fissure. This region of the posterior parietal gyrus apparently receives impulses from all parts of both sides of the body, the largest responses being produced by stimulating the apices of the limbs, the snout, and the tail in lower forms. Responses from ipsilateral stimulation are weaker than those from contralateral stimulation. A face, arm and leg area can be differentiated within this second sensory cortex, the face area being in juxtaposition with the somatic receiving area in the postcentral gyrus. In the monkey, the responses are much more easily depressed by anaesthesia than those in the postcentral gyrus, and they also have a longer latency. Woolsey found too that electrical stimulation of somatic area II can produce movements in the face, arm and leg ; and experimental strychninization indicated afferent and efferent connections between this area and the pre- and postcentral convolutions bilaterally. What functional significance is to be attached to this second area is yet unknown. No detailed location of afferent discharges within it, such as occurs in the postcentral gyrus, can be made out, and much further study is clearly necessary before conclusions of value can be reached. Obviously, present techniques may permit the detection of only relatively large evoked potentials, and wide areas of the parietal cortex may receive afferent discharges from peripheral sensory stimulation, the evoked potentials of which have not yet been recorded. Were this so, Woolsey's sensory area II might only differ from the wider areas of the parietal cortex concerned with sensory process in that evoked potentials in higher forms at least are more readily distinguished from spontaneous cortical rhythms in this region under light anaesthesia.

Evoked sensory potentials in the electro-encephalogram

Dawson (1950) found that responses to the electrical stimulation of peripheral nerves can be detected on the scalp of normal human beings. They are to be found over the central region in sites which correspond with the main sensory fields, close to the central sulcus, but it was not possible to determine accurately whether they arise in the pre- or postcentral gyrus. The responses could be produced by electrical stimulation of the skin, but were smaller than that produced by stimulation of the median or ulnar nerves at the wrist, due to stimulation of both cutaneous and proprioceptive fibres in the peripheral nerve. Electro-encephalographic responses varied with constant stimuli of the peripheral nerve, a change which could not be correlated with any precise phase of the normal spontaneous rhythm, though most probably cortical in origin. The obvious difficulties of carrying out such observations in man, especially the superimposition technique necessary for the detection of small responses, make impossible any precise physiological interpretations. None the less, the results are of much clinical interest.

Strychninization of the parietal cortex

After discussing the limited areas of parietal cortex shown to respond with evoked potentials after sensory stimulation, one may now consider the wide cortical fields over which sensory phenomena can be activated by strychnine. Dusser de Barenne (1916) found that the application of strychnine to a few square millimetres of parietal cortex caused positive sensory phenomena to occur in animals, namely, hyperaesthesia and hyperalgesia. These disturbances were present bilaterally, but greatest on the contralateral side on cutaneous stimulation, and only contralaterally on deep pressure. Three main areas could be located in the expected positions, namely, a leg, an arm and trunk, and a face area. There was only little evidence of overlap or irradiation of affect from one of these regions to another, but their anteroposterior extent was considerable, extending anteriorly into Brodmann's areas 4 and 6, and posteriorly into the boundary of the parietal lobe. Strychninization of a small area within each region would cause the cutaneous over-reaction in the whole of a segment, indicating rapid spread of cortical activity within that area. This same effect could also be seen by recording the spread of the strychnine spike potentials. The role of the precentral cortex might be minimized by attributing the effects to posterior connections of the postcentral gyrus, but this assumption would also render valueless the wide extent of the fields of the parietal lobe, because close connection must exist between this region and the postcentral gyrus. Crude as the method is, it probably gives some indication of the wide and purely cortical fields that may be involved in sensory function. The bilateral effects are especially interesting in view of the strictly contralateral responses (apart from the face area) in the postcentral gyrus following the evoked potential technique, and again suggest that this earlier method may be still relatively crude in the detection of signals entering the parietal cortex.

Another important development of de Barenne's technique has been along the lines of " physiological neuronophagy ". Local application of strychnine to the cortex causes a disturbance to be propagated along various routes of conduction so as to excite other nerve-cells at a distance. This electronic reaction or " pick-up " is demonstrable by electrical methods of recording, whereby spikes of high voltage appear almost, though not quite, synchronously in the electrocorticogram. Such spikes are not to be found beyond the point of neuronic synapses. The rate of propagation of the stimulus can be determined as about 50 metres per second (with extremes of 10 and 100). In this way, the axonal distribution of the cells originally stimulated can be detected. Complicated corticocortical connections are thus revealed. The approximate route taken by such pathways can be discovered by various combinations of undercutting and isolation techniques before and after strychninization. Some of these connections prove to be intracortical ; others subcortical. Homoiotopic projections, that is, between corresponding points in the cortices of opposite hemispheres can also be demonstrated. Strychninization of the sensory cortex in any part causes activity in the corresponding nuclei within the thalamus. By the same technique, pre- and postcentral cortices may be shown to lie in very close anatomical and functional relationship. These findings confirm the view that areas of cortex do not exist as isolated units.

Electrical stimulation

With this method in animals, the early workers noted the contrasts between the abundant positive data yielded by stimulation of the motor cortex, and the paucity and inconsistency of results after stimulation of the parietal lobe. Ferrier found little more than contraction of the pupil, deviation of the eyes to one side, and perhaps turning of the head. He interpreted these findings as the reflex motor effects produced by stimulation of some visual centre, and he associated these results with his ideas that the angular gyrus was a visual centre. Flechsig (1896) and others of his time looked upon the parietal lobe as electrically inexcitable, and therefore a latent or association area. The functional significance was unknown, but it was believed that it was concerned with some type of intellectual activity.

Electrical stimulation of the parietal cortex therefore proved disappointing in animal work, and rewarding only in the case of the unanaesthetized human subject.

Bartholow [1] (1874), Ransom (1892), Cushing (1909), van Valkenburg (1914), Foerster (1936), Penfield and Boldrey (1937), Rasmussen and Penfield (1947) have been concerned with a study of electrical stimulation of this region of the brain, and the evidence abundantly shows that subjective sensory responses can only be comprehended by the intervention of the conscious patient, his understanding and interpretation of the phenomena, and his ability to describe them.

The positive results in man have been obtained principally from the postcentral gyrus adjacent to the central fissure. They show a sensory sequence in general similar to that revealed by the evoked potential technique, except that Penfield (1947), although he has looked for it repeatedly, has found no indication of a separate location of the pre-axial and postaxial surface of the proximal parts of the limbs. He has found no instance in which a sensory arm response has been found between the head and trunk, and also no instance in

---

[1] Bartholow was probably the first to stimulate the brain electrically in a conscious, though feeble-minded woman, who succumbed to this procedure. Through a defect in the cranial vault, he passed an electrode into the posterior region of the brain, first on one side and then on the other. The passage of the current produced a contraction of the contralateral arm and leg, dilatation of the pupils and a strong and unpleasant sensation of tingling in the opposite limbs. A stronger current evoked great distress followed by a generalized convulsion. She died three days later after a series of fits.

which a leg sensation was produced by stimulation above the foot and toe area. The sensations described by the patient comprised numbness, tingling and a feeling of electricity. Less often, a desire to move a part was reported, or a feeling of inability to carry out a movement. A sensation as though the part were being moved was also described. In the tongue, feelings of crawling, dryness, stiffness, cold, warmth and pains have been reported. The sensations, although often quite localized to small regions of the body, were at times more widespread, though they rarely extended outside the areas of the face, arm, leg or trunk. None the less, a sensation referred to the face and chest, hand and foot did sometimes occur, as well as other combined responses. Bilateral and ipsilateral sensory responses occurred only in the case of the face area. The close correspondence between the findings which follow electrical stimulation in man, and those obtained with the evoked potential technique in animals, must be of significance. The sensations produced are crude in nature and are of the same order as those produced by stimulation of a peripheral nerve. It would appear then that electrical stimulation of the cortex can only call forth this effect at the point of entry of the afferent fibres upon the cortex, or from the neurones with which they immediately synapse. Thereafter, the extent and nature of cortical function in conscious sensation are not revealed by electrical excitation. The combined responses are probably due to the spread of excitation in the cortex in the same order of neurones as are affected by the incoming afferent volley. A special observation of interest is that an intra-abdominal sensation, such as a sinking or choking feeling, nausea, or palpitations, could be elicited from stimulation most inferiorly and laterally and more often from the precentral than from the postcentral gyrus. Also, throughout the whole sequence, sensory responses could be obtained from the precentral gyrus, but much less frequently than from the postcentral gyrus. This is in accord with the findings of evoked potentials in the precentral gyrus on posterior root stimulation in monkeys. Penfield has produced some evidence that these sensations produced in area 4 are not dependent on areas 3, 1 and 2 being intact. The reverse is the case in respect of the motor movements produced by stimulation of 3, 1 and 2, as they are absent, at least in animals, when area 4 is ablated.

There are certain inherent drawbacks concerned in the study of the cortex by means of electrical stimulation. These have been clearly stressed in the case of the motor cortex by Leyton and Sherrington (1917), by Graham Brown and Sherrington (1912) and recently by Liddell and Phillips (1950). Specific discussion of the technique of electrical stimulation in the case of the postcentral cortex has been less outspoken. Despite these handicaps there has been an increasing tendency to claim a precision in the arrangement of cortical sensory (and motor) centres. The culmination of such attempts has been found in Penfield's " homunculus " with its minor differences between the motor and sensory sequences within the pre- and postcentral cortices respectively. Rasmussen and Penfield mentioned the complicating factors of deviation of response, facilitation and reversal, but did not proceed to discuss them. The weighty arguments against the propriety of such rigid conceptions in the case of the motor cortex have been forcefully set out by Walshe (1947). The most convincing support, however, lies in the accurate correspondence of the various experimental findings, which seems to establish a meaningful spatial relationship within the somaesthetic area, inside which a limited degree of flexibility obtains. It cannot be gainsaid but that there is a certain consistency of sensory response when experimental conditions as to type and strength of current, duration of stimulus and fixed relationships with regard to preceding stimuli have all been standardized. By and large, dysaesthesiae referable to the hand are obtained most easily, with the weakest stimuli, and with stimuli over the largest cortical territories. Stimulation after local ablation will continue to produce sensory responses referred to the hand.

One of the great theoretical drawbacks of the technique of electrical stimulation of the cortex is the implication that it may have little if any logical connection with the biological function of the cells so stimulated. Just as electrical stimulation of the motor cortex may bear but a remote analogy with the normal physiology of a willed movement, so—even more—electrical excitation of a postcentral region may have little direct bearing upon the problem of normal parietal function.

The finer electrical methods of study, using micro-electrodes, have elicited other interesting phenomena. Stimulation of a cortical cell in the postcentral gyrus sets up a wave of activity which can be followed downwards to that region of the thalamus which lies in direct anatomical relationship. From that thalamic cell a fainter impulse passes back to the cortex. Thence, after a brief delay, it passes back to the thalamus again. This to-and-fro movement of activity continues in a diminishing fashion, and constitutes what has been picturesquely termed a " reverberating circuit ". This phenomenon probably corresponds with Adrian's " after-discharges " as well as with the " multiple responses " described by Marshall, Talbot and Ades (1942). Reverberation may take place over a distance (long circuit) or between nerve-cells in proximity (local circuit). In the case of corticothalamic reverberating circuits, it has been suggested by Hsiang-Tung Chang (1950) that herein lies the anatomophysiological basis for the function of " sensory attention ".

Experimental ablations

While electrical excitation offers an analogy with the acute clinical phenomenon of the discharging lesion, partial or complete ablations of the parietal cortex in animals offers the closest analogy to the natural phenomena of chronic parietal disease. For this reason, it assumes special importance. Research entailing surgical removal of portions of brain-tissue dates from the time of Goltz, who carried out hemispherectomies in dogs either on one side or both. The results were of interest, for the animals not only did not show a permanent and total loss of motor power, but sensation too, though blunted, was certainly not lost. Subsequent generations of physiologists have carried out topectomies, or fractional cortical ablations, and have studied the after-effects, both immediate and remote. Removal of small regions of the postcentral gyrus and of the more posteriorly situated parietal regions have not been as widely studied as extirpation of the motor area. The clinical effects have differed not a little, and many of the inconsistent results seem to turn upon the different techniques used. Cutting, undercutting, electrocoagulation, cauterization, suction, fragmentation by a fine but powerful jet of water are among the measures that have been practised, and obviously some methods are less gentle than others. The more violent techniques are apt to produce traumata to cortical and subcortical areas widely in excess of the actual area attacked. Some procedures may damage the cortical blood-vessels and hence cause ischaemic areas beyond. Technical faults of this kind are probably responsible for some of the unexpected results after cortical ablation. Thus, Ferrier's production of blindness after bilateral removal of the angular gyrus, and of contralateral uni-ocular blindness after destruction of one angular gyrus, can best be explained on the basis of excessive surgical trauma coupled with faulty clinical evaluation.

The results of ablation seemed to tally not only with clinical experiences as afforded by destructive as well as discharging lesions, but also with the results of experimental electrical and chemical stimulation. There seemed to be demonstrable a set arrangement of cortical centres, made up of excitable areas which in turn were connected intimately with specific regions of the somatic musculature. It seemed as though a somatotopic mosaic were demonstrable, analogous to that described within the motor area.

Impairment of sensibility followed parietal removals, but the alterations in sensation were not as intense as might have been expected, and they were not necessarily permanent. As far as could be gleaned from the clinical testing of the experimental animals, the sensory defects comprised both changes in superficial sensibility and also in proprioception. The latter often outweighed the former, and might dominate the postoperative clinical picture.

The difficulties of testing experimental animals for sensory impairment proved to be considerable. Experimenters went to great lengths in devising ingenious test-methods which went some way at any rate towards overcoming the drawbacks of working with inarticulate and non-co-operative subjects. Nevertheless, despite all the resources of experimental physiology, it is well-nigh impossible to study just those very qualities of sensory discrimination which might be expected to be impaired after parietal ablations, namely the more subtle aspects of stereognosis, two-point discrimination, tactile after-sensation, sensory adaptation, and so on. The careful studies of Ruch, Fulton and German (1938) upon the discrimination of weights and of textures are important in that they illustrate not only the successful surmounting of inherent difficulties, but the type of sensory loss which is likely to follow purely cortical removals in the case of primates. The findings suggested that the parietal lobes, though concerned with the power to distinguish small differences in weight, were not the sole areas concerned with this activity. Ruch and his associates concluded from their experience that : (1) the parietal lobes in monkeys are concerned with higher sensory discriminations ; (2) loss of such functions cannot be associated with any circumscribed region of the parietal cortex ; (3) there is no separate localization for tactual as opposed to proprioceptive functions ; and that (4) the parietal lobe is not the sole locus of sensory representation for the contralateral hand. These cautious statements are of particular value when taken in association with the results of other experimental methods of research, and particularly with the clinical evidence afforded by parietal disease.

Much attention has been paid by neurophysiologists to the " hopping and placing reactions " in monkeys with parietal ablations. These have been regarded as useful indices of disordered postural sensibility, though it is possible that impaired motor power may also come into the picture. After removal of the postcentral gyrus on one side, hopping and placing reactions may be severely and permanently affected as far as the opposite limb is concerned.

Peele (1944) and others have described a syndrome, or pattern of clinical defect which may be expected to follow extirpation of the parietal lobes in the monkey. This syndrome is made up of the following : (1) defect in tactile placing, and also in hopping reactions and " proprioceptive " placing ; the first named of these defects is severe, the two latter being milder. (2) Some falling-off in the discrimination of weights of differing magnitude. This impairment, though permanent, is not great. It is more evident in the chimpanzee than in the lower primates. (3) The more extensive the parietal ablation, the greater the defect enumerated in (1) and (2) above ; (4) some delay in the response to tactile stimulation, and probably some raising of the threshold ; (5) inaccurate localization of tactile stimuli ; (6) imperfect tactile recognition of geometrical forms ; (7) a sensory ataxia of the limbs ; and (8) hypotonus, muscle atrophy and sluggish tendon reflexes. These signs were demonstrable long after operation.

Peele sought to correlate types of sensory dysfunction with particular areas of the parietal cortex. Cutaneous sensibility seemed to be chiefly represented within the postcentral gyrus. Discriminative ability seemed to be affected by lesions situated anywhere within the parietal lobe, and the impairment was long-lasting. It appeared, too, that the whole parietal lobe was concerned with proprioceptive stimuli, but other regions of the cortex outside the parietal lobe also seemed to be significant. These views can be compared with the earlier ideas of Minkowski, namely, that tactile sensibility in the monkey is a function of the postcentral gyrus, and also of the superior parietal lobule and the supramarginal gyrus ; that pain is diffusely represented in the cortex ; and that deep sensibility is represented in both the pre- and the postcentral convolutions and also in the rest of the parietal lobe. According to Peele, areas 5 and 7 of the monkey's cortex are probably concerned with the limbs, while the postcentral gyrus contains representation of the whole of the opposite side of the body.

The fact that so often sensory disturbances are incomplete in nature, or transient in duration, even after extensive destructions of the parietal cortex in animals, leads to the question whether other parts of the brain might not be intimately concerned with the normal appreciation of sensory phenomena. Suspicion falls first upon the motor cortex anteriorly ; secondly, the contralateral hemisphere of the brain ; and thirdly, subcortical centres, e.g. the thalamus. Both clinical and experimental data lend weight to the opinion that all three of these possibilities may operate in normal conditions. The importance therefore of extending ablation experiments in the future so as to include other cerebral areas is obvious ; e.g. precentral plus postcentral topectomies ; biparietal extirpations, both fractional and complete ; and parietothalamic destructions.

The " motor " effects of parietal extirpation in monkeys are of interest in that they are comparable with what is often encountered in the natural state in human subjects with parietal lesions. A " loathness " to move, as Peele has put it, in the absence of paralysis, bears an important analogy with the unilateral passive neglect (or disregard) so characteristic of early parietal disease in man. With more severe parietal ablations, there may be so much proprioceptive loss as to bring about gross sensory ataxia, a pseudoparalysis, awkwardness in digital movements, the spontaneous adoption of unusual attitudes, and lastly a failure to correct postures which have been passively produced. To these signs may be added a loss of muscle bulk in the affected limbs, a finding which again can be compared with the hemi-atrophy following parietal disease in man. Whether this wasting can be wholly put down to lack of employment of the limb is not yet certain.

CHAPTER III

GENERAL REMARKS ON PARIETAL SYMPTOMATOLOGY

In taking a case-history, he was urging, begging, ironical, good-natured, even endearing, permitting the patient to express himself freely ; or on other occasions asking him innumerable questions, but never tiring until he was sure to have obtained all possible information.

C. E. LASÈGUE.

Gweddw crefft heb ei dawn. (Technical skill is sterile without inspiration.)

Some preliminary observations are worth while before describing the clinical consequences of disease of the parietal lobes in man. The subject is not a simple one, for, to begin with, the possible clinical manifestations are diverse. Patients are apt to differ widely ; one showing but few abnormal signs, and these mild in nature ; another displaying an intricate clinical picture with elaborate psychomotor and psychosensory features. Why this diversity should be is not yet fully understood. The actual size of the lesion naturally plays a part, though a less important one than might be expected. The pathological nature of the disease-process is significant—that is to say, whether it be neoplastic, ischaemic, atrophic or inflammatory ; and with this factor, the degree of abruptness of onset, the question of progression or regression of symptoms, and the length of the clinical history are, of course, important. Special mention should be made of whether the lesion is a solitary one, or whether it is one of several, for the clinical result of two or three isolated lesions, i.e. metastatic growths, is not necessarily the same as a mere summation of the effects of each separate focus of disease. The age of the patient at the time he develops his parietal affection may be momentous, especially if it be a question of disease of an immature as opposed to a mature nervous system. Lastly, we believe that the type of personality of the patient before the onset of parietal disease may influence considerably the eventual clinical picture. These variables are reminiscent of the " four factors of the insanities " described by Hughlings Jackson, wherein he included (1) the depth of the dissolution ; (2) the rapidity of the process ; (3) the kind of brain in which the dissolution occurs, and (4) the influence of internal and external circumstances upon the patient.

There is yet another set of reasons why parietal symptomatology should be so complex. From the Spencerian point of view, the parietal lobes may be considered highly organized structures, that is to say, far evolved. The consequences of a disorder of such structures might be expected to be anything but simple. Special clinical techniques are required if the case-record is to be adequate. The ordinary routine neurological and psychiatric examination will not unravel all of the characteristic signs. This fact explains why a retrospective study of case-reports prepared by others proves disappointing so often, for doubt may readily arise as to whether a particular sign was ever specifically looked for, and whether a particular technique was ever put into practice. Thus, to take but one example, it is often impossible to be sure from a perusal of a set of notes, whether a Gerstmann syndrome existed during life, or not. Failure to enumerate the constituent components may really mean that the syndrome was not borne in mind, and never actually looked for. These various characteristic " parietal signs " will be discussed more fully in the appropriate places, and with them, the clinical methods which should be adopted for their elicitation ; nevertheless, it is desirable to mention briefly some of the special techniques of examination at this stage :

1. *Sensory testing.* Besides the ordinary employment of cotton wool, pin prick, thermal contacts and vibrating tuning-forks, and the usual tests for postural sensibility, it will be necessary to apply careful and detailed stereognosic tests. The various ways of carrying out these tests will be described in the next chapter. Bilateral simultaneous testing is also important when looking for evidence of parietal disease, and the stimuli so employed may include almost any of the ordinary modalities, though bimanual simultaneous testing for stereognosis often yields the most valuable information. Tactile discrimination as displayed in the compass test is a highly important line of investigation. Various devices for the study of the patient's ability to localize stimuli should be perfected. Discrimination of weights and of textures are often revealing tests. For a more intimate study of parietal sensory affections, recourse may be had to more elaborate techniques, e.g. von Frey's hairs, aesthesiometers, pallesthesiometers, algometers, the use of instruments for testing 3, 4, 5 and 6 points simultaneously applied, " two-dimensional stereognosis " and graphaesthesia. Special tests may be used for the measurement of sensory adaptation as well as of tactile after-sensation. These last-named studies are investigative rather than diagnostic in their scope.

Interesting results may follow the accurate mapping-out of regions of altered cutaneous sensibility, for these areas may be found not to conform to expected patterns, a fact which in itself may prove helpful in diagnosis.

2. The elicitation of *Constructional apraxia* will require special tests. A study of the patient's attempts at reading, writing and arithmetic will also be invaluable. Here too belongs the important group of pencil and paper tests whereby the patient is directed to draw from memory various common objects, especially those comprising a certain symmetry and a certain amount of detail. A clock-face ; a house ; an elephant ; motor-car ; horse and cart ; bicycle ; the head of a daisy ; a man's face—these prove to be very suitable themes. In a special category will belong those drawing-tests designed to reveal spatial, topographical and geographical conceptions as well as the power to revisualize images. Here belong such tasks as the drawing of a map of England ; the making of a plan of the streets in the neighbourhood of the patient's home ; the reading of a blue-print or a street-map ; the construction of a two-dimensional plan of the patient's own house, or living-room, or the hospital ward.

3. Other spatial and constructional test-measures which may reveal considerable defect in patients with parietal disease are the copying of two-dimensional geometrical patterns made with sticks or matches ; and of three-dimensional erections of bricks. The cube-analysis test of Paterson and Zangwill is often helpful. Of particular value is the employment of Kohs' blocks. Form boards, both simple and complicated, may prove useful. The use of various maze-tests may perhaps reveal a defect in the utilization of extrapersonal space.

4. Tests for the concept of laterability should always be made. These should be followed by tests for the ability to point out, identify, or move various parts of the anatomy to command, with particular reference to the fingers. In this latter connection, the examiner should get the patient to identify his own fingers as well as those of others.

5. Visual tests, both complicated and instrumental, may be necessary. Thus, the ordinary perimetric examination should be followed by tests for qualitative defects of vision. These might include tachistoscopic procedures for the recognition of objects briefly exposed ; tests of the ability to recognize two stimuli simultaneously displayed ; tests of the " effective visual field " according to the techniques of Bay, Cibis and others ; estimation of the rate of flicker fusion ; optokinetic nystagmus ; orientation within visual space ; a study of after-images ; the recognition, naming and matching of colours ; the judgment of rate and direction of moving objects ; stereoscopic vision ; the Gottschaldt figures test ; comprehension and appraisal of visual illusions ; and also the unravelling

and identification of superimposed line drawings. It may be necessary to measure dark adaptation ; and the changes in visual acuity according to variable intensities of illumination. Of a more semantic order are the tests of the comprehension of objects ; pictures (both simple and complex) ; humorous " situational " drawings and cartoons ; recognition of human faces as well as of pictures of faces ; and the divinating of the meaning of facial expression. Benton's visual retention procedure is often useful.

6. These foregoing special tests for parietal function may be followed by certain non-specific intelligence tests. Sorting tests (of Weigl and others) may be useful in indicating a general disorder in abstract thinking. Thematic apperception tests may do likewise. Vocabulary tests may be valuable in so far as they reveal the premorbid intelligence level which can be compared with the present performance.

7. Special tests designed to show the integrity of time sense (chronognosia) may be needed before it is realized that this particular faculty is grossly impaired.

There is yet another reason why patients with parietal disease should so often present a difficult diagnostic problem. This turns upon the fact that the patient—for reasons which will be discussed later—may be unaware of the extent and severity of his lessened efficiency. Consequently, the patient's own account of his symptoms may afford a wholly inadequate picture of the real state of affairs. It becomes of more than usual importance therefore to supplement the history with information culled from interviews with the patient's close relatives, friends and business associates. In this way, valuable evidence may come to light as to a change in personality, habits or professional efficiency. The patient's ability to cope with the daily routine of looking after himself, his clothes and his belongings, of finding his way about, mixing with others, reading, conversing, taking decisions, embarking upon new projects, planning ahead—these are all points upon which his own judgment is probably worthless. A consultation with the friends and relatives may also be utilized as a means of gauging the patient's premorbid personality and intellectual level.

A fourth factor still further confuses the picture. The patient with parietal disease is, as a rule, a poor witness, and an unreliable subject under testing procedures. His performance may vary from day to day and even from moment to moment. A very simple instance may be given in illustration : when the patient is tested with a pin prick, his eyelids being closed, at one moment he may proclaim he feels the pin, but at the next stimulus, he may apparently feel

G

nothing. Out of a series of contacts, he may perhaps answer to only 50 per cent of them. That this is not simply due to a rise in the threshold of sensibility is shown by the fact that, if the force of the stimulus is increased, the patient continues to miss some of the contacts. Indeed, the percentage of failures bears no relationship to the strength of the stimulus. The picture may prove still more complicated : the patient may even assert he can feel the point of a pin at a moment when he has not been touched at all.

Faced with more elaborate test-situations, the patient may behave in a still more unpredictable fashion. An object placed in his palm may be recognized at once ; or not at all ; or only after a delay. Or its physical properties may be described, but its identity may baffle him. It therefore becomes difficult to assess this type of performance with a " plus " or a " minus ". An inability to identify an object only after a considerable delay cannot fairly be passed as normal, or rejected as a failure. The only satisfactory method is to record exactly what the patient does and says. In this way, it also becomes important to take note of the patient's emotional reaction to a test-situation which is proving difficult. Evidences of a " catastrophic reaction " in the way of flushing of the face, watering of the eyes, distress, irritability, petulancy or hostility are all worthy of record. So too is an unexpected measure of imperturbability when faced with a series of failures ; or perhaps an undue jocularity or facetiousness, though these latter responses are possibly more suggestive of frontal than of parietal lesions.

Variability of response is equally significant and typical in the case of patients afflicted with agnosic disorders in the visual sphere. The patient may be found to recognize one object but not another : a fork but not a spoon ; a table but not a chair. In reading tests, some words are correctly interpreted, others are not. The examiner should not gloss over these inconsistencies, but he should take note of them and realize them for what they are, the evidences of a brain-damaged person doing the best he can with those cerebral mechanisms which are still intact. At the same time, it would be fallacious to adopt the attitude of seeking for some inherent property in the objects and words missed as opposed to those which are recognized, and thereby trying to identify some specific but artificial type of agnosia, involving this or that kind of symbol or object.

One effect of a catastrophic reaction is to impair the efficiency of the patient's performance. Hence, the paradox may be found whereby a relatively unskilled examiner, who does not possess the knack of gaining the confidence and full co-operation of the patient, may so disturb him as to augment a number of parietal disabilities.

On the other hand, a more experienced physician may encourage a better total performance on the part of the patient. The one, by his maladroitness, may therefore elicit signs which the other, by his greater skill, does not substantiate. But the former has had the advantage of bringing to the surface a greater amount of significant data.

Examples of this variability in performance will be given in the chapters which follow. Here again, it is essential that the examining physician should be alert to this type of characteristic behaviour. He should note it in his written record of the case, and utilize it in his diagnostic evaluation. In this way, the neurologist may perhaps avoid what is actually a very common error, namely, to regard the early case of parietal disease as an instance of hysteria. Similarly, a patient suffering from the effects of advanced parietal destruction may be written off as an example of dementia. The problem of the differentiating of parietal disorders from hysteria on the one hand, and dementia on the other, is discussed in Chapter XI.

Cortical versus Subcortical lesions

In the past, some writers have tended to emphasize a difference between purely cortical lesions, and those which involve the white matter of the parietal lobe, whether in isolation or in addition to the cortex. This is the old problem of " poliopathology " versus " leuco-pathology ", the one being regarded as characteristic of wartime neurology, the latter being the commoner product of civilian practice. This attempt at making a distinction has been especially frequent when sensory manifestations have been under consideration. It is doubtful, however, how far such a distinction is possible or even desirable to attempt. The conception of a purely cortical defect is open to question. Even if such a type of pathology can be said ever to exist, it must admittedly be very rare. True, some obscure types of laminar brain atrophy implicate only the most superficial cell-layers of the cortex, but even here, the axons of the affected cells cannot but share in the pathology, and the lesion thus becomes extended deeply into the white matter, or into contiguous parts of the cortex which are not obviously atrophic themselves. The existence of complex corticocortical ramifications, and of corticosubcortical " feed-back " processes illustrates the fallacy of looking upon small cortical areas of disease as isolated defects. Extra-cerebral space-occupying lesions have been quoted as examples of alleged purely cortical lesions, e.g. subdural haematoma, falcine meningiomata ; but again, any pressure effect upon the underlying cortex must soon be taken up by the subjacent white matter.

Consequently, most lesions—if not all—may be looked upon as subcortical or as corticosubcortical. Nevertheless, it is probably safe to conjecture that the depth to which the lesion extends plays an important part. A small parietal lesion will probably produce different clinical effects according to whether it involves the cortex, or lies immediately deep to the cortex, or between the cortex and the thalamus, or whether it actually infiltrates the cellular structure of the thalamus itself in addition to the ascending and descending thalamo-parietal pathways.

Sidedness

With the advent in *homo sapiens* of cerebral inequality, and the development of dominance, handedness and speech, it is not surprising that parietal lesions should produce in man (as opposed to experimental animals) different clinical effects according to whether the right side or the left is at fault. Broadly speaking, the parietal area of the dominant hemisphere, when diseased, is apt to include among its clinical manifestations, disorder of speech and disorder of " praxis ". To say this is not to assume a localization within that hemisphere of the aptitude of speech, nor of co-ordinate motor activities. It merely emphasizes a greater degree of dysfunction when the dominant side of the brain is deranged. This is not to suggest that there may not also possibly occur some minor degree of dysphasia or dyspraxia with a lesion of the subordinate parietal region. Neither does the foregoing statement assume that disorder of speech and disorder of language are synonymous conceptions.

Nielsen has suggested that, after disease of the major cerebral hemisphere, the minor side may be concerned with the faculty of language, in a manner which is both variable and complex. The change-over may in some cases take place with great facility, with difficulty in others, and not at all in some persons. Visual, auditory and motor aspects of speech may not be transferred to the minor side altogether. The major temporal lobe and the major occipital lobe may not be ipsilaterally located. Russell Brain considered that, in left-handed persons, the role of the two hemispheres is not merely reversed, for the right hemisphere may function as the major one for speech, but behave as the minor one in other respects (1945).

The parietal lobe is of added interest when cerebral dominance is concerned, in that disease of the minor or subordinate hemisphere seems, at first sight at least, to be associated with a greater measure of upset in the integrity of the body-image. The possible fallacy of this belief will be discussed later.

When studying patients with right parietal lesions, one ordinarily is not embarrassed by the complication of difficulties in intercommunication between patient and doctor, or in the execution of elaborate movements on the patient's part. This fact leaves the field clearer for a more detailed probing of the remaining gnosic defects. So it becomes obvious that disorders of corporeal awareness; of visuospatial conceptions; of interdimensional manipulations loom larger in the clinical picture. Whether this greater degree of importance is real or merely relative is open to debate, and will be argued in due course. There is some reason to believe that lesions of the subordinate hemisphere are followed by a greater loss in memory and general capacity for attention, than in the case of the dominant half of the brain. This preponderance applies more especially to frontal lesions, but Pfeiffer has found applicability to parietal lesions also.

We should also mention at this point the evidence now available to suggest that the results of some test-measures depend not so much upon a general impairment of intellectual function as upon sidedness of the lesion. In this category may belong Weigl's sorting test which has been traditionally regarded as a mark of impaired power of abstraction due to a cerebral lesion irrespective of its location. McFie and Piercy, however, found that the incidence of failure on this test bore a significant relation to the presence of disease of the dominant hemisphere (1952). Similarly, in the case of highest level stereognosic procedures, the dominant hand may prove in the normal subject to be more efficient. Sidedness may possibly play a role therefore in determining the degree of astereognosis with a unilateral parietal lesion.

CHAPTER IV

DISORDERS OF TACTILE FUNCTION

La main est à la fois un agent et un interprète du developpement de l'esprit, elle mériterait d'arrêter davantage l'attention des physiologistes et des psychologues qui l'ont un peu negligée.

C. Féré.

He was not thinking, which left his every sense on the alert—his fingers, even when caked with mud and pocket fug, had been quick to distinguish the image on medal or coin, and to tell, by leaf or stalk, plants whose name he did not know. " Hi, there, Peloux lad, just tell us what I've got ahold of here ? " Chéri recalled the ginger-headed lad who, under cover of darkness, would push into his hand a dead mole, a small snake, a tree-frog, an over-ripe fruit, or some piece of filth, and then exclaim, " Blimey, he gets it every time ! "

Colette.

During the actual exploration of an object there is a vivid mental state ; we may call it a tactual perception. Now suppose we think of the object when it is absent, popularly, " have an idea of it " ; there is then a faint mental state, a tactual idea. In both cases the centre for tactual ideas is engaged ; a tactual idea is a faint tactual perception, and a tactual perception is a vivid tactual idea ; the centre for tactual ideation and for tactual perception is one ; it is made up of the same sensori-motor arrangements of the highest centres.

Hughlings Jackson.

Focal (sensory) epilepsy

In the chapter dealing with the experimental physiological aspects, an account was given of the results which follow electrical methods of stimulating the parietal cortex in the conscious human subject. The question now arises as to the nature of spontaneously occurring Jacksonian attacks, associated with cicatricial or neoplastic processes in this region. This aspect of the parietal problem offers an interesting comparison of " natural " (i.e. pathophysiological) events on the one hand with the artificial occurrences or " operations " in the philosophical sense, as provoked in the laboratory.

Ordinarily, the sensation described by the patient is one of a dysaesthesia which may be relatively simple and easy to describe ; or which, on the other hand, may be complex. A tingling ; burning ; numbness ; a feeling of pins and needles ; these are common descriptions. Less often the patient speaks of a coldness ; a wetness (hygric sensation) which again may be qualified as warm, cold, tepid, or hot ; or a freezing sensation. Of considerable interest are the negative

86

feelings, as though the affected segment had disappeared. We do not know whether the sensory experiences are actually diverse, ranging from the simple to the complex, or whether a hiatus lies in the translation of experience into verbal description. It may be that the degree of intraversion, the command of language and the ordinary speech-habits of the patient determine whether the sensation is described in commonplace terms, or in words which are out of the ordinary, even bizarre.

At times, we hear the story that a focal attack is preceded by a feeling " as if the limb were moving ", though actually no movement either deliberate or involuntary is taking place at all. This illusory movement may be highly complex, and sometimes, intensely disagreeable. Thus, not only may a limb seem to tremble, or to twitch, or jerk, or slowly to alter its position, but it may appear violently to twist or contort itself. Complicated phenomena relating to the body-image may develop, belonging to the category of what Bonnier termed " paraschematia ". Thus, a limb may seem to shorten at the expense of the proximal portion, so that the hand (or foot) which may also seem to be in violent involuntary activity, may appear to become telescoped up towards the trunk. The hand may even feel as though it actually entered within the thorax, in which new location it may seemingly continue to be in furious agitation.

" Pain " may also be used as a descriptive term, although admittedly not often. Sherrington (1900), indeed, suggested that pain rarely occurs as part of a focal sensory attack, an argument which he adduced as evidence that the pain-conducting system halts at a level lower than the cortex. Clinical experience does not altogether support this contention. There are case-reports where pain—presumably cortically induced—constitutes a part of a focal seizure. (See Head and Holmes, Case 18 (1911), quoted below.) The pain in such cases is rarely a pure, uncomplicated experience, but is more often an attribute which accompanies a dysaesthesia. Hence, we come across subjective accounts such as " painful tingling like a severe electric shock " ; or " intensely unpleasant coldness . . . horrible ".

As in the case of motor focal seizures, the body-segment most often affected in sensory attacks, or at any rate affected first, is the hand. Occasionally, the site of origin of the dysaesthesia may be elsewhere, and in such cases the tongue, and the circumoral region on one side, are next most often implicated. Not infrequently, several discrete regions (lips and thumb ; hand and mouth ; lips, tongue and fingers) are simultaneously the seat of a dysaesthesia so that the patient is unable to trace any kind of priority. When the hand is chiefly, or primarily, the seat of a sensory attack, the patient may at times specifically implicate a localized portion of this region. Thus, the thumb, or the thumb and forefinger may be primarily affected. Other fingers are less often involved in isolation. The pre-axial portion of the hand seems to be more significant than the postaxial, in this respect.

The subjective sensory experiences, commencing in this or that corporeal segment, may spread to other regions. This march of events is generally in accordance with the principles of contiguity or propinquity of centrally represented body-segments. Experience of sensory focal attacks in patients with cerebral tumours or scars tallies closely in this way with the results of electrical stimulation of the human cortex. As in the latter circumstances, the ipsilateral side of the body may also become involved in the later stages of an attack, and indeed the attack may become generalized ; motor phenomena may participate and consciousness may eventually be lost.

1. *Focal sensory attacks, starting in the fingers.*

Male, aged 47 years (No. 32718), complained of " attacks " of some four months standing, occurring at least once daily. Each would start as a " pins and needles " sensation in thumb and fingers of the left hand. This feeling would then travel up the whole thickness of the arm to the shoulder, then up the left side of the neck to the cheek and temple ; and inside the mouth to the left half of the tongue, where the sensation would assume a curious " tickling " character. Simultaneously, a burning feeling would extend down the left side of the trunk to the groin and perineum ; thence down the left leg as far as the toes as a " pins and needles " sensation. This phenomenon would usually last about five minutes, and when the feeling of " pins and needles " had subsided, a sense of " numbness " would follow and remain for a short while in the same areas. (Case of cerebral tumour.)

2. The following case report taken from Schwob's monograph illustrates a *focal sensory attack, starting in one side of the face.*

Male, aged 52 years, was admitted to hospital in 1932. In 1928, he had a weakness of the left arm lasting some hours. In 1930, he awoke one night with a feeling of " twisting " in the region of the cheek and tongue, which was followed by loss of consciousness and convulsion. For a fortnight before admission, a new type of attack began to develop. These comprised a sensation of creeping (*fourmillement*) in the left side of the face which extended to the arm, then the leg, then ascending once again to the face so as to involve the interior of the nostril. Then would come a feeling as if a ball were trying to pass through an orifice which was too narrow.

3. *Focal attacks of a painful nature, starting in the foot.*

A patient, whose lesion turned out to be a glioma lying immediately beneath the right postcentral gyrus close to the mesial surface of the hemisphere, suffered from attacks of pain of short duration : ". . . like an electric shock " beginning in the left foot, ascending the leg to the hip, then passing up the left side of the body to the shoulder and into the left arm and the left half of the face. At first, the attacks were purely sensorial but later they were always followed by clonic spasm in the left limbs, beginning with the foot, and by jerking of the head to the left. (Head and Holmes, Case 18.)

4. *Focal attacks beginning in one half of the palate, associated with a parietal tumour.*

A patient who proved to have a spongioblastoma growing from the sylvian fissure at a point half way to the vertex, and between the fissure of Rolando and the postcentral convolution, suffered from as many as 30 or more focal attacks a day. Each would begin with a constriction in the throat, accompanied by tremulous jerkings of the Adam's apple, and a numb cold feeling

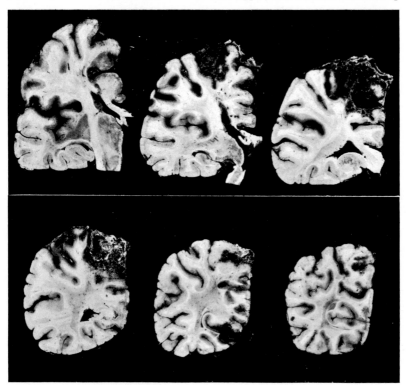

Fig. 48. Arteriovenous angioma involving mesial and upper parts of the right cerebral hemisphere ; Case 5.

over the left half of the tongue, the floor of the mouth and especially the inner aspect of the left cheek. Almost immediately after slow twitchings would appear in the platysma, increasing in strength and frequency. Finally, the twitching would spread to the left side of the face. The whole attack would last up to a minute, and consciousness was at no time lost. (Silverstein, 1931.)

5. *Focal attacks starting in the foot.*

A. B., female, aged 54, was found to have an arteriovenous angioma extending up to the vertex and involving the mesial surface of the right hemisphere (see Fig. 48). Her chief clinical symptom consisted in attacks of a " numby, jagging " feeling beginning in the left foot, extending to the left arm, and then to the head, stopping in the left eye. Sometimes, the sensation, instead of ceasing there, would return into the foot. Synchronous with this sensation, the big toe would move involuntarily up and down. The arm would be jerked about, and the head drawn down towards the left shoulder.

6. *Focal attacks beginning in the nose.*

G. F., female. For two months prior to admission, the patient experienced curious attacks which would start with tingling inside the nose. This would be followed by tingling in the right hand, with a few to-and-fro spasmodic jerkings of the wrist and fingers of that hand, culminating in similar dysaesthesiae and spasms in the left hand. The morbid anatomy proved to consist in a glioblastoma which filled the white matter of the left parietal lobe. (Patient under the care of Dr. Elkington.)

Spontaneous tactile sensations ; tactile perseveration ; polyaesthesia ; hallucinations of touch

Intermediate between the true subjective sensations which constitute sensory focal attacks, and the personal experiences which immediately follow the application of a tactile stimulus, are a number of diverse phenomena. These take the form of a subjective experience which bears only an imperfect, inaccurate, or delayed relationship with an actual stimulus. In this way, they belong more to the category of illusions of touch than true hallucinations. In many circumstances, patients with cerebral lesions are apt to display these phenomena ; and indeed the more careful the technique of sensory testing and recording, the more often such manifestations will appear. It would be needless, however, to be dismayed by these phenomena, and wrong to attribute them to faulty testing. On the contrary, they are important and interesting ; they are actually of diagnostic value in that they suggest a very high level of sensory disturbance.

For example, during the compass test for tactile discrimination, the patient may erroneously proclaim that a single stimulus is really a duplex but simultaneous stimulus, in other words, a virtual diplohaptia. Or again, after a series of stimuli have been applied at short but regular intervals, the patient may continue in a perseveratory manner to feel contacts when there are none. Ordinarily, only one or two such phantom touches are felt, apparently with diminishing intensity so that the patient soon becomes hesitant in his replies and finally quite uncertain as to whether he has been touched or not. The occurrence of these two kinds of tactile illusions is not to be ascribed to the effect of undue preoccupation with very faint stimuli, for the percentage of illusions is the same whatever the strength of the stimulus.

Head and Holmes referred to tactile hallucinations as occurring in patients with cerebral lesions during the technique of graduated tactile stimuli. They did not believe that hallucinations of touch indicated an untrustworthiness on the part of the patient who was indeed able to give consistent replies over the " normal " side of the body. Some of their patients were of high intelligence and were able to explain the occurrence of these spontaneous tactile phenomena. They pointed out that an interrupted touch stimulus felt different over the affected segment, in that the touch seemed to remain in contact with the skin. After a series of touches a continuous sensation would be produced. Upon the background of this persistence of sensation, subsequent touches might or might not be felt, or they might be imagined.

Another type of tactile hallucination is to be found in " spontaneous stereognosic sensations ". With such, the patient has a feeling as if something were lying in the palm of one hand. The feeling may be so vivid that the patient can go on to describe the size, shape, texture and temperature of the object, and he may be astonished to find later that the hand is really empty. As a variant of this phenomenon, the patient may feel stereognosic phantom sensations in the affected hand when an actual object is held in the normal hand. The phantom feelings are usually fainter than the real ones and they tend to fade and disappear even though the normal hand continues to hold on to the test object. Yet again, phantom alloaesthetic sensations may appear in the affected hand some minutes after an object had been held in the other hand and then released.

Such phenomena are graphically illustrated in the case recorded by Allen (1928). His patient had a meningioma removed from the postrolandic sensory cortex of the left hemisphere, close to the midline. As soon as he became conscious after the anaesthetic, he imagined he was holding something in the palm of the right hand. This was a very distinct feeling which was constantly present for two days, although the nature of the phantom object varied. He might feel a smooth rounded object " like a ball which just fits into the palm of the hand ", or else " something rough and jagged and hard like a piece of road granite ". Sometimes, it seemed to be a lady's small mirror ; or a pencil case ; or a matchbox. On the third and fourth days after the operation, the stereognosic fantasies were occurring only intermittently. The patient discovered also that, when a thermometer was placed in the palm of the left hand, he could feel a similar sensation in the other hand as if a thermometer were there also. A matchbox, penny, fountain-pen placed in the left hand was felt and identified, but on each occasion it provoked a similar but fainter feeling in the opposite hand also. When an object was placed in the right hand, he could appreciate the general size and shape, but he might fail to identify it. When the object was withdrawn, the sensation of its presence persisted for at least a minute afterwards. With successive tests, this persistent sensation became weaker and gradually disappeared. On the twelfth day after the operation, another tactile phenomenon occurred. The patient had been smoking a cigarette, holding it between the first and second fingers of the left hand. About a quarter of an hour after he had finished the cigarette, and had thrown it away, he felt as though he were now holding a cigarette between the first and second fingers of the right hand. This feeling was most vivid. There was one more curious tactile fantasy which occurred on the twenty-first day. He put a cigarette between his lips and sought for something with which to light it. Suddenly, he felt as though a box of matches were in the right hand. But the right hand was empty ; so was the left hand. Looking around him, he saw a box of matches lying on the bed. Allen thought that the attitude of the patient's fingers would play a part in determining the presence and nature of a stereognosic hallucination. He also believed that mental fatigue was a factor.

In cases of parietal disease, other tactile illusions may be found. A patient who showed an early Gerstmann syndrome, a constructional apraxia for three-dimensional tasks, and later a visual disorientation, was unable to localize contacts over his right hand or forearm with any degree of accuracy, although postural sensibility was intact. He would hesitate and point to a region in the air somewhere near the midline of the body. Touches on the left hand were accurately localized, as were touches over the left cheek. When immediately afterwards a contact was made on the back of the left hand, he confidently projected the stimulus to the left cheek. This occurred three times in succession. Then once again, when the examiner touched either the right hand or the right cheek, the patient confidently referred the stimulus to the left cheek (tactile perseveration with rostral displacement and alloaesthesia). (Case No. 36459.)

Yet another tactile illusion may be found in cases of parietal disease, whereby a single stimulus is felt and localized correctly perhaps, but a few seconds later is followed by a secondary illusory tactile sensation in some other part of the body. A little later, tertiary and even quaternary sensations may appear. Schilder has given a good example of this type of polyaesthesia. When his patient was touched on the right side near the breast, she felt the stimulus first on the shoulder, but 4 to 10 seconds later she would experience a second sensation near the elbow, a third on the upper part of the leg, and a fourth on the foot. These illusory " palihaptic " phenomena were always duller than the primary sensation. In the same patient, passive manipulations of the fingers of one hand might produce, after a delay, faint phantom feelings of movement in the other hand, in addition to the actually postural sensation in the fingers which have been actually moved. This patient had a vascular lesion of the left hemisphere, believed to be deep within the parietal lobe.

Cortical sensory loss

Knowledge of the nature of the sensory manifestations which follow parietal affections dates from the early part of the twentieth century, and later received a considerable impetus from the traumatic experiences of the first world war (Verger, 1900 ; Bianchi, 1910 ; Head and Holmes, 1911 ; Monakow, 1914 ; Dejerine, 1914 ; Redlich, 1928). As long ago as 1900, Verger laid down as characteristic of cortically produced hemi-anaesthesia, a relatively slight implication of pain and temperature while touch is only qualitatively involved, i.e. inaccurately localized. Dejerine was one of the first to draw attention to the preponderance of impairment of postural sensibility, of tactile discrimination, of the power of tactile localization, and of stereognosis. Tactile sensibility was said to be but lightly involved, and pain and thermal sensitivity impaired but little, if at all. This clinical picture constitutes the " cortical sensory syndrome " of Dejerine and Mouzon (1914). The following year, however, the same two authors described a case-record in which the sensory dissociation was exactly the opposite. Subsequent neurological experience, however, has confirmed that the earlier picture of Dejerine and Mouzon was really the more characteristic. Mme. Athanassio Bénisty reported that the sensory modalities most often affected are the localization of tactile and painful stimuli, tactile discrimination, the appreciation of moderate ranges of temperature ; in short, what she regarded as the " superior forms of sensibility ".

Head and Holmes had much to say about the appreciation of painful stimuli in cases of cortical parietal lesions. According to their findings, purely cortical damage leads to no change in the threshold for measureable painful or uncomfortable stimuli. The patient does not express a greater dislike for these stimuli on one side, than the other. True, a prick may be described as " plainer " or " sharper " on the normal side, but in the opinion of Head and Holmes this difference is due to a defective appreciation of the pointed nature of the stimulus and bears no direct relation to the painfulness of the sensation evoked. In other words, the judgment constitutes an analytical percept.

It should be noted that Head and Holmes specified *cortical* lesions in their monograph ; it will be recalled that we have already discussed the notion that purely cortical lesions must be very rare in clinical practice, and that they are doubtless greatly outnumbered by cortico-subcortical lesions. In the latter case, the threshold for pain might be expected to rise, the more so as the deeper structures are involved. Head and Holmes probably would not have quarrelled with this statement. The same authors also made the point that if the cortical disturbance is recent or progressive, or if it produces convulsions, however slight, remarkable defects may appear in painful sensibility. Touch changes are, they said, due to shock, exhaustion and diaschisis.

The detailed sensory studies after parietal wounds so character-istic of the British, French and German neurology of the first world war have not been approached during the second conflict. Ritchie Russell (1945) and Marshall (1951) have, however, taken up anew this question, with special reference to the integrity of pain sensation after parietal injuries. The former reported a paradoxical state of affairs wherein limited wounds of the Rolandic area (equated with Brodmann's area 3) may often cause permanent loss of all forms of sensation ; while more extensive injuries to the same area (Brod-mann's areas 1 and 2 being also involved) permanently destroy dis-criminative sensory functions only. Marshall, in his study, took pains to anticipate as far as possible various complicating factors such as Head and Holmes had indicated. Thus, he excluded cases where the lesion was anything but superficial ; acute cases (all were examined at least two years after the injuries) ; cases with a long period of post-traumatic amnesia ; those with recent convulsions ; and cases where hysterical elaboration could be blamed. To anticipate Head's distinction between the *pain* of a pin prick, and the discrimination of the *pointedness* of the pin, Marshall used deep thrusts, and, further-more, he had recourse to painful stimuli evoked by intramuscular injection of hypertonic saline. After these precautions had been taken, Marshall found a series of patients where the threshold to pain was distinctly raised. A striking feature in some of his cases, con-firming Dejerine's first war studies, was a striking dissociation of sensory loss. In one case, for instance, deep and superficial pain were normal whilst the appreciation of temperature was almost lost. In another case, temperature sense was delayed. Both these patients are described as having had small cortical wounds. But the first patient had three parietal wounds, two of which were superficial. The other patient had a postparietal wound with a dural tear and a track 4 cm. deep. Marshall sought to explain the paradoxical dis-crepancy between the size of the wounds and the duration and nature

Plate 2

HENRY HEAD

of the succeeding sensory impairment, in terms of the feed-back metaphor.

Nowadays, it is customary to follow the doctrines of Head and Holmes with regard to the type of sensory disturbances which follow lesions limited to the cortex of the parietal lobe. Mindful of the drawback of any attempt to make a sharp distinction between cortical and cortico-subcortical dysfunction, we may nevertheless accept the theorem that with superficial lesions the threshold for simple sensory modalities (touch, pain, heat and cold) may be but little raised, if at all. In contrast, we may find striking defects in the synthesis, interpretation, differentiation, and comparison of these primitive sensory experiences. Head and Holmes, for example, drew attention to the following defects : difficulty in the recognition of objects ; in the discrimination of texture ; in the realization of the duality of two points closely and simultaneously applied ; defects in the precise localization of a stimulus ; and in the discrimination of weights.

All these subtle defects in sensory synthesis are said to occur with an intact sensory appreciation ; that is to say, touch, pain and temperature must by definition be clearly recognized and the threshold of sensory experience must be scarcely altered. Clearly, if a marked hemihypaesthesia exists, it will not be justifiable to speak of defects in the recognition of objects, of the localization of stimuli, the discrimination of weights, and so on.

In addition to the disorders of sensory synthesis already mentioned, parietal lesions—even when superficial—may be associated with marked defects in postural sensibility. To these may be added an inability to appreciate the vibrations of a tuning fork, and also a loss of graphaesthesia (recognition of letters and numerals traced on the skin). Each of these sensory defects may be considered in turn.

The classical doctrines of Verger, Dejerine, Head and Holmes have not escaped criticism. Thus Marie and Bouttier (1922) denied any consistent value to the sensory cortical syndrome, believing that, clinically, a good deal of variability might be found. "...Dans les syndromes corticaux ou sous-corticaux on peut observer les variétés les plus diverses de dissociations sensitives. Certains malades presentent le syndrome classique : troubles très legers ou nuls des sensibilités superficielles avec troubles importants des sensibilités profondes suivant la formule classique. D'autres fois, on observe des dissociations portant sur les sensibilités superficielles : le sens thermique (pour la chaleur) étant particulièrement atteint. D'autres fois, c'est la piqûre et la chaleur qui sont parfaitement reconnues, tandis qu'il existe une hypoésthesie tactile." Similar dissociations were found

H

to occur in the case of deep sensation, and there was no parallelism found for instance between affections of stereognosis, of postural sensibility, of the appreciation of delicate discriminations, and of the sense of vibration.

Pierre Marie's son, André, in his 1924 thesis, was critical both of the cortical syndrome of Dejerine and also the thalamic syndrome of Roussy. He produced evidence to show that subcortical lesions could be followed by syndromes usually regarded as cortical in nature, while purely cortical lesions could also at times be followed by so-called " thalamic " syndromes. " Alors que beaucoup d'auteurs ont pensé que, suivant telle ou telle combinaison des troubles sensitifs, on était en droit de localiser la lésion, soit dans l'écorce cérébrale, soit dans le thalamus, nous voyons, après avoir étudié à ce sujet de nombreux cas, que, pour faire un diagnostic de localisation cérébrale, on ne saurait s'apuyer uniquement sur les modalités des troubles sensitifs."

Delay has affirmed that the sensory cortical syndrome is really a cortical " perceptive " syndrome, a " complex of agnosias ", that is an agnosia of intensity coupled with an agnosia of extensity or spatial agnosia. He went on to state that following lesions of the parietal cortex there may occur two very different types of disorder : (1) anaesthetic syndromes ; and (2) classical cortical sensory syndromes which are in reality not anaesthesias but complex agnosias. Between (1) and (2), however, all types of transition may be found, so that it may be difficult to say whether the anaesthesia is due to a defect of analysers, or to an agnosia.

Hemi-anaesthesia

In most patients with parietal disease, the sensory disturbances cannot be regarded as the manifestations of a purely cortical defect. On the clinical side, this is shown by an alteration in the threshold of sensibility. The patient still feels a light touch with a piece of cotton wool, or a gentle pin prick, but he pronounces the feeling to be less acute—or duller—than on the normal side. Some very light contacts, as by way of the finer von Frey's hairs, are missed altogether. Such a defect may be spoken of as a hypaesthesia ; and, by reason of its unilateral distribution, it usually constitutes a hemihypaesthesia.

This is a defect of which the patient is ordinarily not aware. He rarely discovers it for himself : or mentions it to his doctor. Even when being actually examined, and the sensibility over the two sides of the body is being compared, he scarcely ever volunteers the statement that there exists a difference in acuity—though he may straightway admit it when directly taxed on the matter. In these respects, the patient with a hemihypaesthesia of parietal disease differs from a patient whose sensory loss is due to a lesion of the fillet. The latter type of patient will probably have confirmed this for himself by making personal sensory tests ; he will have discovered the sensory impairment in the bath, or while washing or shaving ; and finally, he will almost certainly mention this discovery to his doctor. Later, however, when the sensory loss is established, and the patient's sensorium has become clear, insight may develop as to the existence of objective hypaesthesia, and the patient may admit to the presence of numbness or deadness. When severe postural loss is also present in the joints of the affected limb, the subjective sensations may even be compelling and complex. Feelings of heaviness may now be couched in such bizarre terms as " like dead meat " . . . " wooden " . . . " like a piece of metal ". The purely sensory phenomenon is now assuming the qualities of a hyperschematia—a disorder of the body-image. Such phenomena are discussed more fully in a later section. Head rather suggested this phenomenon was commoner in monoplegic types of affection : as one of his patients said about his limb, ". . . it hardly seems to count ".

While the distribution of the impaired sensibility has been referred to above as a " hemihypaesthesia ", strictly speaking such is not the case. Unlike the findings in the case of a patient with a posterior capsular disease, or with a lesion of the fillet ; and unlike too, the patient with a hysterical sensory loss, the anaesthesia may not be, and usually is not, evenly distributed over one body-half. Close testing will reveal certain inconsistencies, some segments being more deeply affected than others. Janota (1928) assumed that the clinical features of a lesion in the sensory zone are a relatively greater involvement of the lower limb ; a disturbance of sensation which does not reach the midline ; the occurrence of " strips " of sensory loss similar to segmental or root areas ; and a simultaneous involvement of various body-parts (e.g. face, hand and foot), the cortical centres of which are at a distance one from another.

Roussy and Branche (1918) drew attention to the fact that the hand is often disproportionately affected in cases of cerebral sensory loss. This observation led to the conception of a " main sensitive corticale " or " la main corticale " or simply " la main pariétale ". This distal distribution of sensory loss was noted in the first war to be rather common during the stage of regression in cases of war wounds of the brain. Regnard's thesis (1913) on cortical monoplegias had contained many peace-time records of cerebral disease when the sensory changes were confined to the limbs, sparing the trunk.

When the hand or foot is predominantly involved, the line of demarcation usually runs transversally over the limb.   As Lhermitte (1909) showed, however, there are also cases where there is a longitudinal distribution of sensory loss.   This was confirmed by Calligaris (1910) who, ten years later, described an " anesthésie cérébrale de type longitudinal ".   Mme. Athanassio Bénisty found that in her series of about 100 cases of cortical injuries, the hand was most often affected in a fashion which recalled a lesion of C8.   Thus, the inner aspect of the hand and the three inner fingers were most implicated, the anaesthesia being deepest over the little finger, each finger-tip,

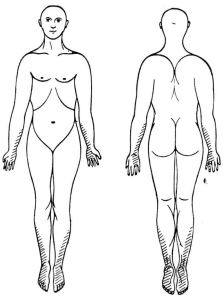

Fig. 49.   A pseudoradicular or axial type of sensory loss in the case of a biparietal lesion.

and the ulnar aspect of the hand.   The sensory impairment sometimes spread proximally so as to involve the inner side of the forearm, and less often, the upper arm.   In some other cases, the opposite picture was demonstrable, with the thumb and outer aspect of the hand, forearm and arm being involved.   Sensory changes were found to be less important over the foot.   Here, the outer side was more often affected than the inner, and the anaesthesia might be traceable up the outer side of the leg and even thigh.   Head and Holmes also drew attention to this type of sensory loss of what they called a pseudo-radicular or axial topography.

Villaret and Faure-Beaulieu (1916) also spoke of sensory loss of a " topographie atypique "—a mixture of pseudo-radicular and pseudo-segmental topography. In addition, there may occur a distribution of sensory loss into "little parcellated zones" (Janota, 1928). Rouquès, according to Schwob, recorded a case of parietal tumour where the loss of sensation to light touch and temperature was confined to small zones *en ilôts* over the inner and anterior aspects of the foot. In other cases, the zones of sensory defect may be confined to the face, the circumoral region, the radial side of the hand. Some neurologists (e.g. Sittig, 1916, 1922; Kramer, 1916, 1917; Goldstein, 1916; Schuster, 1917; Gamper, 1918; Fischer, 1923; Gerstmann, 1930) have regarded these scattered areas as typical of a

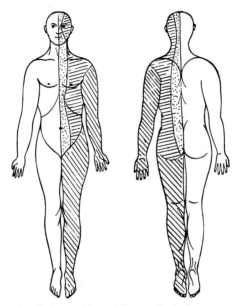

Fig. 50. Gradual transition of hypaesthetic into normal areas.

parietal origin. Schwob (1933) quoted a case with unilateral peribuccal anaesthesia associated with loss of sensation over one thumb.

But there are other case-records again, where the anaesthesia has *spared* the corner of the mouth, together with the radial side of the hand (Goldstein and Reichmann, 1919; Fischer, 1923; Taterka, 1926).

One should be cautious about accepting unreservedly some of these concepts of unusual distributions of sensory loss. Patients with parietal disease, even more than the average, are suggestible subjects. Sensory test procedures at the hands of inexperienced but conscientious and perhaps uncertain examiners are apt to produce zones of sensory loss which are induced rather than natural. The more numerous the examinations, the more established becomes the pattern of sensory loss.   The patch of anaesthesia is now largely iatrogenic and is apt to show unexpected variation at the hands of different testers.   The really experienced clinician steers a course between an over-meticulous sensory examination and one which is merely per-functory ; he will, moreover, avoid too frequent occasions devoted to sensory testing.

Foerster (1916), who has devoted much attention to the varieties

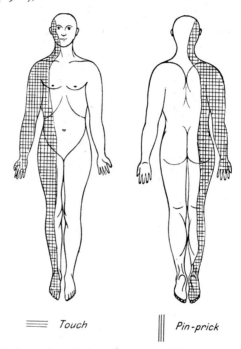

=== *Touch*   ‖‖ *Pin-prick*

Fig. 51.   Distribution of impaired superficial sensibility, not extending up to the middle line of the face, trunk and lower extremity.   (Male, 69 years.   Case No. 32621.)

The border line between touch and pin-prick is diffuse, being about 1 inch wide.

of so-called hemianaesthesia as evidenced by parietal disease, has stressed the following points :

(1) The sensory loss does not possess a sharp area of demarcation, but it merges into the normal zones by way of a narrow area of increasing sensibility.

(2) The sensory loss does not quite reach the midline of the body, the frontier often being formed by a gently curved line situated one or two centi-metres to the affected side of the midline.

(3) Certain regions of the body are spared altogether, e.g. the circumoral, the circumocular and the circumanal areas.

(4) As a rule, the distal parts of the limbs are more affected than the

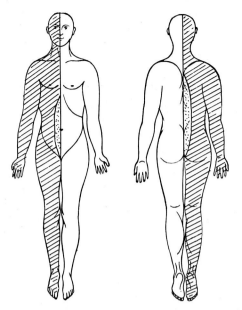

/// Diminution to pin-prick and cotton wool;
cold contacts felt as hot

:·:· Cold is felt neither as hot nor cold

Fig. 52. Hemihypaesthesia which does not quite reach the midline of the
abdomen. (Male, 47 years. Case No. 32718.)
Embolism of the mid-cerebral artery.

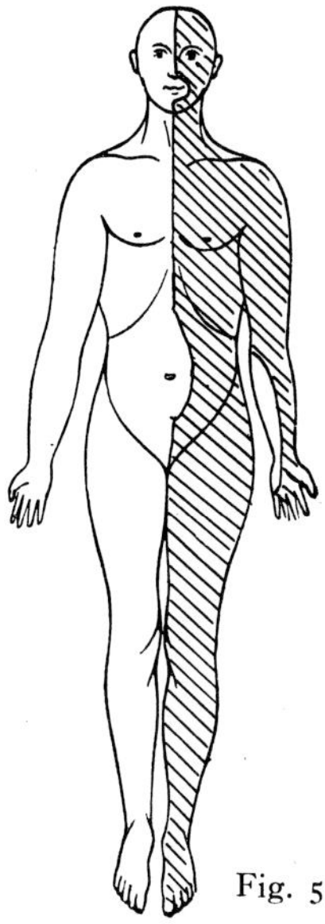

Fig. 53. 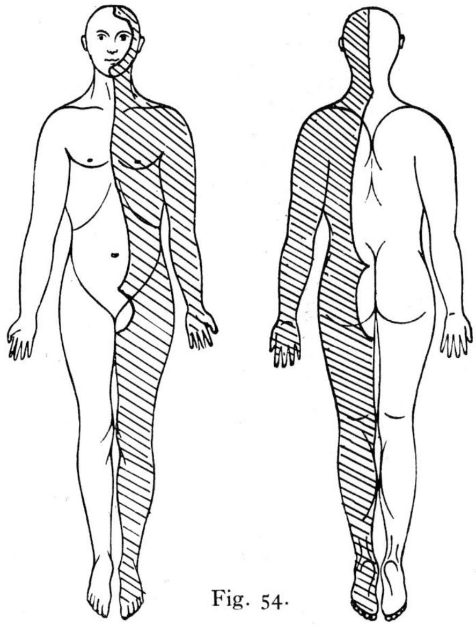   Fig. 54.

Fig. 53. Sparing of circumoral region, and of a crescentic area over
abdominal wall.

Fig. 54. Sensory loss which does not reach the midline of the face or
trunk, and which spares the genital region.

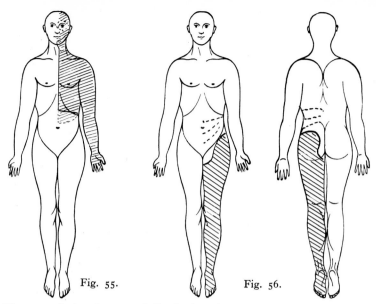

Fig. 55.　　　　　　　Fig. 56.

Figs. 55 and 56.　An unusual distribution of sensory impairment in the case of a parietal lesion.

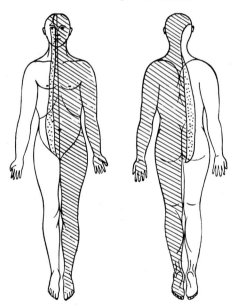

≡≡≡　Diminution of sensation to pin-prick
　　　and cotton wool, and to heat and cold

⋮⋮⋮　Diminution of sensation to
　　　cotton wool alone

Fig. 57.　Right parietal glioma.　(Male, 47 years.　Case No. 32718.)
The area of sensory impairment extends beyond the midline of the body.

proximal. The manner of demarcation in such cases may be annular, so that on the affected side there may be something resembling a sock and glove distribution of hypaesthesia. At other times, the frontier runs obliquely across the extremity.

(5) Ordinarily, the face and extremities are more involved than the trunk, which may indeed escape altogether.

(6) The upper limb is more involved than the lower.

(7) The anterior (or ventral) surfaces are more affected than the posterior (or dorsal).

(8) In the case of the upper limb there may be a greater involvement of the postaxial strip : less often, it is the pre-axial area which is more affected. In either case, the clinical picture recalls a root distribution of sensory impairment, rather than a cerebral.

Anaesthesias which involve not only one half of the body, but which actually transgress the midline to a slight extent, were not specifically described by Foerster. However, such a type of sensory impairment may occasionally occur as an expression of parietal disease, as mentioned by Redlich (1928). In recording such sensory loss, it is necessary to be sure that the spread of the anaesthesia across the midline of the body is genuine, and not merely apparent— the result of slowness in response on the part of the patient.

Although partial hemianaesthesias are the rule in cases of parietal disease, at times the sensory loss can be global, and affect all modalities of sensation, and even be distributed evenly over one body-half (André-Thomas and Ceillier, 1917). That this phenomenon may perhaps be a manifestation of diaschisis, is rather supported by the experience of war-wounds of the brain. In such, an initial hemi-anaesthesia may later be followed by a typical cortical sensory syndrome (e.g. the case of André-Thomas and Courjon, 1917).

Dissociated cortical anaesthesias have many times been described in cases of parietal disease or injury. The sensory impairment in such cases is often both dissociated (as regards its qualitative nature) and incomplete in topographical distribution, though indeed these two factors have not always been clearly distinguished by writers on this topic (André-Thomas and Long-Landry, 1914 ; Athanassio Bénisty, 1918 ; Roussy and Levy, 1926 ; Alajouanine, Thurel and Brunelli, 1934). In Cushing's case, where the cortical lesion was strictly limited, there was impairment to pain and temperature confined to the inner half of one hand, together with postural loss in the little finger only. Gerstmann (1915) described a case of depressed fracture of the parietal bone followed by impairment to pain and temperature over the ulnar region of the hand. Here there was no disorder of stereognosis nor of postural sensibility.

Postural loss

A defect in the recognition of passive movements of the affected joints : unawareness of the direction in which such movement occurs: and ignorance as to the position in space occupied by a limb or a segment of a limb (statagnosia), are all very common sensory manifestations of parietal disease.   They may lead to a number of attendant signs and symptoms, e.g. hypotonus ; lack of steady maintenance of the outstretched arm ; " pseudo-athetotic " wandering movements of the fingers ; and gross sensory ataxia.   Moreover, the patient who is confined to bed often adopts unusual attitudes in the affected arm some of which may be considered uncomfortable, antigravity postures. The patient may thus be observed lying with one arm raised above the head, possibly grasping the bed rail.   Postures of this sort are more apt to be found in patients whose mental faculties are a little dulled, or in whom there is a certain torpor.   If forced grasping and groping phenomena should also be present such attitudes may be complicated by the patient clutching the bedclothes or nearby objects in an unusual fashion.

Another clinical consequence of this postural loss may occasionally be encountered when a hemianopia also exists.   In such circumstances, the patient may be startled to see a hand appearing before his face, out of the blind sector—a hand which he does not recognize as his own for it is devoid of proprioceptive clues.   The stage is now set for a complicating disorder of the body-image which may take the form of an imagined limb in a posture quite different from that taken up by the actual limb.   Thus may arise a " phantom third limb "—a phenomenon which will be dealt with in a later chapter.

Yet again, as already mentioned, and as will be discussed in a subsequent section, the mere outfall of postural impulses may provoke the subjective sensation of undue heaviness of the affected limb so that the victim becomes inordinately embarrassed by the affected arm.   As in so many disorders of the body-image, there is no uniformity or consistency in the manner of subjective experience, and an undue sense of levity of the limb may be noted, or even, in extreme cases, a sense as if the limb were missing or had no existence at all.

When postural loss is confined to one or two fingers, this impairment may easily pass unrecognized during ordinary clinical testing. Especially is this the case when the fourth or fifth fingers are the ones affected, for as a rule postural tests are carried out only upon the index finger.   The fact is less likely to be missed if as a routine the patient is instructed to hold out before him the two arms with fingers extended and abducted, the eyelids being closed.   A slow drooping of the two fingers on the ulnar side occurring outside the patient's knowledge should lead to the suspicion of a defective sense of passive movement and of position of the two fingers concerned. This is the "main instable ataxique" of French authors (Alajouanine and Akerman, 1931).

It is rare in purely parietal lesions for the faculty of recognizing movement to be affected apart from that of recognizing position, although such a dissociation may be met with in a recently leuco-tomized patient. But Head and Holmes found that a patient with a parietal cortical lesion can at times recognize that a movement has occurred without being able to say in which direction or how far the movement has taken place. As regards its distribution, it may be said that the postural loss in parietal cases is always more evident in the peripheral part of a limb than in the proximal.

Postural affections are perhaps the most common objective evidence of parietal sensory impairment, and it is possible that they may occur in the absence of other objective changes. This is a statement which cannot be confidentially supported nor yet denied from a study of the literature, because it is obvious that the whole range of possible subtle sensory disorders at a perceptual level—including the *Funktionswandel* of Stein and Weizsäcker—has not been uniformly adopted as a clinical standard.

Villaret was exceptional in believing that postural loss was a less constant feature of the " traumatic cortical anaesthesia " than for example an astereognosis, as his fivefold classification showed :

(1) Astereognosis, with or without altered tactile discrimination, and with no other disorder of sensibility.

(2) Astereognosis together with loss of tactile discrimination and of postural sense but without any other trouble of sensibility. (This was Dejerine's original " cortical syndrome ".)

(3) Astereognosis, with loss of osseous sensibility, with or without abolition of tactile discrimination but without any other sensory disturbance.

(4) Astereognosis, with loss of osseous sensibility and with diminished superficial sensibility but without postural sense.

(5) Astereognosis associated with bony anaesthesia and altered postural sensibility, with or without discrimination in one or more modalities of superficial sensibility.

Postural loss plays a significant role in determining the patient's mental attitude towards his own disability, that is his acceptance or rejection of illness, the degree of insight into any motor affection which may accompany the postural loss. As will be mentioned in a later chapter, the relationship of impaired sense of passive movement and position to the phenomenon of anosognosia was thought by Barré and others to be integral.

Opinions are much divided as to which parts of the parietal lobe are most significant from the aspect of " deep ", i.e. postural sensibility. Piéron did not consider that any precise localization was possible. Pierre Marie, Chatelin, and to some extent Mme. Athanassio Bénisty implicated lesions of the parietal cortex behind the ascending parietal convolution. Redlich and Monakow associated " muscle sense " with the inferior parietal lobule, the latter of whom, as well as Minkowski (1917, 1923), did not exclude the ascending frontal convolution from playing a role in proprioceptive reception.

In more psychological terms, Head and Holmes pointed out that Munk's idea (1890) as to the function of the cortex as a repository of images of movement is not satisfactory. Change in position is recognized by comparison with the former position. It is not the image of movement which is operative but the summation of perpetual changes in position which brings about the construction of a " schema " or a postural model of oneself. This indeed is the first clear-cut exposition of the idea of a body-scheme in neurological literature (although it may be argued that the meaning has since been elaborated far beyond its original sphere). . . . " Recognition of posture and passive movement implies the combination of every fresh group of sensations with postural schemata outside the central field of attention. The change in consciousness which corresponds to this combination is immediate recognition of an altered position." Thus, instead of Munk's teaching that the cortex is a " repository of images of movement ", Head and Holmes declared the sensory cortex to be a " storehouse of past impressions ", a distinction which in itself does not appear irreconcilable.

An interesting variant of postural sensibility was described in 1928 by Tschlenow under the term "cutaneous kinaesthesia". The test is carried out by the examiner picking up a fold of the patient's skin between the thumb and forefinger, and then displacing the tissue up and down, or to the right or left. The patient, whose eyelids are closed, is questioned as to the direction of the movement. Patients who had lost their postural sensibility, failed to answer correctly, while those with merely superficial sensory defects, were unaffected. Tschlenow considered that his test was a more delicate index than ordinary methods of investigating postural sensibility. Halpern (1945 and 1949) independently revived this test, but under a new term, " dermatokinaesthesia ", and confirmed that when disordered it pointed to an affection of deep sensibility, although the correlation was not quite universal.

Vibratory sensibility

Tests with a vibrating tuning fork are not particularly informative in cases of parietal disease. Vibratory sense is often impaired in cerebral cases, especially when the lesion is deeply located. In other words, the threshold is raised. Rarely does the patient fail altogether to feel a strongly vibrating tuning fork. The fact that there may be a profound loss of postural sensibility obviously does not necessitate a concomitant vibratory loss. A dissociation between postural sensibility and pallaesthesia is therefore the rule with parietal lesions.

Tuning fork tests have been studied carefully in patients with cerebral disease or injury by Holmes, Evans, Fox and Klemperer, among others. Holmes made the statement that such tests are among the least useful in cases of cortical disease, and that, at the most, there is a mere subjective alteration in the corresponding segment of the body. Evans found relatively slight and circumscribed impairment after cerebral ablations. A gross loss of vibration occurred in only one case, namely, where a large excision had been made in and around the supramarginal gyrus. Fox and Klemperer found some impairment in vibratory sensibility in seven out of seventeen cases of cerebral lesion. In all seven, the disease was subcortical in its site. The deeper the lesion, the greater the vibratory defect. Often the little finger and the ring finger showed more impairment than the radial side of the hand. Typical of cerebral cases are various qualitative alterations : delayed perception, uncertainty of response, widened span between thresholds for increasing and decreasing amplitudes, and susceptibility to fatigue (Fox and Klemperer). Sometimes, the patient could not do more than state that the vibrating tuning fork felt " different " on one side than another.

Stereognosis

Tactile recognition constitutes a most important aspect of highest level sensory functions. Touch and vision are partners when it comes to affording us information as to the nature, physical properties and identity of objects around us. By vision alone are we able to guess at the qualities and nature of a remote object, and at times, this prediction is assisted by earlier experiences of either visual or tactile nature. Thus, when we gaze out of a window at a distant scene, we know without the opportunity of recourse to touch, that the objects in view are of such and such an identity—houses, motor-cars, trees and animals. Having made that recognition, we can often correctly orientate them in space, picking out those which are closer to us and those which are further removed. Moreover, by virtue of our previous tactile experiences we can assume, if called upon so to do, that the distant objects seen and identified, have certain physical properties —of hardness, smoothness, warmth perhaps—which tactile contacts, were they possible, would confirm.

Of more immediate importance is the means whereby touch alone can afford information as to the properties of objects within reach, and also to lead to their identification. Note that there are two distinct operations here—a unisensorial recognition of the properties (size, shape, consistency), and a plurisensorial recognition of the nature of the object. This corresponds with what Wernicke had spoken of as *primary identification* (of the qualities of an object), and *secondary identification* (of its identity). It must not be assumed, however, that these two operations necessarily follow one another in time—that one is an earlier stage of the other. Some authors, e.g. Delay (1935), would describe not two but three separate steps in the tactile recognition of an object. Thus, the actual physical properties may be broken down into two categories : first, the recognition of size, shape and weight : and secondly, the recognition of the consistency, thermal properties and structure of the object in question. Some may argue that these two groupings are a little artificial. If, however, they are accepted for the time being, then one can assume three separate activities in recognizing, say, a lump of sugar placed in the hand. Thus, it may be realized that the object is a cubical structure, small in size and light-weight. Delay would then isolate a further process, whereby the article was found to be hard, with a rough surface, and made up of granulations. Lastly, there is the stage whereby this article is identified as a lump of sugar.

Neurologists frequently use a composite term to cover all three of these operations, namely, *stereognosis* ; while a defect of one or all of these operations—most neurologists are vague upon this point— is spoken of as *astereognosis*. (Bing preferred to speak of *stereoagnosia*, but this term, although adopted by Rümke, Verger, Claparède, Raymond and others, has never gained currency.) The historical growth of our ideas in tactile recognition is important, for it shows how muddled thinking grew up and even now is far from being clarified.

Perhaps the earliest account is attributable to Puchelt (1844) who described five patients unable to recognize objects placed in their hands when their eyes were closed. Puchelt did not speak of stereognosis, but merely of a " partial paralysis of sensibility ", emphasizing that the faculty of touch (*Tastvermögen*) was disproportionately great compared with the other sensory changes. In 1885 came Hoffmann's thesis describing sixteen patients with hemiplegia, each with conspicuous inability to recognize small geometrical solid objects in the affected hand. Hoffmann spoke of this defect as astereognosis or a disorder of stereognosis (*stereon*—solid form). Within the next twenty years, many other contributions appeared, and other synonyms were proffered to allude to this general defect of

Plate 3

GORDON HOLMES

tactile recognition—*Tastlähmung* or tactile paralysis (Wernicke, 1876) ; tactile blindness (Williamson, 1897) ; tactile amnesia, psychic anaesthesia (Burr, 1897, 1898 ; Sailer, 1899) ; tactile asymboly, tactile aphasia (Raymond and Egger, 1906) ; tactile agnosia and tactile apraxia.

Delay, who was for a time tempted to describe the total disorder as *anhaptia*, adopted astereognosis as a general term, but he subdivided the defect into (1) an inability to recognize the size and shape of an object, by tactile means alone, or *amorphognosis*; (2) inability to differentiate the material of objects, their molecular qualities (i.e. density, weight, thermal conductivity, roughness)—*ahylognosia* ; and (3) inability to recognize the identity of an object provided there is no amorphognosia and ahylognosia. This specialized defect he called *tactile asymboly*.

Delay's use of the term *tactile asymboly* may be questioned, though apparently sanctioned as early as 1874 by Wernicke. But as Liepmann rightly argued, the term " asymboly " should be used as Finkelnburg (1870) originally intended it to be used, that is, to designate the loss of recognition *of symbols* or conventional signs. In that way, tactile asymboly becomes a misnomer. It would be better to speak of tactile " agnosia " in this connection. Delay also spoke of primary and secondary tactile agnosias, and in his nomenclature tactile asymboly would correspond with secondary agnosia. Looking at the problem rather differently, Delay indicated that amorphognosia was a variety of spatial agnosia ; that ahylognosia was an agnosia of intensity, and that tactile " asymboly " was a semantic agnosia.

" Tactile aphasia " is a general term which has been applied to astereognosis by some authors without, however, any precise connotation. Others have confined it more closely to those cases where the naming of the object within the grasp, is at fault. In such cases, there has even been an attempt to distinguish a " motor tactile aphasia " from a " sensory tactile aphasia ". To warrant the former diagnosis, the object and its function should be perfectly recognized (as indicated by word or by gesture), but the evocation of the name is at fault. This in turn should not be ascribed to an aphasia, but to an agnosic disorder in the domain of touch. Here at once arises a source of scepticism. As Claparède put it, tactile aphasia is, *a priori*, an improbability. . . . " We do not have an autonomous tactile memory, our tactile images are very fleeting. Our visual memory is so much more useful, more synthetic, that it has become preponderant and it has substituted itself for our tactile memory which has become atrophied through disuse. When we handle an object, it is easy to determine that palpation, though entirely tactile, develops in

I

our mind an entirely visual image. Tactile aphasia should not be encountered except in the blind, where it then constitutes the homologue of optic aphasia in the seeing." Carrying the argument further, a " sensory tactile aphasia " (or " tactile alexia ") is conceivable in two circumstances : (1) a sighted person who has lost the isolated and exclusive faculty of recognizing, with the eyes shut, letters or figures drawn upon the skin ; and (2) a blind person who has lost the faculty of reading with his finger-tips braille characters.

Delay has questioned whether such a condition as " tactile apraxia " can really be hypothecated. He quoted a patient studied by Pötzl and Klein who had a bilateral apraxia affecting the right hand more severely. Intransitive, expressive and symbolic movements were relatively well preserved, but any manipulation of objects was apparently disordered. When an object was placed in the patient's hand, her eyelids being closed, she did not know what to do with it : but as soon as she opened her eyes and gazed at the article she made the gestures correctly. Moreover, if the patient were placed before an object, her hand went out to grasp it, but if one put the object into her hand, the movements ceased. Kroll (1929) spoke of tactile and kinaesthetic influences inhibiting motility. The point seems to be that the patient was not apraxic until she was feeling the test-object. Delay, mindful of the sketchy frontiers between apraxia and agnosia (and especially between ideatory apraxia and tactile asymboly) felt that the differences were merely ones of degree.

Unfortunately, many writers on the topic of sensory disorders from cerebral lesions have not been consistent either in their terminology or in their methods of examination. Thus any or all of the foregoing terms have been employed at random, and it is not always clear that the same meaning has been implied throughout. Again, some neurologists have used common objects for testing purposes ; others have preferred special three-dimensional blocks of various shapes. In the former case, the protocols may not make it clear whether their patients recognized the physical qualities and failed to name the object ; or whether they failed to recognize both the identity of the object and its size, shape, and so on ; or whether they belonged to the rare group in which the patient named the object correctly but was unable to describe the spatial and molecular attributes. Scarcely any authors have recorded carefully the behaviour of the subjects as they were being tested—whether they were slow, or hesitant in their replies ; whether they corrected themselves ; whether they were inconsistent in their difficulties ; whether they betrayed anything of emotional distress or embarrassment. Few observers tested both hands simultaneously and listed verbatim the patient's responses. Not many neurologists in writing of astereognosis have tested for astereognosis over skin segments other than the palm of the hand—or have distinguished in their testing measures between placing an object within the hand and allowing the patient to palpate and " feel " the object, as compared with pressing an object into the palm, or moving it passively within the palm ; or pressing against the skin of other parts of the body outline figures of geometrical shape.

An even more serious omission on the part of many writers is a failure to inform us whether other sensory disorders were present in addition to the astereognosis ; and if so, their intensity and their nature.

It might fairly be objected that the term astereognosis should not be used when there is also a defect in the tactile analysers over the area tested. Bing, and Rümke, would prefer to call such a condition *stereo-anaesthesia*. Thus a disorder in the appreciation of light-touch, or of pain, might well be taken as rendering inappropriate the use of the term astereognosis. Other authors might not agree. Delay, for instance, spoke of " astereognosis through anaesthesia ", and also of an " astereognosis through agnosia ". The former arises, he said, from a sensorial deficiency ; the latter, from an intellectual deficiency. Scholl went further and said that whenever astereognosis occurs, there is always some trouble with sensibility. In this respect, he was strongly supported by Dejerine, and also by Vouters. Dejerine regarded astereognosis as an " epiphenomenon of anaesthesia ", devoid of localizing value.

There were others, however, and there still are, who regard astereognosis as a specific sensory defect and who would never employ this term in cases where loss of other sensory qualities is demonstrable. This attitude lends itself to the objection that astereognosis as a " pure " phenomenon is never found, but that concomitant sensory changes of some sort are always present, though perhaps elusive in character and easily overlooked. Wertheim-Salamonson (1888), Schittenhelm (1905) and Strümpell (1918) have expressed their opinion that pure astereognosis in the sense of tactile agnosia is theoretically possible, even though it has not yet been described. The other view is more attractive. The use of the term astereognosis in cases where the sensory threshold to pain and light-touch is raised would appear to be inappropriate, even though it has received the approval of so careful a writer as Delay. On the other hand, astereognosis is commonly found in association with some impairment of postural sensibility, and still more often with some of the highest level sensory defects, e.g. atopognosis and altered tactile discrimination. In some cases no doubt, the sensory change is even more subtle, and conforms to what Stein and Weizsäcker called a *Funktionswandel*.[1] Herein are included such psychosensory deviations as tactile perseveration, sensory dyschronisms, lability of the threshold, delayed sensation, irregularity of response, and other such phenomena. Delay was of the opinion, however, that *Funktionswandel* is not in itself an indication of cortical or cerebral lesions, and that it can occur with lesions at all levels. Consequently, astereognosis associated with sensory dyschronism is not of localizing value.

It may be argued, however, that *Funktionswandel* comprises a great variety of defects, belonging as a matter of fact to differing psychological levels of impairment. In all probability a close analysis of the various defects would permit one to group them and to isolate certain ones which occur only with cerebral lesions. Astereognosis coupled with these cerebral sensory dyschronisms would then be of localizing significance.

We regard stereognosis, therefore, as a mental operation which requires for its efficient working a normal threshold for touch and pain in the palm of the hand. We cannot ask for peripheral sensibility to be entirely intact, however, for we cannot believe that this state of affairs ever exists in cases of true astereognosis. Some degree of postural loss, or of tactile discriminatory defect is almost certainly present. When well-marked tactile loss occurs in the hand, then the patient can scarcely be expected to recognize the properties or the identity of an object held in the palm. But we should not speak of such a defect as an astereognosis. " Astereognosis " in cases of tabes dorsalis or brachial plexus injury is a misnomer. At the same time, despite the handicap of a hypaesthetic palm (from peripheral disease) some patients may succeed in identifying an object in the hand. In such cases we see the influence of a highly intellectual operation which by good luck and almost by guess-work successfully utilizes the scanty clues afforded by the object in the hypaesthetic palm. The identification of the object may be carried out slowly—perhaps hesitatingly. In such a case, the act of correctly identifying the object has thus been more of a test of intelligence than of tactile perception.

[1] This expression, which literally means " lability of function ", is on the face of it obscure. It refers in particular to the threshold of sensibility, and to the fact that this can be altered in one direction or the other by the continuance of tactile stimulation. " Variability of the threshold under the influence of function " is, as Dr. Mayer-Gross kindly indicated to me in a personal communication, approximately the idea behind *Funktionswandel*.

These considerations lead one to the practical use which might be made of such a procedure. Thus, the wearing of gloves during the test of recognizing objects in the hand might, in the first place, be used as a sort of measure of the intelligence of the subject, especially if tested at the same time on a normal individual also wearing gloves of identical texture. In the second place, the glove test might be used as a method of enhancing astereognosis in a patient with a very early or doubtful parietal lesion. For example, he might have passed the tests for astereognosis as carried out in the ordinary way, without errors or undue hesitancies. He then puts on a pair of gloves and is tested again. In these new circumstances, a marked difference may now be found between the normal hand and the one that is contra-lateral to the suspected parietal lobe.

Though it has often been the practice to speak loosely of the " stereognosic sense ", this term should be corrected to " stereognosic perception ", as Claparède insisted. Stereognosis is obviously a process capable of analysis into various stages, whereby semantic, gnosic attributes are combined with sensorial recognition and identification. It is not difficult to understand, therefore, that this aspect of percep-tion is certainly not innate ; but that it grows and develops ; and that it is capable of considerable elaboration. At one end of the scale there is the hand of the congenital hemiplegic, which although not insensitive to touch, pain and proprioceptive stimuli, remains, as far as stereognosis is concerned, une main vièrge. Then at the other extreme is the sensitive hand of the intelligent and artistic blind sculptor, pianist or even braille reader. We may also place within this hypersensitive group some of those crippled individuals who, deprived of the use of their hands and arms, have developed the stereognosic perception and the manipulative dexterity of their toes—with the aid of which they perhaps write, draw, paint, strike matches, fasten buttons and even type. The ability of a blind person to read braille punctographic symbols with the toes is well known, and also with the lips, tip of the tongue and nose (see Fig. 58).

Being a perception, tactile recognition possesses two properties in ordinary normal circumstances. In the first place it is a process so immediate—almost instantaneous—that it cannot be regarded as either an analytical or a synthetical act of recognition. If a subject puts his hand in his pocket, he will recognize his cigarette lighter at once, without going consciously through the stages of perceiving a cold, smooth, hard, flat, oblong object, presumably metallic. It is probable that these stages do not even take place with great rapidity at a subconscious level. Almost certainly, these mediate stages are skipped or by-passed. Knowledge of the whole precedes that of the parts. In the second place the subject does not need to explore the whole surface of the test-object in order to identify it. Experiences with the blinded show this very clearly. The individual may require merely to touch the corner of a piece of furniture for him to identify his desk or the piano. Nay more, it is not necessary for the exploring hand to carry out the ordinary moving contact. Révész (1950) showed clearly that common objects could be recognized when touched, or grasped, and when the observed was forbidden to make

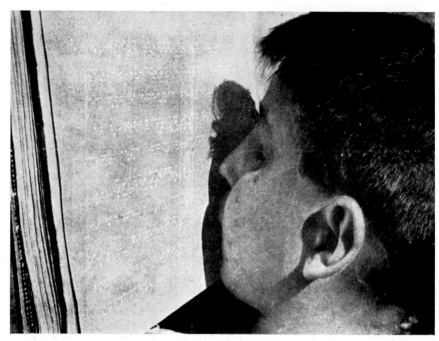

Fig. 58. Blind boy reading braille with the tip of his nose. (Courtesy of Dr. William Gooddy.)

a moving contact. In many cases, too, a static touch of merely part of an object was sufficient to permit the object to be recognized. This is, of course, true of any experienced braille reader, for it is possible for such a one to identify a letter merely by resting the pulp of the index finger upon the punctographic symbol.

Claparède has reminded us how far previous sensorial experiences contribute to the identification of objects tactually. A little ball (*spherule*, *pillule*) lying immobile upon the palm is felt merely as a point of light contact. But if one gently blows upon the ball, it moves. The moving contact is felt as a linear series of touches, but the brain interprets them differently . . . " it is rolling ; therefore it must be a ball ! "

The identification of objects is often materially facilitated when both hands are employed in active touch (bimanual stereognosis). This is particularly the case when a rather large object is in question ; that is, one which cannot be wholly and simultaneously engulfed within the lightly closed hand.   In this way, a blind person may hold the object with one hand and use the other to sweep over the edges and surfaces.   As one such individual said : " . . . by using both hands, the article appears much more clear and vivid to me." Such a statement illustrates the common form of imagery in the acquired blind, who translate tactile sensa into visual synaesthesiae, just as most sighted persons do.

Similarly, the use of two hands in handling rather large objects betrays interesting defects in some cases of parietal disease.   For instance, a patient with a hemianaesthesia may not only fail to recognize an object in the affected hand, but he may also fail to *feel* it. The patient is unaware of the presence of the object.   But if the object, say a large orange, is held between the two hands in such a way that the palms cup the two hemispheres of the fruit, the patient may describe the impressions in one of two ways.   In the first place, he may say : " . . . I am holding an orange," for the perception achieved by the normal hand, although incomplete, nevertheless supplies the deficit which lies within the anaesthetic palm, and so gives an illusion of wholeness.   But there are patients who reply otherwise, and who say : " . . . it feels to me like *half* an orange."   The sensa within the normal hand are being interpreted literally, while the lack of feeling in the affected hand now affords a sort of positive impression of nothingness.

We may therefore indicate at this point the precautions to be taken by the observer in testing for astereognosis, and its various modifications—amorphognosia, ahylognosia, and so on.

The patient should be blindfolded and he should not be afforded any adventitious clues as to the test-objects, either by permitting him to see them beforehand or by letting him hear (smell, taste) them. On the other hand, it may be revealing to show the patient the objects after the test is finished, for the patient may well make some comment which is of significance.

Each hand should be tested first singly and then both hands simultaneously.   If the patient's hand is paralysed, the object may be placed safely within his palm and then moved about.   In addition, the patient's paralysed fingers should be passively flexed on to the test-object, and moved over it in a passive series of palpatory manipulations.

A verbatim record should be made of the patient's statements. Moreover, specific note must be taken as to any delay in recognition ; or slowness ; or hesitancies or changes in mind. In the case of bilateral simultaneous testing, the observer should record which hand first moves so as to palpate the object ; and which object is identified first. When identical objects are placed in the two hands, the patient should be directly asked whether the two articles seem to be of identical size and weight.

Regarding the nature of test-objects employed, it may be said that common objects should always be used. There is an advantage, however, in also using objects which are of geometrical character —cubes, cones, spheres and pyramids. Some of the objects should also include different specimens of material, e.g. paper, rubber, wood, metal, silk, wool, cotton, and so on. Here it may be desirable to choose the textures according to the patient's sex, occupation or cultural level. As Delay found, this test for hylognosis could be carried out successfully in the case of a furrier using a variety of skins. Some French neurologists use *lentilles optiques* as test-objects, the patient being instructed to say whether the lenses are concave, convex or flat. Lastly, and in special cases only, it may be worth while to test for two-dimensional morphognosis by pressing into the palm special outline figures depicting such shapes as a circle, square, triangle, heart- or diamond-shaped designs, and so on. (With this last-named test, skin areas other than the palm may be investigated.)

There is, however, an important difference between the task of recognizing a two-dimensional shape pressed against the skin, and that of recognizing the same figure outlined by a moving contact. The former is a relatively difficult—often an impossible task : the latter is much more within the realm of practicability. Herein lies the fundamental difference between the perception of a static stimulus from that of a kinetic one : the former is a variety of passive contact, the latter being an active type of touch.

There are occasions, also, when it is desirable to test a patient's ability to identify *two* objects placed simultaneously within the palm of one hand. This task is a difficult one for a patient with cortical disease who may display an inability to cope with two problems at once—even though they be presented to one hemisphere at a time as exercises in perceptional ability.

At times, it may be of interest to test for stereognosis in regions outside the palm. Thus, an object, such as an orange, may be placed under the sole of the bare foot. The lack of prehensibility can be overcome by getting the patient to roll the object between the sole of the foot and the ground, in such a way that an adequate moving contact is obtained. Attempts may also be made to test for stereognosis over the trunk by placing objects of adequate size and relatively simple shape under the back of the patient lying horizontal on a couch.

The test-objects put into the hand should include some of small size and some which are much larger, so that in the latter case the patient palpates the object by moving the finger-tips over the edges, or over part or the whole of the object. Here it is necessary to note how much of the object needs to be explored by the palpating finger-tips before its identity is gleaned. A few of the objects may well be of quite small dimensions, and of unfamiliar nature, so as to constitute a more difficult procedure as occasion may demand. Thus, a press-stud, or a hook and eye may prove suitable. The battery of objects should also include a ring and a thimble. When either of these are used, the ring (or thimble) can be placed upon the finger-tip by the observer, who holds the other fingers aside to prevent them being used for feeling the object. This rather more difficult test has the merit of permitting one to test for stereognosis in each finger in turn.

Another method whereby a part of the hand alone may be tested, is to bandage, say, the thumb, index and medius, leaving the annular and auricular free, or *vice versa*. Interesting cases of partially distributed astereognosis may come to light by way of such a technique. (Compare Decourt's case of " astéréognosie dimidiée par anesthésie corticale " and also Krestnikoff's case, 1923.)

Not enough attention is paid in ordinary neurological routines to the question of labiobuccal stereognosis. The exquisite sensitivity of the mucous membrane of the lips and tip of tongue is, of course, well known. Tactile discrimination is nowhere keener ; and whereas the normal threshold for the compass test is 2 mm. over the finger-tips, it is only 0·5 to 1 mm. on the tongue-tip and lips. Blind persons may utilize this fact when extremely fine manipulations are needed such as threading a needle, as mentioned indeed by Diderot. According to Villey (1930) a blind botanist used to put flowers to his lips and tongue in order to study the arrangement of stamens and pistils. In clinical neurology, the interior of the mouth and the membrane covering the tongue and lips may not, as a rule, be implicated in ordinary cortically conditioned astereognosis, though admittedly the number of specific observations on this point must be very few. However, it is in the case of bilateral parietal disease that one would expect astereognosis to be demonstrable, not only in both hands but also within the oral cavity. This is readily tested by using small objects (paper-fastener, button, ring, and so on) secured by a length of cotton.

When the patient's hand is severely paralysed, it may be difficult to test for stereognosis, unless all the precautions already mentioned are strictly observed and the patient's fingers are passively moved over the object. Failure to do this may give a false impression that the patient cannot recognize objects by touch—the so-called *anaesthesia through akinesia* of Chrétien (1902). Delay, however, has rightly stated that such phenomenon has no existence. In cases of infantile hemiplegia, however, astereognosis may be found within the paralysed hand without any accompanying sensory changes. This is due to the fact that the hand has never, by reason of its powerlessness, been used as a palpating organ. It is, as Dejerine would say, a " virgin hand " and the sensory disorder is an *astereognosis through ignorance*, or better still, an *astereognosis through inexperience*, and not through immobility. A patient of my own had a congenital left hemiplegia which she presented at the clinic at the age of 56 years, with an astereognosis as the sole sensory deficit.

The contrary phenomenon is to be found in striking fashion in the faculty of stereognosis existing in persons with a congenital absence of hands or with congenital rudimentary hands. Thus, in a patient of mine suffering from Apert's acrocephalosyndactyly, there were no free phalanges and only very stunted and deformed metacarpals. Plastic surgery had artificially freed an attenuated thumb, thus allowing the patient to acquire an unexpected degree of dexterity with the stumps and a corresponding high level of tactual recognition as well as tactile discrimination (see Figs. 59–62). The skin sensitivity was of the exquisite order that one would expect over the finger-tips of a normal person, and not in the skin covering a carpal stump.

Heller (1904) studied the dynamics of the act of " touching " especially as it is to be found in the blind. He differentiated " synthetic touching " from " analytic touching "—the former being carried out in nearer space by the resting hand while the latter is a process carried out by the moving hand in rather more remote tactile space. As Heller wrote (1905): ". . . the major portion of my *Studien zur Blindenpsychologie* is full of indications that synthetic touch (through the spatial sense of the skin) is not sufficient to provide the blind with adequate concepts. To this must be added touch with moving touch organs (analytic touch). According to my investigation, inadequate synthetic touch can create nothing more than a schematic general picture of small objects, which can only be interpreted by analytic touch movements." Révész could not follow Heller in making this rather artificial distinction, and he preferred to speak of " simultaneous touch " and " successive touching ". Expressed differently, Révész classified the tactile processes as (1) the static tactile process (touching with the hand at rest)—almost only used to test the temperature of an object ; and (2) the dynamic tactile process (or touching with a moving hand). This corresponds with what Monakow called the " kinetic melody ". According to Katz, movements of the exploring hand can determine all modifications concerned with surfaces. Half-way between the static and dynamic tactile processes, there is what Révész called "the holding touch" whereby the observer can determine the approximate size, shape and degree of complexity of the object concerned. Hippius (1934) divided the dynamic tactile process into a number of kinds of moving touch, viz. (1) touching with to and fro gliding movements. By this means the surfaces of an object can be explored and some of the qualities of its material can be detected. (2) The sweeping touch which permits the recognition of the material and also some of the geometrical qualities of the object. This is performed with the index, sometimes also with the medius and annular. (3) Grasping touch, which is similar to (2) but with the assistance of the thumb so that two surfaces can be felt simultaneously, and so tri-dimensional touch becomes possible. (4) Kinematic touching. Here the touch is at once analytic and integrative and permits recognition of all the material and formal qualities of an object.

When the various types of astereognosis are studied, especially in their association with disease of the parietal lobe, the following may be stated :

(1) Cases occur where there is some degree of raised threshold for light-touch and for pain, but where lack of tactile recognition is conspicuous. In other words, the astereognosis would seem to be more severe than could be accounted for by relative hypaesthesia of the palm. Were the same intensity of hypaesthesia present as the result of peripheral nerve, root or spinal lesions, then astereognosis of such blatancy probably would not occur.

(2) More typically, in parietal cases, there is a disordered tactile recognition (astereognosis) with no gross alteration in the threshold for pain and touch. Appropriate testing will show, however, postural defects ; perhaps an impairment of vibration, and certainly subtle psychosensory changes such as poor tactile discrimination ; irregular and inconsistent response, delayed response ; altered sensory adaptation ; tactile perseveration perhaps ; and defective localization of stimuli.

(3) In the case of either (1) or (2), the astereognosis may consist in :

(a) Inability to identify and to name the object though its spatial and molecular qualities are described ; i.e. tactile agnosia or tactile asymboly (Delay).

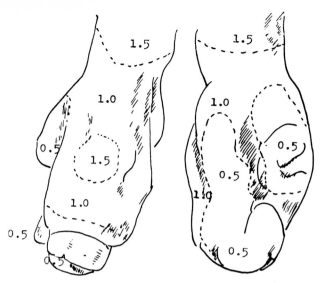

Fig. 59.

Left hand (dorsum on the left ; palmar surface on the right). Two-point discrimination (compass test).

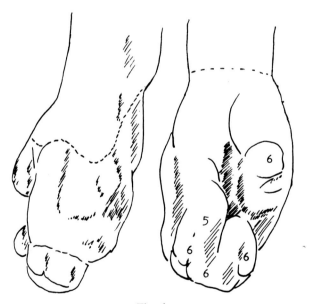

Fig. 60.

Left hand (dorsum on the left ; palmar surface on the right). Multiple simultaneous point discrimination. 6 = 6 points felt as 6. 5 = 5 points felt as 5.

Drawing of stumps of the rudimentary hands of a patient with Apert's disease, or acrocephalosyndactyly (Case No. 35263), showing the type of tactile discrimination present. The thumb-like structure was artificially fashioned by a plastic surgeon.

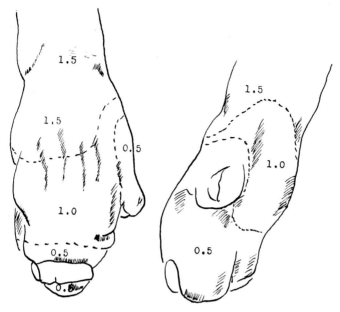

Fig. 61.

Right hand (dorsum on the left; palmar surface on the right). Two-point discrimination (compass test).

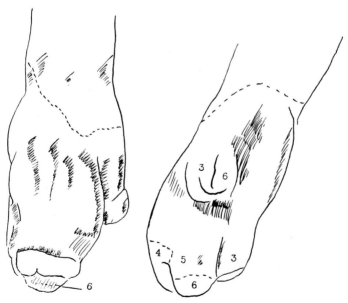

Fig. 62.

Right hand (dorsum on the left; palmar surface on the right). Multiple simultaneous point discrimination. 6 = 6 points felt as 6 etc.

Drawing of stumps of the rudimentary hands of a patient with Apert's disease, or acrocephalosyndactyly (Case No. 35263), showing the type of tactile discrimination present. The thumb-like structure was artificially fashioned by a plastic surgeon.

(*b*) Inability to recognize the spatial quality ; to differentiate the molecular qualities and to identify the object ; i.e. astereognosis through anaesthesia or through ignorance.

(*c*) Ability to identify the spatial qualities, but not the molecular qualities, nor yet to identify the object ; i.e. astereognosis, with intact morphognosia.

(*d*) Ability to name the object but not to describe the spatial qualities nor the molecular properties ; i.e. amorphognosia coupled with ahylognosia.

(*e*) Ability to name the object and to describe its molecular properties but a failure to describe its spatial qualities ; i.e. amorphognosia alone.

(*f*) Ability to name the object and to describe its spatial, but not its molecular properties ; i.e. ahylognosia alone.

(*g*) Ability to identify the object but inability to describe either the spatial or the molecular properties ; i.e. combined amorphognosia and ahylognosia.

From the evidence of such cases of progressive cerebral sensory syndromes as described by Marie, Bouttier and van Bogaert (1924), it is clear that an astereognosis can precede in time the development of a disorder in the sensory analysers. Kato's case was even more important in that as a meningioma developed, there was at first a simple incapacity to identify an object. Later, however, the patient also became unable to recognize the shape and consistency of objects within the hand. If this is true for progressive cases, the same appears to apply to regressive cases, as during the convalescent post-traumatic syndromes. Villaret found astereognosis as the residuum of a hemihypaesthesia, though Delay was sceptical.

Commonest among the relative degrees of astereognosis is a defect which can be regarded as a minor disorder of morphognosis. This defect takes the form of an error in the direction of believing the object to be larger than it actually is, or else smaller—the identity of the article being correctly gauged. Halpern (1945) has spoken of these defects as *macrostereognosia* and *microstereognosia* respectively and has recorded them as occurring in cases of (presumed) thalamic disease. But it is probable that we do not yet know for certain what degree of latitude can be granted to normals. Thus, if a normal individual, with eyelids closed, picks out a series of small articles from a box, there is a tendency to underestimate their size. When the eyes are then opened the objects may appear for a moment unexpectedly large. In cases of mild parietal sensory impairment, bilateral simultaneous testing for stereognosis may often bring to light the fact that objects may appear larger (or perhaps smaller) in the affected hand. Dr. S. Renfrew investigated this problem more closely, only to find that in normal subjects there is a tendency to make errors in comparing and contrasting objects of nearly identical size (e.g. disks of diameters ranging from 9, 10, 11, 12, 13, 14, 15 mm.). The usual error seemed to be to underestimate the size in the case of the dominant hand, and to overestimate the size of objects in the other hand.

The problem of micro- and macrostereognosis also arises out of contrasts between the temperature of the test-object and of the two palms. Thus, if there is a wide difference between the temperature of the patient's hand, and that of the object itself, there is a tendency for the object to be mistaken for being bigger than it really is. A cold piece of metal, for example, will appear bigger in a warm hand than in a cold (Markova, 1900). According to Hoffmann, of two objects identical in size and shape, the warmer one feels a little bulkier than the cold.

This extraordinary complexity of possible modifications of astereognosis, each of which may be found in association with parietal disease, renders attempts at localization more than usually difficult. Indeed, it may even be regarded as futile to try and pinpoint lesions within the cortico-subcortical mass of the parietal lobe, and to expect a strict and consistent correspondence between this and that type of astereognosic defect and a strictly circumscribed region of disease. The different aspects of astereognosis belong rather to differing hierarchies of a psychological process, and hence lend themselves less readily to anatomical scrutiny. Nevertheless, it is of interest to study what neurologists have hitherto noted along these lines of clinico-anatomical association.

Wernicke (1876), Dubbers (1897), Diller (1901), Walton and Paul (1901) have asserted that somewhere near the middle third of the postcentral gyrus there is a kind of " centre of primary identification ", where tactile impressions of different modalities are grouped. This region is very near what is popularly regarded as constituting the hand area. Others would locate such a " centre " within the superior parietal lobule (Reinhard, 1887 ; Williamson, 1897 ; Dercum, 1900; Mills, 1901). There are others, such as Nothnagel, Economo, Kappers, Huber and Crosby (1936), who have implicated the supramarginal gyrus. The propinquity of the visual cortex demonstrates, in their opinion, the fact that ordinarily optic and tactile impulses combine to pass judgment upon the identity of objects. Head's tentative remarks about the localization of different sensory modalities within the cortex would indicate that with lesions of the precentral cortex spatial relations are affected ; with lesions of the postcentral cortex appreciation of similarities and differences ; and with lesions of wide areas lying behind the postcentral convolution, appreciation of intensities.

For the operation of immediate recognition of objects by touch, by-passing the intermediate steps of recognition of physical properties, a gnosic co-ordinating centre (" a centre of symbolic perception "), has been postulated by some writers, such as, among others, Piéron. Delay believed there were good grounds for locating such a centre in the supramarginal gyrus. At the same time, he thought it still premature to speak of psychotactile and sensoriotactile regions, situated within the posterior and the anterior parts respectively of the parietal lobe. Delay equated the function of co-ordinating symbolic perception with other disorders of symbolic or semantic thought, and he reminded himself that Head was tempted to look to the supramarginal gyrus for the lesion responsible for what he called " semantic aphasia ".

We must not blind ourselves, however, to the cases on record which seem to flaunt all our ideas of localization. Thus, we must bear in mind, as Delay has remarked, that tactile asymboly has been found clinically with patients where the lesion has proved to be outside the parietal lobe ; e.g. in the prefrontal region (Pierre Marie) or in the precentral area (Poggio, 1908). As Monakow said : ". . . the stereognostic centre does not represent a simple modality of sensibility, but corresponds with a psychic act to which the qualities of sensibility . . . as much as experience which is constructed on their activity, serves as a base. That is why it belongs truly to agnosia."

We may align ourselves with Delay in his two statements upon this problem : that the integrity of a vast cortical territory is necessary for tactile recognition ; and furthermore, that cortical astereognosis is essentially a parietal syndrome. A more precise localization cannot be ventured.

Of particular interest are those rather uncommon instances of bilateral astereognosis associated apparently with a strictly unilateral lesion. Oppenheim seems to have been the first person to describe this occurrence. Goldstein also described a case in 1916. In a series of papers written between 1913 and 1922, Foix studied the phenomenon of bilateral sensory changes from unilateral parietal disease. As mentioned on page 149, Foix drew attention to a syndrome of hemiplegia, bilateral sensory disturbances, varying degrees of aphasia, and ideomotor apraxia. He regarded the sensory manifestations which, of course, included an astereognosis, as an " anaesthesia arising from an agnosia "—comparable with auditory agnosia. Better still, he might have likened it to the bilateral finger-agnosia of the Gerstmann syndrome. This is the reason for the term Foix suggested, namely anéesthso-agnosie. Foix ascribed the syndrome to a deep parietal lesion situated always, in his experience, in the left hemisphere. Perhaps it would be better to speak of the " dominant " hemisphere, for in 1925, Guillain, Alajouanine and Garcin recorded a case of bilateral anaestho-agnosia, due to a right-sided lesion, but occurring in a left-handed individual.

Possibly—as Delay has said in somewhat different terms—the " comprehension " of the tactile spatial image may be a faculty which is more vulnerable when the dominant hemisphere is diseased. This idea is still further borne out, and also brought still closer in line with the apraxias and the other agnosias, when we find at times that a unilateral astereognosis (usually in the left hand) may be the conse- quence of a lesion of the corpus callosum (Goldstein, 1914 ; van Vleuten, 1907 ; Stauffenberg, 1918 ; Hoff, 1932).

It is obvious from the foregoing remarks that astereognosis is a highly complex phenomenon of perception, which may range from the highest level agnosic defect (which may even be bimanually represented from a one-sided lesion) to an epiphenomenon of cortical sensory impairment, in which case a part only of the hand may be involved (i.e. pre-axial or postaxial). Between these extremes, how- ever, there may exist a wide variety of intermediate types of defect. Time alone will show as the result of more careful and more extensive clinical testing, to what extent astereognosis is a *manual* defect, and to what extent it is a one-sided defect, which may by appropriate test-measures be demonstrable in, say, the sole of the foot, and also the surface of the limbs and trunk. Further work will show how adequately astereognosis can be analysed into two-dimensional and three-dimensional defects. Where the clinical test-procedures of static and kinetic two-dimensional morphognosia (graphaesthesia) belong within the system of stereognosis, is still not clear. To what extent we are really justified in breaking down stereognosis to morpho- gnosis and hylognosis, is also still debatable.

Tests for the *discrimination of the texture* of various objects have conventionally been treated separately and apart from stereognosic tests, as though a specific faculty of perception were concerned here. It is doubtful how true this is, and how necessary it is to try and do so. The ability to discriminate and to identify textures may be conveniently looked upon as a mere aspect of the more general topic of stereognosis, or object recognition : more particularly, it can be allied with Delay's hylognosis and tactile gnosis, differing only in that the stimulus object is for all practical purposes two-dimensional, or apparently so.

Identification of textures is carried out by allowing the patient to handle a number of different materials and by asking him to name them while keeping his eyelids closed. Obviously the patient's ability to carry out this test depends a good deal upon such independent

K

and premorbid factors as his intelligence, his education, his work and his artistry. Perhaps sex is here the most important factor, for a woman accustomed to evaluate and to select textiles, would be expected to put up a better performance than the average man who is on the whole less interested in such matters. Even so, most males can be expected to tell the difference, by feel alone, between such contrasting stuffs as offered by a piece of blanket, or towelling, or a sheet, or fragment of silk.

Practice is highly important here, and no doubt some persons have never utilized their latent potentialities. Conversely, long experience in the tactile appraisal of certain materials, tissues and substances constitutes a professional craft. Silk merchants and tobacco buyers occur to one as exponents of a highly skilled activity which depends upon the intelligent perception and evaluation of tactile impulses. To watch such experts at work is to realize the complicated nature of the active feeling movements they employ with the fingers and hands of both sides, and usually with eyelids closed or gaze averted. The tobacco buyer plunges his hands into a " skip " and allows the slivers of cut leaf to slip between his fingers, as he gently and almost caressingly rubs the grains between the pulp of his thumb and index. In this way he assesses the size, brittleness, weight and moistness of the tobacco. The silk mercer holds the material between the adducted thumbs and forefingers of the two hands, pulling, rubbing, smoothing, scrumpling and hefting the silk in a practised fashion. Obviously it is not a purely two-dimensional activity which is at work, but rather a hylognosis of a much flattened but none the less three-dimensional test-substance.

It scarcely needs emphasizing that the common sensibility of the palm and finger-tips must not be impaired if a test for the discrimination of textures is to serve in the diagnosis of highest level sensory defects.

Head and Holmes also employed another method of testing a patient's appreciation of roughness. This may be regarded as a more " passive " test than the employment of " active " feeling. For this purpose a Graham-Brown aesthesiometer was used, whereby one or more cylinders were made to project to a measurable extent from a smooth metal surface. The instrument was then moved across some cutaneous surface and the patient was asked whether the contact was smooth or rough. All their patients with cortical injuries responded normally to this test of " passive " appreciation of roughness or smoothness. Nevertheless, in all cases the power of appreciation and identifying texture by " active " palpation was lost. " Cotton, silk and stamped velvet are all one to the affected hand, although readily distinguished on the normal side.   When once this test has been applied, the patients often complain that they have lost all idea of texture, saying, ' I can feel it, but I have not the least idea what it is.' "

Ruch, Fulton and German (1938) examined the ability to discriminate weights after parietal damage in the case of apes and man. Their animal studies which of necessity were but little concerned with subjective data, led them to consider simultaneously discrimination of textures and of weights.   They found that parietal damage in monkeys and chimpanzees led to a discriminatory defect which was much more transitory than in the case of man.   An extensive parietal defect in man is followed by an impaired ability to discriminate weight and roughness, a defect which is permanent though relatively slight in degree.   A wide parietal area would seem to be of significance in this faculty, and yet even fairly restricted areas relatively remote from the primary sensory region may when damaged reduce the ability to discriminate weight and roughness.   The degree of recovery is a striking feature, in which re-training plays an important part.   Such re-training would appear to be largely specific, that is individual to the particular testing situation.

Graphaesthesia

Some neurologists practise as a test of cortical sensory disorder the procedure of getting the patient to identify symbols of a numerical, literal or arithmetical kind outlined upon some area of skin.   One side of the body is then compared with the other.   The inference is that patients with parietal disease, whose tactile threshold is little altered, if at all, may be expected to fail to recognize the pattern made by such moving contacts.   The analogy with a variety of two-dimensional stereognosis is tempting.   This test, of numeral-recognition or graphaesthesia, as it has been called, was perhaps first devised by Foerster, who mainly utilized it in cases of spinal disease.   Others since then have extended the technique to cerebral disorders.

Unfortunately, the number of variable factors in this test-procedure are so great, and the normal conditions are still so obscure, that it is not justifiable as yet to make use of graphaesthesia as a diagnostic measure.   It is a manœuvre which still belongs to the experimental stage, and which should not yet be used as if it had achieved the status of a clinical sign.

For instance, the variables include such important points as : the size of the symbol ; the particular area of the body upon which it is outlined, i.e. palm, forearm, cheek ; the type of instrument used for outlining the figure, with such variables as pointedness coming into the picture ; the speed with which the symbol is outlined ; the orientation of the symbol with reference to the vertical axis of the body ; and the essential familiarity of the patient with the meaning of the symbols adopted.

Clinical experience shows that even normal subjects are often in doubt when called upon to identify moving contacts of this sort, at the outset at any rate, though their performance may improve as the test continues.

Discrimination of weights (barognosis)

Two objects similar in size and shape but of different weights may be erroneously regarded by the parietal patient as identical ; or he may be confused and in doubt as to which is the heavier. Special care must be taken during the testing of the patient to ensure that he can adequately handle the objects. Severe paralysis of a limb renders the test impracticable.

Normal subjects cannot discriminate between two weights if the difference between them is small or if the increment is added very gradually. Thus, according to the law propounded by Weber it is necessary to increase the initial weight by a third before a difference is noted (if the hand is supported), and by one-seventeenth if the hand is free to make lifting movements. In the presence of parietal disease, the proportion is greatly increased.

There are various methods by which this test can be carried out. The hand may be supported and various weights of different magnitude placed in the palm. In such circumstances, the patient judges as to differences in weight mainly by alterations in pressure feelings ; or the patient may simultaneously compare two weights by " weighing " them, one in each palm.

Whichever technique is adopted, the patient with parietal lesions may be quite unable to compare one weight with another.

The type of error usually takes the form of an illusory overestimate of weight, when an article is placed in the patient's affected hand. This overestimate may well be related not so much to sensory defects alone but to associated motor disturbances, e.g. paresis or hypotonus. (It was at one time believed that purely cerebellar disorders could cause the patient to be unable to judge weights correctly, an idea which Holmes later failed to substantiate.) But if there is no motor weakness in the affected limb, then the weight is more often misjudged as being unduly light, on the side opposite the diseased parietal lobe.

According to Ruch, Fulton and German, the ability to discriminate weights is disturbed by lesions of the parietal lobe posterior to the

Plate 4

JULES DEJERINE

primary sensory area, in both chimpanzees and man. After partial lesions a considerable restitution is possible as a result of training. (These workers studied the discrimination of weights and also of roughness together, that is, without separating the two aspects of perception.)

Employing their own technique for estimating weights, Bender, Teuber and Battersby (1950) did not find any significant differences between normal controls and a series of patients with wounds of the head, except for six cases of right parietal injury. The sensory defect was present in the left hand only. When, however, they employed a bilateral simultaneous technique a marked defect in the discrimination of weights was demonstrated. In this test, the patient is asked to lift simultaneously a standard weight with one hand and a variable weight with the other. An altered power of discriminating weights was found in the case of lesions of either parietal lobe. The weight held in the affected hand was always underestimated. When the weights were interchanged so that the standard weight was in the affected hand, and the variable weight in the normal, the variable weights were always deemed " heavier ". In other words, a weight in the affected hand was always judged to be lighter.

Inability to localize stimuli accurately

Head and Holmes drew attention to the fact that a patient with cerebral disorder of sensation might be able to recognize quite readily a light touch or a pin prick, but that he will make serious errors when asked to indicate the exact site which has been touched. The terms " atopognosis " or " atopaesthesia " have been applied to this defect. Some difficulty surrounds the actual carrying out of this test. The patient must obviously be blindfolded or have his eyelids closed. The stimulus—say the point of a pin—is applied and taken away. The patient having proclaimed that he has felt the stimulus is then asked to indicate where it occurred. As a rule, the patient responds by pointing to the spot with the forefinger. Provided there is no gross postural loss either in the limb with which the patient points, or in the segment touched, this manœuvre may prove satisfactory. If, however, there is a proprioceptive defect in either limb an added difficulty arises. Thus, to give an extreme example : if the patient's hand is touched and then the arm moved so as to occupy quite a different position in space, the patient may localize the spot stimulated to the place in space which the hand originally occupied, and not the region where the hand now lies. This source of error may be overcome by a different technique. The segment to be tested (say the hand) is placed out of sight, being concealed from the subject's view by the interposition of a bedtable. The patient's eyes are open. On the bedtable is laid an outline drawing of the body-segment which is being tested (i.e. the hand) and the patient is asked to mark with a pencil the spot on the drawing which corresponds exactly with the place stimulated. The examiner afterwards marks the true area with a pencil of another colour, and a line drawn between the true point of stimulus and the point which the patient believed was touched, indicates graphically both the extent of the error and the direction of displacement.

A complicating factor, however, enters this test-procedure and it is one which cannot as yet accurately be adjusted. This factor is constituted by the *duration of the stimulus*. A shortlived jab with a pin, or a fleeting touch with a wisp of cotton wool, will prove to be poorly localized compared with a stimulus which is maintained. This is clearly shown by the way in which the patient in whom a pain stimulus is being maintained will slowly approximate his finger towards the point. The first hesitating essay at indicating this site will probably be very inaccurate, but as the stimulus is continued so the patient's forefinger will steal nearer and nearer to the region of the stimulating pin. Ultimately, the patient's finger may hit off the site of the stimulus, but the time taken for this to come about is probably a matter of 10–20 seconds.

The *intensity* of a pain stimulus also plays a role in the accuracy of localization, in that, other things being equal, a light stimulus is not so accurately located as one which is heavier. This applies both to shortlived stimuli and to those where the contact is maintained.

There is therefore an advantage in using more than one technique in testing for topognosis. When the pencil and diagram method is chosen, the stimulus will need to be one of short duration, and preferably one that can be measured both as to time and as to weight.

When atopognosis is demonstrable, the direction of error ordinarily seems to be far from being haphazard. As a rule the patient erroneously projects the stimulus in a proximal direction, in the case of a limb. Head and Holmes, however, disagreed with Russel and Horsley (1906), who believed that there was a proximal displacement. Head and Holmes believed that the direction of error was really unpredictable. When the patient also has a loss of postural sensibility in the limb, he " gropes " and tends to feel for the stimulus too far proximally. By passively altering the attitude of the limb in space, the direction of errors in localization can also be made to change (Stenvers' " localization of images " (1949)). When, however, the trunk or face is being tested, the stimulus is perhaps more likely to be incorrectly referred to the point nearer the midline of the body.

The extent of the error is not, as a rule, very great, the distance between the point stimulated and the imagined site being not more than an inch or two.

A striking dissociation may sometimes be found between the accuracy of deliberate willed movements towards localizing a stimulus and the automatic pseudo-conscious movements which the patient may make as, for example, when scratching a point of irritation. The former may be much more inaccurate than the latter. *Per contra,* however, automatic movements in a stuporose patient may be observed to be wildly inaccurate when irritating stimuli are applied to the affected side. This is well seen in the syndrome described by Marie and Faure-Beaulieu as *hémiagnosie douloureuse.*

In some exceptional cases, the patient may project a stimulus to a point far removed from the region stimulated. This extreme type of error is most striking when the patient refers the stimulus to the mirror-opposite part of the body : for example, touched on the back of the right hand, the patient indicates the left. (It is necessary to ensure that the patient is not simply confusing right and left, and care must be taken that the patient demonstrates where he believes he is touched, by gesture as well as verbally.) This type of error is spoken of as " alloaesthesia " or " allochiria " (when the hand alone is concerned).

The terminology of this subject is somewhat mixed. Bender has described all errors in localization as instances of " sensory displacement ". This, however, has the drawback of comprising two very different phenomena, namely, the minor errors of atopognosis, and the mistakes in sidedness. Fuchs (1908) spoke of "alloparalgia". " Achiria " and also " dyschiria " have been used to refer to doubt as to localization. Grainger Stewart (1894) wrote of " allachaesthesia ", referring to the minor errors of localization (the " atopognosis " of Head and Holmes). Jones (1907) used " synchiria " for the rare phenomenon of bilateral tactile sensations evoked by unilateral stimulation. Allochiria is in some ways preferable to alloaesthesia, but there is the demerit that " chiria " literally implies " a hand " and it might be considered inappropriate to speak of allochiria of the trunk. None the less, the same Greek term *cheiron* can also apply in a metaphorical fashion to " handedness " or the " handside ", in which case allochiria of the trunk or legs would be quite correct.

The early literature upon allochiria and allaesthesia is cluttered up with a medley of cases of spinal pathology, often cases of tabes, and there is a suspicion that the alloaesthetic phenomena were often produced by suggestion. An early case report by Bosc (1892) dealt with a very different problem, namely, alloaesthesia as a manifestation of organic and localized brain disease. After a lull appeared the case recorded both by Schuster and by Pinéas in 1931, since when about a score of cases have come into the literature. Almost all these cases have been instances of cerebral disease and almost always a lesion has occurred in the right parietal lobe. Probably in every case there has also occurred an imperception for, or neglect of, the opposite half of the body. Complicating this hemi-asomatognosia there have also been present a hemiparesis (in turn associated with an anosognosia) ; a unilateral and minor degree of sensory impairment (but not a total sensory loss) ; a tactile inattention ; and perhaps a hemianopia.

In such conditions, the most plausible explanation of these cases of tactile allochiria is to imagine a unilateral defect of the body-image, without, however, absolute sensory loss. A pinprick applied to the affected side is felt, but it is not accurately projected, that particular half of the body-image being in abeyance. It is therefore naturally transferred to a corresponding point on the intact half of the body-image. This explanation is similar to that adduced by Schilder when he wrote : ". . . it is at least probable that the same mechanism which prevents the patient from appreciating his hemi-plegia and the whole left side of the body is also responsible for the transfer of the sensation from one side of the body to the other. The patient who does not want to know about one side of his body, trans-poses his sensations since he has to acknowledge them, to the other side of the body . . ."

If this is true, it follows that it will be a question of an illusory displacement of the tactile phenomena from the abnormal side to the normal. Clinical experience bears this out abundantly.

In one patient, however, the reverse phenomenon occurred. A man with a right parietal neoplasm developed a spastic left hemiplegia, with neglect amounting at times to unawareness of the affected limb. There was also a left-sided impairment of sensibility. Painful stimuli of the right side of face and chest, and of the right arm were referred to a corresponding spot on the left (i.e. the abnormal) side. Objects held in the right hand appeared to him to be contained in the left. These alloaesthetic phenomena were not demonstrable over the legs, where indeed, bilateral simultaneous testing revealed a left tactile inattention. (Case No. 23617.)

The ordinary explanation of alloaesthesia obviously falls down in such a case. Many features appear to suggest rather a tactile hallucination referred to a side of the body which is occupying an abnormal role in the body-image. It is noteworthy, however, that there is no doubling of sensation (synchiria) and that the hallucinatory percept dominates, or suppresses, or extinguishes the actual sensation. It is rather surprising that one did not find over the abnormal half of the body a hyperpathia, or hyperalgesia, or at any rate a hyperschematia.

There is an analogy in the visual sphere, where in some cases of hemianopia, an actual real object presented to the intact field is displaced across the midline so that it appears in illusory fashion within the blind field. Although a rarity, there are a number of well-authenticated cases illustrating this phenomenon of " optic alloaesthesia ".

Tactile discrimination

Head and Holmes, following the earlier experiences of McDougall (1903), Head and Rivers (1908) and others, paid much attention to this faculty as an expression of parietal integrity. According to Weber's definition, this faculty entails the ability to recognize the duality of two points of a compass, when simultaneously applied and when separated only a small distance. The term " compass test " is commonly given to the technique used for studying tactile discrimination, though French authors speak of the use of " Weber's circles ". Obviously, there is a threshold one side of which, in the normal, two points simultaneously applied, are, by reason of their propinquity, illusorily felt as one. This threshold varies considerably according to the region of the body which is being tested. Thus the tip of the tongue is the area where discrimination of two points is most delicate. The finger-tips occupy a position only a little less sensitive, the most delicate region being an oval area over each palmar pulp—the so-called " touch rosette ". Elsewhere, the threshold is markedly different. However, the degree of tactile discrimination is

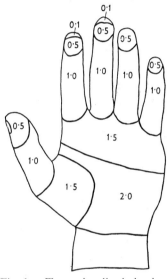

Fig. 63. Two-point discrimination.
Diagram showing areas of relative sensitivity to the compass test. The figures refer to cm. The lines demarcating one area from another are actually not as sharp as depicted in the illustration.

the same for any two symmetrically placed regions, and hence the compass test is a practical and useful manœuvre for comparing two mirror-opposite sides of the body, when unilateral cerebral disease is under suspicion.

The physiology of two-point discrimination has been closely studied by Wundt (1910), von Frey (1896), Markova (1900), Bürklen (1917) and others. When the skin surface is simultaneously touched by two separated points of a compass, two sensory phenomena are appreciated : (1) An appreciation of duality, and (2) an estimate of the distance separating the points. Markova spoke of the former of these factors as " discrimination ", and termed the latter, " spatial cutaneous perception ". It is possible that other faculties also enter the sensory experience, i.e. the recognition of the orientation of the two points, that is whether they lie horizontally across the axis of the body segment, or directly or obliquely in alignment with the axis. There may also be awareness of the equality or inequality in the amount of pressure applied to each compass point.

Should the compass points be applied in rather close apposition, the sense of duality may still be present, but the two sensations are relatively indistinct or dull. They may appear as though united by a bridge ; this phenomenon is what von Frey called the " mutual blunting of adjacent excitations ". It has also been looked upon as a " first stage of fusion ".

Should the two compass points be even more closely approximated, the sense of duality fades. An entirely new " unitary " sensation develops (the " second stage of fusion "). This constitutes the " spatial threshold " (Weber) or the " simultaneous threshold " (von Frey). When the two simultaneous contacts are of equal force, then the " place value " of each individual contact is lost, and is replaced by a sensation located to a point midway between the two actual points of contact. If, however, one of the contacts is more forceful than the other, fusion occurs more readily, and the stronger stimulus outweighs the weaker, and determines the " place value ".

According to Sherrington, tactile discrimination, or the " average liminal distance ", as he called it, is capable of considerable enhancement in the normal by a process of training. Still more interesting is his observation that education of a skin area will not only reduce the liminal distance as tested by compasses, but it will also bring about a similar enhanced sensibility over a corresponding area on the mirror-opposite region of the body. Furthermore, he found that contralateral enhanced sensitivity could be accompanied by an enhanced contralateral motor efficiency.

Head and Holmes' technique of describing the patient's response to this test has the great merit of setting down each reply given by the patient. The attainment of the threshold becomes evident, beyond which all answers are correct and below which all are erroneous. But, unlike the case when thalamic, mesencephalic, spinal and peripheral lesions are concerned, there is a marked tendency for patients with parietal disease to show an incongruity, irregularity and unpredictability in their replies. Head and Holmes brought this point out with emphasis. The threshold thus becomes more difficult to identify than is the case of a patient with a lesion elsewhere in the sensory pathways. A patient may give a series of correct replies ; then make one or more mistakes, without there being an alteration in the stimulus ; then once again he may proceed to give correct answers. Another peculiarity is often evident. The patient touched with one point of the compasses may at times proclaim that he can feel two points. This illusory doubling of sensation is not a consistent phenomenon, however, but it emerges only occasionally, and it rarely persists. Or again, the patient, his eyelids remaining closed, may announce that he feels a touch—either one point or two—when actually he has not been touched at all. This again is an episodic and exceptional phenomenon, which does not continue or behave in other respects as a tactile hallucination.

Head and Holmes also made it clear that in some cortical parietal syndromes the compass points need not be applied simultaneously. In other words, an interval may occur between the application of the one leg of the compass, and of the other, even though the spatial interval between the two points is relatively great. The patient still fails to recognize the twoness of the stimuli. If, however, the time-interval between the application of the first and then the second points be relatively great, the patient may appreciate the second stimulus but independently of the first. He has felt each of the two points, but the duality of the stimulus escapes him.

The system of testing and recording tactile discrimination as practised by Head and Holmes is as follows : ten single and ten double contacts are made in irregular order (after the appropriate threshold for the normal side has been found), on first the normal and then the abnormal side. The results are set out thus :

Affected forearm : separation of compass points, 15 cm.

1		/	/ / /						/	/	/	/	/ /
2			× × ×	×	×	×	×	×				× ×
2+	× ×	×			×	× ×	×		×	×		×

One point applied alone is indicated by (1) ; two points simultaneously applied is shown by (2), and when successively applied by (2 +). A " / " indicates a correct answer, and a " × " an incorrect one.

The use of the compass test, wherein two stimuli are appreciated as one in certain circumstances, must not be confused with the technique of double stimulation. In this latter procedure there is a wide separation in space between the two simultaneously applied stimuli, often indeed involving both sides of the body. The question will be treated more fully under the section dealing with tactile inattention.

Although most interest has been aroused by the phenomenon of *two*-point discrimination, it must be realized that recognition is possible of *three points* simultaneously applied, and indeed, even more than three. That is to say, a finger-tip applied to a series of projecting points can, even without moving the palpating surface of the finger, within certain limits recognize the multiplicity of simultaneous contacts, and their number. The limits of the discriminative perception are determined by the distance separating the points one from another—a distance which must be sufficiently great ; and the total number of points which must not be too many. The test may equally well be carried out in another way, that is like the compass test, whereby an applicator furnished with three or more bristles or projecting points, is laid against the skin. Any area of the body can be tested, but as in the case of two-point discrimination, the tip of the tongue, the lips and the finger-tips may be regarded as the most sensitive regions. The details of the test and the limits of its practicability have not yet been determined.

It is probable that the area for the clear discrimination of three simultaneous stimuli is smaller than for two, and that there is a small peripheral zone where three stimuli give rise—not to a distinct feeling of oneness—but a vaguer sensation, perhaps even an impression of twoness. This latter illusion may perhaps be due to the differing thresholds of separation for duality and triplicity of contact ; or possibly, it may be due to the curving surface of the finger-tips which may make an uneven contact with three points simultaneously applied.

This last statement applies chiefly when the points of three pins are arranged to form a triangle. If, however, they are arranged in vertical series, an additional sensory illusion may come into play. If the hand, for example, be tested from the region of the palm, distally towards the more sensitive finger-tips, the triple-point stimulus will give rise to the following sensations, according to the area touched :

(*a*) Most proximally, there is a feeling of being touched by a single pin.

(*b*) As one approaches the distal phalanx, one enters a zone where the tactile feeling is that of being touched by a linear sharp-bladed instrument, e.g. a short knife-edge.

(*c*) Distal to that is a narrow zone within which there is a feeling as if being touched by two points ; and

(*d*) Within the most sensitive zone, i.e. the tips of the fingers and thumb, there is a feeling of three simultaneous points.

This series of phenomenon takes place whether the pins are arranged in vertical series across the axis of the fingers or in line with it. It is also demonstrable upon the tongue, where the sensibility increases from behind forward, to attain its maximum over the tip.

With four points arranged in a square, the tactile impressions are similarly variable as one passes from a relatively insensitive area (base of fingers) towards the tip. The feeling is first of all a punctate sensation of oneness. Next comes a most diffuse and vague, but still single, type of contact. Then comes a feeling as if one were touching the sharp sides of a hollow square. Last of all comes the sense of four separate pointed contacts. This is usually not achieved immediately but requires a measurable time-interval for its appreciation. The slightest movement of the palpating finger, over a gentle

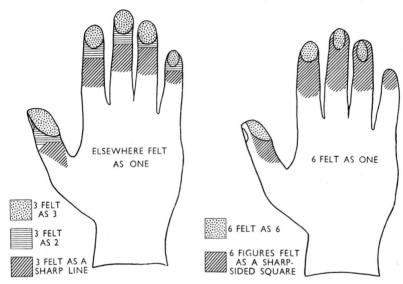

ELSEWHERE FELT
AS ONE

6 FELT AS ONE

3 FELT AS 3

3 FELT AS 2

3 FELT AS A SHARP LINE

6 FELT AS 6

6 FIGURES FELT AS A SHARP-SIDED SQUARE

Fig. 64. Three-point discrimination.

Diagram showing areas of relative sensitivity when the stimulus consists of three points in a line, 0·5 cm. apart, simultaneously applied. The areas are less abruptly demarcated one from another than appears from the illustration.

Fig. 65. Six-point discrimination.

Here the stimulus consists in six points arranged in rectangular form (each point being 0·5 cm. distant from another), and applied simultaneously.

oscillation or rocking along its axis, immediately results in a most vivid tactile image of four distinct pinpoints.

Wundt has asserted that six simultaneous points of contact form the limit of discriminative ability for an isolated area of skin. This experimental finding tallies in a striking way with the empirical contrivance of a six-point punctographic system as the foundation of the braille alphabet for the blind. In this system the great majority of symbols are made up of fewer than six dots.

The immediate and accurate perception of multiple points simultaneously applied to the skin may be compared with a somewhat similar test-situation in the visual sphere. When a group of dots is exposed for a very short period of time, recognition of the numerical total takes place in one of three ways, depending partly upon the number of dots, and partly upon the duration of the exposure. If the stimulus is maintained long enough, the subject can rely upon *counting* to make an accurate assessment. This process is not possible if the time of exposure is short. The subject can now assess the total by an immediate process of *subitizing*, if the dots are less than six in number ; but if they are more than six, he has to rely upon *estimating* the total.

With the simultaneous application of two to six points to the finger-tips, the patient can occasionally rely on a process of immediate subitizing, although more often he will have to resort to a deliberate act of counting the punctate stimuli.

In cases of parietal disease, the discrimination of simultaneously applied multiple points would appear to suffer *pari passu* with faulty performance with the compass test. Considerably more careful clinical study is required, however, before the utility and scope of this test-measure is known.

Tactile inattention

Simultaneous testing with two stimuli may evoke interesting phenomena in patients with parietal disease. This is well seen in the case of stereognosis : if two similar objects are placed in each of the patient's two hands, his eyelids being closed, he may announce that he feels and recognizes the object only on the unaffected side. But when each hand is tested singly the object is promptly felt, and may be even recognized and named correctly. If, again, similar objects are inserted into both hands (the patient feeling the object only in the unaffected hand), and if the object is then gently removed from the normal hand, the patient may now, after an interval of a second or two, proclaim that he can feel an object in the other, i.e. affected, hand. Or, in other cases, when articles are held in both hands, the patient may feel the object on the healthy side immediately, but on the affected side only after a delay. His announcement of an object in that hand may be made hesitatingly ; he may say he feels something there but does not know what it is. Or he may eventually arrive at a conclusion as to its identity. Errors may be made, such as, for example, saying that the object in the affected hand is smaller and lighter than in the other ; or perhaps the opposite.

This technique of bilateral simultaneous testing may be used with other sense modalities, e.g. light touch, pinprick, as well as thermal contacts. In the case of a pinprick, which is maintained evenly, the patient may not feel the pin on the affected side even when the stimulus on the normal side is withdrawn. But if the pin is taken away from the normal side and then applied to the affected side close to the spot which is already being stimulated though not felt, the patient at once states he can feel this fresh stimulus. Still cruder stimuli may be used to demonstrate this phenomenon. Thus, bilateral simultaneous scratching or rubbing may be effectual ; or the application of two vibrating tuning forks ; or the seizure of the patient's two hands by the examiner's. Heterogeneous contacts may also be effective. Thus, cotton wool applied to the normal side at the same time as the affected side is pricked with a pin, causes the latter not to be felt—or seemingly so. Heterotopic stimulation may also act in the same way. Thus, a contact applied to the normal half of the face may prevent a simultaneous stimulus over the affected hand from being felt. At times, this same phenomenon occurs when two touches are made on different parts of the same side ; i.e. the face and the hand on the affected side. In this case, the facial stimulus is the one which is usually felt to the detriment of the contact on the hand. In general, proximal stimuli " take preference " over distal.

Some of these foregoing observations date from 1885 when Oppenheim introduced the term " double stimulation ". Various papers by Bender and his associates, and by Critchley, have emphasized the importance of this test-procedure. Bender spoke of " tactile extinction ", a term which possesses a number of drawbacks and which has been widely criticized. Reider (1946) described his patient as showing " sensory suppression " and boldly implicated the so-called suppressor bands. Vercelli (1947) spoke of " sensory eclipse ". Critchley (1949) gave a number of reasons why the term " tactile inattention ", though not ideal, is perhaps least open to objection.

Incomplete degrees of the defect may be found, and constitute an additional argument against the use of the term " extinction ". These variants are best demonstrated in the technique of bilateral simultaneous testing for stereognosis, as already mentioned. But even in the case of testing with pin prick, variation in responses may be brought about. For example, if the test is carried out many times in succession, the " inattention " phenomenon may break down. Or, if the patient is told to open his eyes and observe closely what is going on, the inattention may pass and two separate stimuli may be declared as felt. Or, with very strong stimulation on one side ; or with stimuli which are maintained for a very long time, the single sensation may slowly give way to a sense of twoness—at first dubiously and then with certainty. Thereafter, the test of double stimulation may for

L

some time fail to demonstrate the inattention (" extinction ")
phenomenon.

In the same type of patient, it may also be found that contralateral
tactile stimuli may be ignored (or " extinguished ") if stimulation of
another sense modality be offered at the same time to the patient
(e.g. the flashing of a torchlight ; the noise of a ringing bell or
jangling keys).

The importance of highest level intellectual function in this test
(whether it be expressed as a faculty of directed attention, or as a
reduced capacity of available nerve energy (Goldstein)) is shown by
one or two clinical experiences. In the first place, a patient with a
parietal defect, whose general mental alertness is beginning to suffer,
may show tactile inattention not only as concerns his affected half of
the body, but at times over the " normal " side of the body as well.
This contradictory finding may not appear at the bedside testing until
after a long interview, during which the patient has shown in the
ordinary way tactile inattention with respect to the contralateral half.
These paradoxical responses, being later in appearance, are exceptional rather than habitual ; but they are, it is submitted, of great
diagnostic and aetiological importance. They indicate at the same
time a parietal defect and a psychological disorder.

The second point of clinical interest concerns cases of bilateral
parietal disease. Here again, tactile inattention may be demonstrated at the bedside, but without any consistency in location. Now
one side is ignored, now the other, when simultaneous stimuli are
applied.

The third point lies in the observation that simultaneous double
stimulation whether of homologous or heterologous areas is liable even
in normal subjects to show that one stimulus " dominates " the other,
at least for the initial tests. In abnormal states (under light general
anaesthesia ; patients with aphasia, schizophrenia, organic psychoses)
and in young children (aged 4 to 10) this phenomenon is demonstrable
still more frequently. A curious pattern seems to be evident in that
simultaneous stimulation of two different segments shows that, if only
one stimulus is perceived, it is the one situated more proximally and
more caudally. The order of precedence would appear to be : face,
shoulder, trunk (breast), penis, thigh, calf, foot, arm and hand
(" rostral dominance "). The results are not always consistent, however, and at certain moments this order is upset. Another curious
phenomenon sometimes found is that simultaneous pin pricks to the
cheek and hand may evoke stimuli apparently referred to both cheeks
(" displacement ") (vide various papers by Bender and his associates,
Cohn, Fink, Jaffe, Kolb, Raines, Schappel and Shapiro).

Probably, therefore, tactile inattention in patients with parietal disease is but the enhanced or exaggerated expression of a process which can be demonstrated in fragmentary or occasional fashion, not only in other morbid states but even in normal subjects. We hark back, therefore, to Lhermitte and Ajuriaguerra (1942), who spoke of the general rule of symmetrical stimulation that strong stimulation of the healthy side suppresses the attenuated sensations on the impaired side ; and even before that, to Heyman's law of inhibition that simultaneous stimuli mask each other (1927). Still earlier authority on this problem is to be found in the dictum of Hippocrates that " of simultaneous pains in two places, the lesser is obliterated by the greater ".

Tactile inattention in parietal patients is probably no more than an instance of local neglect or disregard, which may be demonstrable at times in many other spheres of consciousness besides the tactile —whether motor, visual or spatial. It is not without interest that the inattention phenomenon has been described with bilateral stimulation of the sense of taste when test-substances are simultaneously applied over the two halves of the tongue. This was found to be so by Bender and Feldman (1952) in three cases of parietal injury, and one patient with a right parieto-occipital tumour.

Dr. Hal Gregg has informed one of the diagnostic utility of applying a technique of simultaneous *three*-point tactile testing in patients with early parietal disease. In some patients, normal responses are given to ordinary bilateral simultaneous testing, but errors are made when three contacts are made simultaneously, especially when two contacts are made on the side opposite the brain lesion. In such cases, the more proximal of the stimuli on a limb is the one which is " missed ".

Altered sensory adaptation time

A cutaneous stimulus, if continued, may cease to reach awareness. The factor of attention seems significant here because conscious effort can readily re-arouse the sensation. This is illustrated by the pressure of clothing upon the body-surface, which rarely obtrudes itself into consciousness. " Sensory adaptation time " has been suggested as a descriptive term, even though it carries the demerit of having already been used in a different meaning by physiologists, and by psychologists too, in yet another context.

According to Bender, this adaptation time may be altered over the opposite side of the body, in association with parietal disease. Bender stated that there may be either a shortening or a prolongation, the former being the more usual. He believed that an abbreviated adaptation time was an explanation of the common symptom whereby the patient accidentally lets objects drop out of his affected hand, even though motility and sensibility are not materially impaired. Bender gave another example. One of his marine patients, convalescent from a compound fracture of the left occipitoparietal region, was seated in the parlour *en famille*, his arm round his girl-friend's waist. Presently, a look of displeasure grew over the mother's face, due, it is alleged, to the accidental wandering of the patient's hand so as now to cover a more compromising part of the girl's anatomy.

Bedside clinical testing of sensory adaptation time is not easy, because as soon as the patient directs attention to his sensations, the factor of adaptation disappears. This point would therefore militate against such a test as that of maintaining a pressure with a pin and measuring the length of time throughout which the stimulus is felt. Possibly this phenomenon might be demonstrated in a more objective but less direct fashion by getting the patient to close his eyelids and then to hold for several minutes an object in each of his two hands, simultaneously. An " absent-minded " dropping of the article on the affected side might be taken as indicating that the stimulus had failed to maintain itself in consciousness.

Yet another way would be to allow the blindfolded patient to seat himself before a washbowl with both of his hands immersed in warm water. On the affected side, the sensation of warmth may gradually give way to a " neutral " or " tepid " sensation, whereas the normal hand will continue to appreciate the heat of the water. Here again, the test is impeded each moment the patient focuses attention on the task of comparing the sensations over both hands.

Head and Holmes, however, mentioned more particularly the opposite phenomenon in that interrupted touches were apt, in cases of parietal cortical lesion, to produce a feeling of a continuous touch —what they called the " persistence of sensation ". It may furthermore be noticed in testing patients for the power to judge weights that, when the object is removed from the hand, the patient may continue to feel as though the object were still there, though no qualities of heaviness or lightness may be present.

According to Bender, a reduction in adaptation time is associated with a decrease or abolition of " after-sensation ". This is the name given to the patient's reaction noted after the removal of the stimulus-object. Ordinarily, a sensory impression lasts only a few seconds— according in part to the intensity of the stimulus concerned. It may not be recognized unless the patient's attention is directed to it.

Clinical experience of patients with parietal disease makes one cautious, if not sceptical, about accepting unreservedly some of the data afforded by purely subjective operations, that is to say, data which by their very nature cannot be controlled by objective recording. There are so many complicating factors which are apt to intrude and to invalidate the bedside tests. Drowsiness, unco-operation, mild confusion, are obvious. Less self-evident factors are the psychical reactions which may take the form of unawareness, non-acceptance, denial, projection, repression of disease, or the circumstances of disease, or the physical evidences of a disability. Impaired power of directing or sustaining attention may play a particular role in cases with brain damage, especially of the parietal lobe. Ready fatigue ; variability and even inconsistency of response is a frequent complicating factor in such patients, not only in the realm of sensory investigation. Lastly, we are constantly embarrassed by the problem of spontaneous tactile sensations, or tactile hallucinations, when very delicate tests of sensibility are being attempted in patients with parietal disease.

Anaestho-agnosia

Ch. Foix (1922) drew attention to the possible existence of bilateral objective sensory changes associated with a parietal lesion which is strictly unilateral in extent. The sensory impairment is both more extensive and more profound on the contralateral side. The exact clinical findings in Foix's original four cases were as follows : contralateral hemiplegia, hemihypaesthesia ; ipsilateral postural loss and astereognosis ; bilateral ideomotor apraxia. In three of the four cases, there was also dysphasia. Out of the four cases there was also, on the ipsilateral side in three cases, a very slight diminution in tactile sensibility.

Foix proposed to look upon these troubles as an anaesthesia provoked by an agnosic defect, comparable with an auditory agnosia, or psychic blindness, or aphasia or agraphia. The causative lesion was ascribed by Foix to a deep lesion involving the white matter of the left parietal lobe. It would be more correct to speak of the dominant parietal lobe, for in 1925, Guillain, Alajouanine and Garcin described an instance of bilateral anaestho-agnosia due to a right-sided parietal lesion in a left-handed subject.

Although this original paper dates from as long ago as 1922, few similar cases appear to have been recorded since. (The cases of bilateral astereognosis from unilateral lesions need to be mentioned in qualification of this statement.) This is perhaps all the more surprising in view of Sherrington's study of the bilateral enhancement of tactile discrimination by unilateral training (see page 140) ; and also of Dusser de Barenne's experimental demonstration that strychninization of one parietal cortex in animals produces an objective hypersensitivity over both sides of the body. The still later work of Woolsey and others on the secondary sensory centre is possibly significant here.

Asymboly for pain : hemiagnosia

An unusual syndrome of an imperceptive character in association with pain stimuli is occasionally found in parietal cases. The patient, though not insensitive to pain, displays an altered and unusual attitude towards pain-producing stimuli. The expected evasive or preventive motor reactions are weak or absent. The facial expression may be inappropriate and the patient may smile during painful manipulations.

This syndrome was first noted by Schilder and Stengel in 1928, and in further papers in 1930 and 1931 they extended their clinical conception. They coined the expression " pain asymboly " in this connection. The authors drew attention to a paradoxical or ambivalent attitude on the part of the patient towards pain stimuli. Not only does the patient not resent such impulses as pinpricks, but he may even seem to be unduly interested in his own sensory experiences. He may offer himself for painful stimulation or inflict it deliberately upon himself. Furthermore, the patient appears indifferent to gestures or noises of a threatening character—a fact which prompted Schilder and Stengel in 1931 to regard their cases as evidencing a " danger asymboly ".

A fair number of such cases has since been reported so that the clinical features and anatomical correlates can be described in more detail. Conspicuous among the writers who have discussed this problem are Pötzl and Stengel (1936), Rubins and Friedman (1948), and Hécaen and Ajuriaguerra (1950). Thus, Rubins and Friedman recorded four cases. All the patients could recognize pinprick as sharp, and light touch and thermal contacts were felt normally. Astereognosis was present on both sides together with loss of recognition of textures. Autonomic reactions were present when special pain-producing mechanisms were set in action, e.g. muscle ischaemia, intravenous histamine. All the patients had a marked aphasia of mixed type. They also showed disorders in the body-image, Gerstmann's syndrome, and constructional or ideo-kinetic apraxia.

Hécaen and Ajuriaguerra's patient showed no motor reaction towards pain, a circumstance which prompted them to think of a " pain apraxia ".

In every recorded case, the defect has been distributed in a universal fashion over the body, while the cerebral lesion has in every verified case up to 1950 been situated within the left, that is to say, the dominant hemisphere. Hécaen and Ajuriaguerra's patient had a left hemiplegia, however, and a verified lesion in the right hemisphere ; this patient was described as being ambidextrous. It is interesting to recall that she was not aphasic, but that she showed the usual somatagnosic defects which are typical of a right-brained lesion in a right-handed subject. The frequent co-existence of other disorders, so often associated with parietal disease, would lead one to suspect that in pain asymboly too there is a lesion in or near the inferior parietal lobule. Three cases in the Schilder-Stengel series were verified ; the lesions lay mainly within the left supramarginal gyrus, with some involvement of the angular gyrus and the first temporal convolution. In the Rubins-Friedman series, one patient had a glioma in the left inferior parietal lobule. Their second patient had a gunshot wound of the left hemisphere, with the site of entry of the bullet in the temple and the point of exit in the parieto-occipital region. Hécaen and Ajuriaguerra's patient proved to have an extensive intracerebral haematoma of the right posterior parietal region.

The expression " asymboly for pain " is open to objection in that there is strictly speaking nothing symbolic about a pain stimulus, or the patient's reaction thereto.   " Asymboly " should be restricted, as Finkelnburg argued, to disorders of symbolic thinking, semantic defects and the like : to utilize the words outside those limits leads only to a confusion of thought.   For the phenomenon which Stengel and Schilder described, one could perhaps employ the expression " agnosia for pain " ; if, indeed, it is necessary to find a word at all. " Imperception " for pain is unsatisfactory, in that it might suggest a non-perception of pain, which indeed is not the case. A defective perceptual experience is really what is happening. Pain-apraxia is also terminologically inappropriate. A more elaborate, though rather cacophonous term, would be " algodiaphoria ", meaning a morbid indifference towards painful stimuli.

It is probable that this altered awareness of an attitude towards a painful stimulus does not occur alone, that is to say, independently of other " gnosic " or perceptual disabilities. Such indeed is suggested by the later papers of Schilder and Stengel, in which they pointed out that their patients also displayed an unconcern about visual sensa of a threatening character. Here at once is an extension of the dysgnosic disorder from the narrow sphere of painful stimuli to complicated visual patterns. The problem rather ties up with a variety of prosopagnosia and so comes under the umbrella of the visual agnosias. To speak of an " asymboly for danger " neither adds precision to the terminology nor indicates the fundamental defect which lies behind the clinical manifestations.

The problem of pain asymboly raises the question as to whether any relationship exists between this syndrome and the unilateral phenomenon described by Pierre Marie as " hemiagnosia for pain ". The latter would seem to be an instance of very defective localization of pain stimuli and might perhaps belong better to the category of the atopagnosias (or topo-aesthesias). According to Pierre Marie, a hemiplegic person lying in coma or subcoma, may respond to forceful pinching of the skin of the paralysed side, by emitting sighs or groans, and by vague gestures of protest with the sound hand. Or, if the painful stimulus is continued, upon say the thigh or abdomen, the patient may bring his normal hand up to his face, or he may rub his arm, or grope in the bed ; never does he accurately bring his hand over in an attempt to brush away the painful stimulus. That this failure to hit off the seat of the pain is not the result of obfuscation of consciousness, is shown by the fact that a similar pinching of the normal leg will cause the patient to move his hand down to the exact part stimulated.

" Pseudothalamic syndrome " : hemialgia

The striking clinical picture described by Dejerine and Roussy, and shortly afterwards by Head and Holmes, and ascribed by them to a lesion of the lateral nucleus of the thalamus, is not easily over-looked. Subsequent workers have not found it easy to decide upon the pathophysiology of the most striking feature of the syndrome, namely, the combination of spontaneous pains with over-reaction to sensory contacts. Opinions have swung between the conception of an irritative lesion of the thalamic nuclei, to a destructive lesion of some corticofugal inhibiting pathway. Schuster (1917) has analysed the thalamic syndrome into at least five clinicopathological subtypes according to the vascular topography.

A conception of spontaneous pains being due to the removal of a corticofugal restraint would easily be reconciled with a thalamic syndrome produced by a lesion remote from the thalamus, i.e. within the most proximal part of the corticofugal pathways. Consequently the paper of Foix, Chavany and Lévy (1927) focused attention upon this hypothesis by demonstrating that a subcortical lesion could actually mimic the clinical features of a thalamic syndrome. Špriňgová, even earlier (1926), had demonstrated a patient who developed, among other symptoms, shooting pains in the left side of the spine and in the left leg, mainly when walking. The patient bent over to the left in order to get some relief. An osteosarcoma was found, the size of an egg, compressing the right frontoparietal region of the brain. The conclusion was that central pains could be produced by a cortical lesion. Foix asserted that when a thalamic syndrome of vascular origin is diagnosed at the bedside, and no hemianopia is present, then it becomes necessary to think of a parietal lesion. Whether the clinical manifestations of the " pseudothalamic syndrome " of Foix, Chavany and Lévy are actually identical with those of the thalamic syndrome of Dejerine and Roussy is debatable. Even the so-called " thalamic hand " has been noted in the parietal cases. It could be argued that minor differences distinguish the two clinical pictures. Probably the following case-report illustrates a pseudothalamic syndrome from a lesion of the parieto-thalamic pathways :

Following a stroke, a hypertensive woman of 57 (Case No. 32202) developed abnormal sensations affecting the right side of the body. These comprised a curious and unpleasant feeling in the right half of the face, usually of an icy-cold nature, but sometimes—and especially at night—like a " terrific burning ". At times, the face would feel swollen : at other times, it would seem as though there was nothing there—as though she had half a face. The right side of the face felt as though it had " gone in ". Drinking anything hot would feel " terrible ", like a sore inside the cheek on the right side. The right eye and right nostril often felt as though they were running with water, but each time she wiped them, they proved to be dry. The right arm often felt numb, " like ice ". The feeling in the thumb and fingers was as though they were immersed in soda-water.

Examination showed a mild right hemiparesis with increased reflexes, but a flexor plantar response. There was visual inattention to the right. Objective testing of sensation showed a loss to pinprick over the hands, back and front, as high as the wrist. Over the forearms, almost as far as the elbow, pinpricks produced a diffuse sensation . . . " like many pins ". The most marked sensory changes, however, were to be found over the right side of the face. Cotton wool was lost by the side of the nose, but elsewhere it produced a burning feeling (see Figs. 66, 67 and 68). Pinprick was also lost over a small area on the side of the nose, and elsewhere it produced a spreading and unpleasant sensation. Vibration sense and postural sensibility were both a little impaired on the right side in both upper and lower limbs. There was no tactile inattention, but localization of stimuli over the back of the right hand was not very accurate. Stereognosic tests were well executed, though she had some difficulties with the simultaneous identification of objects in the two hands.

Clinical points which would favour the diagnosis of a pseudo-thalamic rather than a thalamic syndrome are the following :

(1) A limited distribution of objective sensory disturbance ; i.e. restricted to hand ; or face and hand ; or face only.

(2) Marked astereognosis in the affected hand.

(3) More marked motor weakness.

(4) The presence of periodic attacks of focal sensory epilepsy.

(5) Well-marked and consistently demonstrable tactile inattention.

(6) The later development of hypotonus and mild muscular atrophy in the affected limbs.

(7) The presence of paraschematic feelings referable to the affected side.

(8) Less well-marked contracture.

(9) Relatively minor subjective sensory complaints.

(10) An inco-ordination without true intention tremor.

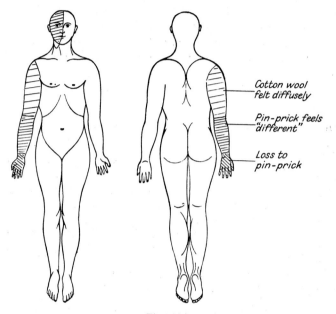

Cotton wool
felt diffusely

Pin-prick feels
"different"

Loss to
pin-prick

Fig. 66.

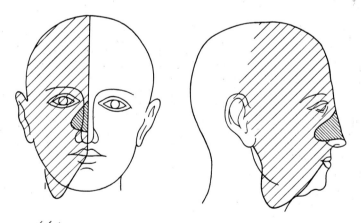

/// Cotton wool felt as "burning cold"

Loss to cotton wool

Fig. 67.

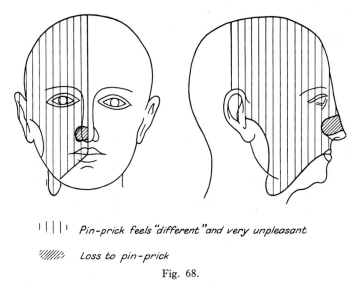

ı | | | ı   *Pin-prick feels "different" and very unpleasant*

░▓▓▓░   *Loss to pin-prick*

Fig. 68.

Figs. 66, 67 and 68.   Distribution of sensory impairment in a case of pseudo-thalamic syndrome from a deep parietal vascular lesion.   (Female, 57 years. Case No. 32202.)

Experience since 1927 has shown that some of the foregoing differential points are not necessarily valid. Roger, for example, thought that the subjective and objective sensory phenomena are much the same in the two disorders, and that it was safer to rely upon the motor signs as evidence supporting a parietal localization. This is scarcely borne out by the verified case record of Lhermitte and Ajuriaguerra (1935), where the motor signs were mild and the sensory features conspicuous. In his important clinicopathological study of the thalamus, Schuster made it clear that differential diagnosis was often difficult and that a similar somatotopic distribution of signs can occur with thalamic as with suprathalamic lesions. Biemond (1949) spoke of spontaneous pain in the pseudothalamic cases (though Alajouanine, Thurel and Brunelli (1934) thought pain was exceptional with such lesions) and in his case—where the lesion was confirmed—stereognosis was intact. Both Jumentié and Roussy, in discussing Foix's original communication, said that it was better to speak of a " parieto-insulocapsular syndrome ", or of a " capsuloparietal syndrome ", rather than to ascribe the picture to a purely parietal origin.

CHAPTER V

DISORDERS OF MOTILITY

It has been suggested to me that the loss of irritability in the cases of spinal paralysis might be owing to defective nutrition of the muscles. I therefore tried the effect of galvanism in a case of chronic cerebral paralysis, or hemiplegia, with much emaciation of the paralytic muscles. I found these muscles, as before, much more irritable than those of the unaffected hand.

MARSHALL HALL, 1839.

Lesions which are confined to the parietal lobe do not ordinarily produce a paralysis. Massive lesions, however, may invade other lobes, or may exert pressure upon motor fibres, so as to bring about a contralateral paresis, possibly associated with signs of pyramidal dysfunction. The frontopontine and frontospinal efferent systems take origin as a sheet-like formation which actually constitutes the anterior frontier of the parietal lobe, demarcating it sharply from the frontal lobe. This layer of fibres is readily indented or invaded by lesions which have their beginnings within the parietal lobe. Some of the cells of origin of this motor projectional system may actually lie behind the fissure of Rolando, in the postcentral gyrus, or even more caudal still. Such motor cells are really parietal constituents, and their implication within a pathological focus might lead to a certain contralateral reduction in strength.

In frontoparietal disease and particularly when of a space-occupying nature, a contralateral hemiplegia of pyramidal type is conspicuous. The relative degree of somatic involvement—leg, arm, face—will naturally depend upon the location of the lesion within the frontal and parietal lobes.

The patient may present himself in the clinic with more unilateral incapacity than can be accounted for on the basis of an associated hemiplegia. Clinical study may reveal other defects which simulate a paralysis, or which intensify it. In the first place, the incapacity may turn out to be largely in the nature of a one-sided neglect—a dropping out of one half of the body from the scheme of activity. This particular sign, more often involving the left side of the body in right-handed persons, will be dealt with more fully in a later section.

In the second place, motor helplessness may prove to be due not to pyramidal affection, but to a profound loss of postural sensibility. The hemiparesis which gradually supervenes with an expanding

156

lesion, or which appears suddenly after an injury or vascular occlusion, is therefore really to be regarded as a frontoparietal, or perhaps a temporoparietal, manifestation. That the parietal lobe is playing a role in the symptomatology may be suspected when certain minor points in the motility-disorder can be demonstrated—sensory and specific parietal signs apart. The chief features which would lead one to guess that the parietal lobe was affected in a case of hemiparesis would be :

(1) Greater poverty of movement than can be accounted for on the basis of paralysis.

(2) A tendency towards the adoption of catatonic-like postures by the affected upper limb.

(3) An unusual psychological reaction towards the disability. (This is a complicated problem which will be discussed in Chapter VIII.)

(4) Flaccidity of the affected muscles going on to actual visible atrophy. (In cases of infantile hemiplegia coming under observation at a later age, a marked hypoplasia of the affected limbs should suggest a parietal involvement.)

(5) An absence of a plantar response on the sole of the affected foot.

(6) Hypotonia, rather than spasticity, in the affected arm and leg.

To these criteria one must, of course, add the presence of sensory changes associated with the paralysis. Field defects, relative hemianopias, deviation of the head and eyes away from the paralysed side, merely suggest a posteriorly situated lesion which may or may not involve the parietal lobe.

With regard to the nature of the plantar reflex on the side opposite the parietal lesion, reference has already been made to the occasional absence of any response at all. (This was incidentally also noted by Athanassio Bénisty.) More often, an extensor plantar response can be elicited. Cohn, however, drew attention to a curious phenomenon whereby bilateral simultaneous stroking of the soles of both feet was followed by a flexor reflex on the ipsilateral side and no response at all on the side opposite to the parietal lesion. When, however, that foot was tested alone, in the ordinary way, an upgoing toe resulted (1948).

Rothfeld's manœuvre for the localization of cerebral lesions (1932) may be mentioned for what it is worth. Passive straight leg raising on one side is said to provoke a contralateral associated flexion movement at the hip, knee and ankle joints in the presence of either a contralateral frontal lesion or else an ipsilateral parietotemporal lesion. If then it is already possible by other methods to determine the hemisphere which is involved, this test is claimed to enable the clinician to determine whether the main mass of the lesion lies in front of or behind the central sulcus.

Apraxia

In addition to the foregoing, there are a number of psychomotor disturbances which have been described with parietal lesions, more especially within the dominant hemisphere. Chief among these is a bilateral ideomotor apraxia in the sense described by Liepmann. The dominant parietal lobe is ordinarily regarded as producing, when damaged, a disorder of motor innervation affecting not only the contralateral paralysed limb, but also the ipsilateral hand and arm. Most neurologists would implicate the supramarginal gyrus in this connection (Strohmayer, Kroll, Stauffenberg, Liepmann, Kleist, Claude and Loyez, Laignel-Lavastine and Lévy-Valensi, Fearnsides, Foix, Morlaas, Bremer, Schwob). Consequently, the apraxic patient experiences much difficulty in carrying out to command pantomimic or sham acts ; none the less, the patient may execute the same motions quite adequately when they appear as automatic or affectively engendered actions. The patient may fumble badly with tools and utensils, held either in one hand or in both together. This maladroitness will be seen whether the activities are deliberate, willed, and " most voluntary ", or whether they be quasi-automatic—" but little automatic ", as Hughlings Jackson would have said. In reflexive movements to command, the patient may make extraordinary mistakes, with hesitancies, delays, untidiness, perseveration, short-cuts or roundabout movements, characteristic of this type of apraxia. The patient may show dissatisfaction with his accomplishment but more often he does not appear to notice his shortcomings. The ordinary daily tasks may even prove too much. He may find it difficult and eventually impossible to dress himself. He may require to be fed owing to his inability to manage a knife and fork. Washing, shaving, despatching a letter, or parcelling up a package soon become quite impossible.

Movement-complexes which have been converted by long practice from a deliberate exercise to a facile automatic act may also suffer in a parietal apraxia.

A woman with a biparietal lesion had for years worked as a fish-filleter. With the development of her symptoms, she began to experience difficulty in carrying on with her job. She did not seem to know what to do with her knife. She would stick the point in the head of a fish, start the first stroke and then come to a stop. In her own mind, she knew how to fillet fish, but yet she could not execute the manœuvre. The foreman accused her of being drunk and sent her home for mutilating fish.

This same patient also showed another unusual phenomenon which might possibly be apraxic in nature (or on the other hand, possibly the expression of an organic deterioration). She could never finish an undertaking. She would begin a job, drop it, start another, abandon that one, and within a short while would have four or five uncompleted tasks on her hands. This would cause her to do such inappropriate actions as putting the sugar bowl in the refrigerator, and the coffee pot inside the oven. (Case of Dr. Hal Gregg.)

A more detailed observation of a patient's performance is informative. As in the case of all organic cerebral disorders, these patients with apraxia should be studied closely and a faithful record made of exactly what the patient does, how he does it and what he fails to do. Thus, a patient, when told to " wave goodbye " may hesitatingly raise both arms above the head and then make a curious gesture of dismissal. These movements may be executed clumsily several times in succession. The next command may be " shake your fist at me ". Again, after a pause, the two hands may come up above the head and the previous pantomimic actions may be carried out, without the patient seeming to be dissatisfied or perplexed. A third command, no less simple or more difficult than the other two, may now be followed by a correct response, perhaps hesitatingly performed but perhaps quite promptly. The next order, however, once again provokes an inadequate, if not totally inappropriate, reaction.

This is not the place to discuss the debatable problem of the essential nature of the apraxias, the classification of the clinical varieties and the extent to which they can be regarded as " focal " phenomena of cerebral disease. Only so far as these questions touch upon the subject of parietal symptomatology are one or two observations permissible. The terms " limb-kinetic ", " ideomotor " and " ideatory " are not altogether satisfactory in that they suggest clear-cut specific entities, with different localizing significance ; both assumptions may well prove to be unwarranted. Nevertheless, it would be unwise to dispense altogether with these working hypotheses for they still serve some purpose in clinical diagnosis. Disease of the parietal lobe in the dominant hemisphere certainly tends to be followed by a bilateral disorder of motility which includes elements of an imperceptive or agnosic type, and which can conveniently be described as an ideomotor, or ideokinetic apraxia. This disability is probably not the same affection as constructional apraxia—a disorder which is most readily demonstrated in cases of parietal disease of the subordinate hemisphere. But when the dominant side of the brain is at fault, then both conditions—ideomotor apraxia and constructional apraxia —may occur in combination and be difficult to distinguish.

Patients with parietal disease are sometimes spoken of as exhibiting a " dressing apraxia ". In so far as this term suggests a specific disability, it is inappropriate, for the difficulty in dressing is usually merely a part of a universal ideomotor apraxic disability. There is yet another disorder of the act of dressing which is even more characteristic of parietal disease, and which is not strictly speaking a part of apraxia. This is the one-sided disability which is apt to follow the active unilateral neglect resulting from a disordered body-image. Such a dressing defect is more typical of right-sided parietal disease, while the apraxic defects of dressing are more typical of left parietal lesions (when dextrad patients are concerned).

From a descriptive point of view, various apraxic errors may be identified. As some of these defects have received specific terms, especially in continental literature, they may perhaps be mentioned. There may be a general paucity of movement—of face, limbs and trunk (hypokinesis). The patient, requested to make a particular movement, may do something quite different (parapraxia or parakinesis). Or a movement may be started correctly but left unfinished (a curtailed reaction). In a complicated voluntary act, some components may be omitted (short circuiting). Vague, pseudo-spontaneous movements may take the place of dextrous manipulation of objects (amorphous reactions). A given movement may be repeated incongruously (palipraxia ; motor perseveration). Or the patient, instead of making a movement to command, merely copies the examiner's gestures (echopraxia). On passive manipulation of the apraxic patient's limb, a contrary, or resistive, movement is initiated (*Gegenhalten ;* counterpull). The patient may be unable to relax a movement at the appropriate moment (tonic perseveration ; tonic innervation).

Sometimes, the patient carries out a movement, utilizing an object or article, with fair accuracy, but a moment later, he may proceed to undo, or erase, or obliterate his earlier response. Thus, if told to take a knife out of a drawer and to put it on the table, he may do so ; but a moment afterwards, he may put the knife back again into the drawer. Told to fill a tumbler with water from the tap, he may do so well enough, but immediately afterwards, pour the water away. To this phenomenon of *katapraxia*, Pinéas (1931) has applied the picturesque term *Penelope syndrome.*

Ataxia

Some attention has been paid in the literature to what is actually a rare manifestation of parietal disease, namely a cerebellar type of ataxia. Loss of postural sensibility will naturally bring about a sensory type of inco-ordination during the execution of a deliberate movement. Gerebetzoff (1938), however, has specifically described a quite different type of ataxia which he termed a *pseudocerebellar inco-ordination.*

Two examples may be given of this phenomenon :

A diabetic arteriosclerotic woman of 53 years (Case No. 5657) developed dysaesthesia and numbness of the right arm and two days later of the right leg also. About a week later, some weakness gradually appeared in the left arm and leg. Examination showed swaying movements and falling away of the outstretched left hand. There was a peculiar inco-ordination of the left arm ; when she attempted to touch any object in front of her with the left hand, it swayed wildly back and forth. This did not occur with the right hand, nor with the left hand when she touched her own nose or any other part of her body. There was no evidence of paralysis, nor of apraxia, nor of loss of postural sensibility, nor of visual disorientation. Both plantar responses were extensor in type ; there was a partial astereognosis in both hands. The case was thought to be one of biparietal softenings, with a " pseudocerebellar ataxia " of the right upper limb.

A boy of 4 years proved, at autopsy, to have a large abscess in the left parietal lobe. His illness had started with an acute otitis six weeks previously. Three weeks later, he developed convulsions in his sleep, and two weeks after that became unsteady on his legs and complained of pins and needles in the right arm and leg. The unsteadiness varied a good deal. When the child performed the finger-nose test, a marked cerebellar ataxia was noticed in the right arm. That limb was rather hypotonic, and rapidly alternating movements were performed badly, more so with the right arm. There was considerable ataxia in the heel-knee test on the right side. No sensory changes could be detected. A cerebellar abscess was diagnosed, and a subtentorial decompression was carried out. No lesion was found other than marked hypertension. The child died two weeks later.

Ataxia without postural loss supervening after parietal lesions is now a well authenticated, if somewhat uncommon, physical sign (Schwob, Athanassio Bénisty, Claude and Lhermitte, Galli, Foix and Thévenard, Alajouanine and Lemaire, André-Thomas, Besta, Roussy and G. Levy, Foix, Chavany and M. Lévy). In a number of these cases, the parietal lesion has implicated the paracentral lobule, and Claude and Lhermitte have indeed described a *paraplégie cérébello-spasmodique*, resulting from war wounds of the vertex of the skull. Decomposition of movement, hypo- and hypermetria, and intention tremor can all be discerned in these abnormal movements, even though the patient directs his gaze upon his hand as he carries out a willed activity. Gerebetzoff believed that the parietal lobe constituted a higher centre connected with the vestibular and cerebellar nuclei, and that lesions at that cortical level were responsible for the defects which he described.

Spontaneous turning movements around the vertical axis of the body are very occasionally met with, and have been specifically described by Hoff and Schilder. These rotatory movements are not ordinarily encountered as the patient lies quietly in bed. On assuming the erect stance, however, and particularly when starting to walk,

M

this disorder may appear. The patient may advance one foot not only in front of the other but also across it, so that he is liable to trip and fall. Indeed, he can only keep upright by executing a turning movement of the whole trunk.

Something of the same character is to be noted in a habit which some parietal patients adopt of averting their gaze, and indeed their head, away from their paralysed arm. This posture has been described as the physical counterpart of a mental reaction of revulsion towards, or morbid dislike of, the hard facts of their paralysis (see Chapter VIII).

A female of 55 years (A. B.), patient of Dr. F. M. R. Walshe, was found to have a very large astrocytoma of the right hemisphere involving the white matter of the temporal and parietal lobes, and also the corpus callosum : her clinical history went back for three months, when she became irritable, unsteady, " difficult " and self-repetitive. Later, she became confused. In hospital, it was noticed that, as she lay in bed, she tended to fall over to the left. When propped up, she constantly slipped downwards and to the left. The head kept turning to the left and backwards—even when she was talking to some one on the right. The head, trunk and limbs would take on bizarre attitudes. Her head would turn to the left and backwards, her back would arch and her hands would approach the head in a slow but powerful tonic spasm. The hands were in frequent, pseudo-spontaneous movement. The legs, when handled, would become rigid, with dorsiflexion of the toes and inversion of the foot. Other signs included a hemianopia, a left-sided ataxia and an astereognosis. As she attempted to walk, the left leg would twist in a grotesque fashion behind the right leg ; she would lean towards the left and almost fall.

Herrmann's patient with a chronic ischaemic focus in the left temporo-parieto-occipital region showed, during life, periodic tonic attacks. Each one of these comprised a turning movement of the whole body, including the head, towards the right ; at the same time, the left arm would be raised in an attitude of extension and adduction. Thus, the patient would come to adopt a sitting posture with a half-turn to the right. Afterwards, the head and eyes would deviate for a time to the right. (Herrmann, 1928.)

Forced movements of this type, and also the unusual ataxia which has been described, have together been looked upon as the expression of involvement within the parietal lobe of cerebrovestibular pathways (de Morsier and Broccard 1937, and others). Van Bogaert (1933) described three chief kinds of hyperkinesias : " roundabout movements " with conjugate deviation of the head and eyes ; movements of axial rotation ; and flexion-extension movements of the trunk. He looked upon these syndromes of *automatisme primitif* as resulting from disinhibition which might result from lesions at various regions— cortex, cerebellum, pallidoluysian system. The most common site of disease was deep in the temporoparietal region. Zingerle's " syndrome of automatosis " (1926) might also at times be ascribed to parietal disease. David, Hécaen and Sauguet (1945) described a case where attacks of " torsion epilepsy ", or forced rotatory movements around the vertical axis used to occur, preceded by visual and auditory hallucinations. It was possible to provoke these episodes, either by irrigation of the left ear, or by stimulation of the anterior end of the interparietal fissure where there was a focal inflammatory area. In the patient's own words : ". . . for some seconds, I can see friends of mine, usually always the same ones, who then vanish, crying out, ' Geneviève, you are going to disappear.' At that moment, I pass out and cannot make a sound. These friends always come from behind me to the right side. They come nearer, and then go away so that they become quite small. They are not in silhouette, but are like coloured shapes. I can't say whether they are real."

De Morsier (1938) has also described three cases of presumed parietal disease, where severe rotatory vertigo was a conspicuous symptom. In his third case, auditory hallucinations also occurred. The author considered that the parietal lobe forms a kind of cross-road where visual, vestibular and somatognosic stimuli meet.

If this anatomico-physiological conception proves to be valid, it raises immediately the question why these pseudocerebellar and pseudovestibular symptoms should be so rarely encountered. They must be looked upon as quite exceptional manifestations of parietal disease rather than the rule, and consequently, no fixed structural defect can be invoked. Furthermore, it cannot yet be claimed that any anatomical evidence exists unequivocally as to these alleged parietovestibular or parietocerebellar connections. The same criticism can be attached to the belief that the motor impulses which try to turn the body around the longitudinal axis have one of their centres in the parieto-occipital region (Hoff and Schilder ; Gerstmann) ; and also to Schilder's view that a parieto-occipital lesion (especially of Brodmann's field 19) increases the postural impulses to turn around the longitudinal axis.

Muscular wasting

The development of muscular wasting in the opposite half of the body in parietal lobe affections is a phenomenon which has received intermittent attention for over a century. Atrophy from disuse ; unilateral " trophic " changes of central origin ; infantile hemiplegia with contralateral dysgenesis, are all of them cognate problems which can be discussed in association. On studying the literature, now very considerable, which bears on this topic, many questions present themselves. In the first place, the inquiry naturally arises as to how often muscular wasting occurs with parietal disease. The total number of cases on record is formidable, and yet in many neurological centres this feature is rarely noted as a physical sign and is probably never looked for. This latter point may be all important, and may account for what one may call the geographical incidence of this clinical sign. Thus, many of the recorded cases emanate from the Philadelphia school of neurology, a fact which suggests a local and traditional awareness of the possible occurrence of this sign ; a vigilance and a routine technique of close scrutiny coupled with palpation of muscles ; and a consequent high score of positive records. In other centres, where muscle wasting is not a familiar sign in parietal disease, and is not looked for, failure to mention this feature means but little. This phenomenon of being unattuned for certain neurological signs is a well-known hazard in clinical neurology and perhaps especially so when parietal symptomatology is in question (vide the Gerstmann syndrome ; constructional apraxia ; disorders of the body-image).

The whole topic of muscle-wasting in parietal disease has been thoroughly discussed by Winkelman and Silverstein (1932, 1935). Marshall Hall (1839-41) is commonly credited with priority in mentioning this physical sign, and among other early neurologists who also recorded it, and even adduced tentative explanations, were Charcot (1879), Gowers (1885), Quincke (1893) and Monakow (1897).

The clinical findings can be described as follows : muscle-wasting develops in the contralateral segments in association with parietal disease. In addition, some slighter degree of wasting has occasionally been noted as also occurring in the ipsilateral side. The muscular atrophy may occur with slowly developing affections of the parietal lobe (e.g. tumours, atrophies), or with abrupt cerebrovascular lesions. In the latter case, the wasting may appear comparatively soon after the stroke ; that is to say, within a week or two. Indeed, an interval of days, or even a single day, has been recorded as intervening between the vascular accident and the first clinical detection of changes in the contralateral muscles. Ordinarily, it is the upper limb which displays the muscular wasting, though occasionally the lower limb has been involved as well, and still more rarely one half of the tongue, and even of the palate and face. Two sites of election are mentioned as likely to reveal the earliest and most striking changes. Of these, the first includes the small muscles of the hand with the muscles of the thenar and hypothenar eminences. Somewhat less often, the wasting may apparently first show itself in the shoulder girdle on one side. From these two regions, that is the hand and the shoulder, the wasting may spread upwards or downwards, so as later to implicate the whole of the upper limb.

Many writers have emphasized that in very early cases the muscular affection is more obvious to palpation than on inspection, for a certain flabbiness of, say, the thenar set of muscles may readily be determined though an actual loss of bulk is dubious.

As the wasting extends and increases, the muscle tonus tends to diminish. Quite often, after an initial stage of spasticity with exaggerated tendon reflexes, the limb gradually becomes more and more wasted and flaccid, and the reflexes become sluggish and perhaps eventually unobtainable. In rare cases, the wasting becomes so intense as to produce claw-like deformity of the hand, and to evoke, indeed, the suspicion of a motor neurone disease or a poliomyelitis. Nevertheless, even in these extreme cases, muscular fasciculation and fibrillation apparently do not occur; nor are the muscles themselves the seat of myotatic irritability. More commonly, the wasting does not progress to such extremes, but merely amounts to a flabbiness, moderate reduction in bulk, diminution in muscle-tone, sluggish arm jerks, and hypotrophic changes in the overlying skin. Head expressed this well in his description of the affected hand of a soldier who had sustained a war wound of the right parietal lobe. He said that it resembled a woman's hand: ". . . it was soft, and its lines were less deep; the fingers seemed to be longer and thinner than the normal side, although by measurement they were actually a little shorter . . . The interosseous

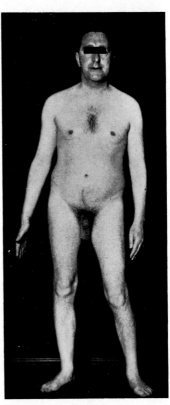

Fig. 69. Case of fronto-parietal oligodendroglioma, with left-sided spasticity and muscular atrophy. (Case No. 18140.)

spaces were not wasted, but they seemed to be occupied by smaller and *softer* muscles." The wasting is, as a rule, slight in degree, and evenly and thinly spread. Gross deformities are rare, and the bony points do not stand out at all prominently. The affected limb appears as a whole smaller, as if the bones too were less well developed on that side.

Electrical testing has been noted a few times and usually it has revealed a quantitative rather than a qualitative alteration in the

reactions.   Chronaxy tests have been but rarely mentioned, but have
been thought to demonstrate a difference from peripherally produced
muscle wasting.   Electromyographic reports are not yet available on
a large scale, but in the personal cases where this test has been carried
out, no qualitative abnormality could be found.

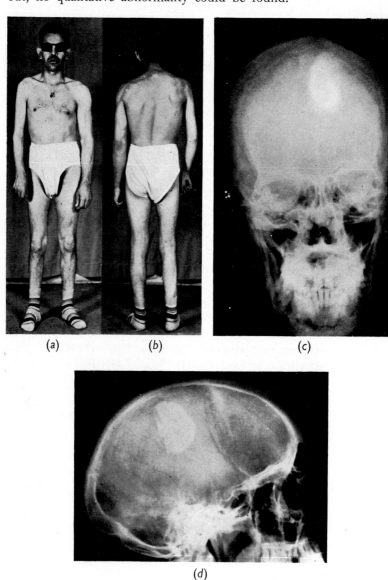

(a)   (b)   (c)

(d)

Fig. 70.   Case of right-sided muscular atrophy, associated with a calcified
tumour in the left parietal lobe.   (Courtesy of Dr. Milton Shy.)

Concomitant " trophic " changes are common and at times are conspicuous. Usually, there seems to occur a thinning of the over-lying skin with a softness to the feel. The hand may be warm to the touch and slightly moist ; or it may be colder than its fellow. Brittle-ness and ridging of the finger-nails have often been mentioned. Uni-lateral shedding of hair has been observed. At times, there occurs a slight oedema or puffiness and in one case at least, this was a conspicuous defect, which masked any possible underlying wasting (Gordon, 1927). Skiagraphic examination of the bones of the hand or arm rarely shows any trace of decalcification, or of osseous hypo-plasia, except, of course, in very longstanding cases of hemiplegia, and particularly those where the causative lesion dates from childhood or infancy.[1]

For a long time, so a study of the literature shows, these cases of muscular atrophy were looked upon as interesting examples of " hemi-plegia with wasting ". At a later date, it became clear that most—if not all—of the cases also had a conspicuous hemi-anaesthesia as well as hemiplegia, and perhaps with especial implication of deep or postural sensibility. Later still, it seemed justifiable to conclude that these unilateral sensory disorders were more consistent manifestations than were signs of pyramidal involvement. Cases began to appear where muscle wasting due to cerebral disease developed in the absence of motor weakness. Gradually then, the conception arose that the unilateral muscle-atrophy was a " parietal " manifestation, and a physical sign which carried with it important localizing value. In particular, the association of unilateral astereognosis with muscle wasting came to be regarded as constituting a " syndrome of the parietal lobe ", especially when there was also present an impairment in postural sensibility leading to a pseudo-cerebellar ataxia.

The fact that muscle flabbiness, softness and early atrophy can occur in the contralateral muscles in cases of parietal disease, promises to be a useful localizing—or at least a lateralizing—sign in comatose patients, for it has on several occasions been recorded that these subtle clinical phenomena were adduceable at the bedside, in circum-stances where the patient was unco-operative or inaccessible.

There is evidence that the process of muscle atrophy may be a

[1] Among the many authors reporting wasting after lesions of the brain, especially of the parietal lobe, may be mentioned : Pitrés, 1876 ; Kramer, 1891–2 ; Anton, 1893 ; Stalker, 1894 ; Bremer and Carson, 1895 ; Packard, 1896 ; Mills, Keen and Spiller, 1900 ; Chatin, 1900 ; Burr and Taylor, 1902 ; Weisenberg, 1905 ; Morton Prince, 1906 ; Stewart, 1906 ; Rhein, 1917 ; Barré and Morin, 1925 ; Gordon, 1927 ; Silverstein, 1931, a, b, c ; Guillain, Petit-Dutaillis and Rouques, 1932 ; van Bogaert, 1933 ; Pitha, 1936 ; Christini, 1937.

reversible one, and that in cases of brain tumour, after a successful removal of the growth, the wasting may gradually disappear and the muscles regain their former dimensions.

A few authors have studied the pathology of the affected muscles. Marked naked-eye and microscopic changes have. been found. Marinesco (1898) found that the affected muscles were pale and yellowish, small in size, and with flattening of the tendons. Winkelman and Silverstein have confirmed this, and in addition, they remarked that oedema is often present as well, so that a yellowish serum oozes from the softened and water-logged muscle-tissue. If there is no oedema, then the wasted muscle on dissection appears " dry, yellowish and mushy ". It may be so fragile or friable as to render it difficult to remove a portion for histological study. The impression is one of " meat that has been cooked too long ". Microscopic studies were carried out by Marinesco and also by Winkelman and Silverstein. Marinesco spoke of a muscle atrophy coupled with a degeneration (coagulation necrosis). The latter workers confirmed his findings. The abnormal muscles stained bluish with haematoxylin and eosin (instead of the usual reddish tint). A very great increase in nuclei is most obvious, but is largely due to a collapse of fibres within the fasciculi. Fibrous tissue increases especially in the interfascicular regions, where collagenous masses and fat are also found. The better preserved muscle fibres show that longitudinal fibrillae and cross striation are both lost. Myogenic giant cells occur, as well as deposits of blood pigment. Small haemorrhages may be seen and at times too, it can be suspected that the blood vessels are wider.

There is, therefore, weighty clinical evidence, supported by pathological data, to the effect that unilateral parietal lesions may be followed by muscular atrophy especially in the upper limb of the contralateral side, but even also, to a slight extent, in the ipsilateral side. Attempts at explaining this clinical observation have been highly ingenious but not altogether satisfactory. Following Winkelman, Silverstein, and others, the main hypothesis can be set out as follows :

(1) *The anterior horn cell* hypothesis dates from Charcot, who found changes in the ventral cornua of the spinal cord in a patient who developed muscle-wasting after a haemorrhage into the substance of the contralateral hemisphere. Charcot ascribed the spinal changes to a pyramidal sclerosis. Similar pathological changes were found by Brissaud (1879) and by Joffroy and Achard (1891) (although in the latter instance there was a discrepancy between the site of wasting and the level of the spinal changes). Steiner (1893) believed that, in children, the anterior horn cells were liable to secondary changes after

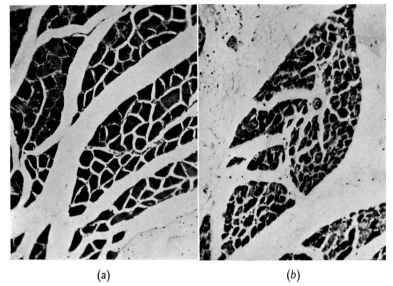

(a)   (b)

Fig. 71.   (a) shows the microscopical appearance of the thenar muscles in one hand,
while in (b) the thenar eminence of the other hand was clinically wasted and
flabby.   Case of right parietal tumour.   (E. B., Case 117,430 (K.C.H.).)

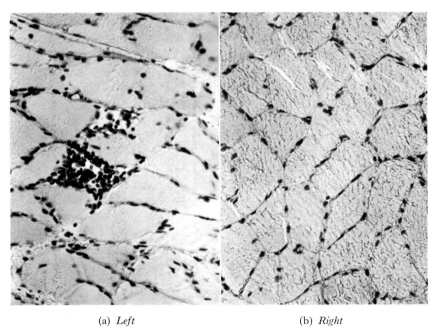

(a) *Left*   (b) *Right*

Fig. 72.   Biopsy of calf muscle from left leg (a) and right leg (b) respectively, from
patient No. 18140 (see Fig. 69) suffering from left-sided muscular wasting
associated with a right frontoparietal tumour.   The muscle-fibres are of equal
size in both specimens, but on the left side foci of cellular regression are
evidence of a degenerative process.

pyramidal disease, while later in life, these cells could at times, though not always, attain a certain independence. Somewhat similar views were put forward by Goldscheider (1894), Schaffer (1897) and Steinert (1903). Kiss (1929) was also a supporter of this theory and he conceived a biochemical equilibrium which normally exists between the motor cortex and the anterior horn cells : pyramidal disease, he believed, upset this state of affairs, and might provoke structural changes within the spinal motor cells.

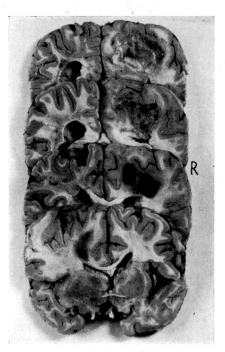

Fig. 73. Carcinoma of bronchus : secondary deposit in right parietal lobe, associated clinically with weakness, hypolinea and wasting of the left upper limb. (E. B., Case 117,430 (K.C.H.).)

(2) *The peripheral nerve* hypothesis of Dejerine (1889) resulted from the demonstration of histological changes in the nerve trunks, in a case of cerebral muscle atrophy, with a normal appearance of the anterior horn cells and roots.

(3) *The hypothesis of joint disease* propounded by Gilles de la Tourette (1897) is tantamount to a notion of arthritic muscular atrophy as the explanation of these cases. It was supported to some extent by Darkschewitsch (1891) and by Bechterew (1894).

Obviously, these three hypotheses fail to account for all of the observed clinical data, and each one of these would fall down if cases could be brought forward where cerebral lesions were followed by muscular wasting in the absence of pyramidal disease ; or without histological changes in the appropriate ventral cornua or roots, or in the peripheral nerve trunks ; and where arthritic or peri-articular changes were not present. Such cases are actually numerous, and to explain them, other speculations will be required. Thus, we are led on to :

(4) The *vasomotor* hypothesis, of Rott and Mouratoff (1891). Vasomotor centres in the brain, wherever they may be located, when damaged would lead—according to this view—to altered circulation

in the contralateral limbs, and thence to muscle-wasting, or " angio-myopathy ", Monakow (1897), Marinesco (1898), Luzzato (1903), Oppenheim (1911). Mouratoff is said to have later recanted, and throwing over his colleague, abandoned his hypothesis for that put forward by Charcot.

(5) The *trophic* hypothesis of Quincke (1893) presupposes a cortical centre which is independent of the motor cortex and which controls the nutrition of the peripheral musculature. In his opinion, fibres from such a locus lie in close apposition to the upgoing sensory pathways within the internal capsule. Quincke's views have been supported to some extent by Steiner, by Patella (1886), Borgherini (1890), Eisenlohr (1893) and by Kirchhoff (1897). With some reservations, Quincke's view has been regarded as the most significant by Winkelman and by Silverstein in recent years.

Related more or less closely to the ideas of both a vasomotor origin and a trophic theory is the :

(6) *Tropho-neurosis* hypothesis. Advocates of this view include a heterogeneous set of cases where hemiatrophy (including even a " crossed " example), or a scleroderma, constitute the clinical findings, and brain changes of inconsistent location are put forward as being responsible ; Howden (1875), Taylor (1878), Luntz (1896), Pelizaeus (1897), Orbison (1908), Meyer (1910), Kraus and Perkins (1926). Most of these cases would appear far removed from the problem of muscle-wasting following disease of the parietal lobe, and the hypothesis cannot be looked upon as impressive.

One must admit that none of these hypotheses carries conviction, and that the problem deserves to be investigated anew. But the clinical observation holds true, and the idea that loss of muscle-bulk may occur in association with parietal disease, seems incontrovertible.

CHAPTER VI

CONSTRUCTIONAL APRAXIA

Human nature comprises an instinct of construction of a very low degree of specialization. Constructive play of children, their delight in making things, especially houses, caves and shelters, and their satisfaction in being within such constructions, are perhaps the most direct evidence of the presence of this instinct in man.

W. McDougall.

Constructional apraxia is an important and commonly occurring event in cases of parietal disease. Nevertheless, it rarely prompts the patient to make specific complaint of its existence. As a physical sign or clinical manifestation it is one which eludes ordinary routine examination of the nervous system and special tests are usually needed. Constructional apraxia lies clinically outside the category of most other varieties of apraxia, and though these other types may coexist in the same patient, this need not be so.

Constructional apraxia may be defined, in simplest form, as a difficulty in putting together one-dimensional units so as to form two-dimensional figures or patterns. Kleist defined it as a disturbance which appears in formative activities (arranging, building, drawing) and in which the spatial part of the task is missed although there is no apraxia of single movements. Van der Horst spoke of an interference with action, especially with action such as drawing from a copy, putting the figures of a puzzle together, or building with bricks. It is essentially an executive defect within a visuospatial domain, and one which bears important associations with other spatial disorders as well as with such visuopsychic troubles as visual disorientation. These aspects will be discussed later.

One of the first references to this phenomenon was made by Kleist in 1912, who spoke of it as " optic apraxia ". The same term was used by Poppelreuter in 1917 in a more detailed study based upon war wounds of the occipital lobe. In 1934, Kleist returned to a discussion of this phenomenon which he now spoke of as " Konstruktive (optische) Apraxie . . . Gibt es Störungen des Handelns, die ich als Konstruktive (optische) Apraxie bezeichnen mochte, bei denen gerade die räumliche Form des Werkes misslingt, ohne dass eine Apraxie der einzelnen Bewegungen vorlage." In his monograph, Kleist mentioned that Rieger (1909) was probably the first to describe this form of apraxia, and that it had also been mentioned by

Reichardt (1918), Liepmann (1912) and by Bálint (1909)—the last-named under the term " optical ataxia ". Other important papers on this subject include those by Strauss (1924), Schlesinger (1928), Lange (1930), Ehrenwald (1931), Zutt (1932), Lhermitte and Trelles (1933), Kroll and Stolbun (1933), van der Horst (1934) and Mayer-Gross (1935, 1936).

Ordinarily, there are two principal methods of demonstrating constructional apraxia at the bedside, namely, by paper-and-pencil tests, and secondly by the use of sticks (or matches). In the former case, the patient is asked to copy a design made by the examiner. These patterns are usually of increasing degree of complexity, but start with a very simple design. The test can be varied according to circumstances. Thus, it can be made easier for a patient by allowing the model to remain in the patient's view throughout the test. Or, the task can be made more severe, by exposing the model for a few minutes and then removing it, before the patient attempts to make a copy from memory.

When sticks are used, recourse may be made to a set of sticks of four standard lengths (15, 10, 6 and 4 cm.), as recommended by Goldstein. Or more simply, ordinary wooden match sticks may be used. The examiner constructs a design and the patient is told to copy it. Here again, the difficulty of the task may be altered. The patient may be given a pile of sticks (or matches) from which he has to make a selection in order to copy the model. This is the more difficult undertaking, for it entails a preliminary and accurate selection of material before embarking upon the act of construction. When this request is beyond the patient's capacity, the test can be simplified by giving the patient the exact number of sticks of the appropriate sizes, with which to work.

Mayer-Gross has pointed out certain qualities in these constructional tests which characterize them and which distinguish them from clinical tests for other types of apraxia. Thus, constructional tests are ordinarily unfamiliar. They have rarely been practised ; hence, the movements are not usually of the secondary automatic kind. The test consequently takes the patient out of the sphere of daily life and its purposes, and transfers him almost into the situation of playing. For example, match sticks are being utilized not for what they were intended but almost as toys. This is not to say that the patient comports himself lightheartedly. On the contrary : the play becomes a serious activity akin to learning, with all the manifestations of trial and error.

As these varied methods of testing entail fundamental differences in performance, it is important that the exact nature of the technique employed should always be stated clearly in case reports. Again—as with every other performance test in parietal disease—it is essential for the examiner to observe the patient closely ; to note the method of going about the task ; and to record any comments, and emotional display, as well as every hesitancy, indecision, change of mind, and type of error. The patient's final design as he offers it at the end of the allotted time may appear good enough, but a record of his manner of carrying out the test may be an eloquent testimony of an abnormal performance.

Although Schlesinger has seen the disability present in the left hand only, the manifestations of constructional apraxia are almost always bimanually demonstrable. That is to say, it matters little, if at all, whether the right hand or the left be employed to hold the pencil in copying, or to manipulate the sticks. The pattern of defect may not be identical, however, when the two hands are used in succession in order to copy the same model.

Patients with well-marked constructional apraxia, although perhaps able to trace designs, show in their eventual copies of geometric figures a number of abnormal features, often in combination. The principal defects can be identified in the case of pencil-and-paper tests as follows :

(1) The patient does not execute his copy boldly in the centre of the sheet of paper before him, but instead, crowds his drawing into one or other corner, usually the top left-hand corner of the page. Mayer-Gross has seen in this peculiarity what he regarded as a " fear of empty space ". Perhaps it would be more accurate to speak of a " neglect " of space to one or other side of the midline—either by reason of an associated visual field defect (hemianopia), or because of a neglect of one half of extra-personal space.

(2) The copy may be considerably smaller than the design ; less often it may be much larger.

(3) The lines drawn by the patient are often wavy or tremulous (see Fig. 74).

(4) One line frequently does not meet another accurately and neatly, but instead there are gaps ; or one line may trans-sect another (= errors of articulation) (see Fig. 75).

Defects (2), (3) and (4) above are not to be regarded as diagnostic of constructional apraxia. The untidiness of the execution may be obvious, for example, in the drawing made by patient with limb-kinetic, or innervation apraxia. There are other and more significant features :

(5) If the patient uses the same sheet of paper as the examiner for his copy, he may actually superimpose his copy upon the model. Or less strikingly, he may construct his copy unduly close to the examiner's design, and portions of the two may actually come into contact. (See Fig. 76.)

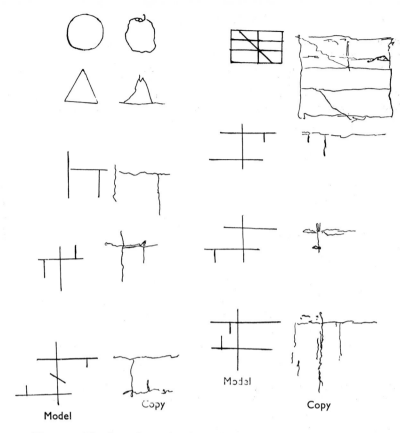

Fig. 74. The lines drawn by the patient are ragged and untidy.

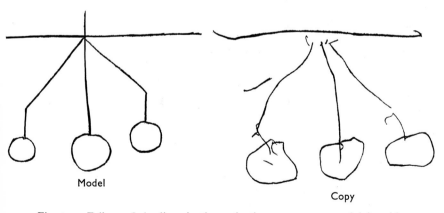

Fig. 75. Failure of the lines in the patient's copy to meet and join with neatness and accuracy.

An abnormal degree of approximation of the copy to the design was described by Mayer-Gross as the " closing-in symptom ".

(6) Conspicuous in the patient's copy may be a tendency towards making all vertical lines oblique, or else tilting horizontal lines upwards or downwards. When this feature is consistently present it should raise the suspicion that the patient may have a variety of oblique vision due to a metamorphopsia of central origin. (See Fig. 77.)

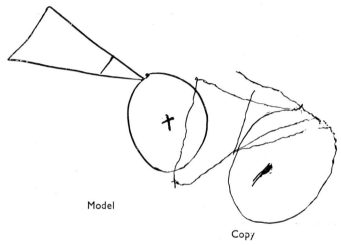

Model

Copy

Fig. 76. The patient not only places his copy too close to the model (closing-in syndrome) but the copy actually superimposes the original to some extent.

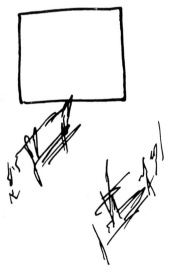

Fig. 77. Tilting of the copies, with approximation of one copy to the model. Note also the graphic perseveration.

(7) One or other of the dimensions—vertical or oblique—may be unduly prolonged. Here again, such a defect, if consistently present, should lead to a search for a visual disorder such as metamorphopsia, or illusory visual spread (Critchley). (See Fig. 78.)

(8) Part (less often the whole) of the pattern may be reversed in a mirror-opposite fashion in the patient's reproduction (see Fig. 79). Possibly these reversals are commoner when the left hand is used in the test. Less often, the reversals take place in a vertical dimension (see Fig. 80).

(9) Occasionally, the patient puts in several lines where there should be only one. The result of this graphic perseveration is a sort of scribble (see Figs. 81, 82). Or the patient may reproduce a linear unit of the design too many times, thus showing a perseveration for details (see Figs. 83, 84).

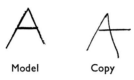

Model   Copy

Fig. 78. Undue prolongation of the horizontal component of the copy. The patient, who suffered from biparietal vascular lesions, also showed visual perseveration.

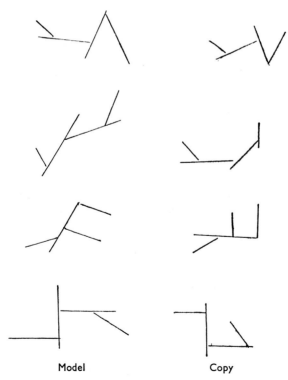

Model   Copy

Fig. 79. Partial and complete mirror reversals.

N

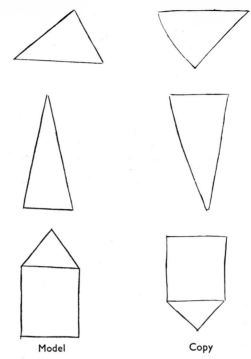

Model   Copy

Fig. 80. The patient inverts his copy.

Model   Copy

Fig. 81. Graphic perseveration.

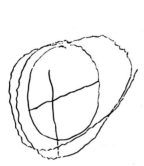

Fig. 82. Graphic
perseveration.

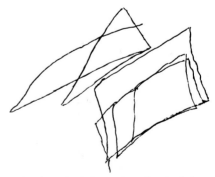

Fig. 83. Drawings of a triangle (left)
and of a square (right) reveal graphic
perseveration, as well as tilting.

Fig. 84. Copy of design. Perseveration of details.

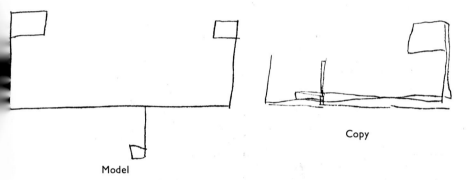

Copy

Model

Fig. 85. The patient omits details from the left-hand side of the drawing.

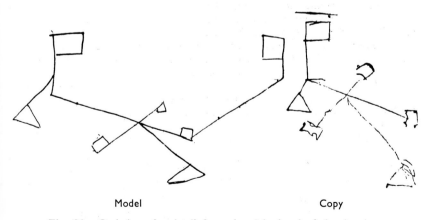

Model   Copy

Fig. 86. Omission of a detail from the right hand of the drawing.

(10) Large sections, and especially lateral components, of the design may be omitted altogether. Such a finding should raise the suspicion of a field defect or of a unilateral spatial neglect. (See Figs. 85, 86.)

(11) Bi-dimensional drawings suggesting solid figures seen in perspective may be copied in such a way as to give no hint of perspective, or a third dimension. Indeed, this copying defect may be the sole evidence of a constructional apraxia.

When constructional apraxia is tested by means of sticks or matches, certain other defects may be noticeable. The stick test is preferable to the drawing test in that the patient's uncertainties and changes in mind are more in evidence to the close observer. As mentioned earlier, it is important for the examiner to distinguish between the patient's performance when the necessary number of sticks is put ready for him. As one patient said, when asked why she was able to perform the test only when the other sticks were removed, " It was easier when you took the other sticks away, because then, it stood alone."

Some of the faults are comparable with those in the drawing tests. Thus :

(1) The patient's copy may be made in a corner, and not in the centre of the available space.

(2) There may be the same crowding-in phenomenon, with the patient's copy resting on top of, or touching, the examiner's model (see Fig. 87).

(3) A special type of defect, which cannot occur with the drawing test, consists in a tendency on the patient's part to remove a portion of the examiner's model in order to make his own copy. This seems to be another instance of *Ich-lähmung*, that is the not uncommon confusion between *meum* and *tuum* which some parietal patients display, and which will be discussed more fully later.

(4) The lines of the model may be tilted obliquely instead of being placed as accurate horizontal and vertical lines.

(5) The constituent parts of the model may not be neatly placed in apposition, but small gaps may be left.

(6) There may also occur mirror-reversals of parts or the whole of the pattern. This defect may be commoner when the left hand manipulates the sticks than when the right hand is used.

(7) Parts of the model—especially the most laterally placed parts—may not be reproduced at all in the patient's copy.

(8) Or, commonest fault of all, the patient may select sticks of the incorrect length, i.e. which do not match the model, and align them inaccurately (see Figs. 88 and 89).

The patient with constructional apraxia who has put up a very inadequate performance during these special tests, may show little if any dissatisfaction with his efforts. A full measure of awareness into the constitutional defects is, indeed, quite unusual on the part of patients with parietal lesions. This is not always the case, how-

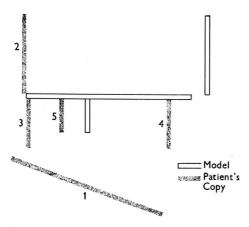

Fig. 87. Stick-test, showing the patient's tendency to put his copy in close apposition to the model. The numbers refer to the order in which sticks were selected and aligned. Right frontoparietal metastatic tumour.

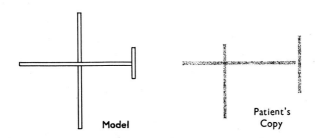

Fig. 88. Selection of sticks of wrong length. Secondary carcinoma; left frontoparietal tumour.

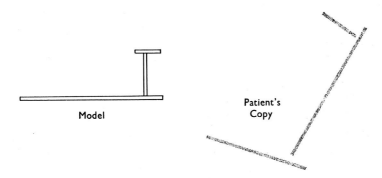

Fig. 89. Sticks of incorrect length selected and aligned quite incorrectly. Bi-parietal atrophy.

ever ; on occasions, a patient with constructional apraxia shows no clouding of the sensorium and may possess fair insight into the disabilities. The patient of Lhermitte, de Massary and Kyriaco (1928) was constantly disturbed by his inability to copy geometrical patterns, as evidenced by his comments . . . " C'est épatant, je ne puis pas comprendre comment je suis ainsi . . . j'ai l'air d'un idiot, et pourtant je ne le suis pas . . . je comprends bien ce que vous voulez me dire mais je ne peux le faire . . . je ne peux plus rien, c'est épatant . . . C'est épatant, moi qui étais ajusteur mécanicien, je ne puis plus faire même des choses d'enfant ! "

Special mention must be made of the use of Kohs' blocks as a test of constructional apraxia. Like so many other intelligence tests, Kohs' blocks constitute an exploration of more than one faculty or aptitude, but it is beyond question that patients with constructional apraxia fare badly. Rarely is it necessary to persevere throughout the whole series of test cards, as failure becomes obvious with the first one or two patterns. As in the case of the stick test, one can modify the difficulty of the test in two ways. Thus, one may present the patient with four blocks, being the number required to construct the desired pattern. On the other hand, the patient may simply be offered the complete box of bricks, and his first task then is to decide how many bricks are needed, in order to copy the design. Before embarking upon this test it is necessary to be sure that the patient is neither constitutionally colour-blind nor afflicted with dyschromatopsia. The manipulation of Kohs' blocks lends itself particularly well to a scrutiny of exactly how the patient comports himself, and even a mere record of the length of time taken by the patient may be significant.

Few patients with constructional apraxia succeed in making a perfect match of the first and simplest pattern, even after considerable deliberation. Certain special defects are worth noting :

(1) The patient may make an " open " square instead of placing the blocks tightly against each other (see Fig. 90).

(2) The patient may attempt to place his bricks on top of the card which bears the pattern—despite the discrepancy in size of the card and the blocks.

(3) The patient may assemble one brick on top of another as if about to make a three-dimensional erection.

(4) In the later figures which require 9 blocks instead of 4, the patient may tend to align them in one-dimension rather than in two (see Figs. 91 and 92). According to Zangwill and his pupils (1944), this particular defect is more often encountered with parietal lesions of the non-dominant hemisphere.

Other bedside tests for constructional apraxia can be tried. Thus, the patient may be given a sheet of paper and told to fold it neatly

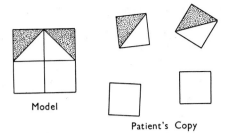

Model

Patient's Copy

Fig. 90. Kohs' Blocks. The correct squares are selected,
but an " open " square is constructed.

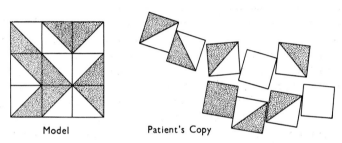

Model   Patient's Copy

Fig. 91. Kohs' Blocks. The correct items are selected but the patient cannot
put them together to form a symmetrical bi-dimensional square.

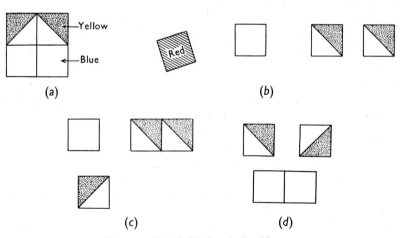

Fig. 92. Kohs' Blocks, design No. 3.
(a) Model. (b–d) Patient's three attempts. Left frontoparietal metastatic tumour.

and place it within an envelope. Or he may be shown a geometrical figure (triangle, circle, rectangle) and told to bisect it. Poppelreuter tested patients by getting them to cut out a star-shaped figure. Schlesinger (1928) and also Pfersdorff demonstrated in their patients with constructional apraxia an inability to copy with one hand the attitude or gestures of the other hand, despite the help of close scrutiny.

Under the term " free construction ", Mayer-Gross has described the activities of a patient who is given a collection of bricks or mosaics and is then told to construct something according to his whim, without any copy or any specific request. The attitude of learning is thus eliminated. Patients with constructional apraxia seem to vary in their response to this particular test situation.

Although it has been stated that constructional apraxia is rarely specifically complained of by the patient, there are occasions when indications of this phenomenon can be detected in the history. There are certain domestic activities which become difficult if not indeed impossible for a patient with constructional apraxia. This may be a disturbance which lies within the patient's awareness : more often perhaps, the patient has little or no insight, and the story of such difficulties emerges from the independent account given by the relatives or friends. Thus, a housewife with constructional apraxia may be at a loss to lay a table for a meal. (This is a practical task which can usefully be presented to the patient in hospital. One patient with a parietal tumour succeeded in laying a table but incompletely so, for she omitted to lay a place for herself.) Or the patient may have lately been experiencing great trouble in dressmaking, in cutting out the material from a pattern, in stitching the pieces together, and in making any necessary alterations.

Indications of a constructional apraxia may also at times be discerned in other activities, e.g. writing and arithmetic. The so-called parietal dysgraphia is characterized by obliquity of the lines ; and in lines which intersect one another or even lie on top of each other. There may be an inordinately wide margin on one side or the other of the paper (see Figs. 95 and 96). But we must distinguish between what may be conveniently termed a " right parietal agraphia " from a " left parietal agraphia ". In the former case, we find all the various defects of arrangement, but in the case of the latter, there also are to be seen numerous and characteristic defects of language. These would include omission of letters and of words ; wrong words ; incorrect spelling ; syllabic reversals ; disorders of grammar, and so on. An excellent example of a very special type of parietal agraphia can be found in the Chinese calli-

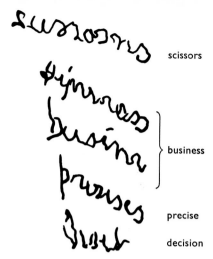

scissors

} business

precise

decision

Fig. 93. Untidy and barely legible writing showing a distinct obliquity in alignment. Case of left parieto-occipital abscess.

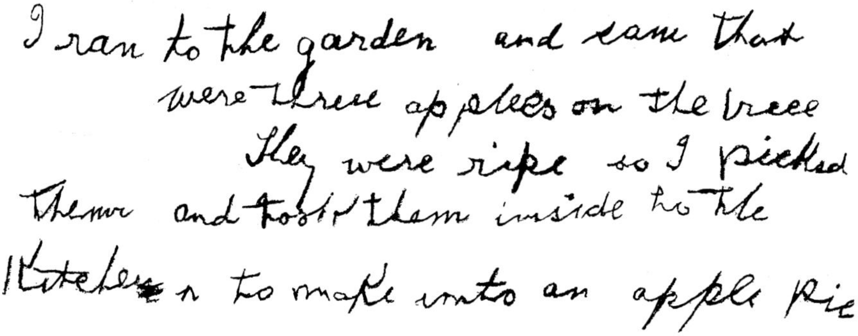

I ran to the garden and saw that were three apples on the tree They were ripe so I picked Themm and took them inside to the Kitchen to make into an apple Pie

Fig. 94. Untidy and ill-arranged handwriting (to dictation). Case of right parieto-occipital meningioma.

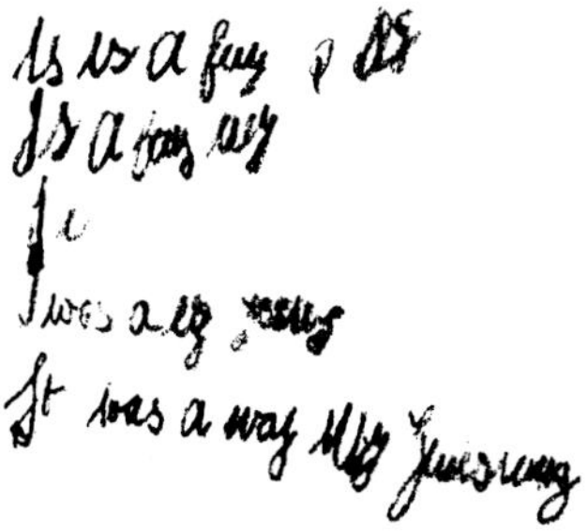

Fig. 95. Patient asked to describe what had happened that day and the day before. Note the peculiar character of the handwriting, and the crowding into the top left-hand corner of the page.

graphy of the patient with a left parieto-occipital tumour described by Lyman, Kwan and Chao (1938). Here, the patient made a number of different errors in writing. Thus, a complicated ideogram might be started correctly but finished wrongly, the substituting symbol bearing some resemblance to the original either in sound or in meaning. Some of the mistakes, though not all of them, could be explained upon the basis of a constructional apraxia. We also recall a case recorded in 1884 by Hamilton of a printer who assembled type upon his compositor's stick with considerable inaccuracy. The

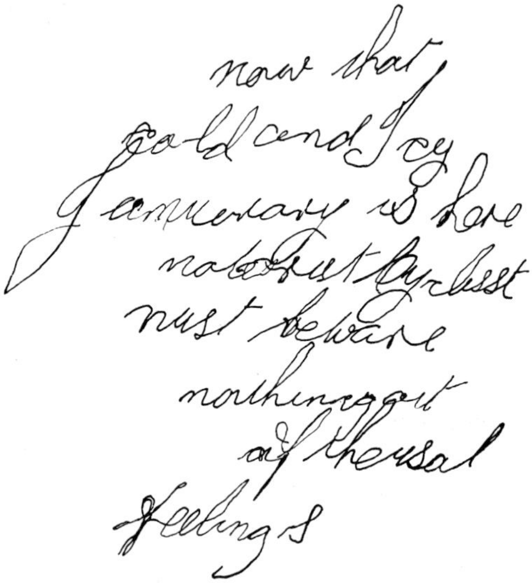

Fig. 96. Writing to dictation : " Now that cold and icy January is here, motor-cyclists must beware." Note the inordinately wide margin on the left.

defect in this case too belongs more to the category of a constructional apraxia than to an agraphia. In doing calculations on paper, a constructional apraxia may be betrayed by incorrect arrangement of figures under each other. This constitutes what may be termed parietal acalculia (see Fig. 97). In hospital or at home, the patient will encounter great difficulty with such recreations as jig-saw puzzles. Another difficulty which the patient's history may bring out is an inability to tell the time readily. This disturbance is emphasized when the patient is tested with toy clock faces : the patient will almost certainly be unable to set the hands at the various points demanded (see Fig. 98). As far as calculation is concerned, the constructional defect may also be obvious in the manner in which the patient reckons upon the bead-frame or abacus. With this article, the patient may pass in a muddled fashion from one row of beads to another, and confuse vertical with horizontal directions.

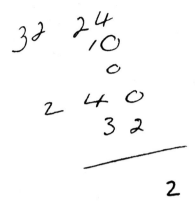

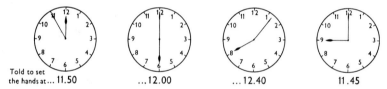

Fig. 97. Parietal acalculia. The patient was told to multiply on paper 32 by 24. Case of right parietal tumour.

Told to set the hands at... 11.50   ...12.00   ...12.40   11.45

Fig. 98. The patient was instructed to set the hands of a clock-face at a given time. Right temporoparietal glioblastoma.

Three-dimensional constructional apraxia

Hitherto, one has considered constructional apraxia as it shows itself in ordinary two-dimensional tasks. It is possible, and indeed useful, to proceed to problems in three-dimensional space, though tests of this character are only too rarely employed. This is a more difficult undertaking, and patients who respond moderately well to the usual procedures with sticks and pencil-and-paper may display gross abnormalities when told to assemble bricks according to a three-dimensional pattern. The examiner first constructs his pattern using bricks of varying shapes and sizes. The patient is then directed to build a similar figure. Here again the task may be facilitated for the patient by picking out for him the required number of bricks, appropriate in size and shape, and leaving him to the business of arranging them in proper fashion. Or the patient may be given a larger pile of bricks of diverse sizes and shapes, and from this stock he has to select the units he needs and then put them in position. Such a task is far more difficult.

There is one other way of conducting this test in such a way as to make it still easier—the patient having failed to master the other two techniques. This method consists in alternate moves by the examiner and examinee. The former takes a brick and places it in position : the patient does the same. The examiner now selects another brick and places it alongside, or on top of the other : the patient should then do the same ; and so on.

When one studies the efforts made by the patient at the end of these three-dimensional tests—whatever method is used—certain types of inadequacy are found. There may be the same sort of

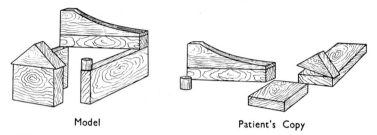

Model   Patient's Copy

Fig. 99.   Three-dimensional constructional tasks.   Left frontoparietal metastatic tumour.

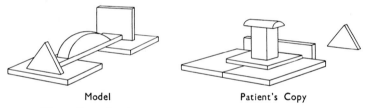

Model   Patient's Copy

Fig. 100.   Three-dimensional constructional tasks.   (The patient was given the appropriate bricks, but he helped himself to two others as well.)   Right temporoparietal glioblastoma.

omission of one lateral half of the construction as in the two-dimensional tests.   Still more interesting is a practice on the patient's part of removing a brick from the model in order to construct the copy—the same type of confusion between *meum* and *tuum* as has been described in the stick test (see Figs. 99, 100, 101 and 102).

The clinical story as given by the patient himself rarely affords any hint as to the existence of this three-dimensional constructional apraxia.   Exceptions occur, however, as when the patient realizes that he is developing difficulty in assembling pieces of machinery or apparatus, e.g. a radio set.   The housewife may have encountered some trouble in making a bed, or in packing and tying up a parcel. Most common of all these natural manifestations of a constructional

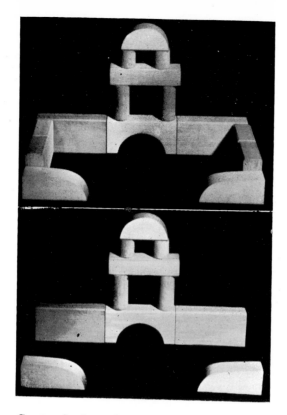

Fig. 101. Constructional apraxia. The patient failed to include the lateral components of the model within his copy.

Fig. 102. Three-dimensional constructional task.

apraxia is a perplexity experienced by the patient in the act of dressing. There are, of course, many clinical varieties of dressing disability (or dressing apraxia, as it is sometimes called). Some of them derive from a mere clumsiness of manipulation : others are due to a unilateral neglect or unawareness of the body scheme. The true constructional apraxic defect in dressing shows itself in a total disarray, whereby garments are put on in the wrong order (shirt or jacket before undervest), or at the wrong end (trousers over head ; shirt over legs).

The nature of constructional apraxia

Kleist, and his pupil Strauss (1924), believed that constructional apraxia resulted from a lesion of the brain-mechanisms controlling optokinetic associations, that is, the linkage between the visual image of the object and the mental image of the movement to be made. Van der Horst was sceptical, basing his opinion not only upon the inadequacy of such schematic views of what are essentially psychological processes, but also upon his study of a personal case. This patient proved to have a number of other spatial disorders involving not only his own person but also the outside world. The impropriety of drawing general conclusions from a single case is obvious, although a common fault. But it is clear that upon analysis, patients with constructional apraxia have some type of defective orientation in space, but a defect which may not emerge until a motor task is attempted within a visual sphere. It is not surprising that most patients with bilateral visual disorientation also prove to have a constructional apraxia. The converse is not necessarily the case, however, and most patients with constructional apraxia are not disorientated in the sense originally described by Holmes and Horrax (1919). Similarly, it is not surprising that a Gerstmann syndrome, whether complete or incomplete, should often coexist with constructional apraxia.

A study of the literature does not perhaps indicate clearly enough the frequency with which these three types of defect are met in association, that is, Gerstmann's syndrome, visual disorientation and constructional apraxia. But the association is actually not rare, as the cases of Laignel-Lavastine and Lévy-Valensi (1914), Pinéas (1924), Ehrenwald (1931), Scheller and Seidemann (1932), van der Horst (1932), Zutt (1932), Stengel (1944), Kammerer and Singer (1951) and others testify. Besides these examples in the literature, a large number of personal case-reports would support this contention. Although it might be tempting to explain away the association upon the grounds of coincidental production of symptoms by a diffuse lesion, or a large lesion, or lesions which are bilaterally placed, it would probably be more correct to try and trace an underlying common denominator, as Stengel has done, in all these disturbances. If such a thread runs through all these complicated patterns, then it is surely one which implies a spatial disorder. " Pure " cases of Gerstmann's syndrome and so on may, it has been suggested, really represent an incomplete manifestation of a more fundamental clinical affection. Mayer-Gross agreed that constructional apraxia is an expression of space-impairment, but he specified that it particularly involves *Wirkraum* or " activity-space " within the sphere of hands and fingers. It has also been said that constructional apraxia entails a difficulty in changing the hand from being a component of personal space into a tool manipulated within extra-personal space. Some qualification is necessary here. Every muscular movement is a spatial operation, but the defects which characterize constructional apraxia involve essentially those movements which are directly concerned with space *per se*, i.e. manipulation of the three dimensions of space, and particularly the translation of an object from one spatial dimension into another.

Constructional apraxia thus seems to include elements of both apraxic or executive order, as well as gnosic or perceptive type ; in other words, to represent a sort of visual *apractognosia*, to use Grünbaum's expression, or an *agnosopraxia*, to quote Kroll and Stolbun. The proportion of the two constituent elements may vary from patient to patient. Thus, in two cases recorded by Marie, Bouttier and Bailey (1922), there were striking disturbances both in visual orientation and in the manipulation of objects according to clear spatial awareness. To this complicated disorder, the authors applied the term *planotopokinesia*—a manifestation of bilateral parietal disease. The word has not received the impress of neurological recognition, largely because the disability can readily be recognized as a mere combination of visual disorientation and constructional apraxia.

Constructional apraxia in ordinary circumstances is a rather delicate index of disturbed spatial relationships. Stengel has indeed suggested that constructional apraxia is an aspect of a more complex " spatial apraxia ". The visual upset can, of course, be severe, as in the case of the various types of visual agnosic defects, scotopic vision, metamorphopsia, and so on. More often, the visual upset is less striking and is of such a subtle character as to puzzle the patient. There is no object agnosia, but rather, a confusion in dimensional relationships. Thus, the patient (Case No. 35427), suffering from a left parietal tumour, when asked to copy a three-dimensional model —failed strikingly. At one point, she selected a brick of unusual shape—a choice which was perfectly correct—but she then proceeded to lay the brick quite incorrectly, placing the long axis horizontally instead of vertically. She was satisfied with her action and seemed quite unable to realize any difference between her copy and the original. For her, the two bricks were the same : that is, identical both as regards their shape and their orientation in space.

The mirror-reversals so often made by patients in their copies with sticks or by drawing—especially when the left hand is used—have been specifically discussed by Stengel. Adopting Mayer-Gross' notion of activity-space, and mindful of Schilder's views on the postural image of the body, Stengel has speculated whether mirror movements in constructional apraxia might not be due to an abnormal tendency to keep quite separate the right and the left halves of external space. Nay more, he even utilized Schilder's suggestion of a projection of the midline of the body into the outer world and went on to speak of the right and left activity-spaces. In his case, the patient seemed to be unable to get the left hand to adopt right-hand activities.

Mayer-Gross and later Stengel have both discussed the tendencies to place lines too close together when copying designs (" closing-in symptom ", *phénomène d'accolement au modèle*). Stengel has referred this to a reversion to the most primitive conception of space as possessed by an infant, that is to say, " nearness ". Conceptions of " above ", " below ", " away from ", " to the right " and " to the left " are developed much later. Muncie (1938) believed he could identify this same " closing-in " phenomenon not only in an arteriopath, but also in a normal child of 3 years and 4 months, as well as in a schizophrenic young man. He ascribed the " closing-in " symptom not so much to a fear of empty space, as to a basic inability to make an abstract copy from a concrete model.

Nothing so far has been said about the spontaneous or prompted drawings of patients with constructional apraxia, for this problem really belongs to the chapter upon spatial disorders. Clearly, however, if the patient is unable to draw lines upon paper in such a way as to copy adequately a simple model : if he confuses dimensions and directions : he will almost certainly make the same type of error with even greater profusion when no model lies before him. Told to draw a horse and cart, for example, he may be expected to confuse utterly the location of the various constituent parts. The question of spontaneous drawing defects becomes of interest in a discussion of constructional apraxia only when the occasional error creeps in to demonstrate eloquently a confusion in the three dimensions of Euclidean space. Thus a patient, when asked to draw a

house, did so adequately enough. When he was then told to draw
a pathway leading up to the front door, he made two parallel lines in
a horizontal direction, that is at right angles to what was expected
(see Fig. 103). This defect may be taken as an indication of a constructional apraxia, or a failure to handle the spatial elements with
confident accuracy. Another patient, when asked to draw a house,
confused the plan with the elevation, so that articles of furniture were
outlined and placed in position, mixed up with the outlines of windows
and doors. When patients with constructional apraxia are asked to
draw a clock-face and to insert the numbers of the hours, and the
hands, there may occur a variety of characteristic defects—crowding

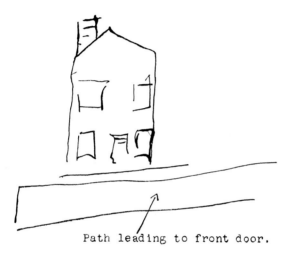

Path leading to front door.

Fig. 103. Confusion of dimensional elements in a spontaneous drawing
of a house.

into one half of the dial, mirror reversals, omissions. Most striking
is a tendency to string the figures vertically one under the other, so
as to transgress the borders of the clock-face (see Figs. 106, 107,
and 108).

Patients with constructional apraxia vary, however, in their
ability to draw from memory the simple geometrical shapes which
they cannot copy. Sometimes their spontaneous geometrical drawings are quite good (e.g. Seelert, 1920). One of Poppelreuter's
patients seemed to lose his constructional apraxia when his eyelids
were closed, for he was then able to draw adequately—though with
eyes open and gazing at the model, he failed. It is, however, only
too evident from a perusal of the literature that cases have often been
recorded in which the distinction between difficulties in spontaneous

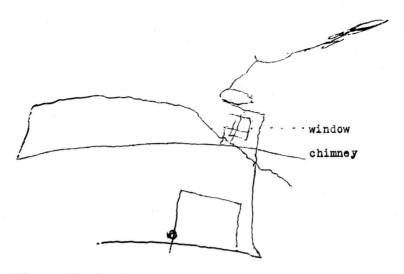

Fig. 104. Drawing of a house, showing neglected left side and disorientation.

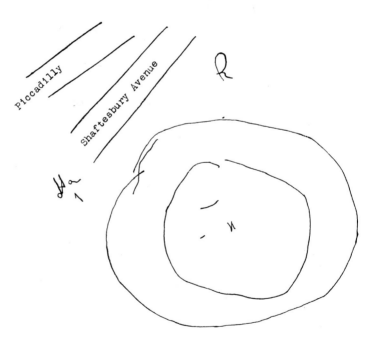

Fig. 105. Patient's drawing of Piccadilly Circus; note that the streets which should run in a radial fashion are depicted in an almost tangential manner.

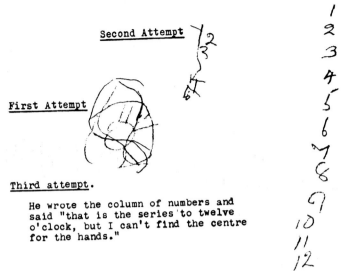

Second Attempt

First Attempt

Third attempt.

He wrote the column of numbers and said "that is the series to twelve o'clock, but I can't find the centre for the hands."

Fig. 106. The patient was instructed to draw a clock-face, complete with hands and numerals.

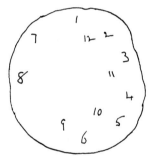

Fig. 107. The dial of a clock. The hands are omitted altogether and the numbers are arranged incorrectly.

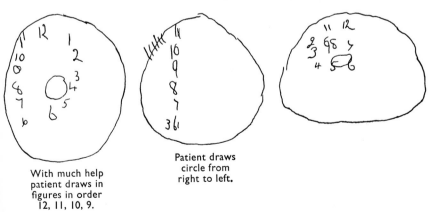

With much help patient draws in figures in order 12, 11, 10, 9.

Patient draws circle from right to left.

Fig. 108. Three attempts by the same patient at drawing a clock-face.

drawing and difficulty in copying has not been borne in mind, or made clear, if indeed such differences occurred.

We may conclude, therefore, that constructional apraxia is a defect which differs from the motor and ideokinetic types of apraxia isolated by Liepmann. Kroll and Stolbun's view, namely, that constructional apraxia is really a mild variant of the other types, is not approved by most neurologists. The majority would agree that two elements at least are at work, one of an executive character, and the other of an agnosic visual type. Lhermitte and Trelles (1933) relegated this condition to that *terrain limitrophe* common to apraxia and agnosia. The term apractognosia is an attempt to express this dual nature. Poppelreuter's conclusion was that there was at fault a lack of harmony or collaboration between visual activity and psychomotor activity. Seelert blamed a suppression of the adaptation of visual images to the innervation of the moving limb, a faulty association between visual imagery and the sensomotorium. Schlesinger blamed a disorganization of a basic function of visuosynthesis, which manifests itself ordinarily in the guidance and directing of voluntary movements by visual impressions. Kleist put the defect down to a disturbance in the reproduction of images and spatial forms, or—in psychological terms—to a rupture in the connections binding central visual functions with kinaesthetic images. It is not necessary for a severe spatial disorder to be present. As Schilder (1931) put it : " One must admit that apraxia can be due to a fault in the transposition of the conceptions of space to manual activity, without the conception of space being in itself disordered." In the three cases recorded by Lhermitte and Trelles, knowledge of spatial data was intact, but there was a well-marked somatagnosia, or troubles in the body-image.

Mayer-Gross, in his second paper (1936) on this topic, utilized some of the views personally expressed to him by Feuchtwänger (1934), who had already interested himself in the problem. Feuchtwänger asserted—in terms which can scarcely be regarded as clear—that in every voluntary activity productive of patterned work, four components could be discerned : (1) the idea of the completed work ; (2) the design of the work as a whole—i.e. the simultaneous image of it, which must be present at the moment when the activity begins ; (3) the constructive plan—i.e. the sum of the partial activities which lead to the formation of the whole, and of the temporal sequence in which they must occur ; and (4) the technique—i.e. the more or less automatic movements of the performing limbs.

These words mean little, but Feuchtwänger regarded only (4) as evidence of apraxia : constructional disturbances being largely

Plate 5

KARL KLEIST

dependent on the lack of sensory control during activity. Feucht-wänger's patient was quoted, a wireless engineer with constructional apraxia, who was nevertheless able to overcome his difficulty in assembling apparatus by using tactile images and by recourse to his theoretical knowledge.

Mayer-Gross's patient—who was particularly co-operative and helpful—was able to cope with spatial problems in non-visual spheres. Thus, she could tap out a rhythm, whether indicated by sound or by touch. Mayer-Gross concluded that, in constructional apraxia, there is undoubtedly a specific impairment of visual spatial cognition, which can be characterized as an inability, when given a real or imaginary visual pattern as a whole, to analyse it, piece by piece, in order to construct it piece by piece. Such visual analysis, with its succession in time, is only acquired and developed in non-automatic activities, corresponding to construction. This is perhaps the best description of the disorder which so far is available. But Mayer-Gross went on to say that such activities are almost always carried out by hand ; that this special visual impairment is so intimately tied to manual activity in space, and so utterly dependent on this activity, that it is almost impossible to conceive of such a function, supposing human beings had not in their hands and fingers so highly differentiated an instrument in space. This idea is, on the surface of it, unlikely, and indeed, Mayer-Gross's ingenious testing disproved the point. His patient was unable to piece together wooden blocks so as to copy a design, not only with her hands but also with her feet. Nor was she able to copy the design by dint of directing another person which pieces to choose and how to arrange them. In other words, the motility factor in the constructional defect is not to be ascribed to purely manual shortcomings, but rather it is the expression of a failure in the general idea of synthesis.

The *localization* of lesions which are apt to be followed by constructional apraxia, needs discussion. The earliest cases were referred to the occipital areas of the brain. Later, the parietal lobe was implicated, and more particularly the region of the angular gyrus. Monakow was an eloquent exponent of the view that apraxia cannot be attributed to a strictly demarcated lesion of the brain. Nevertheless, the accumulation of clinicopathological data is impressive and makes it difficult to escape the suspicion that lesions somewhere within the retro-Rolandic region of the brain are apt to be associated with the clinical phenomenon of constructional apraxia. Questions of localization within the parietal lobe itself, or in relation to the temporal and occipital regions, are not altogether satisfactory. Problems of sidedness are perhaps more rewarding. When

Patient	Side	Pathology	Verified	Remarks
25895	Subordinate	Cystic glioma	+	
E. L.	Subordinate	Meningioma	+	Parieto-occipital
32872	Subordinate	Astrocytoma	+	Parieto-occipital
T. G.	Subordinate	Vascular	o	
E. C. P.	Subordinate	Glioblastoma	+	
C. C.	Subordinate	Papilloma	+	Occipital
11720	Subordinate	Glioma	+	Parietotemporal
18289	Subordinate	Astrocytoma	+	
22775	Subordinate	Cystic glioma	+	
34673	Subordinate	Metastatic Ca	o	Frontoparietal
F. S.	Subordinate	Ischaemic	+	
G. H. H.	Subordinate	Glioma	+	Frontotemporo-parietal
26953	Subordinate	Ischaemic	o	
30075	Subordinate	Astrocytoma	+	Frontoparietal
26779	Subordinate	? Neoplastic	o	Hysterical over-lay
H. R.	Subordinate	Meningioma	+	Parieto-occipital
18287	Subordinate	Ischaemic	o	
39603	Subordinate	Ischaemic	o	3-dimensional constructional apraxia
18700	Subordinate	Abscess	+	Parieto-occipital
26692	? Subordinate (R)	Ischaemic	+	Ambidextrous patient
29536	Dominant	Oligodendro-glioma	+	
35118	Dominant	Glioblastoma multiforme	+	3-dimensional constructional apraxia
36459	Dominant	Metastatic Ca	+	Frontoparietal
12621	Dominant		o	
26634	Dominant	Astrocytoma	+	Temporoparietal
8852	Dominant	Ischaemic	o	
16601	Dominant	Embolism	+	Sylvian artery
F. Z.	Dominant	Ischaemic	o	Parietotemporal
27572	Prob. bilateral	Ischaemic	o	Ambidextrous patient
23452	Prob. bilateral	Ischaemic	o	
34251	Prob. bilateral	Atrophy	o	
A. P.	Diffuse	Ischaemic	o	

N.B. In the metastatic cases, multiple tumours were found at autopsy ; here the earliest clinical features could be correlated, however, with a focal lesion within one hemisphere.

" Verified " means confirmed either at autopsy or operation ; or, in the case of vascular lesions, by arteriography. " Not verified " in the case of atrophic lesions means that no pathological confirmation was forthcoming, though air-studies demonstrated the diffuse cortical atrophy.

constructional apraxia is associated with complicated visual disorientation, the lesions have usually been found to be bilaterally situated. Less complex cases, however, are instances of unilateral disease. Indeed, Paterson and Zangwill at the time of writing their paper on right-sided parietal syndromes (1944) declared that all cases of constructional apraxia hitherto recorded had been examples of diffuse disease, bilateral disease or disease of the dominant hemisphere, and their object was to stress the role of the subordinate hemisphere. In discussing sidedness in this connection, it must be borne in mind that it is easier to apply tests for constructional apraxia to a patient with a left hemiparesis, in that the right hand is intact for drawing and building designs. Constructional apraxia with left-brained lesions may consequently be overlooked, being masked by more blatant defects.

It can therefore be asserted that constructional apraxia may occur in association with lesions bilaterally placed, or right-sided or left-sided. This is shown in the following list:

DIFFUSE LESIONS

CO poisoning	Seelert	1920	
	Solomon	1932	
Hypoglycaemia	Gyárfas	1939	
CO poisoning	Ajuriaguerra, Zazzo and Granjon	1949	
CO poisoning	Steele and Hegarty	1950	
Trauma R > L	Krapf and Courtis	1937	

BILATERAL LESIONS

Pick's disease ; atrophy of both inferior parietal lobules	Lhermitte, Massary and Kyriaco	1928	Verified
Vascular lesions both angular gyri	Stengel	1944	Unverified
Biparietal metastatic carcinomata	McFie, Piercy and Zangwill (case 4)	1950	Verified
Injury	Ehrenwald	1931	Verified
" Migraine " ? tumour	Zutt	1932	Unverified
? Pick's disease	Kammerer and Singer	1951	Unverified
(1) Large deep R. parietal tumour (2) Small tumour in L. post-cerebral gyrus	Roth (case 1)	1949	Verified
Bilateral vascular lesions— R > L	McFie, Piercy and Zangwill (case 1)	1950	Verified

DOMINANT HEMISPHERE ONLY

	Lhermitte, Levy and Kyriaco	1925	
Angular and supramarginal gyri	Kroll	1910	Unverified
(1) Interparietal sulcus (2) Interparietal sulcus	Pötzl	1937	(1) Verified (2) Unverified
(1) Thalamus (L) (2) Border angular gyrus and 2nd occipital convolution (L) (3) Forceps major (L)	Nielsen	1938	Verified
Vascular lesion	Nielsen (case 21)	1946	Unverified

SUBORDINATE HEMISPHERE ONLY

Injuries	Paterson and Zangwill (cases 1 and 2)	1944	Verified by air-studies and/or X-rays
Perforating injury	Bender and Teuber (case 2)	1948	Verified by X-rays
Tumour	McFie, Piercy and Zangwill (Cases 2, 3, 5, 6, 7, 8).	1950	Verified either by autopsy, biopsy or operation
(1) Parieto-occipital tumour (2) Parieto-occipital tumour (3) Parieto-occipital tumour (4) Parieto-occipital tumour (5) Parieto-occipital tumour (6) Parieto-occipital tumour	Hécaen, Ajuriaguerra and Massonet (Cases 1, 2, 3, 4, 5, 6)	1952	(1) Verified (2) Verified (3) Verified (4) Verified (5) Verified (6) Verified
Aneurysm internal carotid artery	Roth (Case 2)	1949	Verified by arteriography

The most interesting clinico-pathological association in this connection concerns the " interparietal " region of the brain. Pötzl was the first to proffer the idea that the special architectonic structure occurring in the depths of the interparietal sulcus represented an associative linkage between the occipital gyri and the postcentral convolutions. Histologically, this is to be found in the " sensory visual band " of Elliot Smith, also termed by Pötzl the " interparietal striae ". Kroll supported this view, as did Lhermitte and Trelles at least in so far as it represented an attractive heuristic explanation of the morbid anatomy of constructional apraxia.

CHAPTER VII

GERSTMANN'S SYNDROME

To begin with the first finger of the left hand, and to tell on to the last finger of the right, is the natural and simple way of *numbring* and *computation* : for, all men use to count forwards till they come to that number of their *Fingers*, and being come to that number, prompted as it were by nature to returne at this bound or But of numericall immensity, (about which all numbers are reflected and driven round,) they repeat againe the same numbers returning unto unity from whence their account began, which we must not account as an accident, but a thing propagated from the fountaine of nature, since it is ever done and that by all Nations. For the *Fingers*, by an ordinance of nature, and the unrepeatable statute of the great Arithmetician, were appointed to serve for casting counters, as quicke and native digits, alwaies ready at *Hand* to assist us in our computations. Hence some have called man a naturall Arithmetician, and the only creature that could reckon and understand the mistique laws of numbers, because he alone hath reason, which is the spring of arithmeticall account : nay that divine Philosopher doth draw the line of men's understanding from this computing faculty of his soule, affirming that therefore he excells all creatures in wisdome, because he can account : and indeed not the least of the more subtill part of reason doth depend upon this Arithmeticall infused quality. Hence we account such for idiots and halfe-sould men who cannot tell to the native number of their *Fingers*.

J. Bulwer, Chirologia (London, 1644).

Διὰ τί πάντες ἄνθρωποι, καὶ βάρβαροι καὶ Ἕλληνες, εἰς τὰ δέκα καταριθμοῦσι, καὶ οὐκ εἰς ἄλλον ἀριθμόν . . . ἢ ὅτι πάντες ὑπῆρξαν ἄνθρωποι ἔχοντες δέκα δακτύλους.

(Why do all men, both foreign and Greek, count in tens, and not in any other numbers ? . . . Is it because all men have ten fingers ?

Aristotle, Problems, XV.)

A shrewd and original communication by Josef Gerstmann in 1924 virtually started a new chapter in the story of parietal symptomatology. The case-record concerned a woman of 52 years, who was found to have a striking inability to recognize her own fingers, or to name them, or to point out an individual digit when so directed. Furthermore, this same inability applied not only to her own fingers, but to those of other people also. The patient had not been aware of this trouble until it was revealed by clinical testing. Isolated finger movements were also difficult, although there was no real motor or sensory loss. Gerstmann regarded this particular symptom as a disorder of the body-scheme and he termed it " finger-agnosia ". Closer study of this patient brought to light some other features.

Thus, there was a right-left disorientation, especially notable for parts of her own body, and for the bodies of other persons. The patient furthermore had an acalculia, and also a " pure " agraphia, the difficulty concerning spontaneous writing, the ability to copy being intact.

Three years later, Gerstmann published another paper, drawing attention to this association of finger-agnosia and isolated agraphia. This paper dealt with two new cases, both being instances of cerebro-vascular disease. In both, there was a " pure " agraphia (copying still being possible), but in the former, it was a question of literal agraphia while the latter was an example of verbal agraphia. As in the case-record of 1927, there was finger-agnosia affecting the 2nd, 3rd and 4th fingers more than the thumb and auricular. Once again, there was a right-left disorientation, and a difficulty in calculation ; and in these cases, some disturbance also in colour-sense. In the interval between his two papers, Gerstmann had come across two an-alogous case-reports in the literature, namely, by Pötzl and Herrmann (1926) and by Herrmann and Kerschener (1926).

Gerstmann, on the basis of his three cases and the two others in the literature, believed he had isolated a syndrome, one which he regarded as a fragment of autotopagnosia, and he suspected that the responsible lesion lay in the region between the angular gyrus and the second occipital convolution.

In retrospect, it seems probable that Gerstmann's syndrome had been foreshadowed a little earlier ; at a meeting of the Berlin Society for Psychiatry and Neurology on February 13th, 1922, Bonhoeffer demonstrated a specimen of a brain with a focus of disease in the supramarginal gyrus and the most caudal part of the first temporal convolution. A second, smaller, lesion lay in the middle of the postcentral convolution. The following year (1923) Bonhoeffer recorded the clinical findings in some detail. The case had been of a young trapeze artist in the Zircus Schumann, who had sustained a stroke during dental extractions under chloroform. There was a sudden loss of speech, which later showed itself as an agrammatism. A mild right hemi-paresis was associated with deviation of the eyes to the left. No hemianopia was present. There was an " apractic disorder of writing " as well as a dyscalculia, and a considerable defect in spatial orientation. This last-named comprised a right-left confusion but at an earlier date all directions were at fault. The patient, when talking, showed considerable impairment in the correct use of adverbs and prepositions indicative of place (*unter, ober, vorn, hinter, auf, aus, in*).

Scrutinizing the literature even more closely, one can find a still earlier but unrecognized example in the famous case recorded in 1919 by van Woerkom. Under the title of " loss of the geometric sense " the author described a patient who suddenly lost his speech and showed inappropriate behaviour. Thereafter, he passed into a curious akinetic state with severe speech defect but no paralysis, no hemianopia and no sensory loss. The patient lost all idea of time and of number, and even the simplest calculations were beyond his power. He had difficulty in localizing sensory stimuli, but a study of the case-notes suggests that this defect was due more to a somatognosia than to an atopognosis. There was trouble with writing and the patient did not set out his words correctly on parallel horizontal lines. He could not copy words constructed with letters printed on bricks. He was unable to indicate spatial directions such as " right ", " left ", " up " and " down ". There was no apraxia, except for " very complicated actions consisting of several stages ". No anatomical study was available in this case, but Woerkom imagined the problem was one of Broca's aphasia with a purely frontal lesion.

It is possible that the two cases recorded by Anton (1899) and the two mentioned by Hartmann (1902), all four of which had shown right-left disorientation during life, should rightly belong here. The analogy is less close, however, in that the four cases were all instances of bilateral disease.

Gerstmann published yet another paper upon this same topic in 1930. He was now convinced from the evidence of his own series and of the cases which had been appearing in print, that there existed a clear-cut syndrome comprising finger-agnosia, right-left disorientation, acalculia and agraphia, and that this syndrome was associated with a well defined brain lesion within the connections between the angular gyrus and the occipital lobe. In this third article, Gerstmann emphasized that the left hemisphere seemed to be the significant one in the genesis of this syndrome : the one exception was the Pötzl-Herrmann case where a tumour had occupied the right parieto-occipital region. But in that example the patient had been ambidextrous.

Since 1923, a considerable number of cases of parietal disease have been recorded or observed, in which this syndrome had been demonstrable. In view of the nature and site of the responsible lesions, it is not surprising that many other agnosic or apraxic defects have been also found in association. Whether any of these other signs are significant, or integral, cannot yet be said with confidence. Kroll (1929), Lange (1930) and von Rad (1930) laid stress upon a homonymous hemianopia, and a loss of optic nystagmus ; while Engerth (1933) was impressed by a defect in the ability to draw. Stengel (1944) considered that symptoms of a constructional apraxia are rarely absent from cases of Gerstmann's syndrome. Rubins and Friedman (1948) drew attention to the common association of this syndrome with the so-called pain asymboly. Olsen and Ruby (1941), and others, observed a defective colour-sense in their patients. Similarly, certain modifications of what may now be termed the " classical " Gerstmann syndrome seem to be possible and will be mentioned in due course.

Whether these other disabilities will prove to be frequent concomitants of the Gerstmann syndrome, time may reveal. In this connection, Zeh's case (1952) may be mentioned where acalculia and dysgraphia (although without finger-agnosia and lateral disorientation) were associated with an inability to understand the meaning of facial expressions in pictures. As a result, the patient could not see the point of a comic situation in a cartoon. Zeh did not think that this defect was an instance of prosopagnosia, that is an inability to recognize faces. Nor did he look upon it as an aspect of a visual agnosia. Until further data is forthcoming, Zeh's case-record is not convincing, even though it can be recalled that Teicher's patient with Gerstmann syndrome had also lost the power of identifying familiar faces, including his own mirror reflection (1947).

The clinical aspects of this syndrome may now be discussed in more detail, with reference to each constituent in turn :

1. *Finger-agnosia* is the most important feature of the syndrome. In the first place, it is tested by telling the patient to point to, or to hold up, the various fingers of each hand. Secondly, the patient is asked to name the various fingers when they are touched in turn. Thirdly, the patient may be told to point to the various fingers on the examiner's hands. Fourthly, the patient may be given a more complicated command as in the following : " Put the third finger of the right hand on the tip of the second finger of the left hand." Again, the patient may be given an outline drawing of a hand. On this chart, he may be told to indicate the finger corresponding to one touched out of sight. Or to indicate on his own hand the finger corresponding to one marked on the chart. Yet another variant is for the examiner to touch or move one or more of his fingers in the view of the patient and for the patient then to touch or move the corresponding finger on his own hand. Finally, very mild finger-agnosic disturbances may be elicited by way of the Japanese illusion. That is, the patient interlaces his fingers and reverses his hands, and then tries to name the fingers which the examiner touches.

It is rare for the patient to give consistently wrong answers to all these tests. As a rule, the patient correctly identifies and names his thumb and also the thumb of the examiner. Again, the patient can often identify and name his own little finger and that of others. But the second, third and fourth fingers are almost always a source of confusion. The wearing of a wedding-ring sometimes assists the patient in the recognition of the annularis. This differentiation of the thumb and index, or the thumb and fifth fingers from the middle group of digits is a most interesting phenomenon which will be considered more fully later.

The finger-agnosia is, of course, bilateral. An exception to this statement seems to lie in the case of Klein and Mallie (1945), where a presumed right parietal lesion caused a left hemiplegia, with sensory disturbances and a left finger-agnosia. But it is rare even for one hand to be affected more than another, unless there is a severe degree of postural loss on one side, in which case there will be a correspondingly greater degree of finger-agnosia.

In advanced cases of finger-agnosia, the patient is also incapable of indicating various other parts of the anatomy ; in other words, the patient is really afflicted with an autotopagnosia. This fact suggests that, ordinarily, the finger-agnosia of Gerstmann's syndrome can be looked upon as a localized, incomplete, or partial autotopagnosia, as indeed Gerstmann suspected.

Some writers, when dealing with Gerstmann's syndrome, have spoken of " finger-apraxia " and " finger-aphasia " in a particular sense, and not necessarily synonymous with finger-agnosia. Thus, the patient may fail in only some of the clinical tests : his chief difficulty may be the indication of a finger at command ; or an inability to touch one named finger with another one. For such a defect, the term " finger-apraxia " has been suggested. " Finger-aphasia " comprises the inability to name the fingers, though they are manipulated correctly to command. To make such clinical distinctions and to make use of such a terminology is neither justifiable nor desirable, however.

2. *Right-left disorientation.* During the ordinary testing measures for finger-agnosia, it will probably become obvious that many of the patient's responses are wrong in so far as they concern sidedness. Unlike the finger-agnosia, the disorientation affects all parts of the anatomy, but it may not extend into outer space so as to involve inanimate objects. It is common, however, for the disorientation to include the anatomy of other individuals. Indeed, it is a more subtle test, when Gerstmann's syndrome is suspected, to ask the patient to indicate sidedness on the examiner's body as well as in the patient's own mirror-reflection. This test can be made still more difficult, if the examiner places his two hands one above the other (and not side by side) and the patient is then asked " which is the right, and which is the left ? " Or the examiner may fold his arms and cross his legs. Occasionally, other spatial dimensions, besides the lateral, are in doubt. Thus, at times, the patient will be uncertain over such concepts as before, behind, above, below. The patient's difficulty with imitating movements made by an examiner standing behind him, but reflected in a mirror, is sometimes spoken of as " disordered kinetic orientation ", or *praktagnosia*.

3. *Agraphia*, or better, *dysgraphia*, forms the third cardinal feature of Gerstmann's syndrome. This may take the form of a disturbance in the execution of letters (literal agraphia), or of words (verbal agraphia). Typically, however, the patient is able to copy. In this way, the ordinary features of a " parietal " dysgraphia with its characteristic signs of a constructional defect, are wanting. Not only can the patient copy in a slavish fashion from the pattern offered, but the patient can also convert a printed model into a cursive script ; or *vice versa*. In other words, the patient can presumably read and understand the content of what he reads.

4. *Dyscalculia* is the fourth characteristic feature of the Gerstmann syndrome. It may comprise difficulties with " mental " arithmetic, but the most striking defects are apparent when the patient attempts to make calculations upon paper. Here, there occur the characteristic marks of a " parietal " acalculia, with incorrect alignment of one row of figures under another. He may be poor at memorizing numbers, and those comprising more than one digit may be virtually impossible. The patient may be unable to arrange numbers in the order of their magnitude. He may fail to count backwards, although he may succeed when told to do so forwards. He may find it impossible to enumerate the odd numbers, or the even numbers, in series. When the patient is tested with an abacus, his performance may be grossly at fault, though again the operation of a coincidental constructional apraxia needs to be borne in mind.

These, then, are the four cardinal manifestations of Gerstmann's syndrome. Occasionally, one of them may not be demonstrable. More often, they are all present, but the emphasis may be uneven, so that one or two of the features are more prominent than the others. There is no consistency in the clinical findings. In progressive as well as in regressive cases, there may occur something in the way of a dissociation. Thus, in Muncie's second patient, finger-agnosia as well as static right-left disorientation disappeared completely to leave an agraphia, disordered calculation and an impaired kinetic right-left disorientation as permanent features. In his first patient, the finger-agnosia and the lateral disorientation were regarded as " mild ", while the acalculia and the agraphia were severe. In Zutt's case, there was no finger-agnosia, while Conrad's patient showed no agraphia, neither did Marburg's patient. Motor apraxia seemed to be the most conspicuous feature of the Herrmann-Pötzl patient, while disorientation in space was the most striking sign in Lange's patient.

The following table sets out clearly some of the inconstancies of the Gerstmann syndrome, as shown in the literature.

Table

	Mayer-Gross, 1936. Conrad, 1947	Mayer-Gross, 1936. Zutt, 1932. Nielsen, 1938, Case 4	Mayer-Gross, 1936	Ehren-wald, 1931	Mayer-Gross, 1936. Schle-singer, 1941. Roth, 1949	Lange, 1930. Mayer-Gross, 1936
Finger-agnosia	+	o	+	o	+	+
Agraphia	+	+	o	+	o	+
Acalculia	+	+	+	+	o	o
R/L disorientation	o	+	+	o	o	+

In the next table, cases are quoted where essential details as to some of the clinical features are not available :

Table

	Juba, 1948 Cases				Engerth, 1933. Peder-sen, 1946	Bender-Furlow, 1945. Ehren-wald, 1931	Schil-der, 1931	Zutt, 1932	Selet-sky, 1936	Kammerer-Singer, 1951
	1	2	3	4						
Finger-agnosia	+	+	+	+	+	o	+	o	+	+
Agraphia	?	?	?	?	?	?	?	?	?	+
Acalculia	+	o	+	?	o	+	?	?	+	+
R/L disori-entation	?	+	+	?	?	?	o	+	?	?

Discussion

Finger-agnosia is, then, possibly a fragment of autotopagnosia as Gerstmann originally suspected. The phenomenon entails an inability to recognize, or to name, or to point out on request, various parts of the subject's own body. It may also apply to the anatomy of other persons : we must admit, however, that finger-agnosia is as far as we know at present practically the only instance of an isolated or localized autotopagnosia. Rümke (1950) has, it is true, written upon a morbid dislike of one's own nose ; while Rubinstein (1941) has described an imperception of the eyelids. These papers do not, however, offer a convincing argument against the validity of the foregoing statement. It becomes necessary, therefore, to suggest a reasoned explanation of why a localized autotopagnosia should almost always concern the fingers and not any other isolated body-segment. The clinical phenomenon whereby a patient names (or points out)

P

correctly and unhesitatingly each part of the body until he reaches his fingers is striking. It is interesting too to observe the patient identifying without trouble each toe on the two feet, but failing when the hands are concerned.

Perhaps there is something unusual about the significance of the hand in the body-scheme which is at the basis of an isolated finger-agnosia; independent, that is, of any other trace of autotopagnosia. The hand plays a peculiar role in human ecology, being a part of the anatomy which is usually exposed ; which is most of the time within the view of the individual subject ; which constitutes the chief and most efficient organ or tool ; and which, if not the most delicate sensory discriminative region is, at least, the principal instrument of touch. The human hand corresponds in biological importance with the trunk in the case of the elephant, or the tail in some of the arboreal apes, but in many ways it surpasses them. Unlike the elephant's trunk, it is freed from olfactory duties. It participates in some of the processes of language far more than the trunk or the prehensile tail. The hand has an important and extensive cortical representation, in that electrical stimulation over a very wide area will produce motor or sensory effects referred to the hand—even though this area is not rigidly predetermined on a point-to-point principle. The manipulative dexterity of the fingers is readily impaired from cortical disease, but very extensive ablations or lesions are necessary to abolish entirely all power of movement from the hand. The sensory and motor accomplishments of the hand far transcend the potentialities of the fore-paw in any subhuman species. If Man is to be regarded essentially as a *homo faber*, then it is the hand with which he uses and directs the implement. Certain anatomical adaptations of the fingers and the hand are peculiar to Man, e.g. the hairless palm, the long and mobile thumb, the wide abductive range of the digits, and the ample pronation and supination of the forearm.

By reason of its attainments, the hand may possibly have become vulnerable. A reasonable case could be argued for the opposite contention, that, because of its important role in the body-image, neuropsychologically speaking, it is thereby firmly established. Klein has tried to show that the hand is largely the organ of the parietal lobe, and that in finger-agnosia, one witnesses a sort of down-grading of the hand to a mere feeding instrument.

The presence of a finger-agnosia does not necessarily interfere with the strength or skill of the fingers and hand, either for movements of a deliberate and highly voluntary character, or for more automatic activities. Whether the ability to " finger-spell " with one hand (as in the American system of dactylography) or with two hands (in the

British European alphabet) would be lost in the case of a deaf-mute afflicted also with a Gerstmann's syndrome has yet to be determined.

Schilder (1931) separated the phenomenon of finger-agnosia into a number of subtypes, according to the behaviour of the patient under selective clinical testing. Thus, he has spoken of an " optic finger-agnosia ", a " constructive finger-apraxia ", " an apractic disorder of finger-choice " and a " finger-aphasia ". He even went so far as to claim that each of these disorders had its own precise localizing significance. Muncie (1935) adopted Schilder's classification. Such a schematization is far too artificial, and although this terminology may serve a purpose in clinical description, it is questionable whether it adds to our understanding of the fundamental nature of the problem.

This symptom of dysgraphia in Gerstmann's syndrome is an interesting one in that in so far as it suggests a disorder of speech, the impairment concerns one sole modality of speech. An upset in the use of graphic symbols of expression, divorced from any disorder of verbalization, or of comprehension of verbal symbols, is on the face of it, anomalous. We should be chary of accepting such a conception unreservedly and either we should seek for other disturbances within the realm of language and thought, or alternatively, inquire whether perhaps some non-language process is not at fault in the case of Gerstmann's agraphia. Other language-disturbances may be present : if only because lesions of the dominant hemisphere are more liable to be followed both by Gerstmann's syndrome and by aphasia than are affections of the subordinate half of the brain. Nevertheless, it is ineluctable that other marks of language-disturbance need not be present, or at any rate, they may prove too subtle for demonstration. A plausible view is that Gerstmann's agraphia is really a writing dyspraxia, and so bears no closer affinity to speech loss than does, say, an articulatory dyspraxia.

The characteristics of dysgraphia need closer attention, including the type of errors in writing and the circumstances in which they appear.

If Gerstmann's agraphia is actually a writing-apraxia, it is probably not a constructional apraxia of writing. In the latter condition, we would expect to find, as already mentioned, certain typical features : (1) the act of copying would be more affected than deliberate or automatic writing, or writing to dictation ; and (2) a particular disorder would exist in the correct alignment of the words, so that succeeding lines do not start neatly one under the other, showing also obliquity, intersection and even superimposition. In Gerstmann's agraphia, there may, it is true, also be found similar irregularities of arrangement, but—most important—the defects would be more marked with spontaneous or dictated efforts, than in copying.   When, however, a constructional apraxia coexists with a Gerstmann's syndrome, as it so often does, then, of course, the agraphia becomes more disturbed and is complicated by the characteristics of that type of apraxic writing.

The third symptom, namely acalculia, belongs essentially to the category of " parietal " acalculia and shows itself on paper in an irregular horizontal and vertical disposition of figures.   Such features are particularly well marked if the patient happens to have a constructional apraxia as well.   The Gerstmann acalculia also shows itself in mental arithmetic, except, of course, when rote memory can readily supply the correct answer to a problem.   Even the handling of an abacus may be faulty in cases of Gerstmann's syndrome.

Speculations of great interest are raised by the association of disorders of calculation with a finger-agnosia.   We are reminded of a primitive use of the fingers in counting, a practice which was indeed so fundamental as to mirror itself in the same word *digitum*, amongst the Romans to stand for both " numeral " and " finger ".   Amongst certain communities, both in remote times and even also today, complicated systems of counting and bargaining are mediated by way of the fingers.

To elaborate this problem would be to venture rather far into the field of anthropology, but a few comments are not out of place.   Counting upon fingers was probably practised universally in primitive times, and today also among primitive peoples, to a much larger extent than is reckoning by the use of objects (pebbles, cowries, etc.).   The practice of " mental " calculation is a much higher and more abstract achievement.   Hence in most primitive languages, a similarity exists between the names given for the numerals, and for the fingers, hands, toes and feet.   This etymological identity is to be found in the language of such widely separated communities as the Malays, the Zulus and the Eskimos.   Thus, the word for " one " is often the same as that for " finger " ;   " five " for " hand " ;   " six " is often similar to " hand-one " (Malayo-Polynesian), or " taking the thumb " (Zulu).   " Ten " may be represented by " hand-half " (Aztec), or " half a man " (Towka Indian), or " both hands " (Melanesian).   After ten, the toes may be incorporated within the system of counting (" hands and feet " or " man ", being the same as twenty).   Schilder gave other examples.   It would thus appear that the early system of calculation was a quinary notation, that is, one based upon fives ;   in turn, based upon the use of one hand.   This system is even mirrored in such a cultured tongue as Latin, where the system of notation is made up of V (IV, VI, XVI, etc.).   A decimal notation, based on tens, implies the use of both hands, and it is interesting to realize that our traditional system of arithmetic has really an anatomical foundation.   Less often a vingesimal notation is adopted based upon a system of twenties, that is, on the fingers and toes, and its terminology may find its way into the language. This is traceable in some keltic tongues, whence it may have passed to such romance languages as French (*quatre-vingts* for 80).

In some other primitive communities, the digital system of counting is replaced by, or augmented by, a metaphorical counting of objects. Nevertheless, calculation based upon the indication of fingers and toes, hands and feet, is the oldest and most widely distributed system (see von Humboldt, A. F. Pott, E. B. Tylor) and is mirrored in the play of children today, and in many systems of silent bargaining adopted by modern Eastern traders.

We can also trace evidence of methods of counting upon the fingers among the ancient Greeks. References can be found in Seneca, Tertullian, Martian Capella, the younger Pliny, St. Augustine, Orontes, Quintilian and Apuleius. Bulwer (1644) pointed out in his *Chirologia* that arithmetical manual gestures are to be seen in various statues and monuments of classic times. Thus, the two-faced image of Janus, Patron of Time and the Ages, shows the fingers of the hands in an attitude which symbolizes the figure 365. Bulwer's treatise gave many illustrations of these hand-signs denoting numbers.

Critchley (1939) has quoted the observation that gypsies are sometimes said to be unable to multiply beyond the figure 5. " They assign a number to each finger of the two hands ; the thumbs are 6, the index fingers 7, the second fingers 8, the ring fingers 9, and the little fingers 10. Multiplication is then carried out as follows : if it is desired to determine 7 times 8, the tip of the left fore-finger (= 7) is placed against the tip of the second finger of the right hand (= 8). The two joined fingers and every finger beneath counts as 10. (In this case, it will be both thumbs, both index fingers and one second finger ; that is 50 altogether.) The remaining fingers are then multiplied, i.e. two on the right hand and three on the left. The product, 6, is then added to the 50, giving the final product of $7 \times 8 = 56$."

The blind idiot savant, Fleury, used a private digital method of calculation. With his right hand he would hold the fingers of his left, and each finger represented units, ten or hundreds.

Strauss and Werner, in a series of papers (1938, 1939, 1942), endeavoured to show in a group of subnormal boys, a significant correlation of deficient appreciation of the finger-schema and poor attainments in arithmetic. Kao and Li (1939) also tested a series of normals and concluded that finger orientation was a special ability, independent of the level of intelligence. Unfortunately for the acceptance of such attractive ideas, the findings of Strauss and his colleagues have been criticized by Benton, Hutcheon and Seymour (1951). Moreover, they repeated the investigation with a series of 22 normal children and 23 defectives. No significant correlation could be found between finger-localizing ability and arithmetical attainment. But when these investigators went on to study the relationship between right-left disorientation and appreciation of the finger-schema, they found in the group of subnormals a positive correlation of moderate magnitude. Breaking down the right-left disorientation tests, they found that tests directed towards the subjects' own bodies correlated better than those tests directed towards the orientation of objects in space. To a limited extent, therefore, it was justifiable to look upon the two functions as expressions of a unitary factor, namely, the body-image.

Right-left disorientation, or " disorder of directional selection ", constitutes the fourth cardinal feature of the syndrome. The patient, when asked to indicate the right or the left hand (ear, eye, shoulder, foot), displays confusion and makes many mistakes in sidedness. An invariable wrong answer naturally is not to be expected, for when handedness is in doubt, the patient has a 50 per cent chance of giving the correct response. The patient will also make mistakes when asked to perform this test while looking in a mirror ; or on the person of the examiner. Right-left confusion will also be displayed when the patient is asked to indicate one or other side in a two-dimensional picture or representation of a human body. Furthermore, this disorientation may possibly apply to inanimate objects, such as a doll or a statue ; and to articles of dress, such as a shoe or glove. Gerstmann, however, thought this would be unlikely.

Most patients with Gerstmann's syndrome show *more* confusion in these more complicated tests than in the case of their own anatomy. Thus, in early cases of progressive parietal disease (and also in late cases of regressive disease) the patients may show no right-left confusion as far as their own anatomy is concerned, but only when the examiner uses tests with a mirror, or his own person, or pictures, puppets or clothing.

This disorientation, oddly enough, applies only, or at any rate mainly, to lateral dimensions in space, for the patient usually does not confuse directions in a vertical or in a coronal plane. Thus, it scarcely ever entails a hesitation as to in front or behind, fore and aft ; and still less so to up and down, above and below. Stengel's patient was exceptional in this respect, for there was also a considerable upset in spatial orientation. It seemed as though " nearness " was the only spatial relationship which she could comprehend ; a regression, Stengel thought, to a more primitive condition.

The nature of this lateral disorientation deserves attention. In the first place, it needs to be discussed whether the defect is perhaps not so much a disorientation—that is a spatial defect—as a semantic one, a mere verbal confusion of the terms " right " and " left ". When similar but mirror-opposite structures are concerned, for example, the two legs or arms, the conception of right-sidedness and left-sidedness may or may not be fundamental. From the point of view of cultural anthropology, the distinction between right and left is, of course, of supreme importance. The " right " hand as the limb which connotes " dexterity ", " rectitude ", " rightness ",

Plate 6

JOSEF GERSTMANN

" good luck ", is contrasted with the " sinister ", ill-famed and unlucky left hand. But it is arguable that the ordinary person knows nothing of the folk-lore which is attached to this concept of handedness, and that to him the words " right " and " left " are mere arbitrary symbols which are associated for no particular reason with the one hand and with the other. Perhaps for him, the contrasting terms might equally well have been the other way round, or else some other empirical label such as " tweedledum " and " tweedledee ". Thus, the child, the immature adult, the dullard, the recruit is notorious for often mixing up the right and the left, or at least being hesitant in making the correct response when the command " left " or " right " is given. Such individuals, be it noted—that is, the youngster, the immature or unintelligent—rarely, if ever, confuse other dimensions in space but only those which pertain to sidedness.

The last point argues strongly for the idea that right-left confusion is not a verbal defect, but a true confusion in spatial orientation. The fact, too, that in minor degrees of this disorder, there is doubt as to the sidedness of external objects or persons rather than in the self suggests very much a spatial and not a semantic disturbance. Schilder imagined that the midline of the body projected into outer space, forms an invisible but none the less formidable barrier. Right-hand activities are thus kept aloof from left-hand activities, and the transposition of the left hand into the right half of space, and *vice versa*, constitute according to him operations of some complexity.

On the face of it, the assembly of four unlikely or unexpected symptoms so as to constitute a clear-cut and frequently occurring syndrome is a matter of surprise. We can safely assume that neurologists, for generations, have been confronted with this syndrome without, however, realizing the fact. This is shown by such case-reports as those of van Woerkom and of Bonhoeffer—and no doubt many others—which antedated Gerstmann's inspired observation. The natural question which now arises, after discussion of the various components of the syndrome, is whether any common principle lies behind the four cardinal manifestations, i.e. the right-left disorientation, the agraphia, acalculia and the finger-agnosia.

When Gerstmann published his first two papers, he was content to put forward the clinical findings, without any attempt to relate them to possible underlying pattern of defect. Herrmann and Pötzl (1926), however, essayed a theory to explain the fundamental nature of the Gerstmann syndrome. They were particularly impressed by the faulty finger manipulations in their cases, and they believed that in all probability a basic apraxic defect underlay the finger-agnosia, agraphia and lateral disorientation. Lange's approach to the problem was more from a psychological standpoint, and he also sought to trace a unitary defect which would satisfactorily explain all four cardinal manifestations of the Gerstmann syndrome. In his first paper, published in 1930, he suggested that there was a fundamental disorder in the patient's idea of direction in space, and in the spatial connections arising therefrom. The same year, Grünbaum was responsible for a number of interesting ideas to try and explain some of the psychomotor difficulties of patients with organic brain disease. In this paper we read of the conceptions of personal as opposed to extrapersonal space. This notion appealed to Lange, who in 1933 issued a second paper upon the nature of finger-agnosia, in which he modified slightly his earlier views, in the light of Grünbaum's hypotheses. Lange now suggested that ordinarily the hand plays the part of a tool which connects the personal space of the subject's body with extrapersonal space as exemplified by the surrounding world. In cases of Gerstmann's syndrome, it was now submitted, the hand had lost its function as an automatic go-between.

Stengel (1944) largely adopted the Lange hypothesis, and expressed the view that both Gerstmann's syndrome and constructional apraxia derived from a basic inability to relate in space objects which form parts of an organized whole to each other and to the patient himself, according to rules acquired by experience. " The complex spatial organization of the outer world is replaced by a most primitive one, the only measure of which is nearness." Juba (1948) looked upon the various components of the Gerstmann syndrome as expressions of a single basic impairment in Gestalt formation, or " globalizing " function.

Also in 1930, Ehrenwald had allied himself more or less with the views expressed by Lange in his original paper, but he furthermore drew attention to a disordered temporal factor in these cases. His idea was that the Gerstmann syndrome arose from a four-dimensional, ordinative disorientation, that is, in space and in time.

The following year (1931) Klein found objections both in the Lange and in the Ehrenwald hypotheses when applied to his own patient's condition. He found, indeed, much difficulty in tracing any single explanation for the whole syndrome as recorded in the literature. He put forward the not unreasonable idea that, just as the clinical emphasis might differ from one case to another, so the fundamental explanation might need to be modified on occasion. In the particular case which Klein was studying, it seemed tempting to submit a phylogenetic theory, and to imagine that the hand had become demoted from its status as a highly evolved manipulative tool, to a mere prehensile organ, as in the case of a child or an ape.

Engerth (1933) traced in his three personally observed cases symptoms indicating an " incoherent body-image ". This disorder was not restricted to the patient's own anatomy, but also involved similar disturbances in the appreciation of mass and space in general.

Benton, Hutcheon and Seymour were sceptical whether there is any close relationship between the four components of the Gerstmann syndrome. They emphasized the numerous incomplete forms recorded in the literature, and came to the conclusion that there is no positive evidence of a high degree of association. In criticism of this rather statistical conclusion, it is necessary to point out that negative cases in the literature only too often indicate inadequate examination, or even ignorance of what to look for.

The phylogenetic notion proffered by Klein should be read in association with the account given by von Angyál (1941) of a special but incomplete form of Gerstmann syndrome, comprising a thumb-mouth agnosia. His three patients, all of whom were suffering from cerebral syphilis, showed a right-left disorientation, a parietal type of agraphia, and an agnosic defect affecting the thumb, and to a lesser extent, the mouth and chin. (And in one case, also the tongue, palate, teeth, lower lip and jaw.) The fingers, other than the thumb, were normally recognized (except in Case 2 where the patient had an agnosia for the little fingers as well as the thumbs). None of his patients showed acalculia. Angyál regarded his patients as exhibiting a variant of Gerstmann's syndrome ; he conceived that, in his cases, the hand had regressed from its status as a counting mechanism, to a mere grasping organ concerned with the function of feeding. This was an explanation of the fact that his three patients were still able to calculate and that they could still identify digits other than the thumb.

Attempts to depict an inherent association of some of the components of the Gerstmann syndrome, occurring in the absence of acquired parietal disease, lead one to inquire whether there exists any evidence of a " congenital " type of Gerstmann syndrome. One such instance can be adduced, namely, case 2, described by Spillane (1942).

A recruit of 25 was sent to the unit medical officer at the instigation of his drill instructor because he could not tell his right from his left. This defect was readily demonstrated by the doctor, who also found that he had great difficulty in indicating his fingers, although he could identify his toes. He wrote slowly and with many mistakes in spelling. He also had difficulty with reading and with calculation. His physical build was that of dyspituitary obesity. Inquiry revealed that his development had been slow. Not until his third year did he begin to walk : he could not talk properly at the age of 5 and schooling did not begin until his 8th year. So slow was he in learning to read, that he was sent to a special school. His sense of right and left was always defective. At the age of 12, he had been sent to a neurologist.

This case seems to be unique, although close study of a wide series of cases of " congenital acalculia " might perhaps yield other examples. In some ways, Spillane's patient reminds one of the case of constitutional inability to learn morse reported in a Royal Naval Cadet Rating by Critchley (1942).

A young man had also been accused by his commander of having confused port and starboard. Close testing showed a superior grade of intelligence but he made unusual errors in spelling, and also curious mistakes when writing numbers to dictation. Thus, told to write down " five million, four hundred thousand and two ", he put down : 5,40002. " Three million, four hundred and five " was written as : 30,40005. He did not realize his errors, nor could he correct them when they were pointed out. His ability to do mental arithmetic was, however, high. With morse flash-light signals he could send slowly but accurately, but was almost completely at a loss to receive. He could not distinguish dots from dashes, nor tell where one symbol ended and the next one began. The question was raised, in discussing the case, whether the defects might not all have been due to some innate disorder of spatial orientation, either of a visual nature, or of a personal character, i.e. affecting the body-scheme.

Has Gerstmann's syndrome any localizing value in cases of brain disease ? In the great majority of cases it is the left, or rather the dominant, hemisphere which has been affected. Exceptions occur in Herrmann and Pötzl's patient (who was ambidextrous), and also in the case described by Seletsky (where a left hemiplegia was associated with slight dementia, acalculia and finger-agnosia). Klein and Maillie's patient (1945) was a right-handed individual who had a left hemiparesis with finger-agnosia in the left hand only. The pathology of the case was not determined. In the bulk of cases recorded where the lesion was verified, or else strongly supported by other clinical evidence, the lesion has been found within the parietal lobe. One important exception might be quoted in the case described by F. Pollak (1938). Here a large meningioma, growing deeply within the left frontal lobe, was associated with right-left disorientation, but with no other component of the Gerstmann syndrome. To specify still more intimately within the parietal lobe itself might be regarded as a vain and unpromising task. Many writers have attempted to do so, however, and most have implicated either the angular gyrus or the region where the angular gyrus impinges upon the most forward part of the occipital lobe. Pötzl presumed the lesion to lie

Cases of Gerstmann's Syndrome with pathological lesions verified at autopsy or at operation

Author	Side	Site of Lesion	Nature of Lesion	Remarks
Bonhoeffer, 1922	Left	1. Supramarginal first temporal gyri 2. Middle of postcentral gyrus	Vascular	
Herrmann and Pötzl, 1926	Right	Junction of angular gyrus with second occipital gyrus	Tumour	Ambidextrous patient
Gerstmann, (1)	Left	Parieto-occipital region	Glioma	
1930 (2)	Left	Parieto-occipital region	Softening	
Lange, 1930	Left	Angular gyrus ; also second temporal and lateral occipital gyri	Softening	
Marburg, 1931	Left	1. Angular gyrus 2. Supramarginal gyri		2 discrete lesions
Lange, 1933	Left	Angular and supramarginal gyri		
Mussio-Fournier and Rawak, 1934	Left	1. From frontal pole to asc. parietal ; below to T1 and insula ; deeply to putamen	Tumour	
Nielsen, (1) 1938	Left	1. Thalamus 2. Subcortical to junction of angular and second occipital gyri 3. Forceps major	Secondary carcinomata	
(2)	Left	1. Postero-temporal and occipital regions 2. Temporo-angular region	Tumour Softening	
(3)	Left	Post-parietal	Tumour	
Lyman, Kwan and Chao, 1938	Left	Subcortical parieto-occipital	Glioblastoma	
Kao and Li, 1939	Left	Parieto-occipital	Tumour	
Olsen and Ruby, 1941	Left	1. Paracentral and upper pre- and postcentral gyri 2. L. angular gyrus 3. L. caudal nucleus	Vascular lesion	At first left-handed ; right-handed through training
Arbuse, 1947	Left	Parieto-occipital (extensive)	Spongioblastoma	
Bertrand, 1950	Right	Post-parietal topectomy (for epilepsy)		Finger-agnosia only ; right-handed subject

Cases of Gerstmann Syndrome where the pathology has been presumed, but not verified

Author	Side	Presumed site of Lesion	Nature of Lesion	Remarks
Gerstmann, 1924	Left	Angular gyrus		
Pötzl	Left	Post. part of sensory visual band		
Isakower and Schilder, 1928	Bilateral	Diffuse	CO poisoning	
Rost, 1931	Left	Parieto-occipital region	Vascular	
Muncie, (1) 1935	Left	Deep parieto-occipital	Tumour	
(2)	Bilateral	Diffuse	Lead encephalo-pathy	
Seletsky, 1936	Right	Not known	Not known	Acalculia and finger-agnosia only
Nielsen, 1938 (Case 4)	Right	Not known	Vascular	No finger-agnosia ; left-handed subject
Stengel, 1944	Bilateral	Both angular gyri	Vascular	
Klein and Maillie, 1945	Right	Not known		Finger-agnosia confined to left hand ; right-handed subject
Zeh, 1950		Interparietal region		Complex case
Kammerer and Singer, 1951	Bilateral	Diffuse	Pick's disease	

Personally observed cases in which Gerstmann's Syndrome was readily demonstrated

Patient	Hemisphere	Nature of Lesion	Site	? Verified	Remarks
15224	Dominant	Astrocytoma	Parieto-occipital	+	Incomplete
35118	Dominant	Astrocytoma	Parietal	+	
C. S.	Dominant	Glioblastoma	Parietal	+	
J. W.	Dominant	Vascular	—	o	
32579	Dominant	Meningioma	Parietal	+	Mild
22019	Dominant	Vascular	Parietal	o	
25140	Dominant	Vascular	—	o	
L. B.-J.	Dominant	Meningioma	Temporo-parietal	+	Temporary
27572	Probably bilateral			o	Ambi-dextrous
A. P.	Bilateral	Vascular		o	
23452	Bilateral	Vascular	Biparietal		
F. E. W.	Bilateral	Atrophy	Biparietal	o	
24033	Bilateral	Vascular	Parieto-occipital	+	
G. T.	Bilateral but chiefly dominant	Metastatic carcinoma	Parietal	+	No R/L dis-orientation
12621	Dominant ? bilateral	Vascular		o	
36459	At first dominant, later bilateral	Metastatic carcinoma	Angular gyrus	+	Early
35427	Dominant at first, later bilateral	Metastatic carcinoma		+	
32718	Subordinate	Astrocytoma	Fronto-parietal	+	Incomplete

within the caudal portion of the sensory visual band, or as he called it, the parietal striae.

Schilder went to lengths which few neurologists today would approve, by associating the fragmentary components or variants of the syndrome with very localized and specific lesions. Thus, he associated " optic finger-agnosia " with lesions near the occipital pole ; " finger-agnosia " with the traditional zone connecting the angular gyrus with the second occipital convolution ; " constructive finger-apraxia ", with a lesion nearer the supramarginal gyrus ;

" apraxic disturbance in finger selection ", with the supramarginal gyrus, and " finger-aphasia " with part of Wernicke's zone. Lange, Bonhoeffer and Zutt all, independently, tended to ascribe right-left disorientation to a supramarginal lesion and finger-agnosia to disease of the angular gyrus.

The above tables set out the clinico-pathological data available in the literature.

In his final paper on his syndrome (1940), Gerstmann emphasized its localizing value in topographical diagnosis. He considered that the syndrome was " . . . related to a lesion of a common apparatus in the region of the parieto-occipital convenity (of the dominant hemisphere), particularly in that part which is represented by the transitional region of the angular and the middle-occipital convolution."

But in addition to the foregoing cases of organic brain defect, there are instances where Gerstmann's syndrome has been discovered *inter alia* as a temporary phenomena during the period of confusion following electro-convulsive therapy. Juba was the first in 1948 to describe such cases, when he gave details of five patients. Benton and Abramson (1952) also reported a series of such cases, most of them schizophrenics. The various components of the syndrome were often dissociated, in their experience. An impressive degree of relationship existed only in the association of agraphia and acalculia. The latter proved to be the commonest single symptom (10 out of 30 patients), the next most frequent being right-left disorientation towards the examiner's body (eight cases). Rarest of the phenomena was finger-agnosia.

CHAPTER VIII

DISORDERS OF THE BODY-IMAGE

I am persuaded that if a peacock could speak, he would boast of his soul, and would affirm that it inhabited his magnificent tail.

VOLTAIRE.

Disease of the parietal lobe is liable to be followed by a variety of phenomena which involve to greater or lesser degree the patient's corporeal awareness. Evidence will be given that rather suggests the non-dominant hemisphere to be more important in this connection. The extent of impaired coenaesthesia, or awareness of self, will be found to vary considerably from one patient to another, depending largely upon three factors : (1) the abruptness of the cerebral lesion ; (2) the clarity or otherwise of the sensorium ; and (3) the question as to whether motor weakness is present or not.

This particular group of phenomena can be roughly looked upon as consisting in alterations of the body-image (*l'image de soi, l'image du corps*) which for the time being may be regarded, following the practice in the literature, as synonymous with the body-scheme (*Körperschema*).

The various modifications of the body-image, as met with in parietal disease, can be tabulated thus :

(1) Unilateral neglect ; motor, sensory, visual.
(2) Lack of concern over the existence of hemiparesis (anosodiaphoria).
(3) Unawareness of hemiparesis (anosognosia).
(4) Defective appreciation of the existence of hemiparesis, with rationalization.
(5) Denial of hemiparesis.
(6) Denial of hemiparesis, with confabulation.
(7) Loss of awareness of one body-half (which may or may not be paralysed) = asomatognosia ; hemidepersonalization.
(8) Undue heaviness, deadness or lifelessness of one half (hyperschematia).
(9) Phantom third limb, associated with a hemiparesis.

A tabulation of this kind must not be taken as meaning that each of these foregoing phenomena are sharply demarcated. Not infrequently one condition merges into another ; or perhaps alternates with another. Sometimes in the course of a single examination the patient will betray evidences of several of these disorders of the body-image, in an inconsistent, if not contradictory, manner.[1]

Unilateral neglect constitutes one of the earliest and most characteristic manifestations of an expanding lesion within the parietal lobe. It is a subtle because transient sign, for as motor weakness appears and gradually increases, the quality of " neglect " or lack of spontaneity is replaced by inability to move. The " neglect " as affecting motor function comprises a poverty of movement, and deliberate willed actions are not impaired in strength. It is important to note that at this early stage the patient is not " paralysed " or afflicted with motor weakness. The patient does not use the affected hand, even in symmetrical bimanual activities, unless his attention is specifically directed to that side, and also unless the bimanual activity otherwise becomes obviously incommoded. A number of simple clinical tests can be used to demonstrate this neglect. Thus to the examiner's command, " Put out your hands ! ", the patient will raise only one hand (in the case of right-handed subjects with right-sided parietal disease it will be the left hand which does not move). When, however, the examiner draws attention to this defective performance by some such command as, " What about your other hand ? ", the patient at once complies by bringing up the " lazy " limb into the required position. Or the examiner may place his hands within the palms of the patient's two hands ; on being given the order, " Squeeze my fingers ! ", the patient grips with one hand only. Again, when the one-sided nature of the response is realized, the patient immediately grasps with the other hand also. In the case of the lower extremity, unilateral motor neglect can be shown by placing a pair of slippers in front of the patient and then telling him

---

[1] The tabulation adopted in this chapter is admittedly an imperfect one, but it possesses certain didactic merits. Hécaen and de Ajuriaguerra (1952) in their recent compendious monograph upon this subject have obviously also encountered difficulties in drawing up a logical classification. Their scheme is built up as follows : (A) Somatognosic disorders associated with lesions of the *right* hemisphere ; and (B) of the *left* hemisphere. Each group is subdivided clinically into three, viz. the hemiasomatognosic type, the anosognosic type and the illusion of absence of *one* half of the body. The authors deal separately with the foregoing phenomena according to whether they occur as sequelae of vascular disease, of spontaneous intracerebral haematomata, of brain tumours, head injury or dementia. Under " lesions of the left hemisphere ", the authors also describe Gerstmann's syndrome, autotopagnosia and asymboly for pain. They devote a special section to paroxysmal somatognosic disorders, dividing them into illusions of absence of part of the body, of bodily transformation, of bodily displacement, of phantom feelings and heautoscopic hallucinations.

to put them on. The patient may respond by putting on one shoe, but one shoe only.

Such tests illustrate a failure on the patient's part to utilize both limbs except to specific command—as if the limbs on one side were occupying a lower level in the hierarchy of personal awareness. In other circumstances, however, both arms (or legs) will be employed naturally as in such a bimanual activity as holding a golf-club or a spade, or operating the keyboard of a typewriter. Automatic actions such as walking will not be marred by any one-leg preponderance nor even by loss of automatic arm-swinging. There is some clinical resemblance between the unilateral neglect of parietal disease and the poverty of movement of unilateral pallidal affections—e.g. early Parkinsonism. The comparison is not far-reaching, however, for the other disorders of motility characterizing pallidal hypokinesia are not to be found. Thus, the patient with unilateral neglect from parietal disease will move the limb in question quickly enough once his attention is aroused. In other words there is no trace of brady-kinesis, nor of delay in the initiation of a willed movement. Further-more, there is no extrapyramidal rigidity, nor any abnormal flexed posture in the limbs at fault.

This subtle unilateral neglect is usually demonstrable at a stage when the patient's general sensorium is not very clouded. The defect lies outside the patient's awareness and it may indeed escape the notice of his close relatives and associates, and even of his medical attendants, unless they are alive to its possible existence.

Somewhat later, however, the clinical picture may change. On the one hand the patient may develop an actual motor weakness in the limb which hitherto has been merely neglected. A new train of phenomena will then result, which will be considered in due course. On the other hand, there may still be no trace of motor weakness, but other clinical troubles, mental as well as physical, may well be develop-ing, as the expanding lesion increases. The patient may by now display a global confusion which will have the effect of elaborating the unilateral neglect in a striking and often bizarre fashion. To passive disregard is added active neglect. The patient may cease to pay heed to one half of his anatomy, to attend to its hygiene and cleanliness. This pathological degree of neglect may even extend to the inanimate coverings of the body over the affected half. At such a time, the patient may be observed to be getting untidy and even dirty in his person. This disorder can be traced to a tendency on his part to omit brushing his clothes over one side only ; or to comb the hair on one half of his head ; or to shave merely one side of the face. A female patient was found to have applied cosmetics to one side only of her face and lips, and to have left her hair unkempt with kirby grips *in situ*—except on the right side where she was soignée and neat. In a bath, the patient may soap only one side of his face and body ; a moment later, he proceeds to dry one half only. His bathing finished, he may step out of the tub with just one leg and leave the other foot in the water ; on attempting to cross the bathroom floor he may then fall heavily.

These grotesque examples of severe unilateral neglect are all the more striking in view of the fact that, in ordinary circumstances, " reflexive " movements (that is movements directed towards one's own person) are more readily carried out over the opposite half. Thus, in lathering one's body in a bath, the right hand naturally performs this act over both legs, the left half of the body, the left arm and left side of the face. The right side of the body and the right arm are largely attended to by the left hand. If unilateral neglect exists, the right half of the body will now be dealt with by the right hand, but the patient will fail in right hand–left body performances. Hence, it is arguable that left-sided " sensory " neglect is paramount, even though the right upper limb is normal.

The rivalry between contending motor and visuo-tactile impulses in cases of unilateral neglect is well shown with the " glove test ". Into the lap of a patient with parietal disease, the examiner tosses a pair of gloves, telling him to put them on. Slowly and with much hesitancy the patient may succeed in putting on one glove, and one glove only. As a rule, he puts on the right glove and leaves the left hand bare. But to do this much, he must have employed bimanual activity, with the left hand indeed playing a more active and important role than the right. Apparently, then, the inattention to the sensory needs of the left hand is a more potent phenomenon than any reluctance to move the left hand.

Regarded otherwise, this defect could be looked upon as a reluctance of the normal hand to cross the invisible frontier of the midline of the body and to make manipulations over the affected side. The affected hand, however—once it is in action—seems to suffer no such difficulty in crossing this midline, in order to attend to the normal half of the body.

The intervention of visual stimuli reflected from a mirror does not serve to correct the patient who shows one-sided neglect in shaving or hair-brushing.

Unilateral neglect, extending from the patient's anatomy (personal space, *Eigenraum*) outwards into adjacent inanimate objects (outer space, *Fremdraum*) is well shown in the act of dressing. The patient may make a correct choice of garments and proceed to don them in the proper order, but he may leave unclothed one half of his body. Thus, he may fail to insert his left lower limb into the left trouser leg; to put on the left sock or shoe; and he may leave the left sleeve of his shirt and jacket hanging empty. This extraordinary one-sided disorder of dressing is often equated with the so-called " dressing apraxia ", as for instance by Russell Brain, Hemphill and Hécaen. To do so is not necessarily correct, for " dressing apraxia " is really a more complicated and diverse disorder than the unilateral defect just described, and may entail a total disorganization in which no orderly breakdown of function can be discerned.

Schuster (1931) and also Pinéas (1931) studied closely a remarkable woman with senile dementia, who, amongst many other agnosic troubles, had a complete loss of the left side of the body which in this case was in no way paralysed. In addition, this hemi-imperception extended into outer space but only on the left-hand side. When this patient was told to make a movement, she always employed the right arm; if specifically directed to use the left, she would use the right once again, without a moment's hesitation. She was obviously convinced she had obeyed the command correctly. After forceful and reiterated insistence that she had acted peculiarly, and that the right arm could not possibly have been at one and the same time both the right and the left arm, the patient might appear perplexed and reply, " Ich weiss nicht ! ", or perhaps, " Das war falsch, Herr Doktor ! " Or, on occasions, the patient might simply react to such cross-examination by bursting into tears. Pinéas did not regard the case as entirely one of absence of the left half of the body-image. He regarded the patient as having and knowing only *one* side and that, by chance, was the right. The patient invariably reacted in the same way, whether one spoke of the " right " and the " left " hand, or the " one " hand and the " other " hand. This represented to Pinéas a true " dyschiria ".

The phenomenon of tactile inattention is probably yet another instance of unilateral neglect, made manifest at that particular moment by a technique of double stimulation. In the same way, visual inattention can also be brought into line with a unilateral neglect as shown here by the medium of simultaneous activation of distance receptors. This same fundamental disorder, namely, unilateral neglect, no doubt enters into the production of such interesting sensory disorders as allochiria or alloaesthesia—tactile, visual and auditory.

Whether a hemi-asomatognosia necessarily accompanies all these cases of severe unilateral neglect, as when one half of the body is omitted from the techniques of washing, shaving and dressing, is still uncertain. More adequately studied case-records are necessary before this can be answered. Certainly, it is probable that, when a profound and subjectively conscious asomatognosia occurs, then neglect of the affected side is likely to follow; whether the reverse phenomenon invariably takes place is uncertain.

Despite the fact that unilateral neglect, or disregard, is one of the commonest, and indeed fundamental, marks of parietal disease, it is rarely mentioned directly in the literature. This is all the more surprising, for it was well described by Bruns as long ago as 1897, who called it " mind-paralysis " (*Seelenlähmung*) and it figured too in Oppenheim's Text-book (1911).

When motor defect accompanies a unilateral affection of the body-image, other psychological disorders are to be expected, as listed earlier. These disorders can be discussed according to degrees of abnormality. Mildest among these is a certain " unconcern " over the presence of a hemiparesis. There is no true lack of insight into the disease, but rather, an inadequate insight as to the implications of the disease. The unconcern is not quite the same as the euphoria, or the unwarranted optimism, or the facetiousness which some neurological patients display towards their maladies. Babinski (1914) seems to have been the first to note the indifference or insouciance shown by certain hemiplegics over their paralysis and its prognosis. As he put it " . . . I have seen some hemiplegics who, without being ignorant of the existence of their paralysis, seem to attach no importance to it. Such a state might be called *anosodiaphoria*."

The following notes illustrate a well-marked case of this sort.

A hypertensive male of 64 years (a private patient) had for the past month been " off colour " and frequently complained of dizziness. A week before the examination he fell in the bathroom, but did not lose consciousness. He made his way back to his bedroom, where he remained. The next morning at 07.30 he was discovered on the floor wedged between the bed and the dressing-table ; he was semi-conscious and he was noticed to be immobile down the left side. That same evening, in the nursing home, he was conscious, though drowsy and somewhat rambling in speech. His brother, who saw a good deal of him at this time, declared when questioned that, at first, the patient did not realize he was paralysed. Later, he did, but he was " jocular about it ", and that he would slap his paralysed thigh, saying that . . . " it wouldn't do what he wanted it to do ". When examined a week after the stroke, he was found to have a Weber's syndrome, with a partial third nerve paralysis on the right and a total paralysis on the left, with a deep left-sided hemi-anaesthesia and a hemianopia. Although there was absolutely no voluntary movement possible in the left arm or leg, and the patient was fully aware of this incapacity, he was quite unconcerned. He replied in an almost facetious manner to requests that he should try and move the limbs . . . " I can almost do it, but it just won't come." He showed no distress, and expressed no anxiety or even interest as to the chances of a return of power. Throughout the consultation, he was cheery and light-heartedly bandied small talk with his doctors.

Presumably he has sustained an occlusion of the main trunk of the right posterior cerebral artery, with a softening deep in the thalamo-parietal peduncle as well as in the occipital lobe and in the upper part of the mesencephalon.

More common, more striking, and better known, is the phenomenon of *anosognosia*, a term which again we owe to Babinski, although Pamboukis has since preferred to speak of a *noso-agnosia*. True, as long ago as 1898, Pick had mentioned a patient with a left hemiplegia who seemed not to be aware of his disability ; Pick did not pursue this question any more deeply. Even earlier, Anton (1896) and F. Müller (1892) had drawn attention to the same paradox. From a strict etymological point of view, the term " anosognosia " indicates lack of awareness of the existence of *disease*. As Babinski employed the word in 1914, however, the meaning was restricted so as to apply to cases of hemiplegia. In his original communication, Babinski drew attention to a mental disorder he had had the opportunity of observing in cerebral hemiplegia which consisted in the fact that the patients were unaware of, or seemed to be unaware of (*ignorent ou paraissent ignorer*), the existence of the paralysis with which they were afflicted. His first patient was a woman who had been paralysed down the left side for years, but who never mentioned the fact. If asked to move the affected limb she remained immobile and silent, behaving as though the question had been put to someone else. Babinski's second patient was also a victim of left hemiplegia. Whenever she was asked what was the matter with her, she talked about her backache, or her phlebitis, but never once did she refer to her powerless left arm. When told to move that limb, she did nothing and said nothing, or else a mere, " Voilà, c'est fait ! " During a consultation, when her doctors were discussing the merits of physiotherapy in her presence, she broke in . . . " Why should I have electrical treatment ? I am not paralysed." In his second paper on the subject (1918), Babinski drew attention to two clinical points in his cases ; both patients had sensory impairment down the affected side, and both had left-sided involvement. " Could it be ", wrote Babinski, " that anosognosia is peculiar to lesions of the right hemisphere ? "

This remark of Babinski's in 1918 was a shrewd one, for clinical evidence since that date had shown that in the great majority of cases lack of awareness of hemiplegia amounts to a lack of awareness of a left hemiplegia. Why this should be so is a matter of argument.

In the first place, it might be that the two hemispheres are equipotential as regards the body-image but that lesions of the left (dominant) hemisphere are followed by the more florid and more obtrusive disorders of speech and of praxia. Possibly, therefore, minor phenomena referable to the body-image might be swamped by these other clinical manifestations. This would seem to accord with the views of Nielsen (1938), and of Dattner (1950). On the other hand, it could be argued that the cerebral representation of the body-image is located exclusively in the right, that is the non-dominant hemisphere. This was Hauptmann's opinion (1927). There is yet a third hypothesis, more of a physiological order ; this points out that the left hand is ordinarily very subordinate to the right as regards usefulness and agility. A lesion of the corresponding hemisphere therefore—so it is suggested—merely exaggerates the physiological trend which is already present. Such a viewpoint was eloquently argued by Schilder (1935). It is rather supported by the observation that the normal infant is said to look at and use the right hand at an earlier date than the left (Tournay, 1922).

Another question not unnaturally arises out of this problem of anosognosia, namely, why the posterior or post-Rolandic regions of the brain should seem to be more significant than, say, the frontal regions in the genesis of this symptom. The answer to the problem is to be sought in the fact that the postcentral or " sensory " regions of the brain are much more concerned with the build-up of a body-image than are any other parts. The body-image is, of course, essentially an imaginal entity, constructed from afferent impulses. It is not surprising, therefore, that unilateral sensory changes accompany the hemiplegia when anosognosia also occurs. This was indeed pointed out by Dejerine in discussing Babinski's original cases in 1914. Barré, Morin and Kaiser (1923) more specifically indicated the importance of a loss of postural sensibility.

Although Babinski's first patient had had a left hemiplegia for a very long time, together with an anosognosia, a protracted disorder of awareness must be regarded as quite unusual. Some neurologists believe that an initial state of unconsciousness is necessarily present before an anosognosia sets in, but a wide experience belies that idea. Ordinarily, anosognosia is more common with vascular disease than with new-growths. As a rule, it appears immediately after an acute vascular lesion of the right hemisphere, and, after persisting for some days, disappears. The development of awareness of the disability coincides as a rule with a return of the sensorium to a state of clarity. As the initial state of confusion slowly recedes, so the patient begins to realize his disability. Two or three different mental reactions may follow the initial anosognosia. The patient may concede that he is paralysed but show little or no distress on that account (anosodiaphoria); the patient may admit the disability but attribute it to some local lesion in the periphery; or thirdly, the patient may realize the trouble and develop a severe reactive depression on that account. Finally, of course, a natural degree of concern may result commensurate with the degree of motor weakness and its progression. This may be regarded as a " normal " response.

Possibly, a milder variant of anosognosia may be traced in those cases of hemiplegia where the patient will take no steps whatever towards helping himself, and refuses to submit to rehabilitation measures or to physiotherapy. This attitude must be regarded as a sort of morbid apathy associated with their disability, and this may perhaps occur more often with parietal than, say, frontal disease.

The patient's attitude towards his inadequate motor performance forms an interesting problem which will be discussed a little later. Suffice it to mention here that in a third paper on the subject (1924) Babinski noted that when these patients were told to raise the paralysed limb, and were then asked to explain why no movement occurred, some would remain silent. Others would insist that the paralysed limb really had been moved. Others again would merely admit that it moved " less quickly " than the right.

Hagen and Ives' first patient (1937) told the doctor that she could move the fingers of her left hand if she tried, and then asked the examiner if he could see them wiggling. Requested to move her left foot, she warned the doctor to keep out of range in case he got kicked. After repeated demonstrations of her disability, she reluctantly acquiesced that she might possibly have had a stroke. But a few moments later she denied the suggestion that she was paralysed.

Anosognosia (for hemiplegia) is not infrequently associated with unawareness of other gross disabilities occurring in the same patient at or about the same time as the paralysis. Thus, the patient may also show an apparent ignorance of, or imperception for, such states as blindness or deafness. Other clinical phenomena may also be concerned, as will be discussed in greater detail later.

From anosognosia, or unawareness of hemiplegia, to an obstinate denial of paralysis, is an easy step in logic, but it indicates a very different level in neuro-psychology. Anosognosia connotes a mere deficiency in awareness, a poverty in insight or perhaps the operation of an organic repression. Whichever explanation is the correct one, no great disorder of the total personality is implied. But to advance from that particular mental attitude to one of denial of the self-evident facts of paralysis is to pass from a faintly abnormal state to a grossly pathological one. The patient has now surrendered himself to a delusional system, and he will probably have to sink still deeper into difficulties in order to discount the evidence of his senses.

Accordingly, it is not surprising to find that most patients who obstinately deny the fact that they are hemiplegic, show a number of other psychiatric features, ranging from a mere confusional to an actual demential state. This organic paranoid reaction is probably not compatible with a clear sensorium and accurate orientation.

Many case reports could be mentioned to illustrate this particular symptom. Lhermitte has quoted the case of a distinguished scientist who, afflicted with a left hemiplegia, not only did not know it but denied it, and was concerned over the sanity of his niece in attendance because she spoke of him as being paralysed.

The patient who not only does not realize his paralysis, but proceeds to deny the fact, is thrust still further into the toils of a delusional system when he is called upon to explain why it is he cannot move his affected limbs. Rationalizations and confabulation now crop up in varying degrees. Simplest among these—and least pathological—is shown by the patient who has but a mild weakness ; who besides not admitting the fact, endeavours to explain an inadequate use of the limb at a medical interview by some intercurrent, non-essential lesion which may have occurred long before. Thus, the patient may blame a rheumatic stiffness in the shoulder ; or refer to a previous sprain of the wrist, or fractured forearm to account for a weakness which the examiner has demonstrated. Outside the environment of a medical interview, the patient probably averts his attention from the disability and represses or refuses to recognize the fact. It is only under the searchlight of a clinical examination, and the inescapable insistence upon an explanation, that the patient is forced to rationalize in this way.

Much more striking, however, even although considerably rarer, are the gross and often bizarre examples of confabulation which some of these patients show when pressed for an explanation of the disabilities which they so perversely reject. The patient may deny the actual existence of the arm which can be seen lying immobile across the chest. Or the patient may admit its existence but repudiate its ownership. Even further, the patient may look upon the paralysed limb as belonging to someone else, whether real or imagined (the *personification anosognosia* of Juba). Sometimes again the hemiplegic person has the delusion that the affected side has been mechanically interfered with in what would ordinarily appear to be a grotesque fashion.

To these curious examples of organic paranoid reaction associated with anosognosia, Gerstmann (1942) applied the term *somatoparaphrenia*.

Examples of these more fantastic disorders of the body-image may be given. Ives and Nielsen's first patient thought that his paralysed left arm and leg " belonged to someone else " (1937). Zingerle's male patient (No. 2) had erotic sensations aroused by his own left side which he imagined belonged to a woman lying beside him (1913). A patient with an embolism of the right middle cerebral artery remembered that in the first days following his stroke he thought his paralysed leg belonged to the man in the next bed. He also developed other corporeal fantasies. . . . " It felt as if I were missing the left side of my body, but also too as though this dummy side were lined with iron so that it was too heavy to move. I even fancied my head to be narrow, but, at the same time, that the left side of the head was filled with bricks." The body felt half as wide as it should have done. When recumbent on the left side, he had a feeling that he was " lying on a void " . . . that he was at the extreme edge of the bed and would soon fall out of it. (Case No. 19450.)

Lhermitte has spoken of a man who had lost his left leg at the thigh and who subsequently developed a left hemiplegia. Thereupon, the patient not only denied that he had ever been amputated but he insisted that he had an intact and useful left leg which he could see and feel. The most that he would concede was that the left leg was " a little shorter " than the right. When a pin was jabbed into the region of the phantom he said he could not feel the point because the doctor was not thrusting hard enough.

Ehrenwald (1931) reported interesting reactions on the part of his patients towards their left-sided paralysed limbs. Some patients regarded the left arm as " strange, ugly, disfigured, artificial, enlarged, shapeless, thickened, shortened, or snake-like ". One patient insisted that a board had been inserted in place of the left side of the trunk and the left limbs.

Hagen and Ives (1937) published a number of comparable cases. Their first patient in the early days of admission to hospital occasionally identified her left hand as belonging to her brother-in-law. When she touched her left elbow she called it somebody else's knee. Of her left limbs, she said ". . . that's an old man who stays in bed all the time." Asked if she had any objection she replied : " Yes, I don't want any spirits in bed with me." Their second patient thought her daughter was in bed with her because there was a strange arm across her chest.

The first patient described by Ives and Nielsen (1937) denied that the paralysed left extremities were his. Questioned : " Whose are they ? " he might answer : " Yours ! " or perhaps, " The doctor's." Asked directly, " Are they yours ? " he would disclaim ownership.

Shown his paralysed arm, the patient said : " It's not the proper one ; it's heavier and bigger than the old one." When asked to show it, he overlooked the left hand which was lying directly before his gaze, and searched under the sheet and particularly around his knee. It might be significant that at the time of the stroke the patient was about to lace up his shoes, and had his left hand resting on his knee. (Ehrenwald, 1930.)

A negress denied that the paralysed arm was hers. When it was demonstrated that the hand was attached by way of the arm to her own body, she replied : " But my eyes and my feelings don't agree, and I must believe my feelings. I know they look like mine, but I can feel that they're not, and I can't believe my eyes." (Nielsen.)

In such cases Kramer, and more especially Pötzl, called attention to the patients' apparent aversion from the paralysed limb. Kramer's patient frequently turned his head and eyes, even indeed the whole body, towards the right hand side. Pötzl's patient refused to look at the left, paralysed, limbs. If they were passively moved so that he could not avoid seeing them, he would declare that the limb was not his ; that it belonged to someone else in the vicinity. Or he would say : " I don't know where it comes from ; it is so long and lifeless, and dead as a snake." One of ·Schilder's patients (1935), however, who incidentally showed anosognosia for a *right* hemiplegia, seemed to show an undue interest in her right limbs and kept looking at them. Her interpretation was abnormal, however, although inconsistent in nature. She usually denied that they were hers : she remarked that they were swollen. At other times, she announced that she had fractured her right arm and leg. Weinstein and Kahn's first patient (1950) thought that her left hand belonged to the nurse.

One of the most extreme cases of somatoparaphrenia concerned a general paretic who sustained a left hypaesthesia. He always lay on his right side, protesting that he had a paralysed brother recumbent beside him and that, disliking this situation, he turned his back on him. Asked to indicate this brother of his, he pointed to his powerless limbs. He would put questions to him . . . " How are you ? " " Will you have a cigarette ? " After telling him to lift his arm, he explained, " He doesn't hear . . . he doesn't answer . . . he has mental paralysis." A couple of days later, the patient asserted that his brother was " one body and blood " with him . . . " half of myself and my own age ". But a week later, he had changed his opinion and irritably admitted that the lifeless limbs were actually a paralysed part of himself. (v. Angyál and Frick, 1941.)

Various authors have afforded evidence in their description of patients with anosognosia, of a somewhat abnormal personality prior to the onset of hemiplegia (Rubinstein, 1941 ; Wortis and Dattner, 1942 ; Rosenbaum, 1948 ; Roth (Case 2), 1949 ; Weinstein and Kahn, 1950, and others).

Thus, Rubinstein's fourth patient had been certified insane for twenty-four years, with systematized delusions of persecution, auditory and visual hallucinations. Her chief complaint was that snakes were constantly attacking her. After a right-sided cerebrovascular lesion, she said : " I can't believe I have an arm. Have you taken it off ? I had a terrible shock this morning when I touched my left hand ; I thought it was the head of a reptile." Asked where her left arm was, she said : " I don't know. Where is it ? I don't feel it." When confronted with her left hand, she said : " That is someone else's hand. Whose is it ? It is not mine. It's a reptile."

Weinstein and Kahn believed they could trace in their patients with organic repression of disease (not necessarily only hemiplegia), a background of much insecurity and a strong drive to perfection and superiority. Such patients reacted to their illness with feelings of guilt or of anxiety. Those who became euphoric had been of compulsive, meticulous and worrisome type.

We now come to another disorder of the body-image which may be found in patients with parietal disease, especially in the right hemisphere. Hemiparesis may or may not be present. The characteristic feature is a subjective sensation as if there existed nothing to the left of the midline of the body. The left arm and leg seem to be " missing " . . . as if the body had been sawn through the vertical midline. This sensation is often a vivid one, but ordinarily it does not assume delusional proportions. The patients insist that the feeling is one *as if* no left arm and leg existed. Only rarely, and in cases where considerable mental confusion exists, does the patient dispense with the term " as if " and proclaim that he actually has no arm or leg at all on the affected side. Paranoid reactions may also occur in such cases. A luetic subject with a paralysed lower limb had the delusion that the leg had gone on a journey to a remote country (Ihsan Şükrü Aksel). Ehrenwald's patient looked under the bed to try and find his arm. A woman with a right hemiplegia told the nurse she had mislaid her leg and asked what was to be done about finding it. The next day, she became agitated, saying she had just seen her right leg and part of her right arm lying on her bedside table . . . " just like you would put false teeth on the table ". (Weinstein and Kahn.)

This feeling of " nothingness " is most often spoken of as *asomatognosia*, or *hemi-asomatognosia*. Schilder called it *imperception for one half of the body*. Ehrenwald referred to it as *hemi-depersonalization* ; Stein, and later still Lopez Ibor, have used the expression *negative phantoms*. Gerstmann spoke of *autosomat-amnesia* or *autosomatagnosia* in this connection. Van Bogaert's *anosognosie vraie ou muette* probably also belongs here.

It is not always easy to distinguish at the bedside, or when perusing the literature, between cases where the patient has an anosognosia for a hemiplegia together with confabulation, and cases of asomatognosia with or without delusional propensities. For example, the second patient described by Ives and Nielsen at one time said that his paralysed left arm felt like someone else's " stuck on ". (This is yet another manifestation of disordered body-image.) Five days after admission, the patient became more lethargic. When asked to identify his left arm held up before him, he said " . . . someone is substituting this arm for my left arm ". Later, he said " . . . my wife rubbed this arm, but it wasn't my arm."

One patient in Ehrenwald's series (1932) maintained that she was no longer herself, she herself having died. A sort of *Doppelgänger* resulted. Ehrenwald regarded this case as an example of unilateral depersonalization of the hemiplegic side.

Hoff and Pötzl's case was even more complicated. The patient was unaware of the existence of the paretic left hand or of her left eye, and she was uncertain of the position of her tongue in the left side of the mouth. Very often she experienced the sensation of having only a right hand. Her answers were variable, however. She refuted the direct suggestion that she felt as though her arm had been amputated, but on one occasion, she admitted to a " strange feeling " on one side of the body.

Asomatognosia may manifest itself to the patient, not so much as a continued phenomenon, but as a recurring episode. Thus, the arm and leg of the affected side may seem to disappear, or to fall out of corporeal awareness. When this happens, there may also be an involuntary deviation of the head and eyes towards the other side, and a feeling of great anxiety may temporarily supervene. The patient may grope with his good hand so as to palpate the paralysed limbs and thus assure himself of their existence. This phase may be accompanied by dizziness and be followed by spontaneous pains in the " missing "—i.e. paralysed—arm (= the *algo-hallucinosis* of van Bogaert). One patient declared : " Mon côte est remplacé par de la douleur." He also had less complete attacks at times, in which the middle third of his affected limbs would suddenly drop out of his awareness, leaving only the most proximal and the most distal portions intact (Hécaen and David, 1945).

Guttmann's case (1931) was more unusual. His patient had sustained a temporary paralysis of the left leg as the result of a shrapnel wound of the right parietal bone. In addition, his left elbow was shattered by shell fragments, later suppurated and ultimately lead to a stiff, shortened and crippled arm. Focal epileptic seizures developed, the pattern of which altered with time. Many years after the injury, his attacks became ushered in by a strange aura of a feeling as if the left hand was no longer part of him ; as if it were strange, and belonged to somebody else.

This symptom of hemidepersonalization (hemi-asomatognosia) is comparatively rare. As already mentioned, it tends to merge with the more common anosognosic phenomena. Other modifications may also occur. Reminiscent of the personification anosognosia of Juba, there may be a tendency for the patient with a sense as if the left limbs were missing, to imagine as his own, other persons' limbs which he can see. This may be nothing more than an illusion (" as if " they were his own) ; or it may actually constitute a delusion.

As an example of the former illusory *identification anosognosia* we may quote the patient who often had the feeling when travelling as a passenger in his wife's car that her left arm and her left hand on the steering wheel really belonged to him, and that it was his right upper extremity. The same patient, when using two-handed shears or hedge-cutters, would be apt to place both his hands upon one handle only. To illustrate the delusional type of identification anosognosia we may refer to the case of Garcin, Varay, and Hadji-Dimo (1938). This patient, who had a left hemiparesis, was tested and actually photographed in the following circumstances : the patient's left arm was covered by a towel. A nurse standing behind the patient placed her left arm around the patient's waist so as to rest in his lap. The patient thought it was his own. When told to take hold of his left hand, he grasped the nurse's hand, gazed at it, rubbed and fondled it. Though the nurse was wearing a diamond ring and a wrist-watch, the patient did not seem at all surprised. " Where is your wedding ring ? " " They took it off me." " And the wrist-watch ? " " I've been given it." " But that hand is whiter and softer than your right hand . . ." " It's got like that because it's paralysed." The left hand of the nurse was pinched under his direct observation. " Do you feel that ? " " No ; because, you see, it is paralysed." The nurse was then told to move her fingers. " Well then, how can you manage to move ? " " I don't understand how it is." But as a sort of after-thought, he added . . . " Well, since it's moving, that hand can't be mine." In this case, be it noted, there was no true anosognosia for his hemiplegia.

It should be made clear that this unusual phenomenon of identification does not necessarily indicate a parietal lesion. A highly intelligent writer described how when very ill with a high fever, he felt as though someone (a person who was no more than an acquaintance) had actually entered his body so that he had become a composite individual with this other person sharing his pains and his discomfort. This impression lasted for days, and he natur- ally believed that all the doctors and nurses knew about it too. Such an account reminds us of the *exchange of bodies* fantasy of Bychowski. A psychopathic postencephalitic, from time to time, had the illusion of " being two people ". He did not actually see or hear his *alter ego* but he would imagine it as occupying a different position in space, the two personalities being situated side by side, but one slightly in front of the other. He would feel that one of his selves was normal and that the other was not. The abnormal self would seem to urge him to do silly things. (*Bi-partition of the body-image :* Lhermitte.)

Nor can we even conclude when such fantasies are unilaterally disturbed that they must necessarily point to a parietal defect. For example, a patient with aural vertigo had attacks of giddiness in which the left side of the body would become " heavy, doughy, as if clamped in a bracelet of steel ". The whole left half of himself would seem to be filled with a foreign substance. Then would come a hallucination within the blind half of his visual field, of a figure standing to the left of himself and slightly behind, which stayed close to him and which seemed to be made of semi-opaque gelatinous material. With the onset of this vision, the feeling of strangeness of the left half of his body-image disappeared (Lhermitte).

A discussion of hemidepersonalization naturally leads to a mention of what has been called *segmental depersonalization*. This comprises the unacceptance or even denial of excreta, or products of menstruation, as having been their personal responsibility. Although this anomaly is chiefly met with in psychiatric practice, it has been encountered after organic focal cerebral disease (Ehrenwald). This phenomenon will be dealt with in greater detail a little later.

If hemidepersonalization is to be related to an organic unilateral lesion of the brain, as seems warranted, one may conjecture as to what the result would be of symmetrically placed bilateral lesions. Possibly the akinesis seen in cases of biparietal atrophy might be related here. Cases of *total asomatognosia* are known, of course, although very rare, but they rather indicate a psychotic type of illness, or else a severe example of the depersonalization syndrome. The feeling produced is that of disappearance of the body, a true aschematia in the sense originally described by Bonnier (1905). The patient described by Deny and Camus (1905) illustrates well the great mental distress which total asomatognosia typically provokes. In an effort to recapture the feeling of the body which she had lost, their patient ran naked into the grounds and flung herself into the snow. A similar " disappearance " or " rotting away " of the body has been encountered after focal cerebro-vascular lesions (Ehrenwald).

Cases of parietal hemi-asomatognosia may include at times such midline structures as the external genitalia. The patient with a middle cerebral embolism, already quoted, also for a time lost the notion of his penis as a constituent of the body-image. Considerable difficulty occurred during the use of a urinal in bed. Penile sensation, and its restoration within the body-image, returned quite suddenly following a spontaneous erection.

So far, using the terminology of Bonnier, we have been dealing in cases of distortion of the body-image from parietal disease, mainly with symptoms of a hyposchematia or an aschematia. Much less often does one find records of parietal syndromes associated with hyperschematic features. In this respect, the literature perhaps gives a distorted view of the facts. Many patients with parietal disease associated with unilateral motor weakness, complain of unusual sensory subjective features of a positive character. Although they can still be regarded as parietal disorders of the body-image, they can scarcely be relegated to the category of anosognosia. Not infrequently, the patient complains that the affected limbs are unduly heavy, and perhaps also swollen. One patient kept complaining in an almost obsessional fashion that his left arm was powerless and that it lay by his side " like a piece of dead meat ".

Another patient, asked why he found dressing so difficult, said : " This piece of dead wood won't co-operate," indicating his left arm. (Case No. 25927, Dr. McArdle.)

A man with a left frontoparietal astrocytoma was afflicted by attacks in which the left hand (i.e. the ipsilateral upper limb) would feel . . . " very strange . . . as if I were extra conscious of it ". Once only the feeling was as though the hand did not belong to him. These attacks would be followed by tremor of the left arm, then of the left leg and twitching would appear in the left side of the face. (Case No. 20727.)

Van Bogaert (1934) has fully described, under the term *painful anosognosia*, a phenomenon which he believed to be allied to algohallucinosis. His case was an unusual one. Afflicted with a right hemiplegia, with severe spontaneous cerebral pain, the patient often developed a bizarre illusion, namely, that the affected arm was abducted and the elbow flexed so as to lie with the hand behind the head. By deliberate employment of the senses of touch or sight he could overcome this illusion, but in the dark, the feeling would be so vivid that he would call out to the other patients to come and alter the position of his arm. Van Bogaert's use of the term " anosognosia " to describe such a phenomenon is open to question, for the problem would appear to be one of spontaneous pains in a limb devoid of postural sensibility, rather than a lack of awareness of, or insight into, a hemiplegic disability.

Here, too, belong these cases of longstanding hemiplegia where the paralysed limb seems to develop a personality of its own but outside the body-image of the patient. A mildly demented arteriopath with a powerless left arm and leg used to refer to the limb as " Toby " . . . a *façon de parler* which was also adopted by her housekeeper and her medical practitioner. " How is ' Toby ' today ? " she would be asked, and her reply might be to the effect that Toby was not so well and was hurting a little. Weinstein and Kahn's patient (Case 7 in their series) used to refer to herself as " he " or " they ", and alluded to her left arm as " he ".

Perhaps one can best explain upon the basis of bilateral (or diffuse) parietal disease, the development of yet another disorder of corporeal awareness. From a descriptive point of view, it combines features of a depersonalization (hyposchematia) with those of an illusory projection into outer space of the body-image. The phenomenon takes the form whereby the belief develops in the patient's

R

mind that he is no longer alone : that some person stands close by, even though he cannot be seen nor heard. This symptom is reminiscent of the *illusion de sosies* which is ordinarily associated with states of exhaustion or delirium. But in the following case, the circumstances were different in that, in the first place, the condition was known to comprise a cortical atrophy, and secondly, because the " presence " was imagined to be the patient's own self :

A woman of forty-three years, with a history of headaches, two seizures, and transient aphasia, developed a left-sided motor, visual and tactile neglect ; a bilateral apraxia ; difficulty in dressing ; dyscalculia ; and spatial agnosia. She also became liable to unusual nocturnal fantasies. She would wake in the night with the very intense feeling that someone was in the room—a person she knew ; indeed, with whom she was very familiar. Sometimes, she was at a loss to decide who this could be, but on many occasions, it would dawn on her that this person was none other than herself. She imagined that the " person " or *alter ego* was somewhere on her left but just beyond her range of vision. The impression was so vivid that she would leave her bed and go from room to room on tiptoe trying to surprise this familiar interloper. At this point, she would often get the idea she was going crazy. But she could not deny that the feelings were to her " very, very real " . . . " real enough to make me get up and look for this person whom I often knew quite well was myself all the time ". (Case of Dr. Hal Gregg, San Francisco.)

Here, then, is a *bipartition fantasy*, which appears as an organic symptom, lying at the cross-roads, as it were, between a temporary depersonalization, a heautoscopic hallucination and the *phénomène de sosies* (or Capgras' syndrome). It corresponds most closely with Janet's *sentiment de dédoublement*.

Illusions of corporeal transformation and of *corporeal displacement* —to use the terminology of Ajuriaguerra and Hécaen—are sometimes met with in association with focal brain disease, particularly as part of a mixed sensori-motor aura. The phenomena may take the form of a sensation as if the extremity concerned—usually the opposite hand—enlarges or swells ; or elongates ; or becomes separated from the body ; or seems to be at a distance away ; or as if it were writhing, or twisting or becoming torn. In the majority of such cases, the affected limb actually is the site of involuntary convulsive movements ; but the quality of intensity of the subjective feelings are not in accord with the actual objective phenomena. Less often, as already discussed, the limb is completely motionless, though the patient may feel as if it were in movement.

These hyperschematic and paraschematic illusions may prove to be associated with parietal disease ; but not necessarily so, for focal lesions in the temporal lobe and the frontal lobe have also been revealed on occasions.

The last group of disorders of the body-image attendant upon parietal disease comprise the illusory feeling of a limb in an attitude which does not conform with the actual posture of the paralysed limb. This is the phenomenon of the *supernumerary phantom*, also called the *phantom third hand*. The patient who has a hemiplegia—usually affecting the left side—may also suffer from an anosognosia ; or a severe degree of sensory impairment. Postural defects are generally conspicuous. From time to time, however, perhaps even most of the time, the patient feels as though the hand and forearm on the affected side were in a position of extension (or flexion), possibly as if they were in contact with the thigh or chest wall, at times as though they were in movement, or at any rate capable of being moved. Usually the fingers and hand are imagined quite vividly ; the forearm a little less so. Ordinarily, the upper arm does not share in the spectral limb, and the lower extremity is rarely, if ever, represented at all.

An epileptic, hypertensive subject developed a left hemiplegia without any preliminary loss of consciousness. Motor power was severely reduced, the patient having full awareness of his disability. Superficial sensibility was blunted over the affected segments. When he was told to stretch his arms out before him, he did so with the right arm but could not move the left. He volunteered the statement, however . . . " it feels as though I have moved it and as though it were sticking out in front like the other ". Most willed activities produced an illusory mirror movement in the phantom arm. When he made rapid wiggling movements with the toes of the right foot, he said it felt as though the left big toe were also moving.

In at least one case, there has been a complex multiple phantom feeling, the patient speaking of herself as possessing a " nest of hands " (Ehrenwald, 1930).

Occasionally, the attitude of the limb is more bizarre.

A man (L. D., case of Dr. Walshe), aged 52 years, with a mild left hemiparesis of 2½ years' standing, had several types of phantom feeling. As a rule, he had no true idea as to the position in space occupied by his paralysed arm. Quite often, and especially in the dark, he would imagine that his left arm was behind his back as if the two hands were clasped ; that is, as if he were a soldier standing " at ease ". His immediate impulse was always to grope and determine the whereabouts of his real arm in case he should accidentally hurt it. As soon as he found the arm, the phantom feeling would disappear. Sometimes, the phantom would feel abnormally short, as if the upper arm had been driven into the thorax, pushing out his shoulder blade backwards. This feeling would startle him and cause him to palpate his scapulae and his real upper limb. Again, the fingers of the hand would feel as though they were going into a cramp-like movement, although actually, his paralysed fingers were quite immobile.

In this patient, there were objective sensory perversions suggestive of thalamic over-reaction, as well as intense postural loss. There was no pyramidal disorder and no hemianopia.

It is possible that we should relegate to this group of phenomena the not very uncommon illusions of movement which patients with hemiplegia may experience in their immobile and paralysed hand. These may take place with variable intensity at quite irregular intervals. They may form part of the stage of restoration of an anosognosia. Or illusory movement may be a vivid and integral part of the pattern of a sensory focal seizure. Thus, Riddoch (1941) described a woman with right parietal atrophy where sensory Jacksonian attacks would begin with a feeling as though she had two sets of toes on the left foot, those of the phantom foot being curled towards the sole.

The vividness of the phantom limb can be modified by pharmacological means. It can be restored, after spontaneous disappearance, by mescaline, and it can be ablated by cocainization of the real limb.

When spontaneous pains appear in the phantom third limb, the illusion is temporarily intensified, just as in the case of phantoms after surgical amputations. This was clearly so in the early case record made by Pinéas (1932), and probably also in van Bogaert's case (1934).

As a rule, the phantom supernumerary arm disappears as soon as the paralysed arm is passively moved so as to mimic the attitude of the phantom. Or if the two actual limbs of the patient are placed in comparable mirror-opposite attitudes. Or it may disappear when the patient looks hard at his actual limb (Birkmayer). Or again, the act of touching the paralysed limb with the normal hand may serve to dispel the phantom (van Bogaert).

We may refer here to a clinical variant of the supernumerary phantom arm. A patient may be liable to transient attacks, not attended by unconsciousness, in which one arm, ordinarily the left, would lose feeling and seem to disappear. Objects would drop from that hand. During the attack, the patient would feel as though the left arm were in quite a different position. Attacks of this sort suggest a transient focal attack at a right parietal level. One excellent example was described by Riddoch.

Yet another variant of the phantom arm phenomenon depends upon a fundamental loss of postural sensibility to which is added an asomatognosia, and a unilateral field defect. The phantom arm now appears not as a tactile or coenaesthetic illusion, but as an impressive visual hallucination. Such a condition must be admittedly very rare, but seems to be well exemplified in the following case:

The patient (No. 25927, case of Dr. McArdle), with a left hemiparesis, frequently, during the month prior to admission to hospital, thought he saw an extra arm at the same length as his real arm, but with no shoulder joint and no movable elbow joint. The wrist, hand and fingers were clearly felt and appeared natural in size and shape. This visual phantom seemed to be stuck out in an attitude of straight-arm abduction at right angles to the chest. He was not able to make illusory movements with it. This phantom supernumerary arm was not constantly present, for it would appear only when he deliberately moved his left arm, that is the weak one. Thus, when stretching out his left arm to grasp an object, his real hand would suddenly and unexpectedly emerge from his blind field of vision into his range of view. The phantom arm had seemed to him as though it were protruding from the body at right angles. It constituted an actual visual hallucination of this phantom : ". . . like a shadow of my real arm ", but this vision was always fleeting and intangible and when he turned to his hemianopic field to study it closer, the shadow would vanish. When asked point-blank whether it was a " feeling " as if he had a limb in an unusual position, or whether it was an actual vision of a limb, he replied that he always " saw " the arm and that it was a very real thing to him.

Such a phenomenon is probably quite rare. It needs to be distinguished from a very much commoner occurrence, already mentioned, whereby the affected hand wanders about in space, often adopting unexpected attitudes. There exists a homonymous hemianopia in addition to a profound loss of postural sensibility in the affected upper limb. Consequently the hand moves about unbeknown to the patient, who neither sees nor feels it, until such time as it passes from the affected to the intact visual field. The hand then suddenly appears before his gaze in what may be a startling fashion.

Rubinstein has stressed certain differences in the attitude of the patient towards his affected limb in cases of anosognosia as compared with patients with phantom third arm. The latter patient recognizes the unreality of the phantom ; he is prepared to examine and scrutinize his paralysed side. The patient with anosognosia does not do so : he may even avert his gaze. He does not attempt to move the limb although asserting he can do so.

Anosognosia is, as a rule, a transitory phenomenon, as already emphasized. The reaction of the patient when forcibly confronted with the hard facts of his paralysis does not necessarily conform to a pattern. Again, other variables must be considered, such as the degree of confusion which the patient happens to display. The nature of the pathological process is important as determining whether the lesion is by nature a regressive or progressive one. The anosognosic patient who is compelled to face his disability may thereupon register a puzzled admission of this disease. Or he may admit the fact with reluctance or, conversely, with unexpected light-heartedness. Other possible reactions include an obstinate rejection of the obvious facts of the handicaps ; or a train of excuse-finding. But the most striking feature is that the patient may in the course of a single interview, run through the gamut of all these psychological reactions, with complete inconsistency. For example, the replies of Sandifer's first patient (1946) might be quoted verbatim :

Ex. : " Give me your right hand ! " (Correct.) " Now give me your left ! " (The patient presented the right again. The right hand was held.) " Give me your left ! " (Patient looked puzzled and did not move.) " Is there anything wrong with your left hand ? "

    Pat. : " No, doctor."

    Ex. : " Why don't you move it, then ? " (The left hand was held before her eyes.)

    Pat. : " I don't know."

    Ex. : " Is this your hand ? "

    Pat. : " Not mine, doctor."

    Ex. : " Whose hand is it, then ? "

    Pat. : " I suppose it's yours, doctor."

    Ex. : " No, it's not ; look at it carefully."

    Pat. : " It is not mine, doctor."

    Ex. : " Look at it—it *is* your hand."

    Pat. : " Oh, no, doctor."

    Ex. : " Where is your left hand then ? "

    Pat. : " Somewhere here, I think." (Making groping movements near her left shoulder.)

Sandifer then went on to say that she denied that the left leg belonged to her or that it was paralysed. The left arm was examined twice more, each time with similar results. At the third test, she was temporarily convinced that her left arm was hers, but when examined a few hours later, she had forgotten this.

    Ex. : " Is this your hand ? "

    Pat. : " Not mine, doctor."

    Ex. : " Yes it is, look at that ring ; whose is it ? "

    Pat. : " That's my ring ; you've got my ring, doctor."

    Ex. : " No, I haven't. It's your hand. Look how different it is from mine." (Patient, bewildered, felt her left shoulder, her left upper arm and followed downward to the wrist.) Then she said : " It must be my hand."

    Ex. : " And do you still say there is nothing wrong with it ? "

    Pat. : " It seems I am wrong."

The patient already quoted (No. 19450), who had a parietal embolism which caused a left hemiplegia, was at first delirious and confused. He thought there was an iron bar lying across his chest, and later, on investigation, he discovered that this was his left arm which had become strangely heavy (temporary anosognosia with hyperschematic confabulation). He discovered an even heavier weight in bed which turned out to be his leg. At first, he did not believe it to be his own ; he thought it belonged to the man in the next bed (personification anosognosia). His body felt half as wide as it should be, at first. He was afraid he would roll out of the bed (hemidepersonalization). Later still : ". . . no one could convince me I was not normal . . . when I kept falling, I put it down to weakness after my illness . . . nothing on the face of the earth could convince me that I couldn't jump out of bed and walk " (anosognosia). It was difficult for him to describe how awareness began to return. There was a sensation of weight on the left, as if lined with iron : ". . . so heavy that I couldn't move it " (projection : hyperschematia). As awareness of the left began to return, so there was a decrease in the subjective sensation of weight on the left : ". . . forcing my left arm and leg was like moving a rusty gate ; the more

I moved them, the less the weight. I became aware of less weight to pull me to the left side." These various stages from complete anosognosia to full insight took place over a period of six months.

Bender, Wortis and Gordon (1949), discussing a series of ten cases of anosognosia, noted certain stages in the recovery-process. At first, the anosognosia was absolute. Later, the patient would become less emphatic in the denial of disturbed functions, and showed variability in responses and uncertainty. The defect was always better demonstrable in the upper than the lower limbs, and the distal parts more than the proximal. Until full restoration of awareness took place, the patients also showed various psychiatric symptoms such as retardation, distractability, fluctuations in performance, disorientation and poor memory.

In the Polish literature may be found a striking instance of inconsistency of response as the somatagnosic patient slowly improved.

The patient, who was afflicted with a left hemiplegia had no idea he was paralysed. He protested that he was " not as ill as they think " . . . that he could walk and would be getting up as soon as they let him have his clothes. Never once did he allude to the fact that he was paralysed ; he explained he was not walking because his socks had been taken from him. Asked to lift his affected leg, he said : " Wait a moment ! " and then lifted his right leg, saying : " There you are ! " A month later, he made the comment . . . " I noticed yesterday that I can't get about on my left leg." Asked whether he could move his left arm, he said he could ; but when told to do so, he countered by saying : " I'm on a bed-pan just now . . . when they've taken it away I'll show you." Told to touch his nose with his left hand, he made no movement at all, but said . . . " I'm not sure whether I can . . . There, now I've done it ! " After a month in hospital, it seemed to dawn on him that his left arm was " ailing ". One day, he said to the doctor . . . " Can you see how my fist has been separated from my arm ? Has it been operated upon ? " Later, he announced . . . " My arm is in three parts and the middle bit is missing ", and he searched for his elbow under the bedclothes. A few weeks later still, he said that his left arm was " different " from the other ; it was " longer " . . . and reached down to his knee. There came a time when he began to feel imaginary movements in the limb. He said that physiotherapy had helped him a lot (actually he still had no voluntary movement whatever). At this time, he would confabulate . . . saying he had missed his train at the station because he had so many suitcases to carry : that he had almost fallen off the stretcher but had saved himself by clutching tightly ; that he had gone shopping and had manipulated his small change. As finally he left the hospital, he was asked in how many pieces his affected arm now seemed to be. He gravely admitted . . . " None. I thought so at one time, but now I have a whole arm." (Stein, 1936.)

We come now to the vexed question as to whether disorders of the body-image can be regarded as the expression of focal disease of the brain : whether in other words there exists in such cases a lesion capable of being " localized ". The problem is far from simple.

Turning for a moment to the allied matter of Anton's syndrome—or anosognosia for blindness—one finds that discussion is still possible as to whether or not this is a focal disorder. Anton certainly believed so, while Redlich and Bonvicini regarded the clinical state of unawareness of blindness as dependent upon diffuse changes not capable of localization.

In the matter of Babinski's type of anosognosia, we are still uncertain. Many writers, such as for instance Sandifer, have drawn attention to intellectual disorders, presumably the expression of diffuse disease. Where such occur, then, he believed, anosognosia may result from lesions at any level. But most writers upon the subject of anosognosia for hemiplegia, as well as allied disorders of the body-image, have approached the matter as a focal cerebral manifestation. The majority of cases certainly point to lesions of the subordinate cerebral hemisphere ; and by going thus far, one is already admitting a localization of a sort. On the other hand, Hoff and Pötzl were able to produce experimentally anosognosia of either limb by freezing the centralateral parietal cortex in patients with skull defects— whether on the right side or the left—who had been injected previously with atophanol. Many neurologists too have not hesitated to go further in the matter of localization, and to ascribe anosognosia to affections of the deep portions of the right parietal lobe.

The evidence needs closer scrutiny, however. To begin with, it is probably going too far to insist that the lesion must be deeply situated. A few records point clearly to a relatively superficial type of pathology. Thus, Halloran's case (1946) concerned a subdural haematoma. One or two have been instances of cortical atrophy. One of the most striking examples of unilateral neglect was found to have a surprisingly small area of atrophy in the opposite parietal lobe (see Fig. 109). Most writers have commented upon the frequent coexistence of sensory changes, an association which some would regard as integral. Indeed, where phenomena like supernumerary phantom limbs are concerned the sensory loss often entails a profound impairment of postural sensibility. Brouwer, however, did not consider that sensory changes were necessarily present in cases of anosognosia. His opinion is a minority one, and it is probable that sensory disorders of some kind are demonstrable in every case where the body-image is gravely affected. The sensory changes may be of such a nature, of course, as to escape notice in perfunctory testing.

Pötzl (1924) was inclined to believe that lesions of the thalamus were significant in the production of this type of disorder. Schuster, as well as van Bogaert, agreed. There are many case-records, however, where thorough pathological examination failed to find any direct involvement of the thalamus. In some of these cases, it would be difficult to inculpate even a pressure effect or distance effect upon the thalamus.

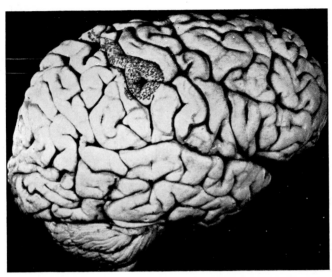

Fig. 109. Right hemisphere. The dotted area indicates the only region where cortical atrophy could be demonstrated. During life the patient showed a striking degree of left-sided active and passive neglect, with tactile and visual inattention. (Case No. 24949.)

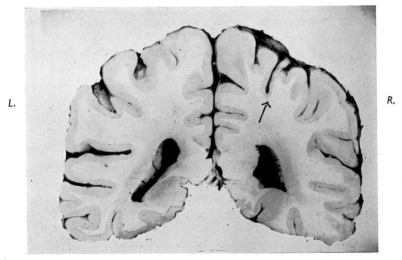

Fig. 110. Coronal section of same brain showing slight degree of cortical atrophy in the depths of a parietal sulcus on the right side.

The main anatomical theories upon this problem therefore comprise the following :

(1) that anosognosia is the consequence of diffuse lesions of the brain ;

(2) that it is the expression of disease of the subordinate parietal lobe, without specifying any particular region ;

(3) that it results from disease of the thalamus of the subordinate hemisphere (Schuster) ;

(4) that it is due to lesions of the thalamo-parietal peduncle within the subordinate hemisphere (Barkmann ; Hagen and Ives). Nielsen would specify a lesion of the thalamo-supramarginal fibres ;

(5) that it is the result of coincidental lesions of the parietal lobe and of the thalamus of the subordinate half of the brain (Pötzl) ; and

(6) that it is the consequence of a lesion of the callosal fibres (Hauptmann).

In addition to these conflicting viewpoints, we also recall that Juba believed that somatoparaphrenia, or that phenomenon which he preferred to call personification anosognosia, was to be ascribed to bilateral lesions of the parietal lobe. For the interesting combination of apraxia with an anosognosia for hemiplegia, we have the contention that a lesion of the visuo-striate band is at fault, so as to constitute an " interparietal syndrome ".

In addition to the foregoing localizationist, " static " or materialist modes of looking at the problem, attention must be paid to a more organismic approach. Reluctance to admit the existence of disease, is, of course, a not uncommon psychological attitude in such people and need not necessarily be regarded as a deviation from normality. According to Goldstein, it is part of the natural process of what he called " the drive to self-actualization ". In organic brain disease there may occur a wide diversity of reaction towards the clinical manifestations. Unwillingness to admit the presence of a hemiplegia may be looked upon merely as an item in the total situation. A tendency to minimize key symptoms, to gloss them over, or to elaborate other non-essential and rather trivial complaints, is often noted when taking a clinical history from the patient. The facts of incontinence of urine and faeces are particularly significant here. In organic cases of brain disease, the patient will almost certainly not have volunteered this symptom, or he may have denied it if directly questioned on that point. When incontinence occurs in hospital, the patient may appear perplexed : or protest that it was nothing to do with him.

Plate 7

JEAN LHERMITTE

Possibly, he may grudgingly admit that the bed seems to be a little damp. Or he may even blame others—whether patients, doctors or nurses—for the soiled bedclothes. Phenomena of these various kinds are particularly common immediately after the operations of leucotomy and of frontal lobectomy. Weinstein and Kahn (1950) have given many striking examples of this sort in a valuable discussion of a series of patients with organic brain disease. Their patients showed such anosognosic defects—in the wide sense of the word— as unawareness or even denial of incontinence, sexual impotence, hemiplegia whether right- or left-sided, vomiting, blindness, involuntary movements and loss of memory. Some seemed not to recognize the fact that they had recently undergone an operation, or that they were in any way ill. The self-evident signs and circumstances of illness were explained away in various fashions, and the same patient in the course of a single short interview may offer diverse and quite inconsistent excuses, which often blatantly contradict each other. There are several types of confabulation. The patient may deny altogether being ill and explain his presence in hospital by claiming that he worked there. Secondly, the patient may claim to have carried out actions which he could not possibly have done. Thus, a bedridden patient may say he had been for a walk : a blind patient may assert he had just visited a cinema or read the newspapers. Or, thirdly, the patient may confabulate so as to over-compensate for an unsatisfactory life-situation.

Disorientation for place was common in their series. Some of the patients in hospital spoke as though they were staying in a hotel : or they would perhaps modify the name of the hospital in an euphemistic fashion. Thus, one patient affirmed he was in the Mount Sinai " restaurant " (instead of " Hospital "). Temporal disorientation was very common. Changes in affect were striking, many showing euphoria and others a sort of " gallows humour ", referring, for example, to an operation for " acoustic aroma ". Another spoke of being in the " Mount Cyanide Hospital ".

Weinstein and Kahn's cases were all instances of organic brain disease, chiefly tumour, though not necessarily involving the parietal lobes. The authors were satisfied that the phenomena of imperception for, or denial of, disease could not be put down to defective memory ; nor to impaired judgment which indeed might be quite adequate in other spheres.

In three of their patients where the anosognosia disappeared, Weinstein and Kahn were able to restore this symptom temporarily by an intravenous injection of sodium amytal.

There is clinical evidence therefore for looking much more broadly upon the problem of anosognosia than has been usual. Anosognosia of hemiplegia, as Babinski described it, and the various elaborations which have been mentioned, may well be regarded as merely an aspect of a common tendency of sick people—and of patients with cerebral disease in particular—to try and disregard, or to repress, or to make light of, some of the uncomfortable circumstances of their illness. Viewed in this way, it seems scarcely necessary to try and pinpoint a lesion to a particular region of the brain, and to regard such focal disease as all-important. One appreciates the attitude of Sandifer in concluding that, when intellectual impairment occurs, anosognosia may develop with cerebral lesions at various levels. *At the same time, it would be vain to ignore the evidence of cerebral pathology that lesions in certain regions of the brain are more likely to be associated with the clinical symptom of anosognosia than are lesions elsewhere. In this respect, the parietal lobe of the non-dominant hemisphere would obviously be identified as the locus which comes most frequently under suspicion.* To particularize further is not justifiable, it is submitted : that is to say, to discriminate between superficial and deep lesions, or to try and narrow down the lesion to a particular gyrus, or subcortical region.

In striking contrast to the cases of organic regression of disease, with anosodiaphoria and anosognosia, are the rare cases where an expanding lesion of the parietal lobe brings in its train a steadily progressive disability, and with it an unconscionable reactive depression. This must be admitted as an unusual sequel. One suspects an exaggeration of a premorbid trait of personality. The following case-reports are illuminating in this respect :

A male patient of 56 years gave radiological evidence of a bronchial carcinoma. He came under neurological care because of a clumsiness of the left hand. When first examined, he had a striking neglect of the whole left side, associated with only a minor degree of motor weakness. He was admitted to hospital a few days later, but by this time the picture had changed. From left-sided disregard he had changed to a state of over-awareness—or hyperschematia. He kept referring to his left arm as " a piece of dead meat " or " a lump of lead ". Indeed, these phrases were reiterated so often that they began to take on the quality of a verbigeration. His motor disability increased and he steadily developed an intense depression with ideas of a nihilistic character.

The previous personality had been one of an obsessional preoccupation with his exceptional physical powers. He had been a professional boxer and had achieved a Dominion championship in his class. The contrast between his former fitness and his present disability constituted a problem to which he was quite unable to adjust. (Case No. 34673.)

A male patient of 56 was admitted to hospital with evidence of cerebral involvement after a bronchial carcinoma, presumably left-sided in this case.

His early signs comprised merely a very mild Gerstmann syndrome. This was followed by unusual tactile disorders (inattention, alloaesthesia, tactile illusions). Shortly afterwards, he became spatially confused and displayed a constructional apraxia at first only for three-dimensional structures. By this time, he had become deeply depressed and agitated. He continually asserted that his " mind had gone " and that he felt " like nothing on earth ". This latter expression amounted to a virtual verbal stereotypy. Later still, he became drowsy and confused and it was only then that his depression receded.

In this case, there were no notable traits in his pre-morbid personality which could offer an obvious explanation for the extreme degree of reactive depression which he developed. (Case No. 36459.)

CHAPTER IX

VISUAL DEFECTS

Harpasten, uxoris meae fatuam scis hereditarium onus in domo mea remansisse . . . Haec fatua subito desiit videre. Incredibilem rem tibi narro, sed veram : nescit esse se calcam. Subinde paedagogum suum rogat ut migret. Ait domum tenebricosam esse.

(You know Harpaste, my wife's female clown ; she has remained in my house, a burden incurred from a legacy . . . Now this silly woman suddenly became blind. The story sounds incredible, but I assure you that it is true. She does not know that she is blind. She keeps asking the attendant to change her quarters ; she says that her apartments are too dark.)

SENECA. *Ad Lucilium Epistulae Morales.* No. L.

Τοὺς δὲ καὶ λήθη ἐλάμβανε τὸ παραυτίκα ἀναστάντας τῶν πάντων ὁμοίως καὶ ἠγνόησαν σφᾶς τε αὐτοὺς καὶ τοὺς ἐπιτηδείους.

ΘΟΥΚΥΔΙΔΟΥ Β. 49.

((In some cases) the sufferers were attacked immediately after recovery (from the plague) by loss of memory, which extended to every object alike, so that they failed to recognize either themselves or their friends.)

THUCYDIDES, Book II, XLIX.

The optic radiations (geniculostriate bundle of Gratiolet) as they stream backwards from the external geniculate body, flatten and splay out in a vertical direction, and become distorted by the temporal horn of the ventricle. In this way, they bend first forwards and then backwards so as to constitute the Flechsig-Meyer loop. During most of their course, the radiations occupy the white matter of the temporal lobe, converging again in a vertical dimension as they approach their end-stations in the upper and lower lips of the calcarine fissure (area striata). The optic radiations therefore lie mainly outside the confines of the parietal lobe, though the white matter subjacent to the angular gyrus comes quite close to the uppermost fibres of the radiations. Although strictly speaking, they lie largely outside the province of the parietal lobe, one can imagine the importance of the contiguous parts of the other lobes, i.e. the temporoparietal and the occipitoparietal regions. This is the border territory which used to be spoken of loosely as the visuo-psychic association area, and lesions hereabouts are generally combined clinically with manifold visual phenomena of a most interesting and complex kind. Pathological processes within the brain naturally do not respect the artificial frontiers erected by anatomists who delimit cerebral lobes. Tumours, injuries, softenings, when occurring in this region, may be followed by clinical signs referable to the temporal and occipital areas as well as the parietal lobe. Shock effects, or diaschisis, still further extend the sphere of clinical disorder. Once again, an argument arises for speaking of a temporoparieto-occipital complex, or of the "hindbrain", as contrasted with those cerebral regions which lie in front of the central sulcus.

A description of the clinical disorders of vision resulting from disease of the parietal lobe, or of this temporoparieto-occipital complex is a matter of peculiar difficulty. There are many reasons why this should be so. In the first place, the clinical phenomena are most diverse, and often far from static. The physical signs are difficult to identify, and they are often equivocal, lending themselves to more than one interpretation. Rarely does the patient himself assist the examiner, for as will be discussed later in more detail, there may be a discrepancy between subjective disorder and objective defect. Purely clinical test-procedures may not reveal the whole extent of the disability, and special instrumental techniques may be needed.

An understanding of central disorders of vision is further complicated by the issue of the sidedness of the lesion. Cerebral dominance enters the problem to some extent. But quite apart from the question of whether the lesion is right- or left-sided is the observation that bilateral disorders of vision may entail more than a mere arithmetical doubling of the effects of a unilateral lesion.

Finally, it must be admitted that the literature upon the subject of central disorders of vision is recondite and difficult to evaluate.

To assist in studying these disorders, a logical schema would be highly desirable. So far no satisfactory classification exists, and it

	Bilateral lesions	*Unilateral lesions*
Most posterior (occipital)	Blindness ; tubular vision ;	Hemianopia Hemianopia with macular sparing
	Colour agnosia Object agnosia Two dimensional visual agnosia	Hemidyschromatopia Agnosia for one half of the extra-personal space
Temporoparieto-occipital	Visuo-spatial agnosia Prosopagnosia Metamorphopsia Visual disorientation	Dyslexia Homonymous visual disorientation
Most anterior	Defect of revisualization De-realization	Visual inattention Constructional apraxia

is difficult to avoid the complicating problem of bilateral versus unilateral lesions. The above table attempts to display the possible
types of clinical disorder, set out according to the proximity of the
lesion to the calcarine cortex.

Central blindness (cortical blindness)

The cerebral lesion responsible for total loss of sight is usually
bilaterally situated and comprises a destruction either of the calcarine
cortex on both sides, or else of the optic radiations. In most cases,
the lesion is ischaemic and consists in a thrombosis of the basilar
artery, or of both posterior cerebral arteries, or less often of both
anterior choroidal arteries. Neoplastic disease would require
bilateral tumours, or else a solitary growth invading both hemispheres. Symmetrical degeneration of the white matter of the
occipital lobes, as in Schilder's disease or in the disseminated intracerebral sclerosis of Foix and Chavany, may also produce blindness
of central type. Trauma, in the way of through-and-through penetrating wounds, can produce extensive bilateral visual field defects,
but total blindness is uncommon.

The outstanding clinical feature is a loss of vision which may be
sudden in onset (as with a basilar thrombosis); or gradual; or
developing in two separate stages (i.e. a vascular thrombosis causing
a hemianopia, followed later by an occlusion of a vessel in the opposite hemisphere). No abnormality is detectable in the ophthalmo-
scopic appearance of the optic disc. The pupillary light-reflex
mechanism will be intact, but there may be difficulty in getting the
patient to co-operate with a convergence-accommodation movement-
complex. The pupils are at times dilated. Photophobia is not
uncommon. Automatic blinking of the eyelids in response to a
threatening gesture will not be demonstrable : nor the phenomenon
of optic (optokinetic) nystagmus.

The outstanding feature of the case, however, will be the patient's
psychological reaction. He may seem not to be aware of his blindness, or at any rate, he may not spontaneously complain of it. As
Lhermitte said . . . " le malade est aveugle même pour son cécité
. . ." Or the patient may admit it as if with reluctance when
directly taxed upon that score. On the other hand, he may deny
the fact altogether and protest that he can see, and he may go on to
describe in a confabulatory fashion objects and persons around him ;
or to speak of imaginary walks he has taken or visits he has paid at
a time when actually bedridden. Other patients again, perhaps
spontaneously, complain of a minor disturbance of vision, or admit
to some falling-off in visual acuity when a direct question is put to

them, but the patient's understatement of his disability does not correspond with the complete nature of the defect. The victim often goes further, and rationalizes his defect by complaining about his spectacles or the poor lighting in the room. The patient may assert that the lamp has not been lit, that the blinds are drawn, or that he is being nursed in a cellar. Frequently, the patient tries to get out of bed and dress in order to return to his business or profession. He boldly walks about, making no effort to feel for obstacles or to grope his way around the room, in marked contrast with the behaviour of one whose blindness is due to ocular disease.

This imperfect awareness of the disability (or even denial of blindness) is usually described comprehensively, and thereby loosely, without distinction as to the precise psychological mechanisms. Although Babinski's term " anosognosia " is usually restricted to a non-realization of the existence of a hemiplegia, it really applies etymologically to lack of awareness of disease of any kind. The most usual term, however, is " Anton's syndrome ", for in 1899 Anton recorded an instance of cerebral blindness where the patient seemed not to recognize the fact of his blindness. (Anton's second patient had cerebral deafness, with no insight into the existence of the defective hearing, and hence " Anton's syndrome " could equally well apply to unawareness of deafness.) Few realize that this pheno-menon was first described nearly 2,000 years ago by Seneca, as quoted at the head of the chapter. (Montaigne's translation may also be given : . . . " This foolish woman hath sodainly lost her sight. I report a strange thing, but yet very true ; she will not believe she is blind ; and urgeth her keeper uncessantly to lead her, saying still, my house is very dark.") *Pari passu* with this defective realiza-tion of the blind state, the patient may often display a condition of apathy (*Indolenz*), wherein he seems resigned or indifferent to his affliction. The patient may even be euphoric. Memory of visual impressions is often lost, though not always so ; this symptom is not necessarily continuous, but may be intermittent. Again, the patient may be unable to recall the colour of common objects (" amnestic colour-blindness "). It is doubtful whether these disorders can rightly be attributed to focal disease, or whether they should not be regarded rather as aphasic manifestations depending upon a general reduction of cerebral activity. The memory of spatial or topo-graphical concepts may be faulty, so that the patient may be unable to describe the arrangement of the furniture in a familiar room ; or he may fail to grasp the relationship in space of one object to another.

The foregoing description applies to the most severe disorder of vision arising from cerebral disease. Some return of function may slowly follow an abrupt onset of blindness, and interesting states of partial restoration of function may be discerned. At other times, however, the responsible pathological lesion does not destroy every constituent of the radiations and cortex, so that vision may remain intact in some sectors at any rate. Redlich and Bonvicini (1908) grouped these varieties of partial amaurosis under the following headings : (1) complete blindness initially, with a return of central vision at a later date ; (2) bilateral hemianopia with macular vision retained ; (3) bilateral hemianopia with the retention of macular vision and also of some degree of peripheral vision ; (4) bilateral hemianopia with the persistence of some slight degree of peripheral vision only ; (5) bilateral hemianopia followed later by complete restoration of vision for light but with a persistent loss of colour sense ; (6) cases with partial return of the fields of vision for light, with a permanent loss of colour-sense ; (7) severe visual defect following a double-sided hemianopia. To these varieties, an eighth might be added : (8) cases of transient complete blindness, clearing up except for a homonymous hemianopia.

(1) *Complete blindness, with a subsequent return of central vision*

In this group, the patient, after a preliminary stage of total amaurosis lasting a few hours or days, regains central vision. Such cases are not quite so frequent as those of permanent blindness ; in 1907, Redlich and Bonvicini were able to collect thirteen examples from the literature. In some instances (Bramwell), the blindness was sudden and was not preceded by a homonymous hemianopia ; at other times, as in Meyer's case (1900), there was definite proof of an antecedent hemianopic defect. Raymond, Lejonne and Galezowski's patient (1906) was totally blind except for two or three occasions when some central vision temporarily returned. The opposite condition may occur, however ; that is, macular vision may be present at the onset of the illness, later giving way to a state of total blindness (Anton ; Probst, 1901). Most of such examples belong to the group of cerebral arteriosclerosis, though the same phenomenon of initial complete blindness with subsequent return of central vision may follow head injuries (Marie and Chatelin, 1916).

(2) *Bilateral hemianopia with retention of macular vision*

The commonest clinical type of double-sided hemianopia is exemplified by those cases where macular vision is retained ; in such, there is no antecedent phase of amaurosis, the patient developing immediately a permanent tubular or pinhole vision. Not only is this the most frequent manifestation of bilateral disorder, but it is the most characteristic. The final defect is easily represented by the association of two hemianopic fields, each with its little hemi-spherical sector of intact sight at the fixation point.

The visual handicap varies in degree from case to case ; in some patients, visual acuity at the fixation point is definitely impaired ; at times, there is a central achromatopsia. Usually, there are obvious associated disorders of spatial orientation and of visual memory. Other patients again (e.g. Bramwell's patient) survive for years with pinhole vision of normal acuity and with full recognition of colours and no defect of orientation or of visual imagery. Such patients can apparently recognize objects and read.

Tubular vision has been described in cases of bilateral neoplasms, and also with softening in the two occipital lobes. It has also followed through and through wounds of the skull (Lister and Holmes (1916), Case 20).

(3) *Bilateral hemianopia with retention of macular vision and also of some degree of peripheral vision*

This is less common than the other types of case, though Redlich and Bonvicini in 1907 were able to quote six cases from the literature. In such instances, the quality of macular vision may be relatively good, in contrast with the impaired acuity in the peripheral parts of the field. Beyond the fixation point, large objects may be discerned but dimly ; at times, movements only can be appreciated. As a rule, recognition of colours is impossible except with the macular fibres. Peripheral vision may not be present from the commence-ment of symptoms, but may develop only during the stage of recovery. In such cases, it may be possible to demonstrate from day to day a progressively increasing field, starting from near the fixation point and extending outwards in a spiral fashion. This has been exemplified in cases of cranial trauma, whether the injury be closed (Kinnier Wilson, 1917) or penetrating (Eisdell Moor, 1915).

(4) *Bilateral hemianopia with persistence of some slight degree of peripheral vision only*

This is a still rarer type of cerebral visual defect : Redlich and Bonvicini could collect only five such cases. Riddoch's fifth case (1917) exemplifies this variety : a soldier, wounded by shrapnel in the occiput, became completely blind. Fourteen weeks later, he said he saw " something moving on his right ", which proved to be his wife's shadow on the wall. Testing showed that he could distinguish between light and darkness. He could detect movements of fingers in the outer part of the periphery of the right superior quadrants.

Stationary objects, form and colour were not perceived. Seven months later, the vision was found to be unchanged.

In some instances, there is a marked improvement in peripheral vision which contrasts with the more permanent defects of a scotomatous type. This is specially seen in cases of sudden injury to the head as in gunshot wounds. (See Holmes and Lister, Case 9; Riddoch, Case 7.) Riddoch's sixth patient lost his sight immediately after being wounded. Two days later, sight returned to the right half-fields, leaving a left-sided homonymous hemianopia. Four months after the original injury, vision began to return in the periphery of the left fields. This continued to improve, but a paracentral scotoma below the fixation point remained as a permanent defect.

(5) *Bilateral hemianopia with eventual restoration of vision for form, but with a persistent loss of colour sense*

This is an even more uncommon manifestation of cortical disease (Alexander, Steppan).

(6) *Partial return of the visual field for form, but with permanent loss of colour sense* is also rare (Boys de Loury, Quaglino).

(7) *Severe visual defect following bilateral hemianopia*

In such cases, there is no true blindness, but a gross reduction of visual acuity is uniformly distributed over the whole field (Fürstner, Therriberry, Uhthoff).

(8) *Transient total blindness followed by a unilateral homonymous hemianopia*

Abrupt lesions of the posterior region of the brain, especially of traumatic nature, not infrequently produce a state of blindness. This phenomenon may also follow an acute cerebrovascular accident (Monakow; Vorster), or it be associated with tumour (Bruns). After a time, vision may be restored in one homonymous half-field.

This phenomenon was well shown in my patient, a man of 53 years, a known hypertensive of unconventional and somewhat hysterical personality, who suddenly lost his sight. Everything went quite dark. Greatly agitated, he was conveyed the same day to hospital by ambulance. He presented himself as a bewildered and intensely anxious blinded individual. His eyelids blinked with unusual frequency; his head was craned forward and turned constantly from side to side. He stretched out his arms gropingly before him. The clinical picture was that of a case of hysterical blindness. When he recognized the voice of the lady doctor, he became highly emotional, and kissed her hand with every expression of relief. Put to bed, he was examined with greater deliberation. He continued to move his head from one side to another and to blink excessively. When large moving objects were displayed before his face, it became obvious that he had a left homonymous hemianopia. In his right fields, however, he began to discern large moving stimuli. A little later, he began to detect comparatively small objects, even at a distance, though overlooking other visual stimuli which were brighter, nearer and of greater luminosity. He would notice small details across the ward, and yet miss others ; he was also unable to synthesize visual stimuli to form a logical whole. Thus, he picked out the black collar to the yellow dress worn by the lady doctor, and also the black piping around her pocket, but he did not notice the much larger and brighter visual target offered by the dress itself. Next day, his vision had improved still more—especially when wearing dark glasses—and he could identify colours even when the target was small. The hemianopia persisted to the left, and optokinetic nystagmus, though present on anti-clockwise rotation, was absent in the other direction.

It was obvious that a vascular accident had occurred, causing a hemianopia. The nature of the initial blindness is, however, problematical, and it cannot be stated dogmatically whether this was a manifestation of hysteria or of diaschisis. (Case No. 27743.)

Other examples of this kind can be cited from the literature in the cases recorded by Marie and Chatelin of war wounds of the head. The period of complete blindness was here a matter varying from some hours to days. In the Lister-Holmes series, cases 3, 4, 8, 11 and 12 may be quoted. Riddoch's case 6 is also of this nature.

The cause of such a phenomenon is conjectural. It is conceivable that a simple anatomopathological explanation might be adduced, and that in the early stages there may be bilaterally situated lesions. Thus, a neoplasm in the hind part of one hemisphere may be associated with much oedema or distortion of the opposite half of the brain. Trauma to the cranium may produce extensive bruising, but an irreversible type of necrosis in one hemisphere only. In arteriopathic cases, a thrombus or embolism blocking the basilar artery at its point of bifurcation may cause a temporary bilateral ischaemia of the visual areas. At a later date, however, a canalization or partial organization of the clot permits a restoration of bloodflow through one posterior cerebral artery, while the corresponding vessel of the other side remains permanently occluded.

Hemianopia

With unilateral lesions of the posterior half of the brain, a quantitative visual loss in the opposite homonymous half-fields constitutes a physical sign of considerable importance. In such cases, there is a tendency for the fixation point to be spared, and this feature is often used as an argument for differentiating a hemianopia due to a posteriorly situated lesion, from one due to an affection of the optic tract. In these posteriorly-sited cases, particularly when the lesion lies in the temporoparietal region rather than in the occipital lobe, the hemianopia is often incongruous, and there is no accurate bisection of the visual field into two regions according to whether visual function is intact or not.

When the parietal lobe is concerned in the production of a hemianopia, the lesion is usually postero-inferior in situation, and the angular gyrus in particular comes under suspicion. Consequently, there may be other clinical features which are usually regarded as the result of destruction of the cortex and subcortex of the angular gyrus (dyslexia, and Gerstmann's syndrome, in the case of the dominant hemisphere).

In cases of hemianopia from posterior lesions, the defect is a quantitative one, and function is usually ablated in the affected sectors. That is to say, the loss of vision is as a rule absolute, and objects are either seen or not seen, depending upon their position within the sectors. Questions of luminosity, colour, magnitude, movement, familiarity and attention are ineffectual in comparison with the simple fact of whether the test object lies entirely within the blind field or not.

In special circumstances, some degree of vision may be possible even within the homonymous blind-fields. This observation, if amply confirmed, would have important theoretical bearings upon the physiology of central disorders of vision. By using small luminous targets as visual stimuli, and by carrying out their perimetric testing in a dark room, Bender and Krieger (1951) have found that there may be some preservation of vision in the hemianopic field. Gradual illumination of the background would cause the target to disappear. Obviously, it is important to be able to exclude diffusion of the light stimulus from the target into the functioning parts of the retina. This phenomenon has also been demonstrated by I. Martin (1952), in the case of a patient with a right homonymous hemianopia due to a head injury. After this test had been carried out, the patient volunteered that he had previously noticed, while lying in bed at night, that he could detect a street lamp in the middle distance within his blind field. If the light in the bedroom was shining, he could not detect the street lamp.

Several points require discussion in connection with the visuo-psychological concomitants of a hemianopia, considerations which are of special interest in so far as other parietal " functions " are concerned. First comes the question of awareness or non-awareness of the hemianopia. Clinical experience teaches that individuals vary in this respect : on the one hand, there is the patient who realizes all too keenly that vision has been lost to one side . . . that " objects are longitudinally cut in two ". By way of complete contrast are those patients who make no complaint about their sight whatsoever, but in whom a complete homonymous hemianopia is found in the course of methodical testing.

Few would claim that the explanation of these contrasting experiences is fully understood. Scrutiny of a large series of cases of hemianopia studied from the standpoint of the patients' awareness brings to light certain suggestive features : (1) By and large, awareness of a field loss is commoner with an anteriorly situated lesion (e.g. one involving the optic tract). This tendency shows itself best when one recalls the obtrusiveness of field defects occasioned by such purely retinal lesions as detachment, trauma or glaucoma. *Per contra*, in cortical lesions, and with disease of the radiations, the patient is more often oblivious of the hemianopia. (2) The degree of abruptness in the onset of the hemianopia may play a role, even though it be a relatively minor one and inconstant. Thus, an expanding lesion of the radiations might be expected to cause less subjective visual complaint, than say an acute affection of traumatic or ischaemic nature. (3) The state of the patient's general intelligence must obviously be considered. No very helpful data emerge, however, for awareness or non-awareness does not seem to correlate well with confusion or mental obfuscation. (4) Nor is there any reliable association with multiplicity of defects. In other words, hemianopia when existing alone does not necessarily obtrude itself upon the patient's awareness to a greater extent, or more often, than when it is accompanied by other outfall symptoms, e.g. paresis, impaired sensibility, loss of speech. (5) The integrity of macular vision may perhaps be significant. Certainly unawareness of a hemianopia seems to occur more often when central vision is spared, as might be expected. This may be due to a relative neglect of the disordered peripheral vision. On the other hand, the factor of macular sparing may simply represent another link in a chain of circumstances which also includes the degree of insight. Both phenomena may be at the same time related to some other causal or fundamental factor. (6) There is reason for believing that incongruous hemianopias are more often perceived by the patient than are congruous ones ; in the same way, quadrantic defects may perhaps be more likely to enter the patient's awareness than are pure hemianopic losses. (7) No clearcut correlation exists between the sidedness of the hemianopia and the degree of awareness, for field defects either to the right or to the left may escape notice or may be realized, to the same extent. Some qualification of this statement is necessary, however. When the hemianopic patient first tries to read, he may find greater awkwardness with a right homonymous hemianopia than with a left ; due, it is generally said, to the dextrad style of writing, and the inability to discern the words in advance. (Presumably in the case of Arabic or Hebrew readers, the rule would apply the other way.) There are weak points, however, both in the explanation and in the evidence. In the first place, many patients with a right hemianopia also have a dyslexia, and finding it difficult, if not impossible to read, give up the attempt without realizing that there actually is a field defect. Secondly, the patient—assuming he is not dyslexic—may learn to surmount the obstacle of a right hemianopia, by unconsciously making small-range lateral movements of the eyes. In other words, he may read and still be unaware of his hemianopia. Then again, it is arguable that even if the act of reading is mechanically hindered more by a right than by a left hemianopia, the opposite holds true for the act of writing. Moreover, a patient with a left hemianopia may experience difficulties in finding the start of the succeeding line, having reached the end of the first line. (To overcome this difficulty, Belz's patient adopted the trick of turning the page through a right angle, so that he would now read in a vertical direction. I. Martin's patient also hit upon the same dodge of reading vertically, but in his case, the hemianopia was right-sided.)

The clinical and anatomical circumstances are obviously complex and imperfectly understood. Similar difficulties surround the meaning of the term " awareness " in this connection. Just as Anton's syndrome was found on analysis to be much more complicated than at first imagined, so it must be admitted that in the hemianopias there are degrees of awareness. It is not just a matter of insight or lack of insight. The patient may realize only too well that he has some visual defect, but he may not understand its nature, and in any event, it may not incommode him. While some patients may be totally oblivious of any visual trouble, others may be dimly aware of impaired function, which they may perhaps misinterpret. The hemianopic patient may declare, or he may admit on direct questioning, that his sight is " misty ", or that it is " not as good as it was ". Or he may refer the visual symptoms to one eye only—a not uncommon clinical experience. Even more characteristic is the phenomenon of projection, whereby the defect is ascribed to some outside source. The patient may attribute his poor sight to the inadequate lighting of the room ; or to his glasses which he says " no longer suit him".

In this matter of insight, we can therefore identify various degrees of awareness (Critchley, 1949) :

(a) Total lack of awareness of a visual defect (a phenomenon which occurs in about a quarter of all patients with a homonymous hemianopia). Some

Plate 8

OTTO PÖTZL

of these patients will even go to the length of denying the visual defect after it has been demonstrated to them ;

(b) Unawareness of the defect itself, but a recognition of its consequences. Thus, the patient may complain that he is apt to bump into persons or objects on one side, without knowing why ;

(c) Realization that the environment is but dimly seen, but the disability is projected, i.e. is rationalized as being due to dim lighting (as in the case of bilateral parieto-occipital disease with Anton's syndrome) ;

(d) Realization that there is something wrong with the vision, though the nature of the trouble is not understood, nor can it be described ;

(e) Awareness of a visual defect to one side, misinterpreted as a disorder of vision in one eye ; and

(f) Full awareness of the hemianopia.

Even this last-named, rare though it be, is not a uniform phenomenon, for degrees of visual disability may be observed. There are " positive hemianopias " and " negative hemianopias ". With the former, the patient who gazes at an object may see it bisected, with one half obscured as if by an overhanging veil. This may be spoken of as a " black hemianopia ", and is only rarely encountered with posteriorly sited cerebral lesions. Or, the veil may be of more neutral tint—the so-called " grey hemianopia ", also unusual in parieto-occipital disease. Commoner, is the negative hemianopia where on the blind side there is an impression not of a veil, but merely of something missing (the *hémianopsie nulle* of Dufour). Still rarer is that type of hemianopia which becomes apparent only in the dark when it shows up as a homonymous luminosity (Brickner). This phenomenon might perhaps be called a " white hemianopia " or *hémianopsie lumineuse*.

In reviewing the problem of impaired insight into the existence of hemianopia, it is tempting to relate it to Anton's syndrome and to regard it as a sort of onesided manifestation of that phenomenon. Furthermore, it seems justifiable to recall other instances of unilateral neglect or disregard, so characteristic of cerebral disease and particularly of parietal lesions. Mention has already been made of unawareness of hemianaesthesia ; and of unilateral motility neglect. Particularly significant here is Babinski's anosognosia, with its unawareness, or even denial of, the existence of a hemiplegia, possibly coupled with other unusual disorders of the body-image.

Macular sparing. The question why central vision should be so often retained in cases of hemianopia due to most posteriorly situated lesions scarcely falls within the scope of a study of the parietal lobes. Any discussion of cerebral function must nevertheless take cognizance of the viewpoint that macular sparing is really an artificial manifestation if not indeed an artefact, and that it is due to a functional shift of fixation towards the blind side in an unconscious effort to extend the area of normal function. Verhoeff considered that the fixation point shifts with posteriorly situated lesions only, on the basis of a hypothetical cortical centre of fixation which is of necessity involved when the lesion happens to involve the optic tract, or the most anterior part of the radiations. This conception also ties up with the opinions of Fuchs (1920) to the effect that patients with cerebral disease are apt to utilize a retinal point slightly eccentric to the natural fixation point. A re-distribution of energy occurs in the intact portions of the fields about a new functional centre of brightest vision. In this way, a " pseudo-fovea " develops close to the old fovea. The former is activated in ordinary circumstances, the eyes being open and the patient gazing ahead. But for attentive scrutiny of a near-point in space, the old fovea is once again made use of by the patient.

One should discuss at this juncture how far a hemianopia necessarily entails a spatial imperception within the homonymous half-fields. Certain hemianopic patients adapt themselves in a satisfactory manner to the handicap of a restricted field. They come to realize that the visual sphere extends in an asymmetrical fashion to the right and left of an imaginary vertical line bisecting their fixation point. They contrive to avoid obstacles lying within their blind field in the same way as a normal person rarely collides with objects outside his vision, when he steps backwards or sideways. By tilting the head to one side ; by making frequent though unconscious horizontal sweeping movements with the head and eyes, the dark regions of the hemianopic field are constantly being explored. More accurately, the intact fields are continually being transferred across the midline so as to compensate for the blind field. In this way, the patient adjusts himself to the ordinary tasks of daily life ; examining his mirrored reflection in order to shave, brush his hair or fasten his tie ; looking at a page of print ; walking through a crowd of people ; writing, drawing, ciphering ; even riding a bicycle or driving a car. This degree of adjustment is probably best seen in patients with good insight into their disability, whose lesions are probably situated far forward within the visual apparatus.

In contrast to such a case is the hemianopic patient, probably with very imperfect awareness of his disability, who bumps into objects, and who finds difficulty in exploring visual space, both two-dimensional (as in a mirror, or in a picture) and three-dimensional around him. One of Gowers' patients consistently left the potatoes uneaten on his dinner-plate, for they lay unnoticed within the blind half of his vision. Such patients do not necessarily display an actual imperception for external space to the one side, although many of them do. (It must be emphasized that imperception for space really means an imperception for the objects contained within space, and not for a true Euclidean conception.) Axenfeld's partition test (i.e. bisecting a horizontal straight line) is often " positive ", in that the patient's estimation of the midpoint is displaced to the side of the intact visual field. This does not necessarily mean an imperception for that portion of the line which occupies the blind field ; a positive finding may or may not indicate a spatial imperception. More suggestive than Axenfeld's test are some of the drawings made by a patient with parietal disease. Thus, when directed to draw an object which is symmetrical in shape, e.g. a daisy head or a clock-face ; or even such an incongruous shape as a map of England, the patient may demonstrate certain suggestive errors. Thus, on the hemianopic side, the patient may omit certain details. For example, when the head of a daisy is drawn, petals may be put in on one side only. A map of England sketched by the patient may show defects, errors or incompletions on either the east coast or the west.

Two explanations of such defects are possible : the figure may be unfinished because one half of it lies within the blind field. This plausible idea is not altogether satisfying. A hemianopic patient, otherwise normal, might be expected to realize the symmetry of a clock-face and a daisy head, and to take pains to complete the elusive details lying to the blind side of the fixation point. By turning the head and eyes—" transporting the macula "—he would be expected to bring the two sides of the drawing into view. Incompleteness should, it might be thought, lead to a sense of dissatisfaction, and the hemianopic patient ought to continue his efforts until he has achieved a suitable representation of his intact mental image.

An alternative interpretation is that the visual defect is associated with a neglect, disregard, or forgetfulness of that half of space which subtends the hemianopic field. In other words, the patient has an imperception for the objects contained within extrapersonal space on one or other side of a vertical midline. The abnormal drawings already described may be put in as supporting evidence. Other clinical tests may confirm this idea. In writing a letter, the patient may leave blank an inordinately wide margin, either on the left or on the right-hand side of the page. If the patient is shown pictures or diagrams or symbols with the regularity of its shape broken up by unexpected gaps or excrescences lying within the blind field, he may not notice them, but goes on to describe the figures as symmetrical. Gaps are filled in, and the added details are missed. Other methods of demonstrating an extrapersonal spatial imperception include a maze test. A more natural test-situation is afforded when the patient is told to cross a room in which chairs and tables stand about as obstacles. He will tend to bump into those on his blind side. Even more impressive is his behaviour when confronted with a series of doorways : he tends to neglect those doors or passages located within the blind field, and to choose those upon which his gaze rests. A patient of Kalanova, who was an orchestral conductor, returned to his work prematurely after a right parietal vascular lesion. It was obvious to all that, not only was he using the right upper limb only while conducting, but he was also entirely neglecting all the musicians who were seated on his left.

Extra-personal spatial imperception is more often witnessed as a left-sided phenomenon. This statement suggests that imperception is not mere epiphenomenon of hemianopia, otherwise patients with a right homonymous hemianopia would display this spatial imperception equally often.

Restoration of function after central blindness, as well as after a hemianopia, is a phenomenon which is difficult, interesting, and still obscure. Not enough cases of regressant cerebral disease have been studied with sufficient thoroughness to warrant firm conclusions. It can be stated, however, that vision returns in a fashion which can be regarded as qualitative as well as quantitative. The latter comprises a gradual shrinkage of the blind field. Vision may return from the periphery inwards ; or from the fovea outwards ; or from a combination of these two. Much depends upon the precise anatomical localization of the lesion. Those parts of the field which correspond with the least affected parts of the cortex or radiations might be expected to recover first ; while the sectors corresponding with the site of maximum damage recover last, if at all. Clinical experience with traumatic cases shows that recovery usually proceeds from the centre outwards to the periphery (Hines). Less often, the reverse is encountered (Riddoch). In the case of scotomata, the recovery is generally from the periphery inwards, whereby the scotoma shrinks. Upper quadrants usually recover before the lower in traumatic cases, perhaps because the causative impact is more likely to have come from above downwards. The returning vision cannot, however, be regarded as qualitatively normal. First comes a completely ill-defined impression, a vague "organ sensation" as it has been called. "As recovery progresses, an elementary light-dark sensation appears on retinal stimulation, at first in dark adaptation to disappear in bright

illumination. This is the most primitive sensory visual function—
a vague formless sentiency with no analysable attributes, a sensation
of brightness, subjectively confusing and even vaguely painful,
objectively appearing as a diffuse irregular lightening of the visual
field, without differentiation or localization and without qualitative
or quantitative relation to the position, extensity or intensity of the
stimulating light " (Duke-Elder).

These qualitative disorders of vision may be discussed
at greater length. The early stages of returning function are
understood better in cases of cortical blindness, and have been
less carefully and less often studied in the recovering hemianopias ; but there is no reason to doubt that the steps are the
same.

Of objective test stimuli, small foci of bright light are first sensed.
Later still, they may be sensed and vaguely localized. The presence
of large moving objects can now be detected. Gradually, smaller
sized objects are sensed, and objects of lesser luminosity ; movement
no longer becomes essential. Later still, there is a recognition of
form, a more accurate localization, and a progressive improvement
in the visual acuity. The identification of white is restored long
before that of colours ; the recognition and discrimination of tints
and shades is very late in appearance. As a transient feature during
the recovery process, there may occur various illusory phenomena,
such as apparent alterations in the size, shape or orientation of objects.
These various kinds of metamorphopsia are to be discussed later. A
medley of defects can be discerned here, comprising a raised threshold
of vision, a dyschromatopsia, appreciation of movement before form,
defective localization, altered stroboscopic and tachistoscopic findings,
reduction in flicker-fusion values, and numerous others. Certain
authors, notably Parsons, have chosen to regard this stage as one of
dissociation between two separate qualities of vision, differing in
phylogenetic age and in complexity. Inspired by the novel ideas upon
sensation which had recently been put forward by Head, Parsons
spoke of " scotopic " or " dyscritic " vision, which he believed was
subserved by the rods. He imagined that it was concerned with
crude differences in luminosity, and a vague perception of form,
colour and contour. A more recent and complex form was
" photopic " or " epicritic " vision, and he considered it to be subserved by the cones. This variety he believed to be concerned with
the accurate perception of luminosity, form, colour ; the perception
of depth ; the perception of movement and its distinction from the
appearance of stationary objects viewed when in movement. The
phenomena observed during the restoration of function after central

T

lesions illustrates, he believed, a temporary dissociation between the two types of vision.

Riddoch emphasized the return of the ability to detect a moving stimulus before a stationary one and he regarded this phenomenon as illustrating a dissociation between a cruder and more primitive function (perception of movement) and a finer and more recent one (perception of form). Although Riddoch's observation of the facts has been amply confirmed, his interpretation has been criticized. Thus, it has been pointed out that the perception of movement is the normal function of the extramacular portions of the retina. As James said, the main function of the peripheral parts of the retina is to serve as sentinels, which, when beams of light move over them, cry " Who goes there?", and call the fovea to the spot. Moreover, dissociation of the perception of moving from that of stationary stimuli occurs, as Holmes has emphasized, not only with central lesions, but also in disease of the peripheral visual apparatus. Thus, in affections of the retina, lens or optic nerves, visual acuity may be reduced to an appreciation of large moving objects which escape notice so long as they are immobile. Lastly, Parsons pointed out that the recognition of movement, far from being a primitive function, is a relatively complex one, entailing an elaborate synthesis of discrete pictures and their differentiation from immobile objects viewed when the subject is moving. Under certain pathological states, this function of synthesis may be lost so that moving objects are no longer seen as such, but as a chain of intercepted polyopic images.

Further consideration of these qualitative, so-called scotopic, visual anomalies will be undertaken at a later stage, when their relationship to the so-called agnosic defect will be undertaken.

The subject of hemianopia should not be left without referring to what Gowers used to call " crossed amblyopia ". As the consequence of a lesion of one angular gyrus, Gowers believed that it was usual to find a severe field defect in the contralateral eye (involving not only the temporal field but also a large proportion of the nasal field). In the ipsilateral eye, there again is found—he claimed—a field defect of lesser magnitude, and in its distribution conforming more to the pattern of a peripheral constriction. Gowers believed that the angular gyrus in each hemisphere constituted a " higher visual centre ", and that it was concerned with bilateral ocular function, but more especially with the fields of the opposite eye. It is not easy to see the basis of this conception of Gowers, and in retrospect, it seems possible that his patients were really suffering from bilaterally placed lesions, with a partial restoration of function according to the pattern cited by Monakow, Vorster, Bruns, Marie and Chatelin, Holmes and Lister, and Riddoch. Gowers was alive to the fact that in space-occupying lesions, a complicating field defect may be due to optic neuritis. Ferrier too was of the opinion that destruction of the angular gyrus would bring about blindness in the opposite eye.

Colour-agnosia ;   achromatopsia ;   hemidyschromatopsia
(Lewandowsky ; Sittig)

It is doubtful whether colour sense can be altered in cerebral lesions without some corresponding disturbance in the appreciation of form. The two modalities of visual dysfunction may coexist as the result of cerebral disease. Colour defect may be restricted to one homonymous half-field, or it may be universally distributed. In the latter case, the responsible brain lesion may be confined to one hemisphere, usually the dominant hemisphere. There may not necessarily be any visual field defect, though in cases of recovery from blindness or hemianopia a small residual defect of absolute nature may be associated with a large field within which there is imperfect appreciation of colour. Colour vision may be more severely affected than perception of black and white in cases of hemi-anopia, and while the latter defect may show a macular sparing, the colour dysfunction may split the macula (Bender and Kanzer, 1939).

The dyschromatopsia may be so complete that the patient is unable to discriminate tone values, that is, the various shades between black and white. In other cases, only certain colours are confused. In Wilbrand's " amnesic colour-blindness " the incapacity is not so much one in identifying colours, or in sorting colours, but rather in supplying the names. Hence, it is more a language defect, an asym-boly, than a disorder in the perception of tints and hues (Lewan-dowsky, 1908 ; Sittig). The patient may achieve his object by means of periphrasis, using such circumlocutions as " grass-colour " instead of " green ", or " like the sky ", meaning " blue ". The substitution of a more concrete attitude is to be noted here.

Undoubtedly, the possible colour defects of cerebral origin are clinically most diverse. There are patients who are aware of different colours but who cannot distinguish them. Some patients see and recognize colours, but only apart from the attendant object, so that the colour seems spread over on a flat surface independently (Gelb). A patient may recognize the various colours in the spectrum only if they are exposed for short periods. With longer exposures, the colours seem to fade into a monochromatic neutral hue (Stein). The term *faiblesse chromatique* applies to a defect where there is no actual colour-agnosia but merely a delay in the time taken before the colour becomes identified (Kries, Guttman and Nagel). An artist, quoted by Holmes (1945), no longer was able to use colours after he had sustained a stroke. He was not colour-blind, however, for he could name most colours and pick out colours correctly to command. When tested, however, with Holmgren's wools, he could not sort colours, that is, pick out the various shades of say red or green. He could not associate colours with objects except by reference to rote memory.

As with so many cerebral disorders, the patient with acquired colour-agnosia, achromatopsia, or amnesic colour-blindness may not spontaneously complain of his disability. He may apparently be unaware of the incapacity ; or indeed, he may deny the fact when questioned.

Quite often other agnosic, apraxic or aphasic symptoms accompany defects of colour appreciation. Spatial disorientation is especially frequent. The coexistence of Gerstmann's syndrome and colour-agnosia may well be more than an accidental association. What fundamental disorder underlies the colour defects and the elements of the Gerstmann syndrome cannot yet be said. It seems unlikely that association merely arises from propinquity of the responsible cerebral lesions.

Whether central colour defects possess a localizing value, whereby the lesion can be narrowed down to a circumscribed area of the brain, is still debated. Gonzalo would not admit of any anatomical specificity, though there are many others who would attempt to do so. Regions that have been suspected in this connection, comprise the second and third occipital convolutions, and first temporal convolution and the angular gyrus.

Visual agnosia ; object agnosia

Our ideas upon this complex subject took origin in an unusual manner, in that they emanated from an experimental physiological laboratory. In 1877, Munk asserted that dogs, after their occipital lobes had been extirpated, continued to see and to avoid obstacles, though apparently they did not recognize the nature of objects before them. As far as could be judged by their behaviour, the animals seemed indifferent to various stimuli—meat, food, fire, whip. They did not recognize their master. Munk attributed these symptoms to a loss of the visual imagery of previous perceptions. His term for this defect was *Seelenblindheit*, an expression which has been translated as " psychic blindness " or " mind blindness ". He found that if, at a second operation, additional parts of the cortex were removed, adjacent to the cut surfaces, then the dogs would become blind.

Munk's experiments were confirmed by other physiologists, e.g. Vitzou (1893). Subsequent clinical experiences, however, led to a reinterpretation of the visual defect in Munk's dogs. Rather than a loss of visual imagery, a lack of recognition of objects viewed became the traditional explanation. The dogs were then regarded as capable of seeing objects but not recognizing them.

Pursuing further the story of experimental physiology, one comes to the researches of Klüver and Bucy (1937, 1938, 1939, 1940). These authors found that removal of both temporal lobes in adult Rhesus monkeys was followed by no loss in visual acuity or visual localization. Nevertheless, the animals appeared not to recognize the identity of objects or persons, and in such state they betrayed neither fear nor anger. All objects were peered at and examined by putting them into the mouth. Their monkeys also seemed to be unable to recognize objects by the sense of smell. Confronted by a collection of articles, the monkey would pick them up one by one, convey them to the mouth and reject them if not edible. In this manner, a comb, a bakelite knob, a sunflower seed, a screw, a stick, a piece of apple, a live snake, a piece of banana, a live rat, were seized and examined. When tested with a form-board, the monkey would respond in just the same way to the cardboard figures as to the food itself. The creatures also exhibited an almost compulsive tendency to attend to, and react to, every visual stimulus. This phenomenon they called *hypermetamorphosis*.[1]

The experience of clinical neurology has brought to light comparable cases in human subjects afflicted with diffuse cerebral disease or with bilateral parieto-occipital lesions. Even before Munk's experiments, suggestive cases had been recorded by Finkelnburg (1870) and by Gogol (1873). Loss of the ability to re-visualize mental images had been noted by Charcot (1890), and also earlier by Wilbrand (1887). One of the most important early contributions to this subject dates from Lissauer's paper (1890), wherein he hypothecated two clinical types of " mind-blindness " which he spoke of as the (1) apperceptive and (2) associational forms. The terms are unfortunate, but the idea was an attractive one, even

---

[1] The ultimate fate of these animals is interesting. Professor Klüver has been kind enough to tell me that the immediate postoperative symptoms of meat eating and of hypersexuality are the first to disappear. The psychic blindness clears up next, while the hypermetamorphosis and the oral behaviour may persist, though perhaps in modified form, eight to ten years after the operations upon the brain.

though it is probably untenable. Lissauer meant by apperceptive mind-blindness a form of agnosia due to a distortion in the appearance of objects viewed. By associational mind-blindness, he referred to an inability to recognize objects despite the fact that visual acuity is intact; or as might be said, without any defect in the visual analysers. To distinguish rapidly between the two alleged types of mind-blindness, recourse could be had to a simple test, namely, that of getting the patient to draw on paper the object which he sees before him, but which he cannot identify. The patient with associative visual agnosia is said to reproduce an adequate drawing of the object, indicating that the shape and proportions of the object have been sensed; identification remains impossible, however. On the other hand, the patient with apperceptive visual agnosia fails to draw the object he sees.

Although Lissauer's classification has continued to appear in the literature, an undercurrent of dubiety has grown up. The statement is sometimes made that Lissauer's apperceptive type is purely hypothetical, and that it never has been demonstrated beyond question. On the other hand, the famous Gelb-Goldstein case (which will be discussed later) has at times been regarded as an example of apperceptive visual agnosia. Most neurologists have believed that the recorded cases contain elements from each of Lissauer's two types of mind-blindness.

The conception of visual agnosia has also suffered from over-schematization, for certain neurologists have attempted to break down the global defect into a series of subordinate visual agnosic difficulties. It is implied thereby, though not always explicitly stated, that each of these various incomplete varieties can exist in " pure " form. Thus, Teitelbaum has analysed visual agnosia into: object agnosia; pictorial agnosia; symbolic agnosia (which again has been further dissected into verbal, numerical and musical forms); colour agnosia; spatial agnosia; body agnosia; and temporal agnosia. Bodamer has spoken of object agnosia, colour agnosia, verbal agnosia and prosopagnosia (or non-identification of faces). To these may be added such conceptions as that of simultanagnosia (Wolpert); and agnosia for animate as opposed to inanimate things (Nielsen and Sanborn).

It is one thing to take a complicated psychological disorder and to trace among the intricate warp and woof of the pattern a number of constituent threads. Such a task is interesting and not without value. But it is quite another matter and probably quite unjustifiable to extricate these various components of the whole and to claim for each one a sort of clinical independence. Although certain aspects of visual agnosia may be conspicuous, while other modalities are relatively subordinate, it would be dangerous to claim that a particular visual agnosic defect can occur in isolation. Pure cases of partial and specific visual agnosia suggest both an incompleteness of the clinical study and an ignorance of the intricate modifications in the patient's total behaviour.

Visual (object) agnosia, or mind-blindness, must be admitted as a rarity in clinical practice. The cases are not only uncommon, but they are difficult and tantalizing problems for study, demanding a shrewd evaluation of such factors as quantitative visual defect, disordered mentation and emotional reactive processes. Consequently, the number of cases in the literature, where adequate documentation is available, is relatively small. Of these few, some have been interpreted in more than one manner, indicating that a gross divergence of opinion is possible in the evaluation of the clinical findings.

Chief pitfalls which commonly form the basis for difference of opinion are the following : (1) the amount of visual impairment of a quantitative sort ; or defect in elementary sensory perceptions (restricted visual field, reduction in visual acuity, defective colour-sense, metamorphopsia, and various qualitative visual disorders to be described later) ; (2) the fluctuation in behaviour shown by the patient ; paradoxical answers ; hesitancies or delays ; self-correction ; day to day and moment to moment variations ; variability in performance according to the examiner ; (3) influence of fatigue ; fleeting attentiveness ; the handicap of catastrophic reactions, and the measures taken to avoid such reactions ; (4) the state of mentation ; degree of general mental confusion ; memory-defect ; disorientation ; (5) intactness or otherwise of visual imagery ; (6) the presence or absence of other associated gnosic or praxic defects, and particularly of dysphasia ; (7) the patient's insight into his own disability and his reaction thereto ; anosognosia ; denial of disability ; projection ; confabulation ; (8) the patient's degree of suggestibility ; his reaction to the meticulous and frequently repeated clinical and psychological test-procedures.

Even after repeated testing, exercising the utmost care and detachment, a conscientious observer may still be in doubt as to the fundamental nature of each of the disabilities shown by a patient with visual agnosia. He may never reach a confident assessment of how much disorder is agnosic, how much is due to visual defect, to dementia, and to a hysterical elaboration. The neurologist who is least in doubt in these respects is only too often a victim of over-confidence. An example of this ambiguity of opinion is admirably shown by the well known case described by Stauffenberg (1914), and even better by the case reported by Goldstein and Gelb (1918).

Stauffenberg's case, as quoted by Monakow, and discussed by Head, may be reproduced as an example of a well documented instance of " visual agnosia ", where the complexities are displayed with all the possibilities and opportunities for differences of interpretation.

The patient, a woman, died at the age of 69 of pulmonary tubercle, associated with cerebral atheroma. She had had a series of cerebrovascular accidents. The first one, at the age of 61, caused some defect of vision, as well as slight loss of speech and her eyesight. At 63, she developed a left hemiplegia, hemihypaesthesia and hemianopia. The last of these persisted, though the first two disabilities improved. At 64, she became subject to attacks of headache, mental confusion and increasing left-sided hemiparesis.

She was under medical observation during the last six years of her life, and was studied as a case of visual agnosia. Her intelligence and memory were described as being " fairly good ", but she could not recognize " with certainty " people, objects, or pictures.

A left hemianopia with macular sparing existed throughout the period of medical observation. Her visual acuity was at first diminished but afterwards improved (the exact measurements were not given).

She could see objects, and avoid them when they constituted obstacles in her way, but she could not identify them surely, without recourse to the aid of hearing, touch, smell or taste. At first indeed, she could not identify objects even by touch, but gradually she lost this disability. She could not recognize a sponge held before her until she felt it with her finger. (This phenomenon was clearly shown by accompanying photographs.) She could not recognize a cigar until she put it into her mouth (though why she should have put it in her mouth Stauffenberg did not explain). A spoon was occasionally recognized, less often a knife or a fork. (Why the one should be identified and not the other raises yet another problem which the author did not discuss.) A key, pocket-knife, and wash-basin were not recognized, or at any rate, their use was not described. Nevertheless, after looking for a long time at a watch, she named the numbers correctly and told the time correctly (the paradoxical nature of these responses was not commented upon).

She learned to identify nurses, doctors, and so on, partly by their clothing, partly by their footfalls, and partly by some trick of gesture, movement or method of salutation. If they spoke, they were recognized at once.

At first, colours were matched according to luminosity and not to colour. Later, her performance improved very much, though always erratic, for at times she would make gross errors.

It was expressly mentioned that her performance with regard to objects, their recognition and their utilization, was most variable. There were days when she scarcely recognized a single article by sight ; on other days, she did well. She was suggestible ; for it was easy to get her to say a sponge was a brush—while at other times, she would deny this vigorously. She would generally employ objects correctly, and better in automatic activities than to command. Her powers of learning were defective : having discovered the nature of an object with the help of touch, she failed to identify the object when it was again shown her.

Sometimes, she could describe the use of an article shown her, but not its name (she had a slight difficulty in finding words) unless it was put in her hand. Shown scissors, she said : ". . . please give them to me, otherwise I don't know them ; you use them when you sew . . ."

Her writing was defective and her powers of reading extremely poor. She did spontaneous drawings reluctantly and badly. She copied a simple drawing with great difficulty and many errors.

At first, she could not find her way about the hospital or ward. After a month, she had learned to do so, though on occasions she made gross mistakes. When, a year later, she returned to hospital, she had not forgotten which was her former bed, and she recognized the passages outside.

After this patient's death from tuberculosis, anatomical examination of her brain showed an extensive softening of both occipital lobes more especially on the right side. In addition, her right temporal lobe was destroyed as well as the second and third temporal convolutions of the left side. The splenium and anterior commissure were degenerated.

In considering this classic example of what would appear to be a characteristic case of visual agnosia, one should note the following :

(1) Visual analysers were defective, in that poor vision (of indeterminate nature and degree) was coupled with a left homonymous hemianopia ;

(2) Her intelligence and memory were only " fairly good " ;

(3) There was a relative spatial disorientation, with a fair degree of re-learning and retention ;

(4) There was a colour-defect, severe at first, later improving but rendering her still liable to unexpected and severe errors ;

(5) There was a naming disability ; and a defect of writing as well as of reading ;

(6) Some degree of apraxia was probably present ;

(7) There was a suggestion of visual perseveration, as noted by Critchley (1950) ;

(8) Performance varied from one occasion to another ;

(9) There was a variability in performance from one test-object to another. Thus, after having failed to recognize (or to state the purpose of) an object as large as a wash-basin or a sponge, she was able to pick out the figures on a watch and to read the time correctly ;

(10) Slowness in visual recognition was noted on the occasions when her replies were correct.

In view of the clinical complexities in this case, it would be unsafe to look upon the visual agnosia here as a specific or clear-cut defect which can be studied in isolation from the other visual and psychological disorders. Stauffenberg, on the basis of his own case, made the generalization that mind-blindness is a symptom which can never exist alone, and that it is always associated with permanent or transitory defects of a higher order, such as those of memory, intelligence, speech, etc. This complex, he said, forms a "syndrome" and is never a pure and isolated loss of function. It is difficult to take exception to this statement of Stauffenberg's.

Goldstein and Gelb's patient, originally reported in 1918, was *Schn.*, a soldier of 24, with a wound in the occipital region. The visual fields in both eyes became markedly constricted. The visual acuity is a matter of doubt, being recorded on one occasion as 6/6, 6/6, and on another as 5/10, 5/15. At first, everything seemed colourless. He could not read letters, except by tracing the outlines with his finger-tip. By making similar outlining movements of the head and eyes, he was able to recognize simple geometrical shapes. With short tachistoscopic exposures, identification was not possible. Nor could he recognize geometrical shapes outlined by dots. There was a simultanagnosia for pictorial scenes in that he identified details, but not the picture as a whole. There was a micropsia, especially in a horizontal dimension. Commonplace objects were recognized promptly. Complicated, unfamiliar, unexpected objects—or objects viewed from an unusual angle or in a strange setting—caused much difficulty. He used roundabout clues to assist identification. This was well shown with a pack of cards : the ten was recognized by dint of the many spots ; clubs were distinguished from spades because they were " slightly brighter ". A moving object seemed to be broken down to a succession of linear stills : it would be described as " now here . . . now there ". There was a defect of revisualization of images especially of letters. Spontaneous drawing was far above the average, though copying of objects and pictures was difficult and depended upon tracing-movements of the head. Persons were often not recognized : on one occasion, he passed his girl friend in the street, an incident which led to the breaking-off of his engagement.[1]

Goldstein and Gelb looked upon their patient as an example (and indeed, one of the few recorded cases) of Lissauer's apperceptive mind-blindness. They considered the defect lay in the formation of total (including primitive) Gestalten, in the sense employed by Ehrenfels.

Subsequent writers held other views. Kleist (1922) regarded the disability in this case as perceptive and not agnosic in type. Poppelreuter (1923) also believed that this was not an instance of mind-blindness, but of a peculiar visual defect. Pötzl (1928) accepted Goldstein and Gelb's explanation, though with some reservations. Quensel (1931) and Lange (1936) doubted the reliability of much of

---

[1] In collaboration with Steinfeld, Goldstein recorded at a later date details of the unusual sexual comportment of *Schn.*, with special reference to his intimate relations with the woman he subsequently married.

Schn.'s evidence. Russell Brain (1941) agreed with Poppelreuter in suspecting a disorder of the " primary phase " of visual perception, i.e. awareness of visual sense-data. He believed that the visual field defect rendered it difficult for the patient to view the whole of a geometrical figure or a picture at once. In the case of common objects, he would be able to deduce the whole from the part which he could see.

Goldstein (1943) defended his original thesis. He maintained that his patient had " only a slight constriction of the field ". During the next years, the visual field extended but the recognition of objects in no way improved. Goldstein repeated the tests of Poppelreuter of gazing at objects through a tube, but came to a quite different conclusion. He denied that his patient was ever able to trace an object with his hand alone. Hand movements were always supplementary to movements of the head. Goldstein affirmed that his patient did not recognize common objects by sight alone, but only by conclusions based on some visual experiences and on tracing movements. He succeeded better at guessing the identity of common objects than geometrical shapes.

Goldstein tried to clarify his conception of the patient's defect. He regarded it as an impairment of that step in the process of perception and recognition where gestalt formation takes place. No sharp division occurs between the process of perception and recognition ; there is a gradual transition from a more simple event to a more complicated one. Goldstein would prefer to call his patient's defect not so much an agnosia as a *Gestaltblindheit* . . . a " disturbance of visual recognition due to a defect in the perceptual sphere concerning the step of gestalt formation ".

The subsequent career of the famous patient *Schn.* is of interest. In 1922, he was studied, at Gelb's suggestion, by Benary, who found severe disorders in calculation and intellectual performance. Conceptions of number and of quantity were defective. Benary implicated a disturbance of " simultaneous surveying " (*Ueberschauen*)—an idea which Goldstein and Gelb had specifically considered but rejected. Mäki in 1928 studied *Schn.'s* ability to draw. Hochheimer (1932) also ascribed the disability to an impairment of simultaneous surveying. The patient *Schn.*, after his discharge from the army with a 70 per cent pension, married, and set up a food shop in 1931. Owing to war conditions and to his wife's illness, he sold this business in November, 1943. In 1944, the patient came under the care of Bay, Lauenstein and Cibis, who later published their findings and conclusions. The patient's subjective visual state had not materially changed. He said that he remained bereft of visual images. Colour vision was still abnormal. Frequently, he failed to recognize people's faces. Testing of the visual fields now showed an incomplete bitemporal hemianopia. His everyday life was not conspicuously abnormal in any way, and contrasted with his deportment in the clinic. The authors concluded that *Schn.* was quite unreliable in his statements, which were full of inaccuracies and contradictions. They doubted whether he had really lost the power of revisualization ; of the perception of movement. In their opinion, the injury had probably involved the optic chiasma. No symptoms of mind-blindness could be found. The authors hinted that the complicated visual picture had developed only after years of repeated psychological examinations. Though not an hysteric in the accepted sense of the word, *Schn.* showed an unusual obligingness and readiness to help. After long training, he had attained a virtuosity which he still displayed twenty years later.

Also in 1949, the case of *Schn.* was rewritten by Jung, though his study of the patient had taken place in 1942, that is, just before Bay *et al.* Jung too was certain that many of the manifestations were the result of suggestion, and of too close and too many examinations. He made the acid comment that, had the patient originally been examined by a psychotherapist (instead of by a brain pathologist and a gestalt psychologist), then there might have been both a different interpretation and also a different outcome.

The latest news of this notorious patient is that at the present time (1952), he is a Bürgermeister in a small town in South Germany.[1]

Heidenhain's patient (1927) had a visual acuity reduced to one-fifth, together with an upper right homonymous field defect. Colour vision was markedly disturbed. The patient could not understand the things he saw, though he recognized differences in size, shading and configuration. He drew surprisingly well even though he might not recognize the object he was drawing. He could not read. He could find his way about familiar streets but not in localities which were strange to him. He could not recognize people, not even old friends. His visual imagery seemed to be good except for colours. At autopsy, there was found a lesion of both occipital lobes, though the pole of the left hemisphere escaped. The basal surface of the occipital lobes as well as the third occipital lobe, and the gyri lingualis and fusiformis were involved.

Comparatively few cases of restoration of vision after its total loss through cerebral disease have been fully documented. Consequently, Adler's case-record (1944, 1950) is of great value, in that the visual agnosia occurred in a young and intelligent subject, and followed an initial period of blindness.

The young woman concerned was a victim of the Boston Cocoanut Grove disaster. She received only superficial burns, but was presumably overcome by carbon monoxide fumes. On her immediate admission to hospital, it was found that she could not see (as she afterwards said . . . " everything seemed dark "). For the first two weeks, she was delirious, excited and

---

[1] Prof. Leonhard kindly informs me (December, 1952) that *Schn.* is now working in the ticket office of a railway station, having resigned his appointment as Bürgermeister.

talkative, showing marked iterations in her speech. After two days, she detected large white objects, actually the uniforms of the nurses and sisters. Her vision gradually improved, but it was found that she could not fix her gaze, and that she could not identify objects, pictures, persons or colours. Although able to write, she could not read. Nor could she calculate. Her condition improved over the ensuing six months, and then seemed to reach a standstill. Adler was able to study her progress, and the nature of the disability. The superficial impression she gave was that of a normal person, but her family were aware of certain incongruous behaviour at home. At first, she got into a muddle when dressing. Twice, she fell down a flight of steps. Difficulty in reading hindered her cooking for she could not understand the labels. Sewing proved too difficult. When doing her laundry, she would overlook soiled parts. Ironing was successful as far as small articles of simple shape (handkerchiefs, towels), but with more complicated garments (e.g. a blouse) she would omit sections altogether. When using a vacuum cleaner, she did not complete the job. Crossing a busy street was hazardous, because she would ignore approaching cars. She seemed constantly in doubt as to the time of the day. She could not manage her money affairs, spending all her allowance at once on trivial things.

This degree of betterment had been attained largely by dint of employing detours, and roundabout methods of performing a task. Special senses were utilized to compensate for visual defects. She would trace the outlines of a letter with her finger-tip ; or she might succeed in recognizing a letter because of its outstanding characteristics—confusing unfamiliar letters, e.g. " q " and " z ". By a process of combining, anticipating and guessing, she made a readjustment to her disability.

It was not easy in this case to estimate the condition of the visual acuity, but by recourse to a method of counting dots at various distances, it was considered that her acuity was normal. The visual fields, carried out with some difficulty, proved to be full, though slightly restricted in the right lower quadrant for colours.

Five years later, the patient was re-examined. Though her general efficiency had greatly improved, the same type of defect could still be demonstrated. The basic trouble was an inability to perceive the whole, but only parts. She often had recourse to guesswork, which sometimes lead to errors. If given enough time, she could now recognize an object. Her errors were greater when judging an object from a distance. She could not recognize patterns, which were made up of curves, owing to an inability to predict the whole from details. Reading of print was much improved (she had mastered *A Tree Grows in Brooklyn* in the course of three months), but handwriting remained difficult for her to interpret. Coloured pictures were promptly recognized, and also those with contrasts in black and white : she found it impossible to disentangle superimposed line drawings. Playing cards were identified in her own way, and she often won at poker or bridge. People were recognized except at a distance or in crowds. An incomplete variety of Gerstmann's syndrome was still present.

Obviously from the foregoing remarks, uncertainty still exists over the nature of some of the classical cases of visual agnosia. The same may indeed be said as to the status of the disability itself. Some neurologists doubt the actual existence of a visual agnosia at all. Difficulty in recognizing objects by sight alone has been ascribed merely to a complex disorder of the visual analysers, whereby objects are not perceived clearly in the first place. One of the earliest to adopt this attitude was Siemerling (1890), who believed he could produce an artificial visual agnosia in normal subjects by altering the optical properties of the environment. Siemerling placed himself and a colleague in a room illuminated by a sodium lamp. This had the effect of reducing all colours to a uniform and unnatural monochrome. Next, the subjects were given lenses to wear strong enough to reduce the visual acuity to $1/30$. The result was that the testees were unable to recognize the surrounding objects which they could still discern imperfectly ; but they at once identified the objects when they touched them, or employed some other sense-modality. (This test may by reason of its constant conditions not accurately mirror the disability in gnosic patients, where fluctuation of accomplishment so often occurs.) Poppelreuter also suspected, though Goldstein would not agree, that visual defects were significant in the production of visual agnosia, and he suspected that the tubular fields of patients with bi-occipital lesions made recognition difficult. In particular, it became hard for the patient to identify a large object, although he could perhaps pick out small items of the whole object. This is a defect which is analogous to the simultanagnosia which Wolpert described in picture recognition, and which might here be looked upon as a sort of visual object simultanagnosia, as opposed to an aphasic or semantic disability. The same handicap has been noted in patients with extremely narrowed visual fields when they endeavour to peer at the faces of bystanders, and Stollreiter-Butzon (1950) has found this symptom in glaucomatous subjects.

Besides poor visual acuity, dyschromatopsia, and restricted visual fields, the peripheral vision may be further upset by various metamorphopsias. Thus, apparent movement of stationary objects, especially if irregular in rhythm, may contribute much towards failure to recognize the nature of surrounding objects. Micropsia, macropsia, teleopsia, crooked vision, any or all of these may be cerebrally determined and may play a very important role in rendering identification difficult.

The intact visual field may be further disordered by defects which lie outside the patient's awareness, but which none the less produce what is really a very limited " effective visual field ". Thus, a multiplicity of surrounding objects may make it more difficult for the patient to identify any single one of them (though he can do so if the others are " blocked out " artificially). There may be a delay in the visual reaction time (capable of being measured tachistoscopically). Local adaptation of vision may be much altered, so that central vision deteriorates to the level of peripheral vision. There may be a reduction in the rate of flicker fusion. There may even be an apraxic defect of ocular fixation so that the patient cannot direct his gaze accurately, or turn easily from one object to another. Lastly, questions of visual attention play an important part in determining the eventual difficulty in recognizing objects within the environment.

But as Jung has picturesquely objected, a myopic patient who takes off his glasses and looks around him, is scarcely a victim of visual object agnosia. He sees things blurred in outline it is true, but he usually identifies them without much difficulty. To this criticism, it may be said that this is partly because the myopic patient has none of the numerous other defects within the visual analysers (impaired colour-sense, metamorphopsia, restricted fields, qualitative visual defects, disorders of fixation and of visual attention). There is yet another and a very important factor, namely, intelligence. The ability to seize and utilize visual clues, to come to shrewd judgments thereupon, to call upon the storehouse of past visual experiences and visual imagery, to adapt to altered circumstances, all these are high-level aptitudes which lie within the capacity of normal but myopic subjects and they assist him to identify the objects he discerns so imperfectly. He utilizes, in other words, what Birkmayer called the " critical detail " of surrounding objects, and from one or two fragmentary sense data, he comes to a correct perceptual assessment.

According to Bay (1948, 1950, 1952), there is no such entity as visual agnosia. What is usually called visual agnosia is really compounded of the primary sensory defect, complicated by a demential state of greater or lesser degree. Objects are seen imperfectly and assessed inadequately. Bay's viewpoint was ably and eloquently argued at a discussion devoted to this subject in the South-West German Neurological Society. His views were debated at some length by Vogel, Scheller, Faust, Jung, Conrad and others. No unanimity was arrived at, and obviously the subject is still one which can be hotly argued. It is tempting to state none the less that the traditional conception of " agnosia " is one which is being drastically modified, if, indeed, it is not already in the process of being rejected altogether. In all probability, the term " agnosia " will eventually be as discarded from the vocabulary of perception as " aphemia " has been in the domain of language.

Can it be that a veritable visual object agnosia may exist, even though a great rarity, and a more complex condition than suspected ? In so far as visual object agnosia seems to imply a bilateral cerebral lesion—and there is no great anatomical evidence to the contrary [1] —there must necessarily be present considerable loss of available cerebral tissue, a basic visual defect, and almost certainly an organic dementia of some degree. Thus, it seems uncontrovertible that Stauffenberg's dictum was a correct one and that mind-blindness cannot exist independently of some disorder at a still higher level. This would suggest that no sharp distinction exists between agnosia and Faust's pseudo-agnosia (that is a condition where object-recognition is imperfect by reason of intellectual debility).

Is there a legitimate analogy in the tactile sphere ? As already discussed, the ability to identify an object by touch alone may be lost in many different circumstances. There may be defect of tactile analysers at a peripheral level, or at a cerebral level. In the latter case, the defect may be subtle, discriminative, and associational in type, not easily demonstrated unless specially looked for, though none the less present. So far, an analogy with visual agnosia is tempting. In the tactile sphere, there may be an ability to describe the size, shape and physical properties of the object, but an inability to recognize it. This tactile agnosia (without amorphognosia or ahylognosia) is comparable with the so-called Lissauer's associational mind-blindness. As already described, the ability to identify an object in an anaesthetic or hypoaesthetic hand may be mimicked by merely wearing a glove. In such cases, the normal subject may perhaps succeed in eventually identifying an object held in his gloved hand, partly by virtue of the bulk or mass or peculiar shape of the test-object, but mainly by utilizing the " critical details " of the object at the highest intellectual level. There will be a difference therefore between the performance put up in the gloved-hand test, according to the intelligence and the experience of the subject. Here too, lies an analogy between the tactile and the visual spheres. Two striking differences obtain, however, which render the analogy between astereognosis and visual agnosia incomplete. Astereognosis is ordinarily a unilateral defect, so that the patient who cannot name an object placed in one hand as a rule succeeds when the object is held in the other. At once a comparison is possible between the two limbs, and one is able to evaluate the " intellectual " role of the patient's ability or failure to identify objects by touch alone. In the second place, astereognosis (tactile agnosia) is ordinarily produced by a unilateral lesion, and by a relatively small and circumscribed lesion. It follows, therefore, that organic dementia, and other disorders of an aphasic, apraxic, or agnosic character, need not necessarily coexist.

The arguments for the hypothetical existence of a pure tactile agnosia are therefore more powerful than for a pure visual agnosia.

Bay would seem almost to be contradicting his earlier views by the publication at a later date (1952) of a genuine case of visual agnosia. In this patient, there was no disturbance of mentation,

[1] It is sometimes said that a unilateral lesion can be followed by a visual agnosia, if the splenium of the corpus callosum happens to be involved. Lotmar's case-report (1938) does not produce any convincing argument to the contrary.

and the traditional sense-physiological examination revealed no abnormality. Special testing, however, brought to light a definite visual *Funktionswandel*, as Bay called it, or what we might term a qualitative disturbance of vision. Though subtle, this impairment apparently was sufficient to produce an inability to recognize objects and faces. Because of its peculiar importance, this case deserves a detailed recording :

A 60-year-old man, almost blind in his right eye from an old injury, woke from a sleep unable to find his clothes, though they lay ready for him close by. As soon as his wife put the garments into his hands, he recognized them, and dressed himself correctly and went out. In the streets, he found he could not recognize people—not even his own daughter. He could see things, but not tell what they were. As he walked, leaning on his wife's arm, he veered to the left. He was taken immediately to an eye specialist and straightway admitted to hospital.

He was found to be hypertensive (B.P. 200/120). For the first few days, he was at times lost for a word, but this symptom quickly disappeared. The first neurological examination revealed a doubtful right extensor plantar response, which soon became flexor. Psychologically, he was completely clear and normally orientated. His rather deliberate reactions were put down to his ordinary rustic clumsiness. Intelligence was rather above average. He responded well to Lange's questionnaire. His mood was initially one of mild depression.

The vision in the damaged right eye was reduced to 2/50. In the left eye, the vision was regarded as normal, i.e. 5/4 (there were initial difficulties in testing him as he could not interpret letters, and he tended to round off the angles of the letters seen). The visual field seemed to be full for moving white objects ; a colour-naming defect interfered with the testing of the colour field.

There was a severe object-agnosia. ". . . One of the purest cases so far described in the literature." Of large objects, he recognized only a bottle of wine. A bunch of flowers was not recognized, though he identified the vase which held them. He wrote, but could not read.

More intimate visual testing then brought to light other disabilities. In a dimly lit environment, a sector defect was found in the visual field, especially for coloured objects, and for immobile white targets. An upper right quadrantic hemianopia was demonstrated by campimetry. Tachisto-scopically exposed pictures were identified only after abnormally long periods of time.

The patient's own description of his vision was interesting. At first, he said he saw everything correctly. Later, he admitted that he could see only the outlines of faces and bodies, and these were not clear. They seemed lighter and clearer on the left, and darker, mistier and smaller on the right. Though he could see the contrasting black upon white of a notice-board, he overlooked the copper name-plate on the brown wall of the specialist's house. Lines of print on Snellen's test-types seemed wavy ; the letters flickered, and kept changing in size. Colours were particularly difficult to distinguish.

Bay concluded that the syndrome of visual agnosia, which was

U

singularly pure, was caused solely by the particularly severe pathological change-in-function in the visual system. He went on to say
that this explanation of agnosia does not apply to every case.

Perhaps " visual agnosia " is still a convenient label to attach to
that particular manifestation of disordered visual perception, whereby
the patient as the result of a comparatively large cerebral lesion loses
his power to overcome the handicap of his disordered sense-data.
Objects are imperfectly and perhaps incompletely sensed, and recognition does not take place in the ordinary and expected fashion. This
may show itself in the clinic. The behaviour of the ambulatory
patient with visual agnosia is often characteristic. He enters a room
cautiously and looks around in a peering fashion, with his head craned
forwards and his eyes turning from one side to another. He obviously
does not fixate normally upon any object. If his gaze fastens upon
one point in space, or if it turns in the direction from which an auditory signal proceeds, he does not readily deviate his eyes towards
any fresh stimulus. Should his eyes come to rest upon the leg of a
table, he does not follow it upwards and thence over the surface of
the table-top. Sometimes the patient slowly moves his head from
side to side as he talks, in a manner reminiscent of the " blindisms "
or motor mannerisms of the peripherally blinded.

Should the patient be questioned as to the subjective state of his
vision, he may assert that it is adequate. He will rarely admit, at
this stage at any rate, that his environment is foggy or misty, that
objects are blurred in outline, or devoid of colour or sharpness of
contour ; or that things around him seem to be in movement, or
distorted in shape. But if he is instructed to look at a particular
object in front of him and to name it, he will often put up a characteristic performance. He will find difficulty in sighting the object
and will probably look beyond it, or above it, or to one side. Or he
will peer at it with his eyes deviated far to one side, gazing out of the
corners of his eyes. At this point, he may project his difficulty by
blaming his spectacles. He may proclaim he cannot see clearly without his glasses. When these are found, and have been put on, he may
say that they are his distance glasses and not his reading glasses ; or
vice versa. Or that they are his old pair which he has outgrown ;
or his newest pair to which he has not yet become accustomed. Even
more characteristic is a trick of taking off one pair of glasses, putting
on another, and then taking these off. Also very typical is the habit
whereby the patient holds up one hand before his eyes, as if shading
them from the sun, or cutting out some of the illumination. When
the hand is posed in this manner his head turns from one side to
another in a searching and bewildered fashion. When asked why

he shades his eyes, he may reply that it " helps his vision ". No doubt this manœuvre assists by cutting down the number of distracting visual objects in the environment.

The patient is now ready to try and name the object before him. At first, this may be difficult or impossible. The patient may make some attempt at describing the physical properties and with that assistance proceed to identify the object in a hesitating, unsure fashion. The next object may, however, be recognized promptly and accurately, but thereafter, further errors occur. Occasionally, after one object has been eventually identified, subsequent objects may receive the same appellation. This defect may be an aphasic one, i.e. a verbal perseveration. Less often, it is an actual visual perseveration, as in the cases of Lissauer, Stauffenberg, Adler and Critchley.

When the object looked at is a large one, i.e. a movable trolley, the patient may slowly identify parts of the object (wheels, leg, blanket, handle) without recognizing the trolley as a whole. This corresponds in the three-dimensional sphere with the simultanagnosia of two-dimensional pictorial representations. The term is, of course, a misnomer, for the process is not necessarily a " simultaneous " one, but may consist in a synthesis or building-up of details so as to form a logical whole.

Although it is commonly taught that the difficulty in recognizing objects is a purely visual problem, this is not always the case. The patient who fails to identify an article before him may also fail to do so when he touches it, though admittedly his performance is a better one within the tactual sphere. Such a combination of defects in gnosis argues strongly in favour of some general defect rather than a circumscribed " pure " disability. This particular finding is an important one, which is apt to be brushed aside, or glossed over (as for example by Stauffenberg).

One should also pay particular attention to that phenomenon whereby the patient with so-called visual agnosia, and who has no aphasia, incorrectly identifies an object as something associated, e.g. he calls a cigarette-lighter a cigarette. Or the patient may mention the use to which the article is put, although unable to name the object itself (e.g. a pair of scissors may be called " for sewing "). If a naming defect can be eliminated, this suggests some defect other than a mere disorder in object-recognition.

Prosopagnosia

But our knowledge of faces is not mathematical. In the first place, it does not begin with the measurement of the parts, it takes as the starting point an expression, a combination of the whole . . . And so, when acquiring a knowledge of faces, we take careful measurements, but as painters, not as surveyors.

PROUST.

. . . Man's Face being composed of so small a number of Parts, as are two Eyes, a Nose, two Cheeks, a Mouth, and a Forehead, which yet Nature hath diversified in so many Compositions and Combinations, that were a Hundred thousand then assembled together, each one has a Countenance, so peculiar and proper to him, that it is a great Wonder, if there appear two that wholly Resemble."

J. HUARTES, *Triall of Wyttes*, 1698.

There have been attempts in recent years to isolate out of the miscellaneous manifestations of visual agnosia a particular variety which concerns the non-identification of the human face. At first sight, this exclusivism of concept is unconvincing : none the less, the thesis has been put forward, and indeed eloquently pleaded, that as the result of bilateral lesions of the hindmost parts of the brain (the exact areas not being named), there may occur an elective disturbance in the recognition of faces, not only of other people but also of oneself as displayed in a mirror. To this alleged deficit, the term " prosopagnosia " has been applied.

Perusal of the literature on the problem of visual agnosia (imperception, asymboly, mind-blindness) reveals that in several cases the patient has been in doubt as to the identity of persons within view ; a doubt often resolved promptly when the bystander speaks. There have also been references to patients who have been at a loss to recognize photographs or portraits of persons who should have been easily identified, in that they depicted well-known individuals, or friends, near relatives or else themselves. Here and there are to be found in the neurological and psychiatric literature accounts of patients who have failed to recognize their own reflection in a looking-glass ; a few, indeed, have declared they could not see any mirror image at all. Study of the literature naturally gives no inkling as to the magnitude or frequency of such phenomena, for the bulk of such cases are never recorded.

We may also refer to a recently described variant of this defect, in which the patient (whose main symptoms consisted in an incomplete Gerstmann's syndrome) could not understand the meaning of facial expressions as expressed pictorially. Recognition of faces and comprehension of facial mimicry were apparently intact (Zeh 1950).

But the conception of a pure and specific prosopagnosia rests upon the demonstration of cases in which lack of recognition of faces constitutes the main agnosic defect ; or at least, stands well in the foreground of the picture of visual agnosia. Such a conception has been built up mainly by Bodamer, though to some extent by Faust, Hoff and Pötzl.

Any such rigidly demarcated impairment obviously seems artificial and unconvincing. Nevertheless, Bodamer's thesis is important and the arguments supporting his contention deserve quotation and scrutiny. His ideas are based upon certain cases in the literature, taken in conjunction with three personally observed instances. The former group includes *inter alia* the patient described by Jossmann, Heidenhain, Charcot, Wilbrand and Wernicke.

All of these are complicated cases in which non-recognition of faces forms a part only of the total picture of imperception. More specific is Hoff and Pötzl's patient, where the defect was so marked and so elective as to suggest a subform of agnosia made up of an imperfect memory for faces.

Bodamer's first patient was a young soldier with a penetrating wound of the occiput. For four days, he was blind, after which he was able to discern fast moving objects of light colour passing before his eyes. Later, his vision improved, but he found he could not appreciate colours ; everything seemed to be in black and white. The acuity of vision measured 5/15, 5/15. There was a considerable reduction in the visual fields. Stereoscopic vision was unimpaired. The patient's ability to visualize and to utilize his visual memory was in no way altered, and included colours. For some weeks, the eyesight was distorted by " irradiation ", in that objects were hazy in their outlines as though adorned with a fringe. There was some defect in the recognition of objects, especially those in daily use. Some other articles (e.g. safety-pin and paper-clip) he did not recognize, although he could draw them. He failed to identify certain unusual objects, the like of which he had never seen since being wounded. The range of objects recognizable on sight gradually increased. Objects rich in characteristic detail proved to be easier. He often succeeded by dint of employing " detours ". He could not synthesize the details in a picture so as to make an intelligible whole (= simultanagnosia). Many difficulties were encountered in the spatial orientation of himself. Thus, he found it impossible to change trains at a railway station ; or to find his way to a seat in the cinema. He wrote easily, although the lines sloped upwards to the right. Reading was difficult, especially at first. Drawing, and copying of designs were normal.

After a while, it was realized by the patient that he had lost the ability to recognize faces, including his own ; to a lesser extent, this defect applied to the muzzles of animals. All faces appeared blank and expressionless. They seemed . . . " strangely flat ; white with very dark eyes, as if in one plane, like white oval plates . . . all the same ". He could see, but not interpret, mimic movements and grimaces. Gazing in a mirror, he described the delineaments of what he saw, but could not recognize the face as his. Together with three other soldiers, he had his photograph taken, but he afterwards failed to recognize his face in the print. The features of his closest relatives, either in snaps or in real life, appeared quite foreign to him. He walked past his mother in the street, and he never got to know the looks of the other patients in the ward. His doctor he knew only by reason of his spectacles : when these were removed, he did not identify him. Ward-sisters were recognized only by their white coats. But he could visualize his relatives and friends quite clearly.

Shown pictures in a book, he made many errors in interpretation. He did not know the face of a very well-known general. A rabbit was recognized by its ears only, but he went on to say that it really looked no different from a man's face. Other animals proved too difficult when shown in pictorial form.

An efficient compensatory faculty developed which doubtless contributed to the protracted unawareness of his defect : he could promptly recognize voices, footfalls, even the individual manner of turning the door-handle. Again, he would utilize such adventitious clues as clothing, eyeglasses, moustaches, hair-styles, and so on, as aids to recognition. At the cinema, he could follow a film only by dint of the sound-track. A simple documentary reel was incomprehensible.

The patient also declared that, when he looked at a face, his attention would become riveted, so to say, on one detail only—usually the eye—from which he had difficulty in shifting his gaze. There were times, too, when he sustained a kind of visual irritation, or fit . . . " the outlines of objects (but only the outlines) would begin to flicker, as if pulsating. Corners, edges, outlines would appear to be alive, as though consisting of fast moving bacilli." Or again . . . " as if coated with luminous paint . . . almost white, as in a fog, or as if behind frosted glass ". This would go on for about ten minutes.

He got into trouble for passing a senior officer without saluting. At that very moment, he had had a visual attack of some sort : ". . . surrounding faces changed, and became snow-white. They no longer looked like faces at all. The eyes became smaller, and, with the mouth and nostrils, pitch black. Faces seemed quite flat."

Bodamer's second patient, originally left-handed but later ambidextrous, was rendered unconscious from a compound fracture of the right fronto-parietal region. Later, he showed a bilateral concentric field defect, with a visual acuity of 6/12, 6/12. There was a left hemiparesis and a hemi-hypaesthesia, together with a transient mixed dysphasia. At first, there was an impairment of visual imagery and memory, but this soon improved. A mild degree of object agnosia was also present for a time, with a more marked simultanagnosia. Colour sense was intact except for a green-blue confusion. Other defects included a geometric visual agnosia ; a right-left disorientation ; a neglect of the left side of the body ; an ideational apraxia of the left arm with a sense of its being foreign to him ; a constructional apraxia ; and slight verbal alexia. He could not visually attend to moving objects. There was an interesting disorder of the sense of time in that everything seemed to move more quickly than normal. Attacks occurred which were reminiscent of a temporary derealization.

The most important finding, however, was an inability to make out persons' faces. In his own words : ". . . apart from the eye, I see the rest of the face as hazy ; I don't see what is characteristic in a face ; I don't see the definite expression of a face. My eye always comes to rest on the most characteristic feature of a face, and in the living person, I find the most characteristic feature to be the eye. When I have seen the eye of a face, I pass on to the other features. But when I look for the special feature in a face, I don't find it." A similar difficulty occurred in the recognition of pictorial representations. Shown a picture of Hitler, he named it by dint of the moustache and the parting in the hair, admitting that he would not have been able to identify the face, which was . . . " just an amorphous mass ". The patient was led into a room where his wife was waiting among a group of nurses : he did not recognize her.

Bodamer's third patient received bomb splinters at the back of the head. For two days, he was quite blind. Later, he was found to have a right homonymous hemianopia and a dyslexia. Strictly speaking, this patient did not develop a prosopagnosia, but rather a kind of specific metamorphopsia involving faces. All faces were strangely contorted, with the features displaced : the nose seemed to be aslant, one eyebrow higher than the other and the mouth diagonal. Nevertheless, the patient was able to recognize faces, including his own, in a looking-glass.

Bodamer looked upon the normal ability to recognize faces as a visuo-gnosic act of a very special kind. He called attention to the work of Pötzl, who had also regarded the recognition of human faces as a fundamental and archaic faculty. The experiences of child psychology were invoked wherein it has been alleged that the mother's or nanny's face represents the first object in outer space upon which a young infant fixates. It has been claimed that recognition of faces precedes the recognition of inanimate objects. Some would go further and assert that facial expression is an *Urphänomen*, that is, a basic primitive function which is not reducible further : and that in the sphere of faces, recognition paradoxically precedes vision—in other words, *gnosis* antedates *opsis*. According to Bodamer, the ability to visualize faces as mental images is not necessarily lost in cases of prosopagnosia, though in a certain number of reported cases, the defect includes both faculties.

Bodamer drew attention to the fact that, in his first two cases, the prosopagnosic defect was not complete. It seemed to spare a part, or segment, of the features, so that these were comparatively well seen and understood. This intact zone was usually made up of the region of the eyes. Indeed, the two patients seemed to have their attention riveted or attracted by this eye-area. This led to the unusual conception that, just as in hemianopia there may occur a sparing of the macular area, so, in prosopagnosia, there may be a relative escape of the eye-area ; or, as Bodamer called it, the *ocula*. The author believed that his hypothesis was supported by the experience of child psychologists like Bühler and Hetzer, who considered that a very young infant can fixate upon the eyes of its mother, to which it reacts by smiling. Kaila spoke of the " figurative element of the eye area ". According to Bodamer, his prosopagnosic patients displayed a regression to an infantile phase of concentrating attention upon the *ocula* of other persons' faces.

Bodamer's hypothesis is arresting and provocative. That many patients with bilateral occipitoparietal lesions fail at times to recognize faces, or pictures of faces, or their own reflection in a mirror, cannot be gainsaid. Several points need emphasis, however :

(1) In none of Bodamer's cases was the prosopagnosia an isolated disability ;

(2) Faces appeared altered ("blank . . . strangely white . . . like plates "), devoid of expression. It was therefore not a question of defective "gnosis" of a normal sense datum ;

(3) Metamorphopsia, habitual or occasional, was apt to mar the appearance of other external objects besides human faces.

That the alleged perceptual disorder is a specific one, capable of occurring in isolated form, is another matter. It seems scarcely credible that human faces should occupy a perceptual category which is different from all other objects in space, animate and inanimate. Can there be any attribute of size, shape, colouring or motility which distinguishes a human face from other objects in such a way as to preclude identification ? Presumably in these patients, a human face is seen, and is also realized for what it is, i.e. a human face ; but the ownership of the face is not recognized. In other words, as the result of cerebral disease, the visual Gestalt formed by the combination of component features—whereby one individual differs from every other person—is no longer recognized.

Many normal persons are notoriously "poor at recognizing people" in that they are slow at attaching an appropriate label to a face which presents itself ; indeed, they may not even be aware that the face is one which they have already seen and should recognize. Such persons would probably also find difficulty in conjuring up a vivid mental picture of the face of a person not actually in view. On the other hand, there are individuals who "never forget a face ", that is, they recognize a face as one they have seen before, and one which they can moreover identify. The problem is actually an exercise in visual Gestaltism, for such a person may previously only have seen the face depicted in two-dimensional form ; thus, many persons and especially women, can recognize in the street some celebrity whose face they know merely from the illustrated press. Indeed, the magazine picture may have shown the face only in profile, and yet they recognize the celebrity when they meet him face to face : or *vice versa*. Many normal persons can recognize a celebrity (or a friend or acquaintance) even though they have not seen him for many years. During the intervening period of time that individual may have altered in appearance—may have aged. Previously seen in out-door clothes, he is now recognized though in his *tenue de soir* : or in uniform : or having lost his hair, or put on weight, or taken to glasses, or even grown whiskers. And yet recognition takes place, perhaps at a glance. Obviously some process of abstraction, or of generalization, is at work, whereby a particular visual Gestalt is identified.

Bodamer's conception of a prosopagnosia is on a par, therefore, with a highly specific Gestalt agnosia, as suggested by Goldstein and Gelb in the case of their patient *Schn.* The fact that prosopagnosic patients identify various individuals only by reason of some attribute of dress (e.g. white coat ; uniform), or of adornment (e.g. moustache, spectacles) is in no way different from the case of normal but absent-minded individuals who are poor at recognizing individuals except by recourse to such clues as associations in time and place ; or by dint of dress.

The analogy with problems in configurational psychology is enhanced by the fact that Bodamer's patients found difficulty in recognizing pictures and photographs even of themselves. Here we are at once reminded of cases of irreminiscence. (Charcot's patient did not know his own reflection in a looking-glass.) But Bodamer's patients, we are told, did not admit to irreminiscence.

Before accepting Bodamer's case-records at their face-value, it is necessary to consider the possible role of a mere reduction in vision. A deterioration in visual acuity might easily bring about a difficulty in recognizing a face, and even pictorial representations of faces. But such a difficulty would scarcely be a specific one, affecting human faces to the exclusion of other objects. There is another peripheral factor, however, which must be considered, namely the role of constricted visual fields. If the fields are much restricted, especially in a concentric fashion, it will obviously be difficult to survey at once the whole details of a scene. In the case of a human face, it would be a matter of visually appreciating small portions of the total area. The perception thus becomes built up feature by feature in a laborious fashion. When the fields are reduced to mere tubular vision, as with bilateral posteriorly situated lesions of the brain, obviously it will be difficult to view the features as a whole and so achieve identification. The closer the subject to the patient's eyes, the more difficult the task will become. Although Bodamer was inclined to discount the role played by peripheral defects in vision, patients with glaucoma also have difficulty in recognizing faces because of their constricted visual fields. In other words, the same prosopagnosic defect can be encountered, or at any rate mimicked, by patients with no cerebral lesion at all. Even normal subjects may temporarily experience a prosopagnosia when they peer at people's faces through a narrow cylinder. Stollreiter-Butzon went even further and emphasized that the ordinary technique of perimetry was not sufficient, for there was often a discrepancy between the area of the intact field charted in the usual way, and that of the " effective " visual field, the latter probably being much smaller. According to this author, it is not only the mere size of the available visual field which determines whether a face is recognized or not, but some higher faculty on the patient's part. A person of normal mental equipment can by a process of " moving the macula " put together the disparate details. This assembling of parts is not enough in itself, for a face is qualitatively more than the sum of individual anatomical structures, being a Gestalt phenomenon. Over and above this process of integration of parts, there must be an intellectual operation of gnosis or perception. This, according to Stollreiter-Butzon, is not a specific prosopagnosic faculty but an aptitude which is more flexible. Her interpretation therefore approximates to the views of Bay upon visual gnosis.

Bodamer's doctrine of an *ocula* as occupying a special role in the surrounding visual world—one which is ontogenetically older and less vulnerable—is not altogether satisfying. It seems improbable that the young infant recognizes the identity of its parents or nursemaid by reason of the ocular or periocular region of the face in particular. The young mother who is in the habit of wearing dark glasses would then run the risk of never being recognized at all by her child. The conception of an *ocula* with some peculiar inherent properties of conveying expression or feeling is really a survival of a popular belief which looks upon the eyes as the mirror of the soul. Even Stollreiter-Butzon in her criticism of Bodamer accepts the idea of a " sparing of the *ocula* ", though she interprets it differently. Like so many lay persons, she also holds the view that no other small region of the face is so " vital " and " expressive " as the eyes. Actually, the range of possible mimetic changes in the eyes, even if one includes the tissues surrounding the palpebral fissures, is relatively limited. Certainly the repertoire of movement is less than in the case of the mouth, which has much stronger claims to be regarded as the medium of emotional expression—if any such conception is seriously entertained.

The problem of the status of prosopagnosia may therefore be summarized. It is not altogether surprising that the recognition of faces should occupy a different perceptual plane than that of many other objects. That the recognition of faces should be impaired in cases of cerebral disease in a conspicuous fashion is understandable. But that it should be involved in an exclusive or specific fashion is not credible.

Metamorphopsia : the visual perseverations

In discussing visual agnosia and its various incomplete subtypes, the point was made that the physical attributes of surrounding objects though altered are none the less identified without much trouble.

These cases illustrate a metamorphopsia without agnosia or imperception. Such patients generally possess a keen awareness of their defects and may complain bitterly of altered vision. This is a point of distinction from the metamorphopsias which form part of a visual agnosia, for in such cases, the patient may not spontaneously complain of poor sight, and even if he does, he may not be able to interpret his disability precisely. Close and laborious study is needed to elucidate the pattern of the metamorphopsia in such cases.

Metamorphopsia, as occurring in cerebral disease, may be a persistent phenomenon, though more often fleeting or episodic. In the latter event, the patient is more likely to be alive to the presence and nature of the illusory distortion of objects. The metamorphopsia may at times be selective, so that only certain objects are altered while others look normal. Here the circumstances are not fully understood. The place of the object within the field of vision ; its size ; its remoteness ; its colour and luminosity, all these are physical factors which may determine whether or not distortion occurs.

Unfortunately, we are dealing with a phenomenon which lies mainly if not wholly within the province of a subjective experience. The examiner is largely at the mercy of the patient's own description of events, and it is not easy to check the accuracy of his statements, and to measure and record the extent of the defect. Questions of intelligence, personality, and insight constantly obtrude and render the examiner's task most difficult.

Merely for convenience, one might attempt a classification (Critchley, 1949/50), always realizing that combinations of defect may occur, and also that the nature of the distortion may alter from one moment to another. Among the simpler varieties of metamorphopsia we can isolate the following :

(1) Alterations in the size of objects : (*a*) enlargement—*megalopsia* or *macropsia* ; (*b*) diminution—*micropsia*.

(1*a*) Alterations in the size of an object in one dimension only. For example, an object may seem squeezed or compressed sideways, or from above downwards. Thus, a patient of Henschens' saw the letters in a book as if flattened.

(2) Obliquity of vertical components, or of horizontal components, or both. Objects may thus appear to be tilted. Lenz's patient had a left-sided hemianopia ; all horizontal lines seemed deflected downwards and to the right. At a distance of 50 metres, the brass plates outside the house seemed as though the right-hand extremity were half a metre lower than the left. When walking, the patient felt as though the pavement sloped up to her left ; in a carriage, she imagined the floor-boards tilted to the right.

(3) As an extreme degree of the above, there may occur *inverted* vision, objects being turned in an illusory manner through 180°. (Wilder, Hoff, Gonzalo, Penta, Klopp.)

(4) Waviness of linear components. Thus, outlines of objects may not appear sharp, but vague, " as if surrounded by a fringe ". This has been called " irradiation ".

(5) Changes in the colour of objects : (*a*) lack of colour—*achromatopsia* ; or (*b*) an illusory monochrome hue—e.g. *erythropsia*, and so on.

(6) Fragmentation of lines ; gaps in the contour of things seen.

(7) Apparent movement of stationary objects (including Bender's " drifting of images "). Conversely, loss of the stroboscopic illusion in the case of an object actually in motion. Or, moving objects may seem to move too fast, or too slowly, or jerkily. Only the outlines of an object may seem to be in movement (to flicker, to pulsate). " Corners, edges, outlines appeared to be alive as if they consisted in fast moving bacilli " (Bodamer's case of G.S.W. left parietal area). This illusory acceleration of moving objects may be merely a part of a more generalized distortion of temporal sense, i.e. the " time-grabbing " (*Zeitraffer*) phenomenon.

The foregoing varieties are comparatively straightforward, and they readily lend themselves to analysis. Some other types of meta-morphopsia are more complicated and entail a change in the association of perceptual processes which ordinarily derive from past experiences. Thus, one may encounter :

(1) *Teleopsia*, where things appear not only small, but " at a distance ", as if viewed through the wrong end of a telescope. The converse phenomenon, which is rarer, is *pelopsia*, where objects seem to loom up directly in front of the subject.

(2) *Loss of stereoscopic vision*, so that the environment appears flat and two-dimensional, as in a picture. The opposite condition is an *enhancement of stereoscopic vision*, whereby near objects seem to be abnormally close, and distant objects seem to be much too far away. There results an exaggeration of the detail of things round about.

(3) *Visual perseveration*, both in time and in place (*paliopsia ; illusory visual spread*). These rare and rather complex experiences will be described below.

(4) Inaccurate orientation of objects in space. This not only includes a confusion of spatial relations within a sagittal plane (teleopsia ; pelopsia), but also in an up-down, or right-left dimension. Most striking of all is an illusory dislocation of an object to the other side of the midline of the body, that is, into the opposite visual field (*optic alloaesthesia*).

(5) Rarely the metamorphopsia affects only a part of the landscape, e.g. distant objects . . . "a disturbance of background (*Hinter-grundfunktion*) only ". (*Auersperg.*)

There are still other varieties of metamorphopsia, which are even more complex in that they entail abnormal affective or conative states of mind as much as, if not indeed more than, purely visual experiences :

(1) Objects (and indeed the environment generally) may appear unduly strange or mysterious, or foreign (as in the psychological phenomenon described by Mapother as derealization). Conversely, there may be an apparent familiarity in the entourage (the *déjà-vu* phenomenon).

(2) Objects may look ugly, sinister or menacing (*kakopsia*), or on the other hand, beautiful, friendly and comforting (*kalopsia*).

(3) Objects may seem endowed with intense personal significance or meaning. Sometimes, the full significance is elusive, and is almost achieved but not quite (*presque vu*).

(4) Sometimes, it is only human faces that appear distorted in a complicated way—a sort of "prosopometamorphopsia". "All faces were strangely contorted and the features displaced ; e.g. the ward sister's nose was deviated to the side by several degrees ; one eyebrow was higher than the other ; the mouth lay at a diagonal ; the hair was dishevelled like a wig askew." (Bodamer's case of G.S.W. left occipital zone.) "Faces would appear big and strange like masks at a ball " (Lenz). " Heads were flattened on the left side with greying hair on that side as if overgrown by a fungus." (Pichler's case of right parieto-occipital injury.) "Faces would come near and then recede, change their size, and assume grotesque forms." (Szatmari's case of occipital injury.) "Everybody looks alike : they all have mongolian faces with slit eyes, prominent cheek-bones, lank black hair and yellow complexions." (Faust's case of head injury.)

Metamorphopsia is by no means confined to patients with organic focal disease of the brain. Indeed, most cases occur in quite different circumstances. Some of them are met with in normal, though sensitive, aesthetic and introspective individuals. Others are indicative of psychotic and psychoneurotic illness. Some occur as epileptic aurae. Many of them are to be seen in toxic or febrile deliria, or in certain drug intoxications (mescal, belladonna, cannabis indica). Some of the simpler metamorphopsias are symptoms of peripheral ocular disease or of vertiginous states.

When focal brain disease is concerned the metamorphopsia may be associated with a lesion anywhere within the posterior half of the brain. Some of the simpler kinds are met with in occipital lesions, while the more complex states (*déjà vu*, derealization, and so on) may denote a temporal lobe disorder. Intermediate varieties of metamorphopsia are more ·often found with parietal disease.

As examples of metamorphopsia occurring with parietal affections, one may quote some illustrative accounts :

" All the mats were crooked " (thrombosis of the right middle cerebral artery).

" The furniture seemed to be turned around " (left parieto-occipital glioma).

" For a minute or so, things seemed smaller than they actually are " (right temporoparietal glioblastoma).

" Objects looked different and were blurred. My husband seemed too big and yet a long way away " (puerperal venous thrombosis in the right parietal area).

" Objects in the intact right field appeared much smaller. At one time, the furniture appeared wider and taller, and at other times smaller than normal " (right parieto-occipital vascular lesion. Van Bogaert, 1934).

" People's faces would frequently change, their eyes would swell and contract . . . ' they look terrible ; the eyes go to nothing at all, then come back like a pimple '. His reflection in a looking-glass appeared dragged down on the right side, especially the cheek and eye." (Biparietal softening.)

Loss of stereoscopic vision was originally mentioned by Holmes as a somewhat rare constituent of the syndrome of visual disorientation, and it was described by Faust (1947) after a bilateral parieto-occipital wound. A particularly striking case was published by Riddoch (1917). The patient was a soldier with a bullet wound extending from the left parietal vertex to the right occipital pole. In addition to a left homonymous field defect and a visual disorientation . . . " everything he saw was flat. People had the appearance of cardboard figures ; they had outline, but no depth. If two persons were standing in front of him, he could differentiate them only by their outlines, for they were featureless and had no rotundity. Their noses might have been painted on their flat faces. Friends were recognized only by their voices. A landscape was like a piece of stage scenery. Trees, hills, everything he saw, were at the same level ; and yet he could recognize light and shade. A ball was simply a circle, an egg, an oval ; and a box, a rectangle. This phenomenon was evident only if the objects were more than a foot away from him."

Although this account describes the phenomenon as if it comprised essentially a loss of stereoscopic vision, obviously other defects were at work. An alteration of the environment from a three-dimensional to a two-dimensional system should not necessarily entail unfamiliarity any more than a photograph or a picture should be unrecognizable. The hint in the clinical description of elements of a prosopagnosia suggests that there was also present some degree of visual agnosia, in that surrounding objects were not only flat and two-dimensional, but they were in addition divested of traits whereby they could be recognized.

No single explanation can be adduced for the occurrence of metamorphopsia, for it is probable that several factors may operate. Thus, when the surrounding world appears changed in a subtle or intangible fashion (" unreal ", " different ", " more vivid "), there may have occurred a divestment of the numerous secondary apperceptive embellishments of a visual sensation. With the simple metamorphopsias of parieto-occipital disease, it is probable that manifold qualitative changes are present in vision, capable of being demonstrated only by special visuo-psychological test-measures (e.g. visual disorientation ; inattention ; fluctuation ; delayed recognition of form or contour ; imperfect synthesis of moving objects ; altered rate of flicker-fusion).

A quantitative test for the accuracy of orientation of vertical and horizontal lines was devised by Bender and Jung (1948). They found in normal subjects an error of never more than one degree. Patients who had recently sustained head injuries showed a much greater error (mean deviation 6·4°). With a parietal, thalamic or frontal lesion, the deviation was to the opposite side. Foci within the brainstem and of the cerebellum produced deviations to either side.

Bender, who has studied this aspect of vision with great thoroughness, found that moving objects, when in close proximity to the borders of an area of actual visual loss, may seem to be travelling along a curved trajectory rather than a straight line ; or the movement may seem to be too fast, or too slow.

Brain (1947) was impressed by the fact that metamorphopsia is a rather rare symptom of a comparatively common disorder, namely, parietal disease. This suggested to him that a specific state of the cerebral cortex of the appropriate region may be operative, as, for example, oedema. In this way, a distortion may possibly occur first of all in the pattern of neural units within a given area of cortex, secondarily of the electrical field, and finally of the conscious percept. Pötzl's patient had a right-sided homonymous paracentral scotoma as the result of a gunshot wound of the head. The vertical dimension of objects seemed shortened while the horizontal meridian looked elongated. This distortion was an oblique one, with the angle of deviation corresponding exactly with the direction of the scotoma, and also with the obliquity of the diplopic image. In general, Pötzl regarded the phenomenon of metamorphopsia as being due to a central defect in the mechanism subserving the fusion of images ;

a disorder of binocular vision, in other words. He regarded the symptoms as lying as it were midway between spatial and agnosic disorders.

Metamorphopsia is an interesting phenomenon in other respects, for it may combine features of a gradation between perception, illusion and hallucination. Often it may not be possible to delimit the phenomena. This same point is well shown in those rare cases of *visual perseveration* (Critchley, 1951). This is a term which applies to the illusory re-occurrence of visual perceptions after the stimulus-object has been removed. This experience is not ordinarily a persistent one, but is intermittent. Only very rarely can it be demonstrated at will. There are two main varieties, namely : (1) visual perseveration in time, or *paliopsia* ; and (2) *illusory visual spread*, or visual extension, expansion or prolongation ; in other words, a kind of spatial perseveration of objects seen.

Visual perseveration is quite often identifiable in the visual illusions of mescal and hashish intoxication. It has occasionally been observed in cases of epilepsy. Ordinarily, however, it is encountered in cases of posteriorly-situated lesions of the brain, as set out in the table opposite.

The brain lesions may be, as is shown, bilateral, right-sided or left-sided. Qualitative or quantitative field defects are commonly present. In Critchley's Case 3, there was a well marked visual agnosia ; in Adler's patient and in Faust's patient, the visual perseveration took place during a stage of recovery from visual loss. Sander (1928) had found something suggestive of paliopsia in normal subjects tested with a tachistoscope at relative high speeds of exposure.

The perseverating phenomena can be illustrated by the following brief records :

" After a person had walked past the foot of the bed from left to right, and then had gone away, she had a moment or two later the impression as if the same person had walked past as before." (Case of right parieto-occipital haemangioma. Holmes, 1931. Critchley, Case 1.)

" At times, objects which she remembered well, or which had attracted and held her attention sometime before, even up to several hours before, would appear within her blind half of vision and gradually float across it." (Case of left parieto-occipital carcinoma. Critchley, Case 2.)

" If he looks at a thing, and looks away, he may continue to see it. Things he thinks about a lot do not go out of his vision quickly, as if they were slow in being switched off." (Case of bilateral parieto-occipital infarctions. Critchley, Case 4.)

" The patient watched a man approach and then pass out of view. Then he seemed to see the man walking past again. This lasted for a second or two." (Case of G. S. W. left parieto-occipital area. P. K. Robinson and A. C. Watts, 1947.)

Case	Nature of perseveration	Visual acuity	Visual fields	Other visuo-psychic defects	Side	Morbid anatomy Site	Morbid anatomy Nature	Verified
Personal 1	Occasional perseveratory hallucination passing from L. to R.	6/12 6/18	L. hemianopia		Right	Parieto-occipital	Angioma	Yes
Personal 2	Hallucinations of well-remembered objects within the blind field	6/18 6/12	R. hemianopia	L. visual disorientation	Left	Parieto-occipital	Secondary carcinoma	Yes
Personal 3	Illusory visual spread	1/18 1/60	Grossly restricted	Lilliputian hallucinations. Distorted vision	Bilateral L. > R.	Frontoparieto-temporo-occipital	Astrocytoma	Yes
Personal 4	Paliopsia	6/36 6/36	Variable R.-sided restriction	Visual dysgnosia. Visual disorientation	Bilateral	Parieto-occipital	Vascular lesions	Yes
Personal 5	Paliopsia	6/6 6/6	Full		Left	Temporoparietal	Tumour	Yes
Personal 6	Paliopsia resembling an after-image	6/24 6/36	Full	Visual disorientation		Idiopathic psychical epilepsy (E.E.G. focus in left frontal lobe)		No
Personal 7	Alloaesthetic paliopsia	1/24 1/18	R. hemianopia	L. visual disorientation and dyschromatopsia	Left	Temporoparietal	Neoplastic	No
Personal 8	Paliopsia		L. hemianopia	Flashes of light	Right	Parieto-occipital	Vascular	No
Personal 9	Paliopsia		R. hemianopia	Loss of visual memory (number-form and topographical)	Left	Occipital	Tumour	Yes
Spalding and Zangwill, 1950	Paliopsia				Bilateral	Parieto-occipital	Traumatic	No
Robinson and Watts, 1947	Episodic paliopsia	6/6 6/6	R. hemianopia		Left	Parieto-occipital	Injury	No
Faust, 1947	Paliopsia		Bilat. constriction lower fields	Visual disorientation; spatial disorientation; simultanagnosia	Bilateral (through and through)	Parieto-occipital	Injury	No
Bender, 1945	Illusory visual spread		L. visual fluctuation and inattention	Visual disorientation and polyopia	Right	Occipital	Injury	No
Adler, 1944	Paliopsia			Visual agnosia	Bilateral	Occipitoparietal	Softenings (anoxic)	No
Stauffenberg, 1914, Case 2	Paliopsia		L. hemianopia	Visual agnosia	Bilateral	R. temporoparieto-occipital; L. temporo-occipital	Softenings	Yes
Lissauer, 1890	Paliopsia			Visual agnosia	Bilateral	Parieto-occipital	Softenings	No

The foregoing cases are examples of paliopsia or visual perseveration in time. Here is an instance of a paliopsia where the object was
also displaced in an alloaesthetic fashion from the intact into the
blind visual fields :—

" A letter which he had placed on a table to his left kept floating about
within the blind right field, on and off for the next two days." (Unverified
case of left temporoparietal tumour. Critchley, Case 7.)

The following is an example of illusory visual perseveration in
space :

" The pattern of a striped or chequered garment would seem to extend
over the face of the wearer. The pattern of cretonne curtains would often
seem to extend along the adjacent wall." (Case of bilateral fronto-occipital
tumours, larger on the left side. Critchley, Case 3.)

Dyslexia

Just as the alleged condition of object agnosia ordinarily includes
an inability to identify with ease and correctness pictorial or two-
dimensional representations, so also the latter state of affairs generally
comprises an inability to comprehend the meaning of printed or written
verbal symbols. It would be difficult indeed to imagine a patient
with a severe visual agnosia who has not lost his power of reading
and of understanding graphic symbols.

This observation is well shown in Nielsen's Case Gilbertine M. (1946).
The patient at first recognized nothing that she saw. Objects were not
identified until touched or until some special sense other than vision was
stimulated. She could not recognize colours. Reading was impossible,
although she could write fluently. When letters or words were put before
her, she could not read them, but she identified them accurately as soon as
she traced the outlines with her finger. She was able to revisualize letters
correctly as evidenced by her adequate verbal description of the conformation
of the printed letters H, O, Q, A and W.

There is some clinical evidence, however, to suggest that a measure
of dissociation can sometimes occur ; that is to say, an inability to
understand printed or written verbal symbols may dominate the
clinical picture. Word-blindness, so-called, may therefore exist with
little if any other evidence of visual agnosia.

Full discussion of this subject will be reserved for a later chapter.
Suffice it to say at this point that Lordat's autopathographic account
of his transitory reading disability, published in 1843, probably
represents the earliest clinical report of this phenomenon. A few
other cases were reported in the course of the next thirty years.
Broadbent's record in 1872 was the first one where anatomical
evidence was forthcoming. The brain showed two cerebrovascular
lesions, one more recent than the other. Of the two, the older lay

in the region of the angular and supramarginal gyri on the left side, and it was this location which Broadbent believed to be of significance. Kussmaul in 1877 first used the expression "word-blindness" (*Wortblindheit*).

At this present juncture, it is advisable to discuss certain aspects of the problem of alexia, leaving the more semantic considerations until later.

In the first place, the role of disease of the angular gyrus of the dominant hemisphere in the genesis of alexia needs scrutiny. It is often assumed that the symptom of alexia (or word-blindness), particularly when associated with an intact power of writing, indicates a diseased angular gyrus. A lesion situated more deeply is believed to account for the clinical combination of an alexia with a homonymous hemianopia. A thorough anatomical study of a larger series of cases where autopsy data is available, abundantly shows that the lesions may be more widespread; that contiguous areas of brain may be involved; and indeed, that the angular gyrus may actually be spared. The contention that an alexia is the specific consequence of disease of the angular gyrus in the dominant hemisphere is untenable. Nielsen has stated that alexia can follow a lesion situated anywhere from the occipital to the frontal lobe. Claims have also been made that alexia can occur as a "pure" affection, that is, independent of other focal or outfall manifestations. Such a phenomenon must be rare, and indeed, one may seriously doubt whether the clinical supporting evidence is really convincing. Incomplete clinical examination will naturally endow the alexia with an appearance of isolation or specificity which may well be spurious. Most dyslexic patients prove to be afflicted by other "parietal" symptoms. Hemianopia is the most obvious of these, but this may be argued as being an epiphenomenon due to an extension of the lesion to the optic radiations. Other disorders often coupled with the reading disability include defective colour-appreciation; impaired spatial orientation; constructional apraxia; and Gerstmann's syndrome. The first two of these were present in Holmes' case of "pure word-blindness" (1950), and although the author admitted that such symptoms had been reported in other cases, he regarded them as accessory rather than essential features. Hamilton's patient, a compositor who developed alexia after an initial difficulty in assembling type, also showed such troubles as an inability to judge distances, to lay knives and forks at the dinner table, or to indicate the points of the compass. Pötzl stated that alexia and colour-agnosia always occur together, and indeed there is an impressive body of data to support this idea.

Alexia has not infrequently been claimed as existing in pure form, that is, without any other disorder of speech. The many instances, where the patient has been able to write with facility and yet cannot read his own writing or anyone else's, are often quoted in this connection. More often, however, the dyslexic patient finds difficulty in writing, and an even greater uncertainty in spelling. A combination of dyslexia with an amnesic aphasia has often been observed. This vexed question of " pure alexia " will be discussed later in more detail. It may now be said, however, that alexia as a " pure " disorder of language is a conception which should be received with great caution, for it is one which largely arises from inadequate study of the clinical facts. The faculty of reading verbal symbols, it should be mentioned, is far from being a simple or straightforward process, but is one which entails a number of operations at different psychological levels. It is scarcely surprising, therefore, that an impaired power of reading should be anything but a uniform clinical event. Some of the difficulties in the matter of alexia can be overcome by looking upon this symptom as representing either a partial affection of language, or else a fragment, or a residuum of a visual agnosia. In this way, there has grown up the notion of a twofold type of alexia —the aphasic and the agnosic varieties respectively. This interesting idea may go some way towards explaining the apparently " pure " cases, by regarding them as cases devoid of other manifestations of an aphasia, or alternatively of an agnosia, but probably not both.

Neurologists who adhere to the belief that a " pure " alexia can exist, independent of other cerebral focal symptoms including dysphasia, often submit that no intellectual falling-off need occur in such cases. In such a thorny question, the responsibility of proof must surely lie upon the claimant. The problem is immediately raised whether aphasia per se implies a disorder of mentation. Without attempting to discuss the conflicting evidence, it may be said that nowadays most neurologists are sceptical about accepting a case of aphasia devoid of some intellectual insufficiency, which may, however, be qualitative rather than quantitative.

That dyslexia is by no means a uniform specific symptom is well shown by the fact that in some cases the difficulty in reading can be ascribed to visual rather than semantic defects. The patient reported by Ranschburg and Schill (1932) is an example. He found that letters and words were blurred, and in movement; it was difficult to concentrate upon the task of identifying a word or letter if others were simultaneously presented to his gaze. Several patients with left-sided parietal lesions have shown difficulty in reading, a disorder which may have attributed to an illusory " running together " of the print, or a side-to-side oscillation of the type.

The distracting property of multiplicity of visual stimuli is probably an important one. Many patients will admit to this symptom if
directly questioned upon the point, although the literature upon the
subject is meagre. The patient, for example, may hold his hand
between the face and page of print, a little below the fixation point.
One patient who subsequently improved considerably, was asked why
he used to perform this mannerism in the days when he had difficulty
in reading. He explained that, by so doing, he cut out of view a
considerable area of visual stimuli which used to bewilder or distract
him.

It is not only dyslexic patients who find aggregations of visual material
too much for them. Objects, rather than verbal symbols, may act in the
same way. One patient, probably suffering from biparietal lesions, could not
look at a bouquet of flowers, or a bowl of fruit without distress, and she chose
to have near her no more than one or two blossoms in a vase.

Heidenhain's dyslexic patient had more difficulty in reading letters than
numerals ; and of letters, those printed in German (Gothic) type were less
well recognized than the more modern Latin type. The difficulties in
identifying the German lettering were probably due to its far greater morphological complexity.

Visual disorientation

Disordered appreciation of the spatial relationship of objects to
each other constitutes an important affection of vision from bilateral
cerebral disease. Our knowledge of this subject dates from the work
of Holmes and his colleagues (1918) carried out during the first world
war. It has been asserted that visual disorientation is actually the
same disorder which Lange had called " visuo-spatial agnosia ", but
Lange's cases were probably examples of a more subtle visuo-psychic
defect. According to Holmes and Horrax, the constituent features
of a visual disorientation comprise some, or all, of the following :

(1) An error in the absolute localization of objects seen. This leads to
an inability to touch them or accurately to point to them. (A simple bedside
test readily demonstrates this defect. The examiner confronts the patient
who is instructed to look fixedly before him. The patient is then told to
touch the examiner's forefinger which is held up in the peripheral part of
the field of vision. A normal patient can carry out this test with fair accuracy
while still looking ahead ; the disorientated patient shows gross inaccuracies.)

(2) Errors in " relative localization ", so that the patient cannot tell
which of two objects is the nearer. Moreover, he cannot indicate out of a
medley of articles put before him, the nearest and the farthest, and the one
most to the right and most to the left.

(3) An inability to compare the dimensions of two or more objects.

(4) Difficulty in avoiding obstacles when walking, and also in finding
one's way about. In the effort to reach a goal which is within his purview
he may set out in the wrong direction. According to Holmes and Horrax,
this defect may be coupled with an impaired topographical memory. (It

would seem possible that these last-named disorders belong more to the category of "spatial-agnosic" defects than to simple visual disorientation.)

(5) A difficulty in counting objects. This applies both to counting by dint of touching each object in turn, and to counting by mere inspection. There may also be a well marked awkwardness in reading. This is due not to an alexia, but to an incapacity to pass accurately from the end of one line to the beginning of the next.

(6) An inability to recognize movement in a sagittal plane, the patient usually being able to recognize lateral movements.

(7) Impaired visual attention.

(8) Disordered ocular movement, including the so-called fixity of gaze, described by Bálint.

(9) At times, loss of stereoscopic vision.

Clinical experience shows that visual disorientation usually follows a bilateral lesion of the brain implicating both parietal lobes. Holmes (1945) drew attention to the fact that Best had previously described a case of visual disorientation where the lesion affected the mesial and upper portions of both parietal lobes. Riddoch (1935) was the first to assert that visual disorientation can occur in homonymous half-fields, as the result of a unilateral lesion of the brain, an observation which has since been abundantly confirmed. In Riddoch's original two cases, new-growth involved both the supramarginal and angular gyri of one hemisphere; the optic radiations escaped. Riddoch believed that visual disorientation is apt to occur when association pathways from the calcarine cortex to other parts of the brain are interrupted, the nodal point probably lying near the supramarginal and angular gyri.

The conception of a visual disorientation confined to homonymous half-fields has not escaped criticism. It has been objected that the disability is not a visual one at all, but that it is due simply to a sensory ataxia in the ipsilateral upper limb. If the pointing tests are carried out by the other hand, crossing the midline, the inaccuracies of touch are said not to occur.

Reference may be made here to a phenomenon which Stenvers has called "localization by means of a mental picture within a peripheral visual field" (1951). To carry out this test, the examiner confronts the patient who has a homonymous hemianopia, and holds his hand up in such a way that it falls within the intact visual field. The patient is told to point to it. At the same time, the examiner also holds up his other hand in a similar mirror-opposite position; as it now falls within the blind field, the patient does not see it. Nevertheless, he is asked to point to where it should be as judged by the analogy of the hand in the intact field. According to Stenvers, the patient whose hemianopia is due to a tract lesion can perform this test well, utilizing the visual stimulus on the one side to form an accurately located visual image on the other. But the patient whose hemianopia is due to a posteriorly situated lesion, fails.

Defective revisualization : " irreminiscence "

The term " Charcot-Wilbrand syndrome " refers to the symptom whereby a patient loses the power to conjure up visual images or memories, and furthermore, ceases to dream during his sleeping hours. This syndrome has at times been equated, quite incorrectly, with Munk's mind-blindness. It is uncertain how frequent this irreminiscence (as Nielsen called it) occurs clinically, for some victims of parietal disease are unlikely to complain spontaneously of such a defect. Nor can a patient whose sensorium is clouded be expected to give an altogether objective answer when a leading question is directly put to him as to the presence or absence of his visual images. However, there are exceptional cases where the patient is a subject of high intelligence, not materially blunted by the cerebral lesion, and can give a convincing account of this impaired imagery. The symptom is all the more arresting if the patient formerly possessed a vivid and predominantly visual type of imagery.

Defective revisualization, if severe, will necessarily include a defect of topographical memory, and also a prosopagnosia. It will probably also entail a cessation of dreaming, or at least, an alteration in the vivid visual component of the dreaming state.

One of the first accounts of this phenomenon constitutes at the same time one of the most striking and convincing examples, though the pathology remains obscure. Charcot's patient (1883) was a cultured man of parts and a polyglot, who quite suddenly found himself bereft of the visual memory of shapes and colours. This was a change so dramatic as to make him feel a different person, as if on the brink of lunacy. In a town previously well known to him, he felt at sea, for he no longer recognized the commonplace landmarks which should have been so familiar (= loss of topographical memory). He completely failed to describe the principal square with its surrounding arcades and the statue in the centre . . . " Je sais que cela existe, mais je ne m'en puis rien figurer et je ne vous en pourrais rien dire." Having also forgotten what his family and his acquaintances looked like, he did not recognize them when he saw them (= prosopagnosia).[1]

---

[1] Charcot asked his patient to compose a letter stating in his own words the manner of disability which afflicted him. This interesting account may be quoted verbatim :

" Je m'empresse de repondre à votre lettre, et je vous prie de vouloir bien excuser ma connaissance imparfaite de la langue française, imperfection qui rend un peu difficile l'expression exacte de ce que je dois vous soumettre.

" Comme je vous l'ai dit, je possédais une grande facilité de me

Furthermore, he had even forgotten his own appearance. Visiting a gallery on one occasion, he found his passage obstructed by a

representer intérieurement les personnes qui m'intérressaient, les couleurs et les objets de toute nature, en un mot tout ce qui se reflète dans l'œuil.

" Permettez-moi de vous faire observer que je me servais de cette faculté dans mes études : Je lisais ce que je voulais apprendre et en fermant les yeux je revoyais clairment les lettres dans leurs plus grands détails ; il en était ainsi pour la physiognomie des personnes, des pays et villes que j'avais visités dans mes longs voyages, et, comme je vous le disais plus haut, de tout objet qui avait été aperçu par mes yeux.

" Tout d'un coup cette vision intérieure a absolument disparu. Aujourd'hui même, avec la meilleur volonté, je ne peux pas me représenter intérieurement les traits de mes enfants, de ma femme, ou de n'importe quel objet me servant journellement. Donc, étant établi que j'ai absolument perdu la vision intérieure, vous comprennez facilement que mes impressions sont changées d'une façon absolue.

" Ne pouvant plus me représenter ce qui est visible, et ayant absolument conservé la memoire abstraite, j'éprouve journellement des étonnements en voyant des choses que je dois connaître depuis fort longtemps. Mes sensations, ou plutôt mes impressions, étant indéfiniment nouvelles, il me semble qu'un changement complêt s'est opéré dans mon existence et naturellement mon caractère s'est modifié d'une façon notable. Avant j'étais impressionnable, enthousiaste, et je possédais une fantaisie féconde ; aujourd'hui je suis calme, froid, et ma fantaisie ne peut plus m'égarer.

" Le sens de la représentation intérieure me manquant absolument, mes rêves se sont également modifiés. Aujourd'hui, je rêve seulement *paroles*, tandis que je possédais auparavant, dans mes rêves, la perception visuelle.

" Comme exemple plus concluant : Si vous me demandiez de me représenter les tours de Notre-Dame, un mouton qui broutte ou un navire en détresse en plein mer, je vous repondrais que, quoique sachant parfaitement distinguer les trois choses très differentes et sachant très bien de quoi il s'agit elles n'ont aucun sens pour moi, au point de vue la vision intérieure.

" Une conséquence remarquable de la perte de cette faculté mentale est, comme je l'ai dit déjà, le changement de mon caractère et de mes impressions. Je suis beaucoup moins accessible à un chagrin ou à une douleur morale. Je vous citerai qu'ayant perdu dernièrement un de mes parents auquel m'attachait une amitié sincere, j'ai éprouvé une douleur beaucoup moins grande que si j'avais encore eu le pouvoir de me répresenter par la vision intérieure la physiognomie de ce parent, les phases de la maladie qu'il a traversée, et surtout si je pouvais voir intérieurement l'effet extérieur produit par cette mort prematurée sur les membres de ma famille.

" Je ne sais si j'explique bien ce que j'éprouve ; mais je puis vous affirmer que cette vision intérieure qui me manque aujourd'hui existait chez moi d'une façon peu ordinaire, et elle existe aujourd'hui, chez mon frère, professeur de droit à l'Université de X... ; chez mon père, orientaliste, connu dans le mond scientifique, et chez une sœur peintre d'un talent assez apprécié.

" Comme conclusion, je vous prie de remarquer que je suis obligé aujourd'hui *de me dire les choses que je veux retenir dans ma memoire, pendant que j'avais auparavant seulement à les photographier par la vue."*

PARIS, *le 11 juillet*, 1883.

stranger of whom he begged pardon ; only to discover that he was confronting his own reflection in a pier-glass (= *le signe de miroir*). He knew that certain colours naturally belonged to certain objects, but could not recall what those colours looked like (= chromamnesia). " Ma femme a les cheveux noirs ; j'en ai la plus parfaite certitude, et il y a pour moi impossibilité complète de retrouver cette couleur en ma memoire, aussi complète que celle de m'imaginer sa personne et ses traits." This same patient began to experience an alteration in the nature of his dreams, in that they now took on a purely auditory quality.

In the opinion of Bay, Charcot's patient had a hysterical disability, and not an organic malady.

Wilbrand, also in 1887, described a similar case :

The patient, an intelligent and polyglot lady of 63 years, abruptly lost consciousness for some hours. Thereafter, she passed into what she called " a curious state " impossible for her to describe. She did not recognize her doctor and she confused persons with inanimate objects. She was regarded as being blind ; but as she afterwards said . . . " When people stood at my bedside and spoke with pity of my blindness, I said to myself, ' You can't really be blind because you are able to see the cloth with the blue border on the table in the sick-room.' " When she was allowed up several weeks later, she found herself in a " strange condition of not seeing and yet being able to read ". It was a sort of dream-state. Vision was restricted on the left and to a lesser degree on the right. Most conspicuous was her loss of memory for places. She could not visualize the streets of Hamburg where she had been born and brought up ; nor even her own house. When taken out of doors, she found that the appearance of the town was strange and entirely changed . . . As she told her attendant . . . " If you insist that this is the Jungfernstieg, and that is the Neuenwall, and that the Rathaus, I suppose I must take your word for it, but I can't recognize them at all." She continued to live a very sheltered life. Four years later, she was studied carefully. Since her stroke, she had scarcely dreamed at all. She had lost the ability to do needlework. Her power of visualizing had improved a little but places still appeared strange to her when she looked at them. " I could quite well walk through Hamburg with my eyes closed, but when I actually stand in the street I don't know which way to turn ; with my eyes shut, I see the old Hamburg in front of me again." Other objects, e.g. the furniture around her, appeared " different " in an indescribable way. On going into her room, she often got the idea she was in a strange room—someone else's. " I myself look quite different in the mirror from what I used to look like . . . people I've got to know since my illness leave no visual traces in my memory. If I meet them the next day in the street, I don't recognize them."

Other remarkable symptoms were also present. She lost her power of accurately estimating time. The sight of a large number of objects or of persons would confuse her. She would imagine objects out of sight to be located in a quite different situation : thus, she had the impression that in the place of her bedroom (which adjoined her sitting-room) was the street ; and that her chest of drawers was outside in the road. This symptom she called " inverted thinking ", and it aroused fears that she might be losing her reason. She developed an exceptional orderliness in the disposition of her belongings, which otherwise she was apt to mislay. It was necessary for her to lead what she called a " mechanical life ".

After a couple more years of strict seclusion, she succumbed to a further stroke. Autopsy revealed widespread ischaemic areas in the posterior lobes on both sides of the brain.

The literature contains many references since then of patients with occipital or parieto-occipital lesions, usually bilateral, who have shown similar defects in their visual imagery. (Müller (1892), Goldstein and Gelb (1918), Grunstein (1924), Hoff and Pötzl (1937), Lyman, Kwan and Chao (1938), Brain (1941), (1947), etc., Adler (1944), Holmes (1945), Arbuse (1947).) Nielsen associated a loss of revisualization with a lesion of Brodmann's area 19. Most attention has been paid to the topographical aspects of this symptom, as tying up with a spatial agnosia, often to the neglect of the other evidences of impaired irreminiscence (to employ Nielsen's terminology). Some authors have spoken of *l'amnesie des occipitaux* to describe this defect. The case of Dide and Botcazo (1902) was a particularly severe instance, for not only was visual memory gravely at fault, but the patient was confused and disorientated, believing himself to be still an employee at a railway station although he had left that job years before.

Spalding and Zangwill (1950) reported an interesting case where the patient lost visual imagery and memory, as well as the power of calculation, after a left parieto-occipital bullet wound. As the patient had ordinarily been one of those persons whose imagery for numerals had conformed to a certain geometrical pattern, more vividly than is perhaps the rule, it was interesting to note a loss of this imaginal number-form as a consequence of a cerebral lesion. The loss of number-form also lead to considerable difficulty in calculation. Associated troubles included an impairment in visual memory, and in topographical sense.

Humphrey and Zangwill (1951) published three cases of head injury where the patients ceased to dream after they had been wounded. Their case-reports are all the more valuable because the patients were men of superior intelligence, and also because they had spontaneously mentioned this cessation of dreaming. The exact site of the lesion in these cases was never demonstrated but it was obviously in the nature of severe trauma to the after part of the brain, right-sided in two cases, and bilateral in one. The loss of the habit of dreaming was associated in each case with a poverty in visual imagery, all the more conspicuous since one patient at least had, before his injury, been a strong visualizer. Humphrey and Zangwill brought forward some interesting analogies between language and imagery. Visual thinking, dreaming and imagination are, they suggested, liable to organic dissolution in a manner comparable with the dissolution of symbolic thought in aphasia. They pointed out, however, that neither hemisphere was of specific significance in this connection.

Qualitative defects in the visual field

With improved techniques for testing vision, it is probable that minor defects can now be demonstrated in association with cerebral lesions. Some of these disorders cause little if any disability, so that the patient may be unaware of any trouble whatsoever in the visual sphere. Other patients may realize only that something is vaguely wrong with their sight, but the extent of the impairment proves on testing to be much greater than expected. Sometimes, there is an actual sector defect in the visual field, with these more subtle disabilities lying alongside, that is to say between the area of lost vision and the normal field. As Bay has truly said, the shape and size of a visual field defect depends to a large extent upon the choice of the stimulus-object. An actual field loss, due to cerebral injury, may even improve with the passage of time, leaving a series of what might be called qualitative field defects. Some of these defects have been recognized for years : others are less familiar. They include :

Visual disorientation
Metamorphopsia
Visual inattention
Altered visual adaptation rate
Loss of appreciation of small stationary objects
Defects in colour sensation
Altered rate of flicker-fusion
Delayed recognition-time
Loss of optokinetic nystagmus.

The question arises as to what terminology should be used to describe in the aggregate these minor disabilities. German neurologists are in the habit of referring to them as the marks of a *visuelle Funktionswandel*, but this term is not one which lends itself to translation. The English equivalent, lability of function, is an abstract term which as it stands is almost meaningless. Parsons spoke of scotopic vision to include all these disabilities. He based his ideas, however, upon the now discredited views of Head, who in the tactile sphere, sought to distinguish two types of sensation phylogenetically of different degrees of maturity, namely, epicritic and protopathic sensibility. For Parsons, scotopic vision corresponded in the visual sphere with Head's protopathic sensibility. Perhaps the least objectional term which can be adopted provisionally at any rate would be simply to speak of " qualitative visual defects ", implying a series of defects as enumerated above.

Bay has emphasized the value of testing for *Funktionswandel* or qualitative visual defects under unpropitious technical circumstances. Thus, some of these disorders will only be revealed in conditions of poor illumination. This is what Bay has termed " examination under stress ".

According to Allen (1948), *visual inattention* was first described by Anton (1899) and by Oppenheim (1900). Head and Holmes rediscovered it in 1911, and it was independently described on the continent by Poppelreuter during the first world war. It had been found in the course of the confrontation test for visual fields that some patients were unable to detect a visual stimulus on one side, if a rival stimulus were simultaneously presented on the opposite side. The role of the point of fixation in this manœuvre is not altogether clear. With progressive lesions, a state of visual inattention might later be followed by an actual hemianopia. Hence, the term *hémianopsie rélative*, which was suggested by Thiébault and Guillaumat 1945. Although the early cases were mainly examples of penetrating wounds of the parietal region, the morbid anatomy of the phenomenon cannot be said to be clearly established. It is generally assumed that a relatively superficial cerebral lesion is at fault ; that is, one lying between the cortex and the optic radiations.

More detailed testing has since shown that the phenomenon is more complex. Although as a rule the simultaneous stimuli are exposed at mirror-opposite points within the visual fields, at times it is possible for a stimulus lying within a lower quadrant on one side to cause a stimulus in a diagonally upper quadrant on the other side to be neglected. An inattention phenomenon can even be demonstrated within a single homonymous field. Thus, a stimulus lying above the meridian may be neglected when a stimulus is displayed below the meridian : or *vice versa*.

An inverse relationship can be traced at times between the size or luminosity of the intact stimulus and the one which is lost through inattention. That is to say, a large target may cause one of lesser size in the opposite field to be neglected, while a smaller stimulus will not be operative. Bender and Furlow therefore advocated the term visual " extinction " rather than " inattention " based upon the idea that a strong stimulus extinguishes or suppresses a weaker one. They believed that the term " attention " is a misnomer in this connection, although their arguments on this point are not altogether convincing. They spoke of extinction, obscuration and dulling of the image concerned, and they noted that there was a tendency towards fluctuation in vividness. They emphasized that " rivalry, dominance and attention mechanisms " are normal psychological functions of the cortex. When one hemisphere is diseased or damaged, rivalry and consequent dominance of the normal over the pathological side may be so pronounced, according to the authors, as to cause complete extinction of the form, colour and movement of the image within the affected field . . . " The more the normal is stimulated, the less the affected half perceives." It may perhaps be objected that the particular patient who formed the basis of Bender and Furlow's original paper was not altogether typical. Visual inattention is usually not discovered until specifically looked for, most patients being unaware of any defect which may arouse suspicions on the part of the examiner. Bender and Furlow's patient, however, had already noticed, and had made spontaneous complaint, that if he stared for a long time, his vision on one side would begin to blur. For this reason, he could not visit a cinema, and he could not read much ; moreover, the patient had something reminiscent of visual perseveration, for he went on to say : ". . . if I look at one object long enough, and look away, I still can see it."

Allen's review of the subject is the most detailed in the literature. His series comprised ten cases where unilateral visual inattention was present, with normal visual fields. There were also three cases with visual inattention combined with minor homonymous defects in the visual fields. Assembling his cases, and collating them with others garnered from the literature, Allen found that they fell naturally into two main groups : (1) those in which field defects were (or had been) present ; and (2) those in which there were not (and had never been) any defects in the visual fields. Within the first group, the main features that he observed were : (1) impaired visual attention to one side was associated with minor defects of the visual field to that side ; (2) impaired visual attention to one side had succeeded an earlier defect of the visual fields to that side ; (3) awareness of movement in the affected portion of the visual field was regained when there was still inability to perceive a stationary object (during recovery from a visual field loss) ; (4) interruption of some of the stimuli up to the level of the visuo-sensory cortex was a feature ; (5) in cases where it was impossible to chart the visual fields with precision, an homonymous defect of the visual fields could be confused with a defect of visual attention to that side ; (6) partial and quadrantic homonymous defects of vision were, in his experience, not usually associated with visual inattention to that side ; and (7) the lesion lay at a subcortical level near the convex surface of the opposite cerebral hemisphere in the hinder part of the temporal lobe, or in the neighbourhood of the angular gyrus, usually associated with a still deeper lesion.

Analysing the second group of cases, Allen found that unilateral visual inattention occurred in ten cases without field defects, in which the morbid anatomy was demonstrated. There was an attention loss over the whole of the temporal field of vision on the affected side, and in suitable cases, over the whole of the corresponding nasal field. The cases were mainly neoplastic, but one was vascular in origin ; increased intracranial pressure was commonly present ; the inattention phenomenon was present on the side opposite the lesion, but it varied in appearance according to the degree of intracranial tension. There were always signs indicative of parietal disease, including sensory changes.

Allen ascribed visual inattention to a disintegration of visual impulses at a physiological level higher than that of the visuo-sensory area of the opposite cerebral hemisphere in cases in which the lesion has involved the cerebral cortex extensively in its outer and posterior part, or in which there have been extensive changes in the cerebral cortex with a lesion of the upper and inner portion of the parietal lobe. He endeavoured to study the phenomenon not so much as a psychological manifestation, but as one along lines of neurophysiology and anatomy.

Bender (1945) has drawn attention to another possible though infrequent consequence of visual inattention, namely monocular diplopia or polyopia. These symptoms, which may be transient, may be explained partly on the basis of occipital damage, and a disturbance in the mechanism of ocular fixation. In addition, however, Bender implicated the phenomenon of fluctuation, obscuration or extinction of visual images—as the result of rivalry between the healthy and diseased hemispheres. Abnormal ocular deviation may result, and this may cause the visual image to impinge upon some retinal point other than the true macula. A conflict between the visual sensations evoked at the two retinal points, leads to defective vision, or even double vision.

Altered visual adaptation time

The technique of field testing employed by Cibis, and utilized especially by Bay, Lauenstein and others, brought to light another important aspect of vision, one which concerned temporal qualities. Thus, if an object was detected when exposed in a peripheral part of the field, it was in certain circumstances apt to fade and to disappear while the stimulus-exposure was actually being maintained. This rapid fading of a test-object was often met with in patients with posteriorly situated lesions of the brain, whose fields of vision were intact on ordinary perimetric testing. This phenomenon was spoken of as alteration in the adaptation time, and was regarded as a type of asthenopia, or undue visual fatigue. The conception of a temporal factor in visual perception is a very important one and is also an attractive idea. It falls readily into place alongside Monakow's chronogenic factor in perception, and it also represents the logical extension of the principle of tachistoscopy in vision.

Bender and Teuber did not accept the notion of altered rate of adaptation without certain reservations. They were of the opinion that had Cibis and others allowed the visual target to remain a little longer *in situ* after it had faded from view, it would probably have reappeared as a sense datum and then perhaps faded again. In other words, Cibis' increased visual adaptation was probably only a part of (and the first phase of) a phenomenon of visual fluctuation. This criticism may or may not be justified, but it does not essentially assail the fundamental importance of Cibis' technique, which entails the essential need of introducing a time-factor into every test of visual perception.

Visual efficiency can therefore be charted in a graphic fashion, employing a campimetric technique of testing for the speed of onset of local adaptation. A contrast can thus be made between sectors where the appreciation of visual stimuli is maintained in a normal and indefinite manner ; and sectors where stimuli are sensed but only for a limited period of time. This former sector of the visual field can be qualified by terming it the " effective visual field " in contrast to the whole area where simple perimetry shows no gross changes. In this way, a " damage curve " can be constructed. No clear-cut borders are said to exist between lost and intact parts of the field. Even with small cerebral injuries, the visual field tended to be affected as a whole, in the direction of altered adaptation time. Certain parts of the field showed rather more change than others, but gradually sloped towards areas with a smaller loss of function. Cibis and Bay interpreted these findings as evidence against any point-to-point projection of the retina on to the visual cortex, the macula being diffusely represented.

Defects in the appreciation of colour

This impairment refers not to any colour agnosia, or amnesia for colour naming, but to a localized disorder of the appreciation of colour, limited to a sector or area of the visual field. Within such an area, colours can perhaps be distinguished one from the other but they appear " muddy " or " impure " in hue. There may be a tendency for the colour of a small visual target to approximate to the colour of the background, so that sharp differentiation does not occur. The change in hue of the target is consequently an inconsistent one, and may take on chromatic properties which differ according to circumstances.

Bay and Cibis have used Nagel's anomaloscope to demonstrate this " colour asthenopia " after cerebral lesions.

Altered rate of flicker-fusion

Specific tests may show that after cerebral lesions, there may be a lowering in the critical frequencies for fusion of visual flicker (c.f.f.). The test is particularly revealing when a difference can be shown between one homonymous field and another, though as a rule the change is most evident in the centre of a field.

Here, again, the test is important in that it is betrayed only by special techniques. Most patients are unaware of any change in this stroboscopic faculty, and unless specifically looked for, the defect will not be found. On the other hand, some of the patients noticed an illusory acceleration of moving objects, through areas of the field where the rate of flicker fusion was depressed (Teuber and Bender).

A word is necessary to point out the inherent difficulties of the testing procedures, which demand a strict standardization of technique with natural and uniform illumination. The endpoint is not a very sharp one, and being entirely a subjective evaluation, cannot be checked independently. The rate of flicker fusion is one which varies considerably in the same subject according to numerous endogenous factors, including fatigue. Despite these inherent drawbacks, the test is a useful one in that it can demonstrate at a particular sitting, in a given set of circumstances, a possible difference in the subjective appreciation of an illusory fusion of a rapidly moving object. It is the difference (rather than the actual numerical reading) which is of importance.

Optic nystagmus

Localizing information has been sought in cases of cerebral disease by recourse to the technique of optic nystagmus (optomotor ; opto-kinetic nystagmus). This test promises to be of particular help in cases where a homonymous hemianopia exists. It forms an addition to the battery of tests of visual function, even though its utility is still under discussion.

The test was introduced by Bárány (1921), and was studied by Brunner (1922), Stenvers (1924, 1925), Cords (1925), Strauss (1925) and Ohm (1926). The first detailed account of the value of optic nystagmus in neurological diagnosis was made by Fox and Holmes

(1926). Their series included cases in which there was hemianopia but optic nystagmus could not necessarily be elicited ; they found that visual inattention in itself was not the immediate cause of the loss of optic nystagmus. Fox and Holmes agreed with Stenvers that optic nystagmus is a cerebral reflex with a centripetal centre in the occipital lobe, and a centrifugal centre in the frontal lobe, these two centres being connected by a reflex path. A large proportion of the lesions associated with the loss of optic nystagmus lay in the inferior part of the parietal region, or in the temporal lobe. Nystagmus to the opposite side seemed to be affected by lesions of the supramarginal or angular gyri of the adjacent portion of the parietal and temporal lobes, of the posterior end of the second frontal convolution, or by lesions situated along a line joining this with the angular gyrus.

A series of papers by Fox and his associates (1926 to 1936) lead to more intimate knowledge of the nature of optic nystagmus. Fox (1932) concluded that disorders of optic nystagmus cannot be explained solely on the basis of imperfect recognition of visual objects emerging from contralateral " inattentive " or blind fields. Thus, the response may be disturbed with lesions in the temporo-parieto-occipital region, in cases where the contralateral visual fields are either normal or else slightly indented, visual attention being unimpaired. Interruption of the corticofugal system or optomotor pathway (the internal sagittal stratum of Sachs) at any point in its course disturbs the ocular response to a certain direction of movement of the visual field. According to Fox, a defect in this corticofugal system is the primary cause of a disturbance of optic nystagmus, regardless of whether the corticopetal system, or sensory visual radiation, happens also to be involved.

Stadlin (1949) confirmed these views, but in a single case. His conclusions were : (1) if hemianopia exists with normal optokinetic nystagmus, the lesion may lie anywhere within the higher optical pathways ; (2) if there is hemianopia with loss of optokinetic nystagmus, the lesion must be situated high up towards the striate area ; and (3) if optokinetic nystagmus is abolished in the absence of hemianopia, the lesion affects the fibres connecting the optomotor area with the " centre " of lateral gaze, near the 6th nerve nucleus.

Henderson and Crosby (1952) have dealt with the problem experimentally in the case of monkeys. They found that intact pre-occipital and occipital eye-fields (areas 19 and 18) are essential for normal optokinetic responses. If both these fields are ablated on both sides, such responses are abolished. Should the appropriate portions of the preoccipital and occipital eye fields be destroyed on one side, optokinetic responses are not elicited on rotation of the drum

Y

away from the side of the injury. If there is destroyed a portion of one preoccipital eye-field, functionally related to conjugate horizontal deviation of the eyes, the homolateral eye-field may still produce an optokinetic response in the expected direction.

Tachistoscopy

Valuable information as to the nature of visual perception has been afforded by the procedure of tachistoscopy. Pictures are exposed for very short periods of time, and the subject is instructed to describe, identify, and better still, make a sketch of what he has seen. The picture can be projected so as to overlie the fixation point of one eye or of both. Or, by projecting the picture a little to one side of the fixation point, one homonymous field can be compared with another. Shapes, colours, forms—both simple and complex— can be used as stimulus figures, and a wide range of exposures can be utilized extending usually from 1/200th sec. up to 2 secs. The technique of tachistoscopy can be used in normal subjects in an effort to investigate the normal act of visual perception. It can be utilized in cases of brain disease, including both diffuse as well as focal lesions, and understanding of the various visual agnosic disorders and the qualitative visual defects (*Funktionswandel*) is assisted. Perhaps there have not been enough studies comparing the performance of normal subjects at high speeds of exposure with that of patients with brain disease shown pictures at slower exposures. Indeed, the technique of tachistoscopy has still not received the attention it deserves at the hands of clinical neurologists.

The problem of defective visual object recognition is admirably shown by the case described by Garner and Berlin (1951). Their patient complained of being blind, but it transpired that he was able to identify the colour and nature of objects if exposed for a period of 5 secs. or longer. With briefer glances, he failed : with deliberate and prolonged inspection, he succeeded. Cases such as this are unintelligible to the associationists, for the performance cannot strictly be marked in terms of either a plus or minus. The introduction of a chronogenic or temporal factor into the matter of perceptual efficiency necessitates a dynamic or organismic line of explanation.

Adler's patient was shown the figure 18 on a card. The " 1 " was recognized at 1/150th sec., but the other figure was doubtfully described as a ' 6 ', or a ' 3 ' . . . " Or is it a ' 5 ' ? " At 1/100th sec., she said it was a ' 6 ' ; at 1/50th sec., she said, " Oh, it is an ' 8 '. All the time I have seen only the lower loop, and therefore I thought it was a ' 6 '." She was then shown a meaningless black form (which is correctly perceived by normal subjects at 1/150th sec.), and was told to draw what she had seen. It was obvious that the patient had gleaned only a very vague idea of the shape at that particular speed. The procedure was repeated at progressively slower speeds. Her drawings demonstrated clearly that she could not perceive details simultaneously. She could detect parts only, and by gradually tracing around the contour, would add these parts together. Each time, she would begin at the top part of the figure, and usually on the left side before the right. Finally, after a 5 sec. exposure, she recognized all the details of the figure, saying in explanation . . . " I could not get all the little marks at first because it was so fast. I only got the two upper ones first."

Birkmayer has afforded us the most detailed information obtained from the largest series of brain injured subjects studied tachistoscopically. He used two test-pictures : (1) a circle with a star below and to the left, and a triangle with its point downwards, below and to the right ; and (2) three shoes of different pattern arranged in a row and coloured blue, red and black respectively. The patients were instructed to draw what they thought they had seen. With the first of these pictures, most patients behaved as follows : they saw at 1/200th sec. a flash of light, sometimes combined with something grey and amorphous. At 1/100th sec., three figures would usually be seen in correct spatial arrangement, but the forms could not be perceived. At 1/50th sec., the circle was almost always identified, and generally one other figure (either the star on the left or the triangle on the right). The question of which lateral figure was seen depended upon which side attention was weaker. Recognition of the shapes and spatial relationships of all three figures was achieved at speeds between 1/5th to 2 secs.

The foregoing was the usual type of performance. A number of variations were encountered, however. Thus, one patient saw the triangle on the right at 1/200th sec., and did not see the circle and the star until exposures of 2 secs. were attained. Sometimes, the circle was drawn as a ring : or fused with the star to constitute a shape like a ship's wheel. Sometimes, at 1/100th sec., the triangle on the right was seen together with a central figure described as a square. At times, at 1/50th sec., all three figures were recognized, but in an incorrect spatial alignment. A sort of alloaesthetic displacement of the lateral figures sometimes occurred. Sometimes the circle did not seem to be in the centre of the three objects but to be displaced to one side or the other. Or the star and triangle seemed to be unusually low down in their situation as regards the circle. One patient saw the star only at 1/200th sec., and at 2 secs., he still saw nothing but the star (= Bálint's compression of the visual field).

As regards the second test-picture, most patients with 1/200th sec. exposures saw nothing but an impression of light, or perhaps a red spot. At 1/100th sec., several unidentified objects were seen. At 1/50th sec., there were perceived three objects in a definite spatial arrangement. At 1/25th sec., it was possible to say that the central object was red, the one on the left was not clear, the one on the right being dark. Red was always the first colour to be detected. At 1/10th or 1/5th sec., the red central object could generally be identified as a lady's shoe ; with another shoe either to the right or to the left (according to the side to which attention was weak). It took an exposure of 1 sec. before all three objects could be recognized. At 2 to 5 secs., the correct spatial arrangement was also realized (though there were two patients who were successful at 1/100th sec.).

Variations of the above order of events occurred at times. Some patients received the impression of redness with a very short exposure (e.g. 1/100th or 1/200th sec.). In such cases, the colour-recognition blocked the subsequent recognition of form for an undue length of time ($\frac{1}{2}$ to 2 secs.). Sometimes, the blue colour (ordinarily last identified) would be projected to the black shoe on the right. There were cases where recognition of form and detail appeared earlier than for colour ; indeed, early recognition of colour seemed to block the recognition of further figures. Faults in the detection of the spatial arrangement were common. Often only two out of the three figures were perceived, the other one not coming into awareness until after comparatively long exposures.

Birkmayer believed that brain-damaged patients behaved much as normal individuals as regards the various stages of accomplishment. First comes an amorphous impression, which Butzmann called a " primary mist ", and Birkmayer refers to it as a *petite perception*. Next comes the second phase of a vague circular contour, which marks the beginnings of a simple spatial arrangement. Then comes the recognition of a partial figure which in brain-damaged patients often retarded further differentiation. The same blocking effect occurs with premature recognition of colour. Birkmayer spoke of the partial figure early recognized as the " critical detail " of the object. It is at this stage that patients with cerebral lesions begin to make errors, especially in spatial orientation. (Geometrical metamorphopsia.) The so-called " inner plane " of the figure makes its appearance very late, if at all, in patients with cortical disorders of vision. The ultimate picture makes its appearance suddenly. Here, again, it may be blocked by a premature grasping of a detail.

Most of these tachistoscopic data have been studied upon patients with occipital rather than parietal disease, though there would be scope for interesting work in the latter type of case. It is interesting to note that Bender and Teuber found at times that tachistoscopy would reveal retention of visual function in areas in which perimetric studies indicated amaurosis. (These particular patients exhibited ring scotomata and/or tubular fields.) In Bay's interesting case of visual agnosia with qualitative defects, only a dark brown leather purse with a rectangular metal fastening, placed at a distance of 1 metre from the patient, was exposed for varying short periods of time. After 1/100th sec., it was described as a " dark spot ". At 1/50th sec., he said it was " like a square of dark colour ", and upon a repeated similar exposure, he noticed " something " (i.e. the fastener), " low down ". At 1/25th sec., he described two objects . . . " darker on top, lighter below ". At 1/10th sec., his description was . . . " like a quadrangular box, black in colour ; underneath there is something painted ". After 1/5th sec., he thought it resembled a " sugar casket ". When the object was exposed for an indefinite period of time, the patient stated that it was " like a clock ; somewhat light in the middle . . . an alarm clock ". But when the object was brought forward from 1 metre to 20 cms. distance from the patient, he at once proclaimed it was " a purse ".

CHAPTER X

DISORDERS OF SPATIAL THOUGHT

It is scarcely possible to give any other definition of space : space is what enables us to distinguish a number of identical and simultaneous sensations from one another : it is thus a principle of differentiation other than that of qualitative differentiation, and consequently it is a reality with no quality.

HENRI BERGSON.

With the discovery of the relativity of simultaneity, space and time were merged in a single continuism in the same way as the three-dimensions of space had been before. Physical space was thus increased to a four-dimensional space which also included the dimension of time. The four-dimensional space of the special theory of relativity is just as rigid and absolute as Newton's space.

ALBERT EINSTEIN.

Earlier chapters have repeatedly indicated that parietal lesions are often followed by anomalies in spatial considerations. For instance, the various disorders of corporeal awareness can be looked upon as defects involving the body-image in its capacity as a unit within a three-dimensional environment. Constructional apraxia can be regarded as a difficulty upon the patient's part in breaking down and building up again an object either in two or in three dimensions. Gerstmann's syndrome involves more complicated difficulties, both in the realm of personal space (body-image) and of outer space. Many of the visuopsychic manifestations that have been described, as well as some of the tactile disorders, involve spatial components as well as more simple perceptual factors. But there are still other disorders of spatial thought which may be demonstrable at times in patients with parietal disease, and the subject is one of such importance and peculiar difficulty as to warrant a more detailed discussion.

The literature which treats this aspect of neurology is far from easy to follow, not the least for the want of clear thinking and clear writing upon the part of some authors. Certain fundamental points are often confused, and the terminology has thereby increased in a highly artificial and unsatisfactory fashion.

As an illustration of the extraordinary elaborate language which has been employed at various times, one may mention that the following terms have been used, if not synonymously, at least in close apposition : spatial agnosia ; visuospatial agnosia ; agnosia for spatial orientation ; agnosia for spatial relationship ; apraxia for spatial articulation ; disordered visual space perception ; planotopokinesia ; visual constructive derangement or disability ;

disturbances of geometrical vision ; disturbance of space-image ; inaccurate spatial localization ; space-blindness ; loss of abstract spatial relations ; visual-spatial cognition ; deform.tion of visual co-ordinates ; disorganization of discriminative spatial judgment ; disorientation ; impaired sense of direction (*Richtungsvorstellung*) ; and, quite simply, "k" (a group factor closely concerned with the ability to obtain, manipulate and utilize visual-spatial imagery). Lange distinguished four types of agnosicapraxic disorders of visual space perception, viz. (1) " dyslexia " (due to oculomotor ataxia) ; (2) defective visual perception of number (as shown by an inability to count) ; (3) visual-spatial agnosia ; and (4) apractognosia for spatial articulation.

It is desirable to try and simplify this difficult problem. Various levels and hierarchies in the matter of spatial thought may be distinguished both for the sake of clarity and tidiness, and also because a dissociation may occur through neurological disease, leaving one aspect more or less intact, while another is ablated. Thus, one can isolate as separate problems : (1) spatial perception ; (2) conceptions of space ; and (3) various spatial manipulations.

(1) *Spatial perception* is a complicated process in which visuo-tactile sensa play a chief part, but which may also include impressions of auditory, vestibular and even olfactory type. Each of these sensa possesses, according to James, an essential quality of voluminousness, or extensity. Previous experience also assumes an important role, as do active movements of the head and eyes. Finally, there comes an intellectual operation of synthesis and deduction which may take place with great rapidity and at an unconscious level. This is spatial colligation, or the process of blending of discrete impressions into a single spatial perception (described by Mach, Hartmann, Birkmayer and others). Parietal disease may in certain circumstances interfere with this final stage of co-ordination and interpretation of sense-data.

This faculty may be impaired in parietal disease because of physiological defects in the visual sense data. These are subtle in nature and are not likely to be discovered unless special methods are adopted. The patient himself is usually unaware of any corresponding disability until appropriate tests have brought them to his notice. Most of these disorders of spatial perception have already been described in the previous chapter, and need not be discussed again in detail.

The chief spatial perceptive disability to obtrude itself upon the patient's awareness comprises those metamorphopsias where dimensional factors are concerned. Here belong such phenomena as illusory obliquity of vertical or horizontal directions ; teleopsia ; pelopsia ; and the very rare cases of inverted vision.

Most other spatial perceptual disorders are not obvious to the patient. They include among others : loss of stereoscopic vision ; illusory acceleration (or retardation) of moving objects ; inability to discern readily the units of superimposed line-figures. The patient may also be unable to detect the alternatives in visual rivalry tests ; or to be deceived by visual illusions. Paterson and Zangwill's " cube analysis " test (where the patient is instructed to estimate the total number of bricks made up of three in each dimension) may prove impossible. Some of the many difficulties encountered by a patient with visual disorientation also belong here. Thus, a patient may be unable to count a collection of objects before him (even with the help of touching each article in turn). He may find it hard to decide which object lies farthest away and which is nearest to him ; and which are most laterally sited. From a collection of sticks of different sizes laid out in haphazard fashion before him, he may be unable to show the longest and the shortest. When reading a paragraph, he may experience difficulty in moving his eyes directly from the end of one line of print to the beginning of the next line.

Inability to count is also well shown in cases where there occurs not so much a visual disorientation as a defect of attention. Certain of the objects to be counted may, by reason of their particular location within space, tend to be disregarded or overlooked. This defect of counting has been interpreted as an inability to " partition space ".

Just as the patient may be unable to choose the longest or the shortest out of an assortment of sticks before him, so too he may prove to be incapable of arranging a set of miscellaneous articles according to size (though well able to do so in terms of colour, weight or texture).

The mechanical difficulty in reading is a sensorimotor defect of eye movements, which become ataxic and do not pass easily from the end of one line to the start of the next. Some writers look upon this defect as the expression of a disorder whereby the smooth flow of attention is interrupted by both an undue distractability, and also by a tendency to fix too long upon a visual stimulus.

Among these examples of visual disorientation (looked upon as spatial disorders of perception) is the inability to point accurately to an object in space. This is ordinarily demonstrated in the visual confrontation test, objects being held up in the periphery of the fields and the patient is directed to point to them or to touch them. As already stated, this type of visual disorientation becomes more inaccurate the more peripheral the visual stimulus. The disorder may be limited to one homonymous half-field or even to a homonymous sector. Much more gross defects may occur, especially in cases of visual object agnosia. The patient may be unable to take in an object as a whole by passing from one detail to another. Thus, the patient may see, recognize and indicate a lighted cigarette, but not the individual who is smoking : he may pick out a handbag but fail to realize his wife is seated by his bedside : he gazes at and identifies the window-latch but not the window itself. The factors of compulsive fixation ; of disordered attention ; of apraxia of ocular movements may also be operative in such cases. Again, the patient may be unable to point out, to command, the various objects with which he is surrounded even though he sees them. Such a defect is rare. It is more often demonstrated by dint of certain manœuvres, i.e. after the patient has been shown the objects around him as he stands in the centre of the room, and is then passively turned through an angle of 90° or 180° ; or after his eyes have been blindfolded ; or after being instructed to lie down. A defect which seemingly entails apraxic (or at any rate apractico-agnosic) elements is shown by the patient being unable to manipulate two or more objects placed before him. Thus, after correctly pointing out a box of matches and a candlestick, he may find it impossible to pick up the one and set light to the candle.

The patient may lose stereoscopic visual perception, and the surrounding scene may appear as flat as a coloured picture. Rarely does the patient mention this phenomenon, either because it is too tenuous for him to appreciate, or because it is complicated by other visual symptoms which are more obtrusive. The defect is demonstrable, however, by means of the stereoscope, when it will be found that the ordinary illusion of exaggerated depth does not appear, and one image cannot fuse with the other.

Among the exceptional cases where the patient was subjectively well aware of a loss of stereoscopic vision is the following : A woman of 49 years underwent a hysterectomy. On recovering from the anaesthetic, she noticed double vision, followed within 24 hours by a defect of sight to the left ; dizziness ; and a list to the left when walking. A few weeks later, she realized that she was unable to visualize the location of objects at home ; as she ordinarily possessed an exceptional and " photographic " type of visual imagery and memory, her present disability was all the more striking. At the same time, she discovered that she had lost stereoscopic vision and that everything she looked at would appear " flat " and uninteresting. As she gazed out of her window, she could see a wall and beyond that, the street. Now, it would seem to her that people strolling along the pavement were actually walking on top of the wall. She also tended to lose herself in her block of flats and in the street. The condition was almost certainly one of a right parieto-occipital vascular lesion, although never confirmed. (Case No. 32288, Dr. D. Brinton.)

Only in very rare cases does the patient confuse a real solid object with a coloured pictorial representation of the object. Yet occasionally this does happen. A scenic view, realistic in colouring, tonal quality and chiaroscuro may in an appropriate setting deceive the patient with a parietal lesion. Similar confusion may be shown by animals and by young children ; and even at times by normal adults, provided that the environment is sufficiently life-like.

Special tests for binocular depth perception may reveal impairment which had been unsuspected by the patient. Birkmayer has relied upon four techniques for this purpose, namely, a dropping test, the three-thread test, the stereometer apparatus as used in the *Luftwaffe*, and also Pulffrich's cards (stereoscopic landscapes). These four tests can afford discordant results in a single patient, for the faculty of depth perception is by no means a simple one. Most successes were achieved with the " dropping " apparatus, showing that depth perception of moving objects is easier.

Some tactile disorders characteristic of parietal disease also entail spatial modalities. Loss of postural sensibility ; astereognosis, especially when it includes an amorphognosia ; atopognosis ; " sensory displacements " ; alloaesthesia ; all these belong to the category of spatial defects.

(2) *Conception of space,* that is the idea of a three-dimensional world enveloping and surrounding the body-mass of the subject, is quite another matter. It constitutes an age-old controversy in metaphysics to which Locke, Berkeley (as subjective idealists), and Kant have been conspicuous among philosophers, while Lotze, Cyon, James and McDougall have contributed much to the psychological aspects. Many persons of poor intellectual endowment, or of sketchy educational attainment, have little or no conscious notion of space or spatial imagery. With others, a conception of sort may exist but bear little, if any, relationship with reality. In this respect, the conceptions of space held by a philosopher, a mathematician and an artist are probably very different one from the other, and all of them are quite unlike the naïve ideas of the ordinary layman. A person blind from birth will have his own peculiar conceptions of surrounding space. There are no fundamentals, therefore, which can be said to lie at the basis of common experience or belief in so far as spatial ideas are concerned. Consequently, it is more difficult to determine whether parietal lesions are ever responsible for an upset in spatial conceptions, as opposed to perceptions ; and, if such really do exist, to study and demonstrate their nature.

Being largely an intellectual or learned faculty, combined with a plurisensorial image, the conception of space is to some extent a personal or highly individual aptitude, unobtrusive and essentially subjective. The nature of spatial thought continues to be a matter of debate, with nativistic and genetic theories standing in frank opposition, and with associationists, sensationists and Kantians remaining unconvinced by each other's arguments. It is not surprising, therefore, that examining neurologists find it difficult to assess how far spatial notions are upset, if at all, in parietal disease, especially if the patient is also confused or lethargic. There are reasons for imagining that some alterations probably occur. Loss of sight, for example, brings about a certain change in spatial imagery, even though—like the altered body-image—it may not be uniform in its nature. Highest level visuopsychic disorders (visual agnosia, so-called) will cause as much, if not more, subjective spatial disturbance than simple blindness. This is demonstrated when the patient is given certain tasks to perform which are in the nature of inter-dimensional manipulations.

The analogy of the blind may be quoted, in so far as it throws light upon the difficulties of a patient with parietal disease. The spatial world of the blind, especially of those born without sight, is largely made up of tactual and auditory sense data which are constantly being renewed, and which are the object of close attention. Those who have become blinded in childhood or later also possess a vivid recollection of past visual experiences, which, however, are no longer being augmented. The blind man's spatial conception is largely an aspect of haptics, though to a variable extent, depending upon such factors as the original intelligence and personality, the sum-total of past visual experiences, the educational status, and the cultural and aesthetic background. In his imagery, he may seem to dwell in the centre of a number of co-tangential spatial circles ; the innermost one comprising his own body. Beyond comes manual space within which he can grasp and feel objects, and move his fingers and hands. A little beyond lies brachial space which he can explore merely by stretching out his arms. Beyond that again lies a spatial terrain which is readily investigated by taking a few paces : this can be spoken of as ambulatory space (or available space). At a greater distance away lies the touch horizon, which forms the boundary of remote space, somewhat mysterious and vague, coming to life only by virtue of its sounds and noises, and dropping out of imagery in conditions of complete silence. The louder the auditory stimuli within this " space-shell ", the less remote it appears to the blind person.

A blind man's spatial imagery is deficient in various dimensions, and does not correspond with Euclidean space. It extends little, if at all, in a posterior direction. The blind man's head constitutes the nodal point as it were, rather than the trunk or limbs, so long as he remains immobile. When touching an object (or reading braille, making a basket, operating a switchboard), the focus of most vivid imagery descends to the region of the hands. The spatial conception of the blind does not extend in an upward direction with any clarity or degree of precision. Consequently, differences in vertical dimensions are elusive and unconvincing. Greatest definition applies to notions of laterality, and also to small-range differences in a fore-and-aft direction, close to the patient's body. The factor of symmetry is an important spatial conception for the blind person, whereas strict accuracy of vertical and horizontal co-ordinates are not important. Tilting, obliquity, loss of alignment are not as disturbing to the blind as they are to sighted persons.

These anomalies of spatial imagery in the blind can be gleaned mainly by way of the introspective analysis of intelligent subjects. As regards patients with parietal disease, the neurologist is less advantageously placed.

Perhaps it is also a question of a change in spatial conceptions when the patient informs us that his environment appears " confused " or " jumbled ". This is (as already described) a common remark made by patients with one type or other of visual agnosia, even though they may immediately go on to say that each individual object is clearly seen. The sum total of visual sense-data is, none the less, in some indeterminate way, " not right ". Neurologists may endeavour to explain away some of these intangible visuospatial anomalies by speaking of them as examples of derealization or of depersonalization. In so far as these states of derealization and depersonalization may arise from focal structural brain disease, they may well belong to the category of organically determined disorders of spatial conception.

Parietal (or temporoparietal or parieto-occipital) disease may perhaps produce a state of affairs analogous to some toxic states, including temporary alcoholic influence. In such circumstances, the environment becomes vaguely distorted, so that distant objects and persons seem unduly far away and, losing their importance as units in the present scene, tend to drop out of awareness and to be disregarded. On the other hand, persons and objects in the immediate proximity become all-important, and temporarily dominate the subject's spatial world. Some such distortion, or alteration in the relative values of objects in space, may well account for the behaviour of a patient with a posteriorly situated cerebral lesion. His indifference to what goes on around him (except for objects and events which happen to concern him intimately for the moment) ; his apparent preoccupation ; his variability in response to test-procedures ; his inattentiveness, or rather his inability to switch his attention easily and quickly from one concept to another: all these symptoms of brain disease may perhaps be marks of an organic depersonalization.

Other neurological studies of spatial thought may be mentioned. Fischer (1932) was interested in spatial orientation from the standpoint of comparative physiology. He distinguished " near " from " far " orientation in space, the latter term being applied to the long distance homing sense possessed by certain birds, as well as by dogs and horses. In Fischer's opinion, there is still no adequate explanation of this " far " orientation. Birkmayer (1951) regarded the idea of space as being built up of concentric space-shells (*Raumschalen*), of which the innermost is constituted by the subject's own body. This shell is ontogenetically the earliest, and is the one which is most generously endowed with sensory material. Beyond lies the area of grasp, or of touch (*Greifschale*), and beyond that, the area of vision (*Sehschale*). Within each shell, the constituent sensory qualities are fused by means of a faculty of orientation. With each space-shell the subject commands different ranges of freedom. Boundaries between the various space-shells are not absolutely rigid. Each different type of orientation is liable to its own pattern of dysfunction in cases of cerebral affection. Orientation in the outermost (visual) shell is regarded as most vulnerable since only one sensory system is concerned. The relative frequency of the different types of disorientation is said to be shown statistically. Out of a series of 3000 cases of brain injury, there were about 150 instances of visual disorientation (including optic agnosia); 60 examples of disorientation within the touch-shell (right-left confusion, tactile agnosia and apraxia); and less than 10 cases of disorientation within the body-shell (autotopagnosia, alloaesthesia). Gooddy and Reinhold (1952) in their recent study of orientation in space successfully avoided most of the neologisms of the recent literature in a commendable fashion: they used the term orientation for the ability to integrate all, and perceive certain, of the sensory impulses arising from the entire body, and to relate—not necessarily at a conscious level—one set of sensory information to another. They have emphasized that the human individual, being symmetrically arranged about a longitudinal axis from head to foot, orientates himself in a manner directly related to this structure. This central longitudinal axis forms the " fixed point " around which the mobile and symmetrical body-segments move in a rotatory and also a parallel direction, and so form the basis for orientation. Schilder's conception of the importance of the midline of the body is emphasized.

The important and detailed study of spatial organization of visual perception by Bender and Teuber (1947–8) is mainly an analysis of the phenomena of visual disorientation, interpreted along the lines of the theories of vector psychology.

Such concentric limitation of the horizon of attention recalls Stengel's views as to the spatial world of a patient with constructional apraxia. A regression to an infantile notion of space in which " near " and " far " are the sole spatial distinctions has been envisaged. If this is so, it would mean a substitution of the ordinary geometric ordinates of up and down, left and right, before and behind, by a single quality of distance—irrespective of direction.

In advanced cases of parietal disease, when disordered conceptions of space are associated with marked impairment of spatial manipulations, other signs may be found. Autotopagnosia, or inability to point out various parts of the body, may be interpreted *inter alia* as a disorder of personal space. Striking defects may be observed at times in patients with parietal disease, the features of which depend upon the nature of the underlying psychological defect. Thus, in cases of hemi-asomatognosia, the patient may readily point out anatomical landmarks which lie within the normal half of the body or the midline, but finds difficulty in touching parts of the body on the affected side. He may continue to indicate the mirror-opposite locations. A spatial defect may be witnessed when the patient also fails to point out parts of the body depicted in a picture of a man ; or in his mirror-reflection. When a doll is held up, the patient may be able to touch the ear, eye, limbs upon one side only. Or else, the patient may succeed in pointing to the various parts of the doll, but make errors in lateral identification (calling the left limbs " right ", and *vice versa*). But at a later stage still, it may seem as though the frontiers between personal and extrapersonal space become less sharp. This is the *Ich-lähmung* of psychiatry, where there is an illusory fusion (" oneness ") with the environment. Ego blends with non-ego. This may show itself by the patient confusing his own limbs with those of the examiner, or *vice versa* (" Autoheterosyncisis "). Particularly is this likely to happen when the examiner holds one of the patient's limbs : the patient may then imagine that the examiner's hand is his ; or that his own leg is part of the examiner. When a pin is stuck into his arm, the patient, whose eyelids had been shut at the time, may point to a similar region upon the examiner's limb, as being the spot stimulated. This phenomenon needs to be distinguished from the illusory indication of some point in space between the bodies of the patient and of the examiner, as the region touched. This faulty localization is not at all rare : it may, of course, be an evidence of gross postural loss, but more typically, it is a dissociation between an intact sensorial appreciation of a pin prick and a distorted body-image. (Shapiro, Fink and Bender (1952) have termed this phenomenon " exosomesthesia ".) A similar confusion of *meum* and *tuum* has already been mentioned in the stick-tests of patients with constructional apraxia ; in these cases the patient may incorporate part of, or the whole of, the examiner's model into his own copy. Possibly belongs here also the not uncommon error whereby the patient, working with Kohs' blocks, places one or two of his bricks upon the card which bears the pattern.

(3) *Interdimensional spatial manipulations.* The third problem of spatial thought is simpler, and is one which clearly lends itself to neurological investigation. Many patients with parietal disease display considerable difficulty with what might be called automatic, or quasi-automatic, spatial manipulations. These are diverse in nature, and parietal disease does not necessarily impair every one of these operations. Indeed, it is much more usual for only some spatial tasks to suffer while others are unaffected. The distinction between spatial conception and interdimensional relationship corresponds with the dissociation between implicit and explicit spatial awareness (Paterson and Zangwill, 1944).

Spatial defects when present in severe form constitute a considerable handicap, even more so than a straightforward loss of sight. This statement has been borne out by the contrasting performance of two of Scheller's patients. One of these was a totally blind man (without any specific spatial loss) who travelled on foot 15 kilometres, hid himself in the grounds of a house, killed a woman and then returned to the place whence he had started. The other patient had a bilateral hemianopia with intact tubular vision and ability to read small print ; but she could not correctly carry out a right-angle turn, or find her chair, having risen from it and moved away a distance of 18 inches. As Scheller put it, any blind person can confirm that integrity of vision has relatively little to do with orientation.

The more important of these interdimensional spatial adjustments, or manipulations, may be listed and then discussed, with particular reference to the effect of parietal lesions : visual imagery (topographical memory) ; topographical " sense " (or ability to find one's way around) ; " spatial aptitude " ; " sense of orientation " ; " homing sense " ; ability to read a clock, and also to set the hands of a clock to a given time ; drawing from memory ; map reading ; construction of a plan or map of a familiar place ; self-extrication from a maze ; assembling of jigsaw puzzles, of Kohs' blocks and of manikins ; construction of machinery or buildings from a blue-print ; form-board tests ; ability to point to various parts of one's own anatomy on command (or to parts of the anatomy of others) ; mirror tests ; visual orientation ; perception for, or awareness of, external space, or of one half of external space.

To these may be added some other tasks which entail spatial considerations to a more limited extent, viz. dressing ; reading ; as well as remembering in correct order various historical events and personages, or scenes and characters in a work of fiction, or propositions in a textbook. The judgment or estimation of the passage of time may also be included.

The various forms of impaired spatial manipulation which are so often found in patients with parietal disease may now be discussed.

First among these may be mentioned *a loss of the ability to cull up visual images of a topographical or geographical sort.* This defect may be merely a part of a more profound irreminiscence (Charcot-Wilbrand syndrome), as is well shown in the original case-records made by these two authors. It is possible, however, that in some cases of parietal (as opposed to occipital) disease, the loss of visual images may entail places rather than persons. In such an event, the patient finds it difficult to conjure up a mental picture of a familiar environment— his home, bedroom, office, the streets in his neighbourhood and so on. This impairment may occur independently of other visual images. Thus, one patient who had lived for the past ten years in the South Kensington district, was quite unable to describe the Fulham Road, or Piccadilly Circus, but he could give a satisfactory description of his wife's appearance. (Metastatic tumour of the right parietal lobe.) When such a disorder is severe, the patient may even fail to recognize the buildings and furnishings among which he has lived and worked. Or he may recognize them with some dubiety, asserting that they look " unfamiliar, different . . ." To this special defect, the term *loss of topographical memory* is often applied, and it is generally adduced as the explanation of a good many other disabilities to be described later. Wilbrand's patient with loss of visual images also suffered from an inaccurate conception as to the spatial relationship of objects which were out of her range of vision. Thus, she would imagine that the street lay just outside her parlour (where actually the bedroom was situated), or that a piece of furniture was out in the road. This symptom she called " inverted thinking ".

Independent of all questions of topographical memory and imagery is the faculty of what can be vaguely called a " *sense of orientation in space* " ; a " *homing instinct* " ; " *spatial aptitude* " or " *topographical sense* ". This essentially consists in an ability to find one's way about without getting lost. In straightforward circumstances, this ability concerns an environment which is ordinarily well known (such as is comprised by the streets around one's home or office), or even, indeed, extremely familiar (as exemplified by one's own house or apartment). But many normal persons are also able in an uncanny fashion to navigate themselves without much difficulty in a district which is quite unfamiliar. By relying upon subtle visual clues, a well-developed sense of orientation may direct one undeviatingly towards a goal. Obviously, normal subjects differ as regards the sensitivity and accuracy of this particular skill.

In patients with parietal disease, the symptom of losing oneself often constitutes a conspicuous feature in the case-history. This may possibly bring to the notice of the relatives the fact of illness, though oddly enough, it rarely distresses or even interests the patient himself.

A number of such examples may be quoted:

". . . has found herself in the scullery looking for the dining-room. Once she arrived at the wrong end of the village looking for the butcher's."
(Unverified right parietal disease : Case No. 18025, Dr. Elkington.)

". . . was observed to have great difficulty in finding his way around the hospital (more than could be ascribed to his right hemianopia), and when faced with two or three doors or passages is unable to choose the correct one."
(Unverified left (? bilateral) parietal lesion : Case No. 12621, Dr. D. Williams.)

". . . has difficulty in finding her way about, and was recently almost lost on a familiar allotment of which she could not find the gates. In hospital, was noticed to be in constant doubt as to which was her bed."
(Unverified case of biparietal atrophy : Case : F. E. W., female, aet. 56 years. Dr. Riddoch.)

". . . has no mental image of his own home where he has lived many years ; he cannot describe his bedroom . . . his own home has seemed unfamiliar. One of his chief troubles was disorientation in space and time : e.g. he was unable to find his way around Bellingham—where he had been living for 15 years."
(Verified case of metastatic carcinoma of the brain, with bilateral parieto-occipital tumours. J. W., male, aet. 52 years.)

". . . he went far past his proper destination in a bus, and walking back, found great difficulty in finding his house. Indeed, he will often pass his home without knowing that it is his, and wander round for many minutes trying to decide where he does live . . . His geographical sense eventually became so impaired that, when he went out, he would ask his wife to leave a light on so that he could recognize his house more easily."
(Verified occlusion of the right middle cerebral artery : F. S., male, aet. 49 years. Dr. J. P. Martin.)

". . . has at times walked past her house on her way home, only realizing she had done so after she had gone a little way . . . In hospital, she was constantly losing herself, mistaking the dressing-room for the kitchen, going towards the ward when she meant to go to the dining-room, and not knowing her own bed from the others unless she placed some object belonging to her beside it for her to recognize."

z

(Right parieto-occipital meningioma ; verified. H. R., female, aet. 52 years. Dr. McArdle.)

". . . when he was about to take a bus home, he could not remember which bus he wanted ; for a time, he waited in the wrong queue. With some difficulty, he managed to get home. As he drove along, he could not ' for the life of him ' believe that this was the countryside he should have known so well. His home and surroundings are no longer familiar, although this does not apply to persons. On his way to the White City, he suddenly felt lost in Victoria Street, and had no idea how to get to his destination. He got on a tram which took him to the north of London. Then, he realized he had gone astray. A stranger re-directed him with instructions on a piece of paper. Eventually, he got to the White City, but failed to recognize it. A passerby had to help him find his seat. Afterwards, he had to be conducted home to Kingston, but could not recall where he had left his suit-case . . . On subsequent occasions, he sometimes took wrong turnings. In the hospital, he kept losing the Day-room."

(Right middle cerebral arterial thrcmbosis ; verified by arteriography. Case No. 28749, Dr. D. Williams.)

". . . he loses his way in the estate in which he lives. Perhaps this is due to not recognizing landmarks, but he feels this is not the whole explana-tion. He does not lose his way in his home in the daytime, but does so in the dark. He forgets his ' sense of direction '."

(Verified right parieto-occipital astrocytoma. Case No. 32872.)

". . . today, on the way to the hospital, he did not know at which under-ground station to alight, and at Russell Square he was completely at a loss to find his way to the hospital, and relied entirely upon his wife, although he had been there many times, and had formerly found his way about without any trouble."

(Unverified biparietal softenings. Case No. 27572.)

". . . in the past week, he has become lost about the house on several occasions. He has often had difficulty in finding the toilet, or when he had succeeded, he might miss the pan and urinate on the floor alongside."

(Right parietal atrophy ; verified. Case No. 24949.)

". . . she easily gets lost in a strange house or place. While at a con-valescent home earlier in the year, she often got lost in the building. Appar-ently, on one floor there were three doors of which she always opened the one on the extreme right. This always caused trouble as it belonged to the Board Room. While out in the town, she would get lost."

(Unverified case of biparietal atrophy. Case No. 34251.)

". . . he never seems to know where things are. He cannot find the door in a room he has known all his life."

(Case of cortical atrophy. H. D., male, age 37 years.)

". . . when visiting friends, he often went past their houses, although he knew them well. He took the wrong turning on coming to a road junction on his way to see a friend, along a route he knew quite well. He realized his mistake after having driven some distance, because he became vaguely aware that the layout was not quite right. In hospital, he would frequently ' over-shoot his cabin '."

(Right parietal cyst ; verified. Case No. 22775.)

". . . she has become lost in her house more than once. Once, she started off for the toilet and found herself on the porch outside. She has lost herself in the neighbourhood, on her way to the store. The wrong turning is almost always to the right ; that is, she would turn to the right instead of to the left. This is also the case indoors : if she intends to go into a room on the left of a hallway, she will enter a room on the right."
(Case of brain atrophy ; unverified. Patient of Dr. Hal Gregg.)

". . . she went to visit a neighbour, but knocked at the door of another's house three doors away."
(Verified right parietal astrocytoma. Case No. 21630, Dr. Walshe.)

". . . whenever she left the ward to go to the bathroom, she had to place her blue bedjacket across the bed so as to be able to identify it . . . On leaving the hairdresser's (where she is in the habit of visiting), she turned right when she should have turned left in order to get home."
(Right parietal thrombosis ; unverified. Case No. 38299.)

". . . the patient, who had been in hospital with the effects of an abrupt parietal vascular lesion, returned one month later to his home in Portslade. The chauffeur did not know the district and relied upon the patient to give directions. This proved impracticable, however, and they got lost, taking right-hand turnings instead of left, and overshooting the destination. At home the patient lost himself indoors, and also when taken for short journeys in a wheel-chair, he would be in doubt as to the shortest way back."
(Embolism right middle cerebral artery. Case No. 19450.)

One of the tasks which perplexes a patient with spatial disturbance is undertaking a long journey. It is not so much a problem of finding one's way through the streets, as more especially an inability to change trains at a railway station. Another difficulty lies in making one's way to a seat in a cinema, especially if the lights are dimmed at the time.

Neglect of one half of external space (*or imperception for one half of external space*) is another example of a defective interdimensional manipulation, probably first described in 1931 by Pinéas and in 1932 by Scheller and Seidemann. As already described in Chapter IX, it consists largely in a disregard of the objects which occupy one half of outer space (and not a disregard of space itself). Most of such cases also show an homonymous defect of vision. This lends itself to the plausible argument that the neglect of objects to one side of the midline is entirely due to the fact that they are not seen. In other words, the problem ties up with the phenomenon of visual inattention, but differs in that the presence of visual objects on the intact side plays no part in determining whether objects on the other side are neglected or not.

Not all patients with an homonymous hemianopia also show an homonymous spatial imperception : in fact, probably only the minority do so. Most hemianopic patients, whether aware of their visual defect or not, automatically adjust themselves within their restricted environment, and hence sweep their gaze in a lateral direction in order to look for, and if necessary avoid, external objects. Yet another important piece of evidence supports this argument : well-marked unilateral visual imperception may occur in some patients in whom no quantitative field defect exists. (Pinéas, 1931 ; Kroll and Stolbun, 1933.)

Imperception for one half of external space may be detected by various manœuvres. The patient who walks across a large room cumbered up with chairs, tables and other articles of furniture may

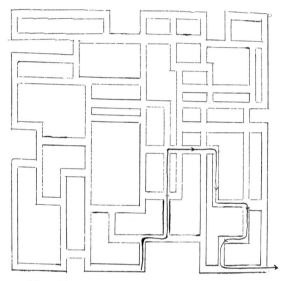

Fig. 111. Maze Test. The patient avoids most left-hand turnings.
(Right parietal lesion.)

collide with or bump into objects on one side only of the midline. (Of course, some patients with hemianopia behave in the same fashion, in the early days of their disability, at any rate.) A more convincing demonstration of homonymous spatial imperception is found by tracking the route taken by the patient on his way through a large building. He will be expected to show a preference for turnings or doorways to one side of the midline, i.e. he will always turn to the right (rather than the left), or *vice versa*. Such a performance is perhaps less readily explained upon the basis of a mere homonymous field defect. The test is a clumsy one, however, which scarcely lends itself to practical use. (A more revealing procedure would be to put the patient into a maze or labyrinth and to follow him, noting carefully his itinerary.   This procedure has never been carried out, as far as can be determined.)   A bedside test along the same lines, but in miniature, utilizes a plan drawing of a maze.   The patient marks with a pencil the route he would take in an attempt to extricate himself. (See Fig. 111.)   The most useful method of discovering whether a patient has an imperception for one half of space is to be found in Poppelreuter's visual searching test.   A consistent hesitancy in matching patterns from a medley of designs situated on one particular side of the fixation point affords a convincing demonstration of a different degree of visual significance of visual sense data on one side

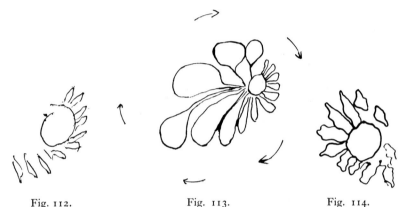

Fig. 112.   Fig. 113.   Fig. 114.

Fig. 112.   Incompleteness of the left-hand side of a daisy head, drawn by a patient
with a right-sided parietal cyst.
Fig. 113.   Patient, when asked to draw a daisy, drew in a clockwise fashion, making
the left-hand petals disproportionately large.   Right parietal tumour.
Fig. 114.   Patient's drawing of a daisy head, with inadequacies on the right-hand
side.   Case of left parietal syphilitic vascular lesion.
(Courtesy of Reinhold.)

or the other of the midline.   This test can be carried out upon a blackboard before an audience, and timed with a stopwatch.

Unilateral spatial disregard may also show itself in a number of free-hand drawing tests.   The patient is instructed to draw from memory some such symmetrical object as, for example, the head of a daisy.   Imperfections on one side as compared with the other may demonstrate a one-sided spatial neglect.   (See Figs. 112, 113, 114.)

Objection may again be made that this imperfect performance is entirely attributable to the field defect, and as a supporting argument, the example may be quoted of the inaccurate bisection of a horizontal line, so often shown by hemianopic patients.   The argument is not really valid, however.   A horizontal line is not a symmetrical, closed figure, and the hemianopic patient who bisects the line inaccurately does not really display an inattention so much as a blindness as regards the full linear extension on one side.   The patient is not afforded any clue as to the nature of the error that he is likely to make. A straight line inaccurately bisected is just as satisfying as one which is marked correctly in the midpoint. A daisy head with petals drawn on one side only might be expected to leave the patient uneasy or dissatisfied. The ordinary hemianopic patient would not be content with such a drawing, for he would realize how a daisy usually looks, and that petals grow out in radial fashion all around. Only the patient with homonymous spatial neglect (whether he happens also to be hemianopic or not) fails to notice that his drawing is not completed.

The patient with parietal disease who cannot perform free-hand drawings is often at a loss to explain the difficulties. There is no trace of defective revisualization in such cases, and the patient who has a clear mental picture of what he wishes to draw fails entirely to make a pictorial representation. Ehrenweld's patient, for example, said : ". . . I know very well what it looks like, but when I try to draw it, I can't."

A female diabetic who had suffered at least two cerebrovascular accidents found it almost impossible to draw on paper, although she previously was well able to carry out applied arts. Nevertheless, she had a very clear image of places and persons, and though there was no obvious constructional apraxia, she failed entirely to draw a house or a daisy. (Case No. 41513.)

Difficulties in reading or drawing maps, plans, charts and blue-prints usually form conspicuous evidence of spatial defects in patients with parietal disease. To transfer an actual landscape, or a topographical mental image, into an accurate and well-proportioned sketch-map is an operation which entails the conversion of a three-dimensional concept into one which is two-dimensional. To some normal subjects, this is both an unfamiliar and a difficult task, but not beyond the capacity of anyone of normal intelligence. Patients with parietal disease usually fail badly to carry out a request to draw a plan of their bedroom ; their house ; the streets in their neighbourhood ; or some such familiar or well-known location as, for example, Piccadilly Circus. The patient, confronted with such a task, often demurs ; protesting that this is a technical procedure beyond his ordinary competency . . . that he " never was any good at drawing ", and so on. These protests are usually rather unconvincing, and should be interpreted as evidences of a deliberate evasion of a difficult task, or one which he fears might prove revealing and too much for him.

The final result, after the characteristic hesitancies, slowness and indecision, usually reveals numerous mistakes. Some of these recall the efforts made by patients with constructional apraxia and, of course, a number of subjects may be expected to suffer from both conditions, that is, constructional apraxia as well as spatial disorientation. But spatial defects may occur without constructional apraxia. The features which suggest spatial disorganization include a tendency to confuse the three-dimensions of space. Thus, a patient who is told to draw a plan of the ground floor of his house may introduce chimneys or roof-tops into his sketch. (See Fig. 115.) Quite often,

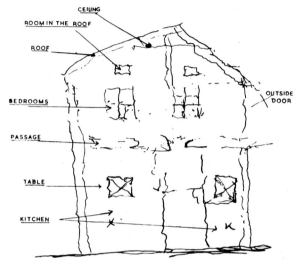

Fig. 115. Confusion of dimensions, revealed in a patient's drawing of a house. Case of right parietal softening.

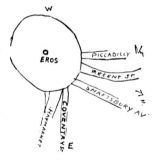

Fig. 116. A sketch-map of Piccadilly Circus, with neglect of the detail in top and left-hand sides. Case of right parietal lesion.

an incompleteness can be detected which involves only one side of the drawing, indicating a unilateral spatial neglect. In severe cases again, there may be a total disorder so that the pictorial attempt is quite unrecognizable.

Sketches representing Piccadilly Circus are particularly appropriate for the Londoner. Being largely a circular landmark with

streets emerging in radial fashion, the drawing readily betrays a unilateral neglect if this should be present.   The patient should finally
be instructed to insert the points of the compass upon his sketch :
this, in turn, may reveal a spatial disorientation.   A further useful
test is to draw a map of a familiar country and insert any five or six
cities.   Maps of Great Britain or of Ireland, being islands, are particularly valuable, for in cases of unilateral neglect, either the east
coast or the west may be imperfectly drawn.   Spatial defects are also
well shown by an inaccurate placing of the towns selected.   Some-

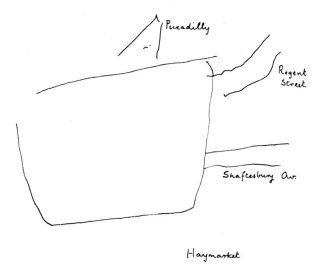

Fig. 117.   Another patient's drawing of Piccadilly Circus.   Case of right
parietal lesion.

times, it is possible to demonstrate a " dislocation " of cities to the
east (or west), even to the extent of their being sited within the
surrounding sea.   (See Figs. 118 to 121.)

An analogous, though opposite, task consists in map-reading,
that is the translation of a two-dimensional schema into a mental
image of a three-dimensional terrain or structure.   Some normal
individuals show little or no bent in this respect, but when a patient
with a putative brain lesion has obviously deteriorated as regards the
power of finding his way about with the aid of a chart, then a spatial
disability can be suspected.

When parietal disease afflicts such skilled subjects as engineers,
mechanics, constructors or architects, it may be that the patient can

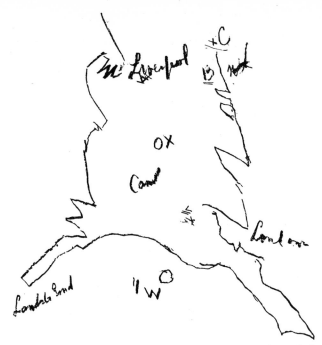

Fig. 118. Camb = Cambridge, I.W. = Isle of Wight, Ox = Oxford. Note C (= Cardiff) and B (= Bristol) both placed on east coast. Case of biparietal vascular lesions.

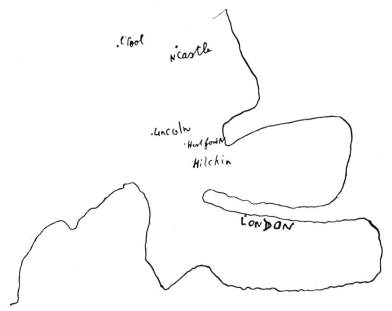

Fig. 119. Patient asked to draw a map of England and to insert any six towns (note omission of the west coast). Case of right parietal tumour.

no longer read a two-dimensional blue-print of a building or a piece of machinery. This difficulty is essentially a spatial agnosic one. A coexisting constructional apraxia will entail the additional inability of working to his blue-print.

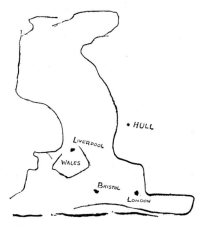

Fig. 120. In this map of England the city of Hull is sited too far to the east and is actually outside the map; and Wales is also shifted inland. Case of right parietal lesion.

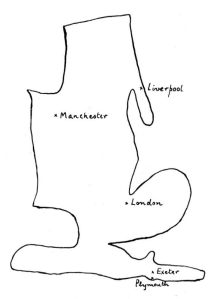

Fig. 121. Polycythemia vera with thrombolic lesion in right parietal lobe. Map of England and Wales drawn as requested and named towns indicated by patient. Plymouth and Exeter are marked as though in the eastern counties. Patient remarked that he was born and bred in Devon and knew exactly where Exeter was.

Free-hand drawing tests, as opposed to copying, often display in eloquent manner a difficulty in coping with the spatial elements of a composition. Certain themes may be adopted as standard tests, in that an anomalous performance is readily discerned, and the defects can be analysed. For this purpose, the patient may be asked to draw " out of his head " a bicycle ; an elephant ; a horse and cart ; a clock-face ; a chess-board ; a motor-car ; a human profile ; or a house. (Allowance must be made for the social, education and racial aspects of the case, and it must be borne in mind that some patients may have had a limited experience of bicycles or of elephants.) These particular test-themes are useful in that they entail the fitting together

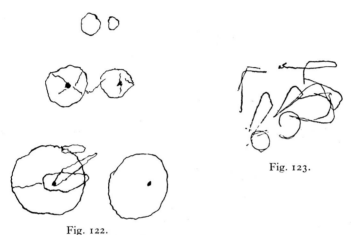

Fig. 123.

Fig. 122.

Fig. 122.   Attempts at drawing a bicycle.   Case of left parietal syphilitic
vascular lesion.
(Courtesy of Reinhold.)

Fig. 123.   Freehand drawing of a bicycle.   Case of biparietal vascular lesion.

of a number of constituent parts (especially the bicycle) and that a confusion of two and three dimensions can easily be identified (especially in the case of the house or human face). Most of these objects are " closed ", if not indeed symmetrical in outline, so that unilateral neglect is easily recognized. (See Figs. 122, 123 and 124.)

As in so many other tests for parietal dysfunction, the patient's attitude to the task is important. Very often, the patient is most reluctant to undergo the trial, excusing himself by saying that he " never could draw ", or that he has mislaid his spectacles and cannot see clearly. There may be a frank catastrophic reaction, with annoyance, embarrassment or distress. Sympathetically encouraged, he may betray hesitancies, slowness of execution and change of mind. In addition, there may occur the numerous graphic characteristics of a constructional apraxia, indicating again the common combination of the two conditions. Consequently, one may find the drawing being crowded into one corner of the page ; the closing-in sign ; obliquity of lines ; tremulousness ; inaccurate intersection of co-ordinates. (Too much attention should not be paid to mere errors

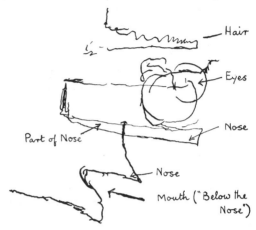

Fig. 124. Attempt at drawing a human face by a patient with biparietal vascular lesions. (Writing not inserted by patient.)

in perspective as these are all too common even in the drawings of normal subjects. For example, the classical Necker Cube Test is generally drawn incorrectly by the examiner himself.)

Paterson and Zangwill emphasized the various technical errors in drawing shown by their patients with disordered spatial thought.

Fig. 125. Form-board.

These included : (1) abnormal representation of perspective and depth ; (2) confusion of planes ; (3) anomalies of relative size and articulation ; and (4) a piecemeal approach.

Various *form-board tests* may also reveal spatial difficulties besides the more obvious features of a constructional disorder. This is well shown in the simple oblong form-board illustrated in Fig. 125. A patient with parietal disease, when given the constituent pieces and told to fit them into the gaps, usually finds it hard to arrange the two right-angle triangles so as to form the isosceles triangle. This defect is partly a constructional and partly a spatial one. But after turning his attention to the other geometrical shapes, the patient may remain satisfied even though he leaves uncompleted the figure which lies at one or other extremity. The patient's satisfaction persists despite the fact that the piece of wood lies ready to hand in such a way as might be expected to suggest that the task was still uncompleted. This particular feature indicates a neglect or disregard of an object in one lateral half of external space.

More elaborate form-board tests are not necessarily more informative. The Halstead board, though thought to be useful in cases of parietal disease, is probably too difficult for the average hospital patient. The Rey-Davis form-board constitutes a different type of test, for it brings out the factor of visual recall as well as definite spatial components. Most patients with parietal disease fail completely when tested with this form-board.

Another type of test for the efficiency of inter-dimensional manipulations comprises the assembling of jigsaw puzzles, Kohs' blocks and the manikin figures (as used by McFie, Piercy and Zangwill). Ordinary commercial jigsaw puzzles should be avoided as being too elaborate. A more simple and workable test is to take a straightforward coloured picture (as may be found in a child's book), to cut it into four quarters, and then to give the pieces to the patient for him to assemble. Even such an easy task as this baffles a patient with severe disorder of spatial thought. Kohs' blocks constitute a very informative test, the value of which has already been described in the chapter dealing with constructional apraxia. But it is interesting to note that a patient may fail badly at this test, even though no constructional apraxia exists whatsoever. This is not surprising since the use of Kohs' blocks test is an investigation into more than one aptitude or faculty. The manikin test consists in a figurine with head, arms and legs detached from the torso : the patient is directed to assemble the parts of the body in an appropriate fashion.

More severe cases of disordered spatial thought may prevent the patient from adopting natural postures ; for example, he may be unable to sit comfortably upon a chair, or to lie down on a couch. This defect, which bears some superficial resemblance to a trunkal apraxia, is not a common one. It occurred in the patients described by van der Horst, by Zutt and by Reinhold and Gooddy.

A variety of this upset in personal, corporeal relationships is shown by the patient who is asked to walk with his eyelids closed. He tends constantly to deviate to one side or the other, so that his route eventually takes up a sort of stellate course (Babinski's " star-walk test ").

The patient may also be muddled over the correct spatial orientation of verbal or numerical symbols. Thus, when a cardboard letter such as E, L or N is put before him, he may be puzzled as to which way round the letter should be placed. (A minor degree of this same spatial disorientation is sometimes found in the barely literate, who may confuse N and И ; S and Ƨ. Normal persons are rarely in doubt over E and Ǝ ; L and ⅃ ; and never do they mix up E with Ш.) Spatial disability is shown by those patients who are unable to hold a rod or a stick in a vertical or horizontal direction on command, or to alter its position appropriately as it lies upon the table. The letter-completion task is more complex, though it certainly entails spatial qualities. (In this test the patient is instructed to complete a capital letter drawn in an unfinished manner upon a sheet of paper or on a blackboard.)

Comprehension of the meaning of such adverbs of place as *up*, *down*, *in*, *out*, *back*, *front* may be defective, as judged by the patient's inability to demonstrate their significance in dumb show. One particular type of confusion has been specifically noted, namely an inability to distinguish *below* and *behind*. If, when looking at a picture, the patient is asked to indicate the portions which lie below, he may point to the back of the picture. This defect has been likened to the error of some young children who try to find a continuation of the pictorial scene upon the reverse of the page. Something similar was found in the case of a patient with a right parietal tumour, who set out to write a letter. The first line went horizontally across the page in the usual way ; but the second line was written on the back of the sheet of paper, the patient having turned over the page.

Spatial difficulties are displayed by those rare patients with hemi-depersonalization, who, unaware (or neglectful) of the existence of one half of their own bodies, cannot cope with sidedness as applied to other persons or inanimate objects. For example, a patient who maintained that her hemiplegic left arm (which she called " George ") seemed to be non-existent (and that, on inspection, it did not seem to belong to her) had great difficulty in identifying the right and left limbs of others. Shown a teddy-bear, for example, and asked to name the various parts of its anatomy, she as it were projected the midline of her body forward into space. Thus, the teddy-bear's limbs lying to her right were spoken of as its right arm and leg (actually the left). When the teddy-bear was turned around so that its back was towards herself, she correctly named its right arm. When the teddy-bear was placed horizontally, but with its face towards her, the upper limb was correctly termed the left. Before making a reply, the patient would in every case hesitate, and come to a conclusion on the question of sidedness only after raising her own right arm, looking at it and saying quietly to herself, " my right side ". If her right arm was covered with a blanket, she would not answer until she had moved the limb. If it were passively immobilized, she would become distressed and unable to answer. (This patient figured in Gooddy and Reinhold's series, as their case No. 4.)

The transformation of thought into articulate speech may also be considered as entailing spatial manipulations. Van Woerkom paid particular attention to this aspect of language, and especially to some of the mental operations which precede the act of speaking (the preverbal processes of thought). Aphasia, in his judgment, is closely bound up with a " loss of the geometric sense ", and a disorder in numerous non-verbal but spatial performances is often demonstrable. For example, some of his aphasic patients could not assemble shapes to copy a model, nor extricate themselves from a maze, nor reproduce rhythms by means of tapping. Temporal as well as spatial difficulties were therefore present, and the notion of correct sequence of ideas was often faulty. It will be recalled that one of van Woerkom's patients has already been quoted as exemplifying a Gerstmann syndrome, even before Gerstmann's first description (p. 204).

A simple but outstanding defect lies in a difficulty which many patients betray when asked to read the time. They look at the dial but fail to interpret the position of the hands of the clock. Often, they give a reply which would be correct were the big and little hands reversed : or were they arranged in a mirror-opposite fashion. The time-telling disability is furthermore demonstrated when the patient cannot set the hands of a dummy clock-face to command. Many different errors may appear, including a tendency towards mirror-reversals. The adoption of a more concrete type of response to these various clock tests (receptor and effector) is illustrated by the patient who reads the clock as indicating " supper-time " instead of half-past eight. With a dummy clock-face set at 3.20, one patient was asked to move the hands so as to read 4.30. After some hesitation, the patient seized the big hand and moved it through 380°, that is all round the dial until it rested in the " half-past " position—just as she probably would have done in moving on the hands of a real clock that was slow.

There are still other ways in which a patient with parietal disease demonstrates spatial difficulties. Thus, the act of dressing may be most disordered. The patient may be unable to play draughts : to cut out a star-shaped figure from a sheet of paper : to write down neatly the constituent integers of an arithmetical sum : to fold a letter accurately so as to fit into an envelope.

Most interesting and complicated of all are those spatial disorders which also involve the conception of time, or order, or sequence. Thus, at the simplest level, is the patient who is able to count, but not backwards : to recite the days of the week (months of the year, or letters of the alphabet), but not in reverse order. Some disorders of spelling can be regarded less as grammatical errors than as a spatio-temporal disability. This is well shown by those interesting cases of imperfect spelling of numbers (which are more abstract than words, and less concrete). Thus, the patient may be unable correctly to write down the numerals standing for " twenty million, two hundred and one ", and gets into difficulties with the noughts and the commas. A less obvious defect is shown by the patients who cannot visualize in correct order a list of monarchs or prime ministers ; who mix up the sequence of historical events. It may even be difficult to read a book, or recall a film, because of a tendency to forget the logical and chronological order of characters and incidents. The converse difficulty may also occur, whereby the patient finds it hard to arrange the constituent pictures of a story without words, so as to make sense (= Buhler's test). This particular disability has been associated more with frontal than with parietal lesions (McFie and Piercy), although Birkmayer related it to damage to the occipital lobe. It is a disability which may preclude the patient from playing any but the simplest card games.

Pure temporal disorientation, that is, occurring independently of spatial disorders, is a rarer phenomenon, for more often, the two are combined, especially in the case of massive space-occupying lesions within the middle third of the cerebral hemisphere. As Ehrenwald pointed out, one must distinguish between a primitive time sense, and a gnosic time-conception (by which is meant an understanding of chronological order). In such cases, a number of defects may occur, not necessarily within the patient's own knowledge : such disabilities include :

(1) Inability to judge the passage of time ; i.e. the length of time occupied by a medical interview. (The presence of an affective disorder must be realized as a complicating factor if it should happen to coexist with an organic brain lesion.)

(2) Difficulty in estimating the approximate hour of the day, except by a laborious process of recall of the meal last partaken, or of some other such clue.

(3) Gross disorientation in time, i.e. confusion of the season of the year, or the month, is more likely to be an aspect of dementia,

outside the category of a strict parietal lesion. The same applies to confabulatory adjustments to long amnesic gaps.

(4) The patient may develop altered temporal associations with simple habitual activities. Thus, an action may be accompanied by a refreshing sentiment—almost one of unfamiliarity—as if the patient had not performed this task for a very long time. Or the opposite phenomenon may take place, as if the patient had already carried out the performance earlier that day, e.g. shaving or taking a bath.

(5) Time may appear to pass too quickly. This phenomenon may be compared with an illusory acceleration of moving objects, and it may constitute what has been called the " quick-motion " (*Zeit-raffer*) phenomenon (Pichler ; Wagner). For Bodamer's patient, everything looked at moved too fast—people in the street, motor-cars, his own propelling-chair. Also, the passage of time was speeded up. Persons seemed to be talking too fast and too loud, with intolerably shrill and piercing voices.

Some of these combined temporal and spatial defects are illustrated in the following case-reports :

". . . he would turn up very late for meals and would spend as much as three hours lying in his bath . . . no idea of time . . . He made a journey to London for a business interview on the wrong day . . ." Physical examination included evidence of visual disorientation and constructional apraxia with paligraphia.

(Unverified case of right fronto-parietotemporal astrocytoma. Case No. 30075.)

". . . when shaving he would often imagine he had already shaved that day. The recent past seems ' flat ', and the future ' ill-defined '. Cannot tell when meals are due. He cannot remember whether he had been on an errand that day or the day before : whether the next meal is tea or lunch . . ."

(Left mid-cerebral arterial occlusion ; unverified. Case No. 28749, Dr. D. Williams.)

". . . severe disorientation in time and place. Says he left the Service 5 years ago (incorrect). It is now autumn . . . but several months since Christmas (actually January)."

(Multiple metastatic carcinomata of the brain. J. W., 1938.)

". . . after being in hospital three days, she asked when was the doctor going to see her as she had already been there for months."

(Case of unverified right parietal lesion. Case No. 18025.)

Anatomical considerations

Something should be said as to whether spatial disorders can be looked upon as focal manifestations of cerebral disease, and if so, what regions of the brain are most often concerned.

Clinical experience indicates that some or all of these symptoms

A A

may follow bilateral or unilateral lesions of the brain : in the latter case, either the dominant or the subordinate hemisphere may be at fault. Finally, evidence can be gathered to suggest that, although certain regions of the brain, when diseased, are more likely to be followed by spatial disorders, nevertheless they have been known to follow lesions situated anywhere from the frontal to the occipital lobes. These observations therefore suggest that spatial difficulties are not necessarily the clinical expression of diffuse disease of the brain, but that they may at times show themselves as if they were focal, outfall phenomena.

Bilateral disease of the brain, and especially of the parieto-occipital regions, may be followed by the most conspicuous spatial disorders, especially entailing visual disorientation. This is well shown in the original case-records of Holmes and Horrax, and also in the planotopokinesia of Marie, Bouttier and Bailey. But unilateral disease can also be operative, in that it may be followed—not perhaps by universal visual disorientation, but by other spatial difficulties. Some authors have attempted to distinguish between different patterns of spatial upset, according to whether it is the dominant or the non-dominant hemisphere which is diseased. Thus, some have contrasted topographical memory and topographical " sense ", equating an upset of the former with a lesion of the dominant half of the brain, and an impairment of the latter with disease of the subordinate hemisphere.

In practice, there is a slight bias in the direction of suspecting the subordinate hemisphere, but again (as in the case of aberrations of the body-image) the absence of complicating disorders of language may cause the spatial defects to be discovered in all their profusion. The following table indicates the siddeness of the lesion in a random series of 19 cases, where spatial disabilities were well marked :

Right hemisphere	.	.	.	verified	.	.	.	9	} 11
Right hemisphere	.	.	.	unverified	.	.	.	2	
Left hemisphere	.	.	.	verified	.	.	.	0	} 1
Left hemisphere	.	.	.	unverified	.	.	.	1	
Bilateral .	.	.	.	verified	.	.	.	2	} 7
Bilateral .	.	.	.	unverified	.	.	.	5	

Here, the terms " right " and " left " refer to subordinate and dominant hemispheres respectively. The bilateral cases are not altogether easy to interpret for they were instances of multiple, metastatic carcinomata of the brain. In one, at least, of these, the presenting lesion was in the left hemisphere, and spatial defects were obvious. Her condition deteriorated, however : other symptoms developed ;   and at autopsy, many tumours were found occupying both halves of the brain.

As regards localization of lesions within the hemisphere, it can be said that the posterior parietal, or the parieto-occipital regions, are the ones most often the seat of disease.   So common is this association that the clinical occurrence of marked disorder of spatial thought should, at the bedside, lead to the strong suspicion of a lesion of the hinder part of the brain, and more precisely of the territory linking the parietal, occipital and temporal lobes.   Other things being equal, it is the right or subordinate side of the brain which comes under greatest suspicion.

The literature holds records, however, of lesions located elsewhere. In Pollak's case (1938) there was a massive tumour of the left frontal lobe.   This led Pollak to conclude that the act of orientation in man was an automatism which consisted in three components : a parieto-occipital ; a vestibulo-labyrinthine ; and a frontal one.   He believed the frontal terminal component served for the execution of direction. Marie and Béhague (1919) believed that frontal wounds, of either side, could produce gross defects of orientation in space, provided the lesion was extensive enough.   Feraro (1921) repeated the clinical tests for orientation which Marie and Béhague had used.   He found defective performances in so many normal subjects that, in his opinion, the Marie-Béhague test was valueless as a pathological symptom of any sort, and still more so as a pathognomonic sign of frontal lobe lesions.

CHAPTER XI

DISORDERS OF LANGUAGE AND
OF SYMBOLIC THOUGHT

> . . . We feel in one world ; we think, we give names to things in another ;
> between the two, we can establish a certain correspondence, but we do not
> bridge the interval.
>
> M. PROUST.

Lesions of the parietal lobe of the dominant hemisphere are at times followed by impairment in symbolic thought. The principal evidence of such a disorder consists in disturbances in reading and in calculation. For the former type of disability, the terms alexia or dyslexia are commonly used, meaning " a form of verbal amnesia in which the patient has lost the memory of the conventional meaning of graphic symbols " (Bateman).

Reading defects have already been described in Chapter IX as a manifestation of what is usually looked upon as an " agnosia ". But alexia may also be considered as an impairment of semantic or semiotic nature, in that letters when combined so as to form words constitute linguistic symbols. As a consequence of cerebral disease, the meaning [1] of certain verbal symbols may be obscure, even though the symbols may continue to be recognized as symbols, spelled out perhaps, and grammatically declined. This paradoxical state of affairs explains, though it does not excuse, the use of the terms contrasting

---

[1] " Meaning " is used here in its conventional, broad connotation. The flexibility of the meaning of a word and its dependence upon the sign-situation has been fully discussed by Ogden and Richards. The " meaning " of a word is so imprecise that we cannot be sure that any two normal individuals attach the same associations to a word or set of words. Vigotsky, like Paulhan, has tried to distinguish between the sense of a word, and its meaning, the sense of a word being the sum of all the psychological events aroused in our consciousness by the word. According to Paulhan ". . . the sense of a word is practically unlimited. A word receives its sense from a sentence ; the sentence itself receives its meaning from the context of a paragraph ; the paragraph from the context of the book ; the book from the context of the whole work of the author." The mutability and demerits of signs and symbols have been ably discussed by a large number of writers, including in particular Holbrook Jackson. Rémy de Gourmont wrote : ". . . words, which are signs, are almost always ciphers as well . . . But cipher implies deciphering. It is not easy to understand even the sincerest writing, and the author himself goes astray because the meaning of words varies not only from one man to another, but from moment to moment in the case of the same man. Language is thus a great cause of deception."

" word-meaning-blindness " and " word-sight-blindness ". In that cerebral disease affects the ready attachment of logical associations to the sight of the printed word, no simple or universal formula of explanation is to be expected. At times, it may only be the ultimate and esoteric significance of a complicated sentence, couched perhaps in technical terms, which baffles the patient. In other cases again, it is the aesthetic properties of language rather than its semantics which elude the patient with cerebral disease. Thus, the actual meaning of a verbal proposition may be appreciated, but the tonal and phonetic qualities, the stylistic virtues, and the exquisite nature of the prose may pass unnoticed by the patient, just as though he had been reading a text written in a foreign language, of which he had but a mediocre knowledge.

To those neurologists whose ideas upon cortical localization are static and conventional, the problem is simple enough. A focal lesion (located, it is claimed, around the left angular gyrus, though others would implicate the fusiform gyrus) is followed by a clear-cut " pure " dyslexic type of aphasia, where speech is intact save for an inability to read words (or perhaps only letters). Henschen even went so far as to refer to " an angular aphasia ". Such viewpoints do not accord well with present-day ideas in neurology. It has already been asserted that the term " pure " alexia is a misnomer, in that other defects of visual perception are to be expected, assuming that the examiner knows what to look for and is prepared to take pains in his investigation. The same criticism applies to the conception of " pure " alexia as an aspect of disordered language. Accepting the definition of speech as " symbolic formulation and expression ", it is *a priori* a challenge to submit that the understanding of merely the visual components of so complex a cultural integration as language could be involved alone. The contrary contention is submitted : either dyslexia is found on appropriate testing to be an incomplete defect and an inconstant one, or else other aspects of speech are demonstrable in alleged cases of " pure " reading disability.

As an exercise in logic, the problem is somewhat unsatisfactory. One's conception of alexia is largely an attitude of mind. To the atomist, or associationist, questions of psychodynamic subtlety are meaningless. Superficial testing reveals certain defects : other qualities are apparently intact, and the case is recorded as such in the literature. On the other hand, the organismic neurologist is more interested in the total behaviour of patients with brain defect, and he finds beneath the façade of clinical simplicity, manifold though thinly-spread difficulties. Surveying the case-records in the literature, he cannot but suspect that other disorders of such and such a type must also have been present but remained unrecognized : but obviously, this attitude is one which can scarcely be sustained nor yet refuted.

The phenomenology of acquired reading defects may be considered in more detail. The patient may apparently be unable to recognize single letters. This disability usually proves to be variable in degree, however. Some patients recognize letters as being letters, but they cannot identify each one. Others can understand large printed letters (e.g. headlines in a newspaper), but not the smaller type. (This defect should lead to the suspicion of a so-called " agnosic " type of dyslexia, where a metamorphosic distortion may occur in the appearance of visual symbols.) Some patients may recognize letters for what they are, but fail to orientate them correctly in space, confusing Ǝ with E or even with ɯ. More commonly, the patient recognizes some letters but not others. In such cases, certain patterns of error may be traced in their performance. There may be a recognition of commonly occurring symbols, but not the rarer ones. Or those symbols which are simple in morphology (such as I, O or X) may be identified, and not the more complex shapes (W, F, Z). Literal symbols may often be mistaken one for another. Errors may depend upon mere proximity within the alphabet (e.g. L and M ; S and T ; V and W). Or upon phonetic similarity (G and K ; J and Y). Or upon comparability in form (O and Q ; F and E). Certain letters may possess a peculiar relationship within the patient's own language-system. His own initials, for instance, may be recognized when the letters stand in correct combination, but not when separated. One of Dejerine's patients could identify the letters R and P when they were displayed together and surmounted by a laurel wreath : but outside of that particular symbolic setting, they meant nothing.

A patient may be unable to interpret a given letter, though he can say whether it belongs to the beginning, middle or end of the alphabet. He may perhaps be able to recognize letters printed in roman script but not in gothic (as in the case of German patients) ; or a polyglot may perhaps find it easier to interpret letters in one language rather than another, e.g. English, but not Russian or Greek. Even within the framework of a particular language, he may find differences according to type-founding, recognizing, for example, letters printed in one type face but not in another. More usual is a dissociation between graphic symbols written by hand, and those appearing in print.

Then there are patients who find difficulty in recognizing letters but none with numerals—a not uncommon state of affairs (perhaps because there are only 10 as opposed to 26 symbols to be understood). Some can recognize musical notation or mathematical signs, but not verbal symbols.

Paradoxical performances such as these are interesting, and tempt one to seek explanations drawn from various fields of experience. Unfortunately, most of these ingenious hypotheses fall down when it is realized that the patient himself may be quite inconsistent in his accomplishment ; and that to speak of a precise or orderly pattern of error is really not justifiable.

Much attention has been paid to the trick manœuvres which lead to a sort of pseudo-reading. Wilbrand found that his patient could not read printed symbols at a glance, i.e. by a purely visual act, but he could interpret them if he traced the outlines of each symbol with his finger. Such a manœuvre is sometimes referred to in the continental literature as " Wilbrand's sign ". Kinaesthetic memories or engrams in this way have been regarded as affording adequate clues towards a non-visual identification of visual forms. This notion was expanded considerably by Goldstein and Gelb who found that their patient *Schn.* could " read " in this way. He also succeeded if he moved his head or eyes in such a manner that the fovea swept over the outlines of the symbol. These tracing movements were unconscious, and were, it seems, still operative some twenty-five years later. Patients who employ tracing methods so as to identify symbols : or who rely upon an all-or-none recognition of a given Gestalt, are hindered when confronted with a literal symbol which is crossed out or scribbled over (⊰⊱) ; or when shown a letter which is not quite complete (Ą Ƅ Ɍ Ṃ). On the other hand, some dyslexic patients apparently attend only to a part of the visual morphology, and by dint of guess-work, attempt to identify the symbol as a whole. This may be demonstrated by getting the patient to copy in script printed letters.

From literal alexia, one passes to verbal alexia.[1] This term

[1] The autobiographical account of dyslexia which befell Dr. Lordat in 1825, and which was published in 1843 is probably the first of such records. " Whilst retaining the memory of the significance of words heard, I had lost that of their visible signs. Syntax had disappeared along with words : the alphabet alone was left to me, but the function of the letter for the formation of words was a study yet to be made. When I wished to glance over the book which I was reading when my malady overcame me, I found it impossible to read the title. I shall not speak to you of my despair, you can imagine it. I had to spell out slowly most of the words, and I can tell you by the way how much I realized the absurdity of the spelling of our language. After several weeks of profound badness and resignation, I discovered whilst looking from a distance at the back of one of the volumes in my library that I was reading accurately the title ' Hippocratis Opera '. This discovery caused me to shed tears of joy."

suggests that there are some dysphasic patients who fail to read words, though understanding individual letters. The fault concerns the synthesis of isolated visual units into language. Any sharp distinction between a literal and a verbal dyslexia is, however, unconvincing. A word is not a unit of language, but only of grammar. A few single letters may in certain languages constitute words (e.g. " i " and " I "); it is unlikely that the letter would be identified but not the word. Rarely, if ever, is there a total and consistent unawareness of the meaning of written or printed symbols. The normal act of reading is really far too complex a process for a specific global defect to occur in isolation. Ordinarily, a skilled reader skims a page and gathers the gist of the argument without interpreting individual words. A complicated or unusual phrase may slow up the act of reading so that each word is now studied *seriatim*. In the case of the poorly educated, a difficult word, if not glossed over altogether, is pondered over, and perhaps spelt out. Silent movements of the lips and tongue often accompany the visual act when an unfamiliar symbol is being pondered over, or the individual may be observed to whisper the text quietly to himself.

With parietal disease, some of these activities which ordinarily go to make up the complicated process of reading may become impaired. At times, there seems to be a dissociation between silent reading and reading aloud. The latter may perhaps be possible only at the sacrifice of meaning (Joffroy's " psycholexia "); as if the simultaneous operation of two or more processes was too difficult, and had to be broken down into successive functioning.

Ordinarily, the patient is able to read many easy and familiar words but fails to read difficult, polysyllabic, technical or unfamiliar terms. (The same patient will probably find that some of the letters are easy, while others are puzzling.) Sometimes, the patient can do little more than identify the Gestalt of a word which stands in particular personal relationship (e.g. his own name). Something similar occurs in the case of a print collector who can recognize the signatures of the well-known Japanese artists though ignorant of the language. In the same way, a young child, quite unable to read, may be able to select gramophone records by means of the configuration of the writing upon the different labels.

A discrepancy between the familiar and the unfamiliar constitutes the commonest pattern of dyslexia in parietal disease. And yet, the disability may at times seem to be quite different. Thus, the patient may understand the longer and apparently more complicated words, but not the shorter ones. At first sight, the paradox seems difficult to explain. On reflection, it may be realized that the longer terms often comprise the substantives, adjectives and verbs, i.e. those terms which are most endowed with concrete significance. These are the ones most likely to be picked up first while learning a foreign language along natural lines. Shorter words would largely be made up of the articles, conjunctions and prepositions, all of which are far more abstract in their linguistic connotations. Such words are less readily acquired in a foreign tongue.

Dissociation between the understanding of " big " and " small " words in cases of dyslexia is therefore adequately explained along the Goldsteinian views upon the dissolution of function in cerebral disease. It leaves unanswered, however, why this particular type of reading defect is apparently the exception, and not the rule, after brain affections.

In dealing with aphasia, not enough is made of the fact that the patient typically shows a blatant inconsistency in performance. This variability has been stressed repeatedly in this present discussion of parietal disease. The observation applies particularly to patients with parietal types of dysphasia, and cuts across many of the theoretical attempts to " explain " the various kinds of dysfunction. Within a single paragraph, at a single sitting, the patient may succeed in reading the very same word at one moment but not the next : in one context perhaps, but not another. Even to use the term " reading " is ambiguous, for the patient may be unable to read the words silently, i.e. to understand them : or he may be able to read them aloud, but without comprehension. At other times, he can perform one or other of these functions but not both. And yet again, he may succeed with both tasks. Five minutes later, his performance may be quite different ; it may have improved, or it may have worsened. With one examiner, he may fare badly ; with another, he may do well. The circumstance of the test ; the typography ; the subject-matter concerned : each of these factors may play a significant part. The patient's own physical and emotional states may be even more important. An emotional display (catastrophic reaction) brought out by a particularly poor attempt may cause the immediate subsequent performance to deteriorate still further : while initial success may encourage the patient and lead to fewer mistakes.

Some writers have spoken of a kind of " intermittent claudication of verbal comprehension ", whereby the patient reads a word or two and then comes to a halt : after a pause, he can venture a little further (Berlin and Bruns). Although ready fatigue and quick recovery are not infrequently discerned in dyslexic patients, it is perhaps safer to speak of a variability of performance, rather than to seek any such consistent pattern of deficit.

The foregoing discussion refers to cases of aphasia where the disability is mild and relatively limited. In most cases of parietal injury or disease, the speech affection is far more serious, and other aptitudes besides reading are involved. We may quote the experiences recorded by Schiller (1947) of aphasia due to head injuries. Following parietal traumata, the pattern of aphasia showed gross impairment of writing, spelling, reading and calculation. The ability to construct was also at fault. Perseveration of speech was common in the case of large lesions, with or without stammering. Intellectual loss seemed to be greater the further back the lesion lay. Parietal aphasia has also been described as a conduction aphasia (*Leitungsaphasie* —Hilpert, 1930–32), or a word-meaning aphasia (*Wortbegriffs- aphasie*—Kleist, 1932). The parietal lobe has been looked upon as standing in such an anatomophysiological situation as to involve associational processes connecting acoustic, visual and tactile concepts. Marie and Foix (1917) from an experience of war wounds thought they could isolate a number of clinicopathological types of aphasia, including two which related to the parietal lobe. In one, associated with injury to the angular gyrus, an almost complete alexia was coupled with involvement of the calculation and the comprehension of speech ; writing was said to be intact. A hemianopsia (or perhaps only a quadrantic defect) always occurred. In the other, there was no hemianopia, but there was a global aphasia together with a slight brachial monoplegia, a hemianaesthesia, and often a bilateral ideomotor apraxia. This syndrome was associated with a lesion of the supramarginal gyrus. Other examples of this latter variety were recorded by Fearnsides (1915), Bremer (1921), Brun (Case 13, 1921– 22) and Bailey (Case 1, 1924). (See also Foix, 1925.) Bianchi (1925) attributed a specific type of optic aphasia to parietal lesions, particularly of the inferior parietal lobule of the dominant hemisphere. After stating that " word-blindness " with transient " word-deafness " may occur (with or without agraphia), Bianchi stressed a special kind of disability which may affect educated, well-read and scholarly individuals. They lose their versatility in imagery and thought, though still able to pass short, immediate comments upon certain events in their environment. They cannot, however, indulge in complex thinking, nor can they connect words, names and grammatical peculiarities in a logical fashion. There results a kind of dementia, as shown by verbal amnesia, inability to form sentences, dyslogia, paralogia, paraphasia and agrammatism. This is the " aphasic dementia " characteristic of those previously accustomed to read and write much, who have sustained a parietal lesion.

That variety described by Head as semantic aphasia also bears

Thus, disease of the dominant hemisphere is more often followed by severe disorders of calculation than disease of the subordinate half of the brain. Frontal, occipital and parietal " types " of acalculia have been distinguished, only the last of which needs discussion here.

Dr. Hal Gregg's patient with brain atrophy (already quoted in another context) lost her usual ability to calculate her earnings at the end of each day's work. Ordinarily, she would multiply the number of pounds of fish she had filleted by 0·033 ; this would give her the amount of money due to her. She was accustomed to carry out this calculation in her head, quickly and accurately. Now, it was proving too difficult : the decimal point seemed to be too much for her.

When the lesions lie in the dominant parietal lobe, the patient's acalculia may show certain specific and recognizable features. These comprise ideational, verbal and constructional deficiencies. The

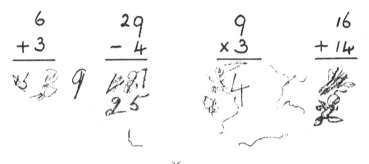

Fig. 126. Type of graphic response to simple arithmetical problems set out by examiner on paper.

ideational aspects may be severe. The patient may lose the meaning of numbers although possibly still able to identify and to name the various numerical symbols. But he may not be capable of deciding whether 7 is greater than 6, for example. Even such fundamental conceptions may be wanting as the idea of bigger or smaller ; addition and subtraction ; plus and minus ; part or whole. This, however, is rare. There may be more subtle defects. The patient may no longer recognize the meaning of place-value in arithmetic. Perhaps too he has difficulty in recognizing numerical symbols, though this defect need not necessarily be present. Indeed, understanding of numerals may often be intact while recognition of letters may be almost impossible. Confusion is increased if the patient displays perseveratory tendencies, which cause numbers to crop up inappropriately.

A third kind of defect which may be discerned in cases of parietal acalculia stems from constructional or spatial difficulties. The power of arranging figures upon paper so as to assist written calculation may be severely impaired. No longer are units neatly placed beneath units ; tens below tens. Horizontal and perpendicular dimensions may be hopelessly muddled. Indeed, the essential idea that figures need to be placed in a set arrangement in order to manipulate them may be wanting. This defect has been termed " constructive acalculia " (Krapf, 1937).

The characteristics of the parietal type of dyscalculia have been set out by Boehlke, as : a lessened memory for numbers ; a disturbance of counting ; a tendency to invert numbers when expressing them in words ; and a slowing-down of number-operations. Most of these various disorders of calculation are well illustrated in the case of puerperal thrombosis described by Wagner.

A difference in performance may be noted according to whether abstract or concrete numeration is at work. Thus, the patient with parietal disease (as also to a lesser extent with frontal, temporal or occipital affections) may experience greater trouble with dealing with figures " in his head " than on paper. In part, this may be due to a disorder in the revisualizing of numbers, and perhaps to a loss of the imagery of numerical form (Humphrey and Zangwill ; Leonhard). Still further, the patient may show greater facility in manipulating objects rather than digits. Thus, he may be able to calculate when handling actual coins, or counters ; or the beads of an abacus. But when confronted with a pencil-and-paper task, the difficulties may prove greater : and with mental arithmetic, greater still.

Grewel discussed the unpredictable behaviour in some cases of dyscalculia. A patient may fail to subtract 6 from 9, and yet a moment later, if asked the result of 6 + 9, may answer " 3 ". Or, having failed with the sum 1 + 8 + 3, soon afterwards, when told to construct a number containing a 1, 8 and 3, answers " 12 ". This kind of performance has been put down to an " impairment of distributive attention ".

The term " Leonhard's syndrome " would not be inappropriate when applied to the clinical combination of dyscalculia, agraphia (the power of reading being intact), constructional apraxia and temporal disorientation, described by this author (1952). Leonhard was wisely cautious about ascribing these four symptoms to any single underlying basic disorder, and he pointed out that they might merely be epiphenomena. The role of the different types of pre-morbid mechanism of mental arithmetic was stressed in so far as they may well determine what type of dyscalculia will occur after brain disease. In this connection, the existence of a vivid imagery for numerical forms and sequences will play an important part.

Dysgraphia

Regarding the writing disability which so often coexists with a dyscalculia, it has been said that the defect mainly entails the translation of printed symbols into script. This faculty (or " acopia " as

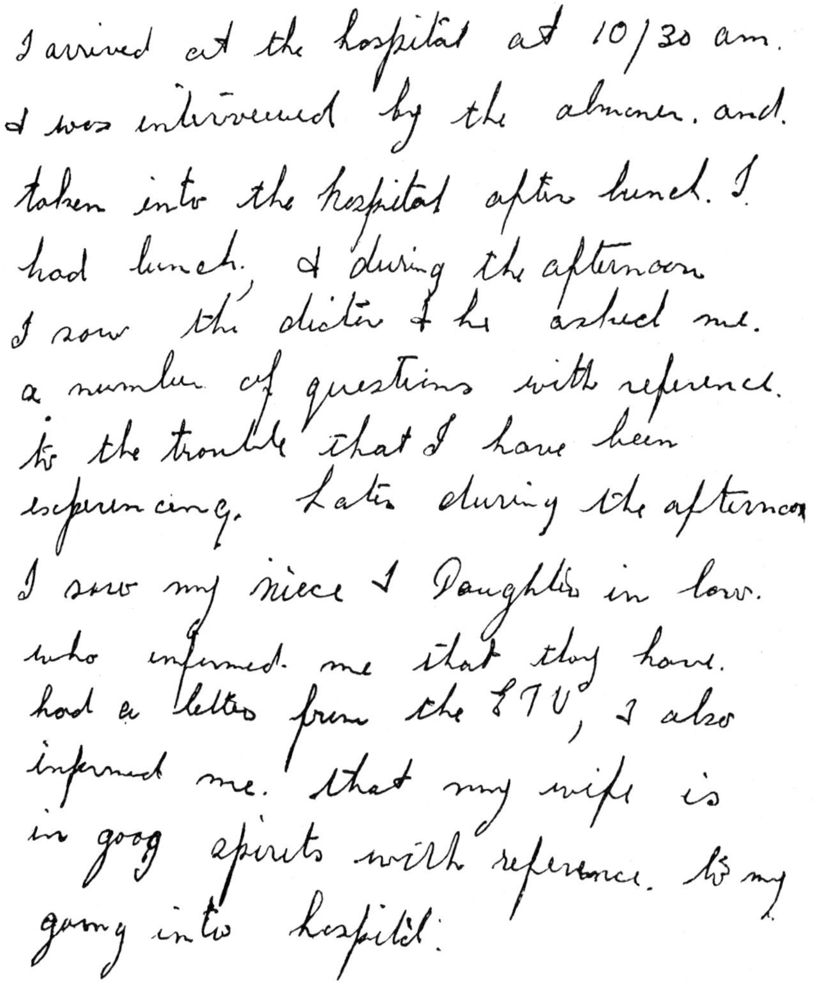

Fig. 127. Spontaneous writing performed by a patient with a left temporoparietal astrocytoma. He was unable to read back this script.

it has been called) differs from ordinary spontaneous writing in that it is necessary for the patient to be able to read in order to make a copy which is not simply a slavish reproduction : or alternatively, the patient must be able to memorize certain symbolic associations. The trouble is therefore a variety of dyslexic agraphia. Specimens illustrated in Figs. 127 and 128 show this discrepant performance. The patient who had a marked disorder of calculation was able to write spontaneously an adequate composition (Fig. 127). Afterwards, he could not read back his text, once the recollection what he had written had faded. His imperfect attempts at copying printed letters into script are shown in Fig. 128.

The combination of dyscalculia with dysgraphia, finger-agnosia, and disorientation of lateral relations, already discussed in Chapter VII, is really not a surprising one, in that each phenomenon entails a spatial component (Lange) or a spatiotemporal one (Grünbaum).

Difficulties in the act of writing have already been discussed in earlier chapters. To bring the problem logically within the section dealing with disorders of symbolic thought consequent upon parietal

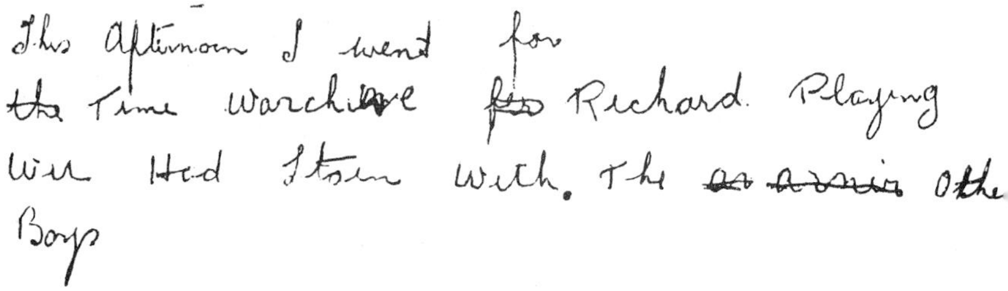

Fig. 128. Copying of print into script, as performed by same patient whose spontaneous writing is shown in Fig. 127.

disease, certain conclusions can be made. The characteristics of parietal agraphia are the following:

(1) Deterioration in the actual calligraphy. This usually takes the form of an exaggeration of the specific traits which characterize a person's handwriting. A previous tendency towards sloping the script backwards will become enhanced. Natural flourishes will become more elaborate. Small handwriting will become still smaller. At the same time, the curves will be more spiky or angular and the flowing lines tremulous and quavering. (See Fig. 129 *a* and *b*.)

(2) An upset in the orderly arrangement of lines, if very apparent, will give evidence of the probable coexistence of constructional apraxia. A patient may even finish the line at the right-hand margin, and then turn over the page to begin the second line.

(3) Inordinately wide margins on one side or the other will suggest a spatial neglect to the corresponding side of the midline. (See Fig. 130.)

(4) Greater difficulty in copying than in spontaneous writing may be noticeable, and will suggest either a constructional apraxic defect, or else a concomitant dyslexia.

(5) " The patient writes as though his eyes were closed." This
statement emphasizes some of the features of the dysgraphia of the
dyslexic patient, which were noted over 90 years ago (Forbes Winslow,

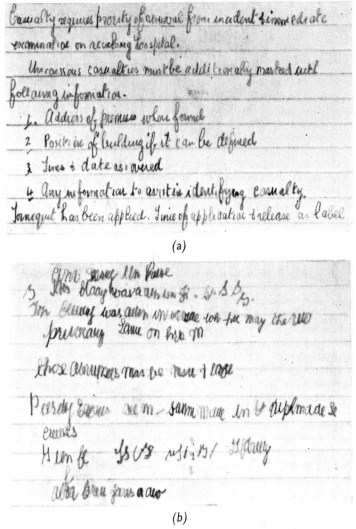

(a)

(b)

Fig. 129.   (a) Writing before illness.   (b) Writing after illness.   Note the
exaggerations of the natural graphic peculiarities.   Case of left fronto-parietal
secondary carcinoma.

1861 ; Falret, 1864).   Irregularities may occur in the alignment or
in the formation of letters : or in the separation of one word from the
next.   Errors and omissions are not necessarily elided or rectified.

(6) In addition to the foregoing defects must be added the semantic disorders properly speaking. These include incorrect

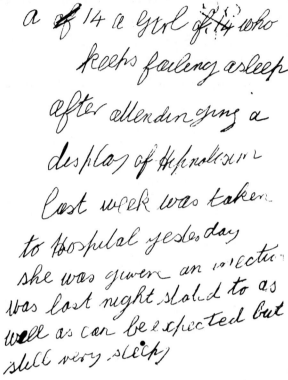

Fig. 130. Writing executed by a patient with a right frontoparietal metastic carcinoma (not verified). Note the inordinately wide margin on the left side.

spelling ; repetition of letters or syllables ; paragraphic substitutions of the word in question by another word or by a neologism. Some,

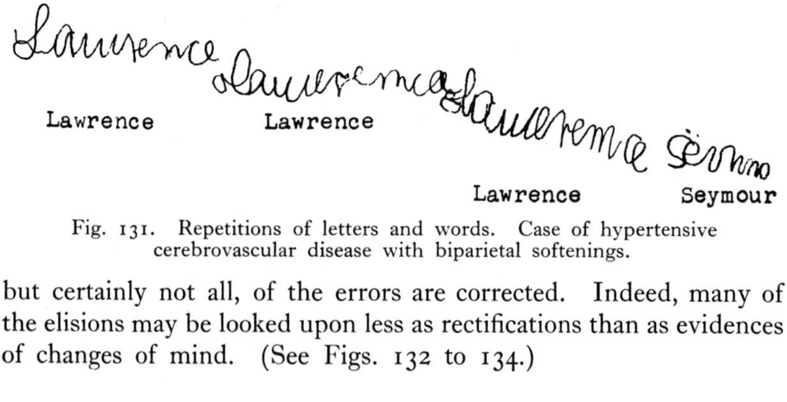

Lawrence   Lawrence   Lawrence   Seymour

Fig. 131. Repetitions of letters and words. Case of hypertensive cerebrovascular disease with biparietal softenings.

but certainly not all, of the errors are corrected. Indeed, many of the elisions may be looked upon less as rectifications than as evidences of changes of mind. (See Figs. 132 to 134.)

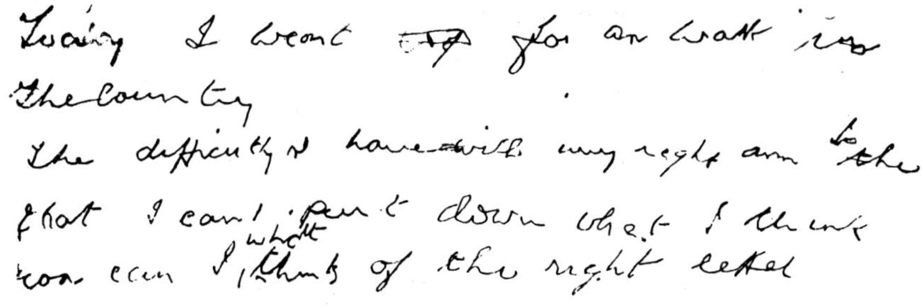

Fig. 132. Specimen of handwriting. Left parietal meningioma.

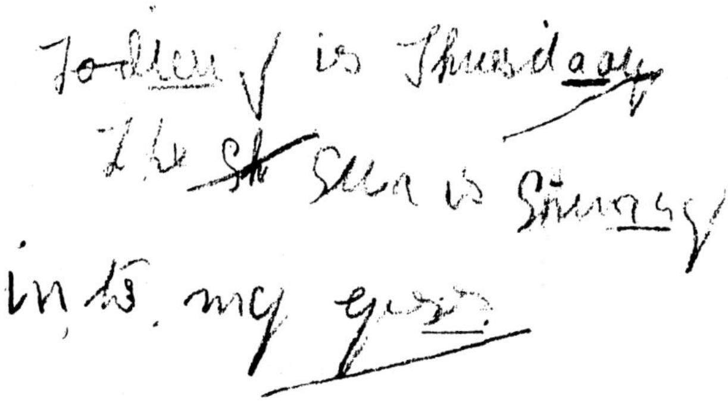

Fig. 133. Right temporoparietal astrocytoma. Spontaneous writing.

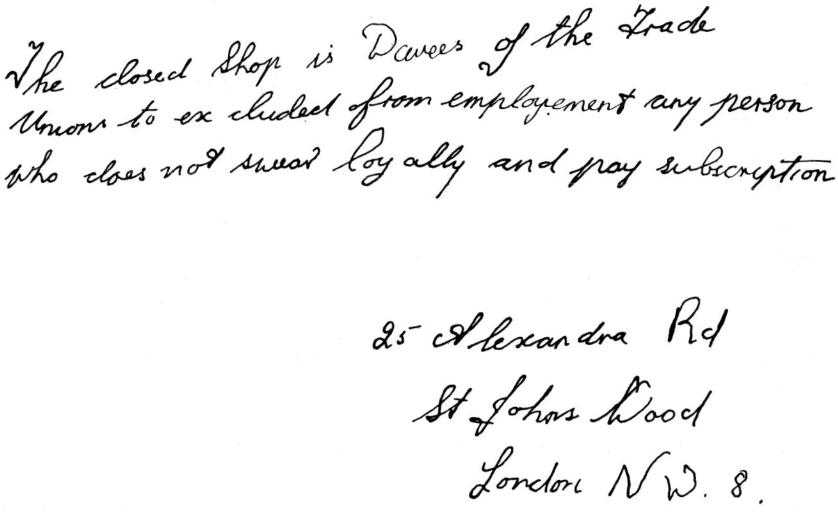

Fig. 134. Writing to dictation. Right temporoparietal meningioma. Note omissions of words.

(7) In advanced cases, the handwriting may deteriorate into an amorphous and illegible scribble. (See Figs. 135 and 136.)

Errors in spelling over and above those usually found associated with dysgraphia deserve special note. The selection of the appropriate letters and their precise and orderly conjunction is a process which entails qualities of both spatial and temporal nature. Patients with parietal disease might therefore be expected to show errors in this field, even right-handed patients with lesions of the right parietal lobe. The spelling mistakes of patients with parietal disease differ somewhat in nature from those made by dysgraphic patients with

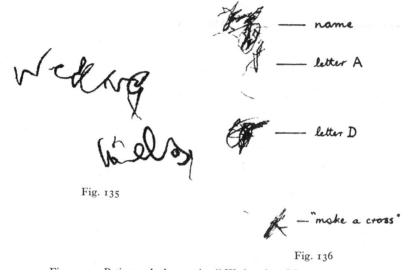

Fig. 135

Fig. 136

Fig. 135. Patient asked to write " Wednesday, May 13, 1948."
Case of cerebrovascular disease.
Fig. 136. Attempts at writing. Case of cerebral atrophy with dementia.

frontal or temporal lobe lesions. In the first place, the spelling errors may occur in the absence of any real dysgraphia (omission of words ; use of wrong words ; grammatical errors ; disorderly arrangement of script ; undue number of erasures). Particularly is this the case with patients with disease of the subordinate parietal lobe. In the second place, the spelling errors are unexpected in character, even bizarre in type. Perseveration of letters or of combinations of letters may occur. Reversals of the order of letters within a word or syllable may be conspicuous. These features may be quite unlike the type of spelling error made by the patient with a frontal lobe lesion, and also quite different from the sort of mistake made by normal persons who are inherently bad spellers, or who are poorly educated. As already mentioned, a " parietal " type of spelling error is often very readily demonstrated in the act of writing long numbers to dictation (numerical spelling). (See Fig. 137.)

Interpretation of pictures. Reference has already been made to the difficulties encountered by patients with cerebral disease in interpreting pictures. The disability is not pathognomic of lesions in any one region of the brain, but it can be truly said that such a defect often occurs in cases of disease of the dominant parietal lobe, especially when aphasia also exists.

The phenomena should be studied more intimately. By far the majority of patients recognize the pictures as being pictorial. That is to say, the patient does not confuse an actual object with a coloured representation of an object. In the rare cases where this does happen, the confusion forms part of a high-grade defect of visual perception. Ordinarily, the patient looks at a picture and imagines he interprets it adequately. When, however, he is questioned as to what he sees,

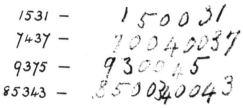

Fig. 137. Incorrect spelling of numbers. Case of right frontoparietal metastatic carcinoma (not verified).

he is apt to indicate details only. The meaning of the picture as a whole seems to escape him, even though he rarely realizes his short-comings. Thus, in a sporting journal, he may point out a racket, a ball, persons in shorts or flannels, but he fails to mention that the picture depicts a tennis tournament. Pictures of celebrities will possibly be identified (though not always), but the theme of the picture—what the personages are doing, and where the scene takes place—is not understood. This is the defect described by Wolpert as simultaneous agnosia (*Simultanagnosie*), though the term is not a particularly happy one. The phenomenon may be most striking at times. The patient may pick out a minute detail only and ignore the great part of the available surface area. Just why that particular detail should be chosen is often obscure, for it is not necessarily the most significant item, nor the most optically con-spicuous. With such a high-grade simultaneous agnosia, it is prob-able that the patient does not bother to look at illustrated papers by choice, even though when questioned directly on the point, he may protest that he can still do so with enjoyment.

The disability is capable of explanation along more than one line. To speak of a defect of surveying the total scene (*Ueberschauen*) is more descriptive than explanatory. A disorder of attention has also been envisaged. Thus, Hillebrand has implicated a defect in the " flow " of attention ; while Pötzl preferred to talk of a lack of " change " of attention.

The less severe grades of simultaneous agnosia may pass unrecognized not only by the patient himself, but also by the perfunctory examiner. Thus, a picture may be described well enough, details being correctly named, and the subject-matter or topic of the illustration moderately well evaluated. Closer testing would show a disturbance, however. If the patient is confronted with a political cartoon, or a humorous drawing, or an allegorical picture, he may be at a loss. The primary significance may be understood, but the patient will probably miss altogether the point of the picture, that is the inner or ultimate meaning. In this connection, Birkmayer used the expression " last refinements ", and pointed out that these are the final aspects of a language to be acquired, and that they are very vulnerable to cerebral disease. A comic picture, especially one without printed captions or text, and one which depends for its wit upon some situational incongruity, will fail to raise a smile. Indeed, the patient may even be unaware of the fact that the picture purports to be humorous. For the purpose of such a test, drawings from comic papers like *Punch* or the *New Yorker* may be chosen ; continental investigators have often used the cartoons of Caran d'Ache. Unfortunately, it is not possible to draw firm conclusions from the results of these tests, as the norms have never been determined. Only too often has it been discovered in the neurological clinic that some of the control subjects are unable to detect the point of a comic drawing.

It is possible (though still quite unproven) that a different kind of simultaneous agnosia for pictures may exist. As the result of cerebral disease, a patient may perhaps no longer be able to evaluate the aesthetic properties of a picture. In other words, he ceases to be able to discriminate a good picture from an indifferent one. It is necessary, of course, to satisfy oneself that the patient could have done so at an earlier period, and that the defect is an acquired one and not innate. Another obvious difficulty is that of " marking " a patient's performance against that of a normal control. But that aesthetic judgment or pictorial taste can deteriorate as a result of brain disease can scarcely be doubted. Whether it can also follow circumscribed lesions of the brain, e.g. the parietal lobe, has yet to be determined.

Language, as a symbolic means for the expression or interchange of ideas and emotions, obviously entails systems other than verbal and mathematical agencies. In enumerating parietal disorders of language, it would be unwise to omit reference to musical expression, drawing, signalling and pantomime.

The first of these fields is concerned least of all in parietal disease, for executive and receptive aspects of " amusia " are believed to be associated more particularly with frontal and with temporal lesions within the dominant hemisphere. Indeed, the converse phenomenon is much more characteristic of parietal affections, i.e. an integrity of musical faculties together with a receptive disorder of speech. One patient, for example, who showed a gross jargon-aphasia due to a glioma of the left temporoparietal region was conducting his orchestra up to the day before admission to hospital. (Case No. 26634.)

Impairment of the ability to draw has already been discussed in its relationship to parietal symptomatology. In a rather special category is the case recorded by Foster Kennedy and Wolf (1936). Here the patient, an art student, as the result of a left frontoparietal head injury, temporarily reverted to an infantile type of drawing. Gradually, as her condition improved, her artistic execution became more mature and eventually returned to its pre-accident level. There did not occur any aphasic disturbance. The focal nature of the disability was supported by a slight weakness of the right hand which cleared up in three days.

A regression to a juvenile type of drawing was well shown in the papers by Engerth, Angyál and Lorand, and by Allison, the last-named dealing with a series of cases of carbon monoxide poisoning with presumed lesions in the parietal lobes. In the diabetic arteriopathic patient already referred to (p. 342), an inability to draw was a conspicuous defect despite the fact that she had previously been fairly accomplished in this respect, and despite too an intact visual imagery. She owned a business for the manufacture of teddy-bears, and it was her job to cut out patterns from a sheet of felting. In the early days of her illness, she found that she was incapable of drawing the outlines of the pattern upon the material, but if someone else did this for her, she was able to perform the task of cutting-out.

In one case personally observed, the style of artistic accomplishment changed considerably in character after a left-sided temporoparietal lesion, though it could not necessarily be regarded as having deteriorated. The patient was a professional artist and photographer, whose original technique was of a meticulously detailed, highly representational order. On this account, he was frequently employed as a fashion artist by *couturiers*, and by editors of weekly magazines. After his stroke, he developed a transient mild right-sided weakness, and a mixed aphasia not only for his native German but even more so for French and English. When encouraged to draw, he began to sketch with bold and effective delineaments, using a marked economy of line. The new style which contrasted completely with the old was in many ways more significant. It was tempting to suggest that the vascular lesion had acted somewhat like a leucotomy, and had liberated the patient from the burden of obsessional traits. As in the case of musical accomplishments, artistic power may often persist despite a severe defect of speech. This was very well shown in Alajouanine's case of aphasia occurring in a professional landscape artist.

Critchley (1942) has described cases of " aphasic disorders of signalling " occurring in Royal Naval signalmen. No pathological data were available in any of these cases, but in the third patient, the presence of an alexia and of a left-sided hemianopia was suggestive at any rate of a right parietal (or temporoparietal) lesion.

This was the case of a retired Chief Yeoman of Signals, aged 57 years, who rather suddenly noticed some trouble with his vision to one side, and also a failure to comprehend printed words. Examination revealed a left hemianopia ; a dyslexia ; a tendency to misname colours ; a semantic type of simultaneous agnosia ; and a gross upset in the power of map-reading. When tested with various flags (ensigns, and hoists of signal-flags) he made a striking number of errors. He also made mistakes over the interpretation of ships' lights. On the other hand, he was quite efficient in the reception and transmission of signals in the Morse code (either visually by means of flashlights, or acoustically as by means of a buzzer).

The role of pantomime and gesture has been studied in some detail by Critchley (1939) in relationship with the aphasias. Briefly, it can be stated that in very severe cases of speech loss, there may occur a limitation of the language of gesture (" asemasia "), more marked in the propositional domain of pantomime than in the more affective symbology of gesture. The most important cases, however, concern those patients who, deprived of the faculty of spoken speech on account of a deaf-mutism, have later lost their acquired gesture-language because of cerebral disease. Critchley (1938) recorded one such case in full, and although no pathological data were available, a deep parietal location of the lesion seems justifiable. Three other such cases have since that date been observed (by Critchley), though not published. The literature now includes a little series of cases, made up of the patients described by Grasset (1896), Burr (1905), Critchley (1938, 1939), Leischner (1943) and Tureen, Smolik and Tritt (1951). The lesion in Grasset's case was probably in the frontal lobe, as it was in the patient described by Burr, and by the last-named authors. Leischner's patient, who was studied clinically in great detail, died, and at autopsy proved to have a vascular lesion affecting the left supramarginal gyrus.

It must be remembered that pantomime does not always become impaired in cases of aphasia, and that in certain special circumstances, it may actually be exaggerated.

Elsewhere, attention has been drawn to the possible existence of an unusual form of language defect which might be expected to follow a lesion of the parietal lobe within the dominant hemisphere (Critchley, 1953). Persons born blind, or persons who lose their sight early in life, usually learn and adopt a tactile process of reading in such a fashion as to act as a substitute for the visual reading of ordinary sighted individuals. This braille reading may be an aptitude mediated by the index finger of the right hand, or the left hand, or of both. In some braille readers, other fingers besides the index may participate. A defect which is tantamount to a " dyslexia for braille " has not yet been described, but it can be surmised as likely to follow cerebral lesions, and to be demonstrable if specifically looked for. Whether focal lesions of the brain can provoke such a defect, time alone will show. That the dominant hemisphere is likely to be the more significant in this connection can be suspected. It is possible too that a lesion situated within the parietal lobe may cause more upset in braille reading than a lesion elsewhere.

CHAPTER XII

GENERAL PSYCHIATRIC CONSIDERATIONS: THE RELATION OF PARIETAL SYMPTOMS TO DEMENTIA AND TO HYSTERIA

. . . Sometimes the convolutions are simply reduced in volume, at other times they are puckered ; in other cases, there is induration. The patient lives a life of a mere excito-motory and nutritive kind. The cerebral functions are obliterated. The true spinal and ganglionic functions remain alone. There is much for the physiologist to investigate in this singular *return* to a sort of infantile existence.

MARSHALL HALL, 1839.

To a series of neurologists early in the century belongs the credit of having unravelled the tangled skein of the organic dementias to the extent of isolating and extracting various syndromes of an aphasic, agnosic and apraxic character. Such disorders have thus been " purged from the stigma of dementia ". These early studies have since been so elaborated that the sum-total of specific outfall symptoms of an apraxic, agnosic and aphasic nature have multiplied and now constitute a formidable collection of nosological entities. As the matter stands today, it is worth while reviewing the problem in order to determine, as far as possible, in what manner and to what extent these specific syndromes differ from a global dementia. In cases of parietal disease the question is particularly pertinent, for neurologists of considerable experience and ability are apt to differ in their judgment of a given case. To one person, the clinical picture may appear as a straight-forward dementia : to another, it may seem that the inadequate performance is the outcome of an agnosia (or apraxia, or aphasia). The manner of carrying out a prescribed task, the behaviour in a given test-situation, may be so similar both in the case of the dement and in the patient with a small and circumscribed parietal lesion that there is room for a legitimate difference of opinion. Indeed, an over-confident judgment is only too often the mark of inexperience.

Dementia, as the word is used today in English neurology and psychiatry, refers to a deterioration in intellectual capacity which is, by definition, irreversible. Whether it is proper to insist upon this irreversibility is open to criticism, but ordinarily that property is taken as being integral. Dementia must therefore be distinguished from some of the psychiatric states of stupor where a considerable

378

degree of improvement is possible. It must also be separated from a deterioration of personality, which may, of course, accompany a dementia, though actually another problem. We must also realize that most cases of dementia are examples of an organic dementia, in that pathological changes in the brain can usually be demonstrated.

Mayer-Gross and Guttmann have classified the term " dementia " by listing some of the fundamental defects which constitute this picture of diffuse disease. They specified : (1) a difficulty in retention (the amnesic syndrome); (2) disturbance of attention (*Einstellstörung*), and more particularly, difficulty in focusing attention ; (3) lack of spontaneity (*Antrieb*) ; occasionally, an excess of spontaneity ; (4) poverty of ideas ; (5) forced responsiveness to stimuli (*Reizgebundenheit*) ; or perhaps an extreme selectiveness for stimuli (*Reizdurchlässigkeit*) ; (6) some degree of disturbed consciousness ; (7) undue tidiness ; or on the other hand, slovenliness ; (8) affective disorders ; and (9) proclivity to various catastrophic reactions. Some of Goldstein's conceptions have obviously been incorporated.

The circumstances in which focal agnosic symptoms are likely to occur are also those in which a dementia might well develop. Manifold outfall manifestations due to multiple softenings or metastases may stand out against a background of global dementia. The two conditions may therefore coexist and it may prove most difficult, if not indeed impossible, to place the various findings into their appropriate category.

Attempts have been made to trace a thread, if not indeed a basic pattern, in the symptomatology of diffuse disease, especially as expressed in psychiatric form, although the clinical emphasis is variable in such conditions. If this is admitted, and here all psychiatrists might not agree, then the task of disentangling a concatenation of focal symptoms from the picture of diffuse brain disease becomes more difficult still.

In distinguishing these two kinds of manifestations, i.e. focal and general, certain differential points are helpful. The following may be considered as evidence supporting a global dementia :

(*a*) Conduct which is incongruous, inappropriate, or anti-social is more suggestive of a demential state than of an agnosia. This statement is particularly true when the patient shows no drowsiness or noticeable clouding of the sensorium. Urinary and rectal incontinence require special mention here. This is a symptom which is both frequent and early in cases of frontal lobe lesions. But here, the defect may fairly be looked upon as demential and not agnosic. Patients with parietal disease are not incontinent until relatively late in the evolution of the disease, when lethargy, stupor or unawareness of the environment have supervened. Particularly suggestive of dementia as opposed to agnosia is the occurrence of incontinence by a patient who is not at all drowsy, in circumstances which make the act blatantly offensive or improper. The patient who exposes his person and urinates in the dining-room, for example, is not for a moment behaving like a victim of a lesion in the after part of the brain. Similarly, sexual offences, indecencies, financial extravagance or miserliness are not usually encountered in patients with agnosia.

(b) An affective state which is inappropriate to the occasion is common in demented subjects. It may take various forms, with apathy, depression or euphoria as the prevailing mood. In addition, there may be emotional lability with impaired control over the expression of the feelings, especially in the arteriopathic dements. Truculency and irritability may occur, especially in alcoholics. In the case of the patient with a circumscribed organic lesion of the posterior part of the brain, certain mood changes may be demonstrable, but these are fairly characteristic. Organic repression or defective awareness of the disability is common ; as has been seen, this anosognosia may be elaborated into definite paranoid and confabulatory directions, with denial of disease, projection and so forth (the " denial syndrome "). These latter states may, it is true, be regarded by some as transcending a simple agnosic defect or focal symptom, and can be argued as indicating a complicating demential state. Then again, a patient with a parietal lesion (or indeed with a defect elsewhere in the brain) may so modify his behaviour as to simplify his milieu and thus avoid catastrophic reactions. Such adjustments do not necessarily mean a dementia. Excessive reactive depressions with enhanced awareness of a paralytic or sensory defect may occasionally occur, as already described, but again, this may betray a psychotic state though not a dementia.

(c) Disorientation involving the three modalities of time, place and person alike suggests a dementia. Agnosic patients are more likely to show an uneven defect in this respect, with spatial uncertainty being conspicuous.

(d) An ignorance of current events, coupled with an impairment in recent memory, is rather more suggestive of a dementia than of agnosia, aphasia or apraxia. One must make allowances, of course, for the acutely ill patient, who, because of a recent stroke, or the march of symptoms of an expanding lesion, has been cut off from news, and has not read the papers or listened to the radio. But questions of such a type as the capitals of European countries, the names of recent monarchs or premiers, lists of common objects (flowers, animals, vegetables, and so on) should be well within the competency of an agnosic patient with a circumscribed cerebral defect. Failure with such tests would suggest either an inherent mental deficiency (which can be confirmed by other means), or else a dementia.

(e) Impaired memory may be associated either with the agnosia of focal lesions or with the dementia of diffuse brain disease. In the latter case, there is more likely to be a global defect, with an impairment of retention and of recall. On the other hand, remote and middle distance memory may be better preserved in the demented subject than the memory for recent events.

(f) A study of the patient's language may afford important clues as to the state of the mentation. While it may fairly be argued that severe affections of speech—especially when receptive as well as expressive aspects are at fault—almost of necessity imply a dementia, the reverse is not the case. That is to say, a demented patient need not display an aphasia nor indeed

Plate 9

KURT GOLDSTEIN

any gross affection of speech. The adjective " gross " needs emphasizing, for it is probable that qualitative changes of a semantic or syntactial sort may be demonstrable in dements who are not aphasic. A progressive poverty of speech is, of course, an obvious anomaly in the case of the demented subject, and may often be coupled with a tendency towards iterations, repetitions and stereotypy.

(g) The demented patient, in the same way, need not display any apraxia : just as an apraxic patient does not necessarily suffer much intellectual falling-off. However, the problem is more complicated than would appear from such a bald statement. Ideatory apraxia probably implies some degree of dementia. A patient with ideomotor, or with constructional, apraxia may also be demented. Whether here the dementia and the apraxia are causally associated, or whether they are merely linked as epiphenomena, is not easy to decide. Often, it is a matter of opinion. Any patient who is grossly demented will be expected to show considerable impairment in the orderly and co-ordinate execution of a motor act. He may be unable to stand, or to walk, to feed, or dress himself. Whether these defects in motility can be logically placed within the framework of an apraxia, is arguable.

(h) An important differential point concerns the presence of certain regressive signs in the nervous system : features which can be looked upon as " neurological anachronisms ". This term would include such manifestations as forced grasping and groping ; sucking movements ; lip and snout reflexes ; pathological laughter and weeping ; a compulsive tendency to put objects into the mouth. These signs may occur as marks of a focal cerebral lesion ; they may also appear in the dementias. To evaluate these signs and to decide whether they betray focal or diffuse disease, one pays attention to the point whether the " anachronisms " are unilaterally or bilaterally distributed. Then a one-sided grasping propensity (or grasp reflex) has a certain localizing value which a bimanual forced grasping does not possess. The same statement obviously holds true in the case of a unilateral extensor plantar response, as opposed to one which is bilaterally demonstrable.

The last arguments are important in that a patchy distribution of neurological signs, or an uneven involvement of intellectual functions, can serve as an argument in favour of an agnosic type of defect or defects. Per contra, a bilateral symmetrical occurrence of morbid neurological findings suggests a diffuse process ; and if coupled with a global involvement of cerebration, a dementia is probable.

(i) The demented patient is essentially unable to undertake novel enterprises or deal with new and unfamiliar problems and situations. In the early stages, he can still carry out routine work as well as the chores of daily life, but as soon as unexpected demands crop up and necessitate that he turns his attention to some task which is quite unfamiliar, he fails conspicuously. This is one of the characteristic disabilities of a demented patient, and is one which does not necessarily apply to the person with a focal lesion of the brain, unless he too happens to show a global falling-off in intellectual capacity.

The foregoing points may serve as guides in distinguishing agnosic affections from demential states. Nevertheless, one must beware of being led astray by over-simplifications. We have really been contrasting the mental effects of a circumscribed focus of disease with those due to lesions which are either diffuse, or else multiple. Let us admit that a global dementia can at times follow a circumscribed lesion, and hence act like a focal symptom. The mental state associated with some cases of massive frontal lobe tumour may be offered as an example. The question may perhaps be asked whether the clinical difference between focal and diffuse disease is not merely one of degree. May not the algebraic summation of a number of single lesions be tantamount to a dementia? The problem is well illustrated by the example of multiple secondary tumours of the brain. The first cerebral metastasis, if deposited in an appropriate region of one hemisphere, may be followed by symptoms of, say, a Gerstmann's syndrome. A dementia, in the strict sense of the word, cannot be said to exist. In a short while, other manifestations develop, for instance, a dyslexic type of aphasia. The patient is still *sensu strictu* not demented. Then shortly afterwards, he becomes drowsy, apathetic and taciturn, though capable of being aroused and conversing sensibly. Still later, he becomes bed-fast. He may need help at meal-times. Urinary incontinence may occasionally occur. Some confusion as to time and place becomes obvious; his memory grows uncertain; his attention cannot easily be seized or maintained. By gradual stages the patient has passed into a dementia, which proves at autopsy to have been the clinical expression of half a dozen or more metastatic growths scattered throughout the brain. Few would venture to assert at which point the cerebral outfall symptoms entailed an incipient dementia. If, then, one admits that the transition has been gradual, the argument becomes admissible that right from the start the first focal manifestation was potentially productive of a dementia. Expressed otherwise, a Gerstmann syndrome, or a dyslexia (or maybe a tactile or visual agnosia, a constructional apraxia and so on) may each one of them represent a little dementia or perhaps a subclinical dementia. Such a view would indeed accord with the most recent ideas upon the nature of agnosia, but the subject is one where unanimity does not as yet obtain. As far as the apraxias are concerned, the problem has not really been broached, although it is a familiar aspect of contention in the aphasias. In other words, we are harking back to the viewpoint of Pierre Marie that aphasia necessarily connotes a *petite démence*, to which a specific disability may be added.

The foregoing remarks are essentially clinical in scope, and they are based upon conventional neurological and psychiatric conceptions of dementia. One may now turn to the province of pure psychology and enquire whether the problem can thereby be clarified. To equate the dementia of the clinician with a quantitative deterioration in intelligence would be tempting, were there only a clear-cut conception among psychologists generally as to what is meant by intelligence. Briefly, there are at least three main hypotheses, which bear upon the present question. The first conception presupposes an underlying common function of intelligence (Spearman's " g ") ; the second considers that intelligence is made up of a number of group factors (including verbal, spatial, numerical, as well as others connected with memory and reasoning—inductive and deductive). Thirdly, there is a compromise in the suggestion that numerous special abilities exist subordinate to a general factor at a higher level. Based upon these hypotheses, at least three opinions are possible as to the nature of dementia. It might be looked upon as a reduction of Spearman's common factor of intelligence (a state of " minus g ") ; or, as a falling-off in the efficiency of some (or all) of the group factors, whether evenly or unevenly spread. Thirdly, dementia might represent a combination of a deterioration of both the common and the group factors : each of these suggestions assumes that dementia represents a simple quantitative reduction of intelligence ; that is, uncomplicated by any qualitative changes in the pattern of dissolution.

Psychologists have in the past largely concerned themselves with the organization of intelligence (rather than its dissolution), and with the integration of various aptitudes such as learning, retention, and so on, into the framework of the intellect. The question remains unanswered whether focal cerebral disease can cause a focal and specific deterioration in intellect, or whether a general deterioration alone is to be expected ; and if the latter, what would be its nature.

This leads to one of the most important topics in present-day neuropsychology, namely, the unitary hypothesis of mental function. This view submits that the site of a focal brain lesion is of minor importance, as compared with, say, its sheer mass or volume. The resultant clinical picture is a specific one, according to Goldstein, who combining shrewd clinical observation with an attachment to configurational psychology has made one of the most significant advances in our knowledge of the results of brain damage. Goldstein focused attention upon a minute study of the total behaviour of patients with head injuries. If the patient, or rather the organism (as Goldstein says) is confronted with tasks within its capacity, it will perform them in a harmonious, orderly fashion. Faced with a task with which it cannot cope, it betrays a catastrophic reaction. The life of the organism becomes therefore bound up with the need to find an environment which makes few demands. Many of the apparent symptoms are really only expressions of the sick man's flight from catastrophic reactions. To achieve a satisfactory milieu, numerous devices may be adopted, e.g. self-exclusion ; avoidance of company ; or by restless over-activity ; or a cloak of indifference ; or excessive orderliness. The patients are unaware of their altered personalities, and even perhaps of the nature and extent of their disability. The degree of readjustment is directly proportional to the severity of the defect. Goldstein formulated, moreover, a number of principal forms of disintegration in neurological lesions : (1) the threshold of excitation rises, and there is, moreover, a retardation (leading to slowness of performance) ; (2) once excitation has occurred, it lasts an abnormally long period of time (hence such clinical phenomena as perseveration) ; (3) external factors influence the patient unduly (causing distractability, and also the phenomenon of being " stimulus-bound ") ; (4) there is an ever present difficulty in distinguishing essentials from non-essentials ; or in the Gestalt metaphor, to distinguish " figure " from " ground ".

Perhaps the most important of Goldstein's views is his teaching that the brain-injured person loses the ability to assume a categorical attitude. In other words, he can no longer emerge from an elementary passive type of concrete behaviour. This alteration in the total personality is one which is mirrored in numerous little ways in which he comports himself in his daily life, as well as in his behaviour in test-procedures, and also in his speech.

Goldstein's work possesses outstanding merits, though also certain demerits. In the first place, it substitutes for a bald mathematical score on the part of a psychometrist, an objective and detailed description of the patient's performance with special reference to the delays, slowness and inconsistencies—factors which are difficult to " mark ". Goldstein's work takes into consideration the fluid or dynamic nature of the patient's behaviour. It accords with the newer schools of psychological thought, as well as with neurology. He has offered ideas which are stimulating, refreshing and illuminating. Unfortunately, his work is not sufficiently supported by statistical or other scientific evidence. Questions of localized as opposed to diffuse disease of the brain are not deeply discussed. Of focal lesions, neither the site, nature, volume nor degree of acuteness are noted in detail. Most of his early case-records comprised young adults with brain injuries, and the problem might well be different in patients with steadily expanding lesions. A serious drawback consists in the lack of information as to the relative incidence of the various traits of abnormal behaviour. As much of the performance is typically variable, being demonstrable on one occasion, but not the next, this is perhaps understandable, though the scientific value of the data thereby suffers.

The ideal solution to the present unsatisfactory state would be for Goldstein's careful studies to be consistently applied to a diversity of cases with brain lesions, and for the data to be scored psychometrically and then evaluated statistically. Research of this kind is, indeed, under way at the hands of many psychologists such as, for example, Zangwill, McFie, Piercy, Shapiro, Jackson, Etlinger and others. But it is most important that the battery of tests should be adequate ; that each should be scored more flexibly, and be accompanied by verbal description (rather than a plus or minus, or a numerical " marking "). In particular, a better test is needed for a study of abstraction than mere recourse to Weigl's colour-form sorting test, and the verbal similarities subtest of the Bellevue Scale. For instance, in the valuable paper by McFie and Piercy, left-side lesions were found to show more frequent impairment of a process of abstraction than right-sided lesions. The evidence, however, was simply based upon Weigl's test, and the ability or not to pass within a limited space of time (not stated) from one system of sorting to another. The results may be true, but the method is perhaps unsatisfactory. The " test of life " is at the present time still the best index of a loss of categorical attitude.

Diagnosis from hysteria

Several difficulties in the distinction between hysteria and parietal disease are apt to occur in clinical practice. In the first place, a patient whose malady is wholly a hysterical one may be incorrectly diagnosed as suffering from a parietal lesion. This is actually not a common mistake and it is unlikely to occur except at the hands of an inexperienced neurologist who, beguiled by a compelling interest in parietal syndromes, errs in finding phenomena where they do not actually exist. The opposite type of error is much commoner ; that is, to regard the patient with a parietal affection as suffering from a psychogenic ailment, and in particular, a hysteria. This is specially liable to happen when the organic lesion involves the right hemisphere rather than the left ; or both halves of the brain. This kind of mistake is more likely to arise with atrophic lesions than with tumours, where the more compelling symptoms of headache, vomiting and lethargy may afford a clue to the diagnosis. A third type of diagnostic difficulty arises in those cases where there is a hysterical elaboration of organic parietal manifestations : or where a parietal lesion develops in a person of notorious hysterical personality. It then becomes most difficult to judge whether the disease picture is organically produced or psychogenic : or whether both aetiological factors play a part : and if so, what is their relative importance.

Even competent and experienced neurologists are at times in doubt in the face of such diagnostic problems. Once again, the neurologist who is over-confident in his assessment of a difficult case is only too often blind to the complexities of the problem.

A striking example of a case where diagnostic doubt has occurred is the famous patient *Schn.*, described originally by Goldstein and Gelb in the most painstaking detail. The authors' conclusions have been criticized either in whole or in part by numerous neurologists, though supported by others. Later, the patient came under the care of other neurologists whose opinions were at variance with those of Goldstein and Gelb. Some, indeed, have asserted that the patient, *Schn.*, showed hysterical features which complicated the organic manifestations of cerebral injury. Even today, the status of the case *Schn.* remains a matter of dispute.

Certain attributes of a patient with parietal disease foster the error of believing that the problem is a psychogenic one, and that the symptoms are those of a hysterical disorder. A routine neurological examination—one which does not specifically investigate highest level psychosensory and psychomotor features—may fail to uncover any evidence clearly indicative of organic trouble. The patient's mental attitude towards his disability—his apparent apathy, his seeming content—may suggest to the unwary examiner the *belle indifférence* of the hysteric. Again, the occasional lapse into catastrophic reactions may lead to the mistaken conception of a neurotic emotivity with an evasion of intolerable situations. The variability in level of performance, especially at the hands of different examiners, may again bring to mind the inconsistency of the hysteric. The lack of distress over the existence of a disability (e.g. the anosodiaphoria of an hemiplegic) may readily be mistaken for a fatuous euphoria of a dullard with hysterical features.

Some of the clinical phenomena of parietal disease are so bizarre in their type as to suggest a psychiatric disorder. The complicated descriptions of corporeal sensations put forward by patients who have various organically determined disorders of the body-image : the grotesque somatoparaphrenias of the parietal patient with delusions as to his own anatomy : the depersonalizations and derealizations so similar to the manifestations in neurotics : spatial disorders leading to a tendency for the patient to become lost in his own home : unexpected errors of sensory localizations, and especially the alloaesthesias : tactile and visual perseverations : dressing disability : disorders such as these are neurological phantastica which superficially suggest psychiatric affections and among them hysteria. The demeanour and behaviour of a patient with cortical blindness bear many common features with the phenomena of hysterical loss of sight. Even the signs of the various visual agnosias are not easily distinguished from a psychogenic illness. The asthenopias, or lability of visual function, may show on protracted testing a concentrically reduced field of vision which may easily be misinterpreted as hysterical. Prolonged states of semi-stupor, with mutism, which may follow biparietal cortical atrophy may be confused with a hysterical somnosis.

Among the few writers who have boldly discussed the clinical difficulties which surround attempts to distinguish between hysterical states and the manifestations of an organic reaction has been Reinhold (1952). She has contrasted the catastrophic reactions of a patient with structural lesions of the brain, with the benign acceptance of disease displayed by the hysteric. The latter tends to dissociate and to disintegrate. On the basis of Goldstein's teaching, she has described the various psychopathological measures adopted as a protection against these catastrophic reactions. The brain-injured patient may develop traits of unusual orderliness : he may show trick movements or various other manœuvres : he avoids hazardous situations : he often employs sense modalities other than the one at fault (i.e. he utilizes *détours*) : and he is apt to invent plausible excuses for his shortcomings. From her series of patients with brain tumour (many of them situated within the parietal lobe), Reinhold has illustrated each one of these psychological mechanisms. One patient with a right parieto-occipital lesion would seek to limit the number of surrounding visual stimuli, as the sight of " many things at once " somehow distressed her. Large bunches of flowers, and bowls of fruit, caused visual embarrassment, and she would select one or two blossoms and put them in a vase, and place one or two apples on a plate. Shown a tray upon which many small articles were jumbled, she tidied them into little heaps. Her possessions were kept " fantastically tidy ". (Case No. 38299.) (In this respect, she exactly recalls Wilbrand's original case, where the morbid anatomy was eventually revealed.) Her patient adopted tricks or dodges to assist her. To cut out some of the multitudinous visual stimuli, she would cup her hands over her eyes. In order to mark her bed within the ward so as not to pass it on her return from the toilet, she would place her coloured bed-jacket on the counterpane. There was a patient with auditory agnosia who (like certain mild aphasias) would dominate the conversation by means of a stream of small talk. In this way, the embarrassment of a failure would be avoided. (Case No. 17289.) Asked to describe an object before her, a patient with visual disorientation would, in an almost compulsive manner, always stretch out her hand to feel it. (Case No. 34717.) Excuses which an organically diseased patient might proffer in a plausible, though inadequate fashion, were instanced. "Being out of practice" was often adduced as sufficient explanation for defects in writing or drawing. Impairment of memory might be put down to a long illness. All these kinds of behaviour had at one time or other been erroneously dubbed hysterical in cases which were unquestionably organic.

Reinhold also pointed out that a patient with a brain lesion may be chary about volunteering a symptom which strikes him as bizarre. With growing confidence in the doctor, however, he may sheepishly attempt to describe his strange troubles, characteristically prefacing his remarks with some such phrase as, "I know it sounds rather silly . . ." The patient, indeed, is often quite unable to do justice to the complicated nature of his subjective state. Thus, the patient with visual agnosia may get no further than the statement that everything looks "muddled" or "in a mess".

CHAPTER XIII

THE LEFT VERSUS RIGHT PARIETAL LOBE

There are works which wait, and which one does not understand for a long time ; the reason is that they bring answers to questions which have not yet been raised ; for the question often arrives a terribly long time after the answer.

OSCAR WILDE.

There is one principal and as it were radical distinction between different minds . . . that some minds are stronger and apter to mark the differences of things, others to mark their resemblances. The steady and acute mind can fix its contemplations and dwell and fasten on the subtlest distinctions ; the lofty and discursive mind recognizes and puts together the finest and most general resemblances. Both kinds, however, easily err in excess, by catching the one at gradations and the other at shadows.

FRANCIS BACON.

This chapter will deal chiefly with the clinical syndromes of parietal disease according to the lateralization of the lesion. Localization of this or that symptom within the parietal lobe itself (or rather of the lesions which are followed by the individual syndromes) will be avoided. The two parietal lobes, however alike in morphological structure and convolutional pattern, and however comparable as regards the evidence of experimental physiology, are to the clinician anything but equipotential. In the case of the ordinary right-handed members of the population, the left parietal lobe, when the seat of disease, is followed by outstanding clinical defects which do not occur when the right lobe is affected, or at least not to the same extent. When the right parietal lobe (in right-handed subjects) is at fault, certain other clinical phenomena appear which are rarely seen with left-sided lesions. The problem so far is straightforward in that there would seem to be characteristic clinical disorders specifically bound up with disease of each of the two hemispheres. Difficulties begin to arise, however, when discussing the 5–10 per cent of the population who are in general terms spoken of as being left-handed.

Before embarking upon a discussion of cerebral dominance in relation to parietal symptomatology, it may be useful to display in the form of a schema the main types of clinical defect which are liable to follow disease of either parietal lobe, irrespective of the patient's handedness. Table 1 shows these characteristic fundamental parietal defects arranged in as logical a fashion as possible.

Of these clinical manifestations, three at least require comment.

Table 1

UNILATERAL DISEASE (I.E. RIGHT OR LEFT)

Disorders of sensibility
" Cortical syndrome " → hemianaesthesia
Pseudothalamic syndrome

Disorders of motility
Unilateral muscular atrophy
Unilateral passive and active neglect (?) → mild hemiparesis
Spontaneous turning movements

Visual disorders
Qualitative visual defects in homonymous half-fields
Metamorphopsia : visual perseveration
Quantitative field defects → hemianopia
Neglect of one half of external space (occasionally)

Constructional apraxia (?)

Under disorders of motility, unilateral passive and active neglect (eventually amounting to an actual hemiparesis) is mentioned as a phenomenon which may be demonstrable in either the right arm or the left, being in other words independent of the side of the lesion. Some neurologists would query this viewpoint and some would even deny its validity. Certainly, unilateral motor neglect is more often seen in the left arm than in the right in the case of right-handers. But it would be wrong to deny that this phenomenon does not also at times involve the right upper limb in the case of right-handed people. It is possible that this unilateral neglect is not a specific defect peculiar to lesions of the subordinate hemisphere, but that the circumstances of common usage and habitual activities of daily life draw attention to a motor or sensory defect in the master hand (i.e. the right hand), so that its demerits are likely to be noticed early. Hence, neglect or disregard of minimal handicaps are less likely to occur. The fact that the right hand is used more favours early recognition of any disability, and therefore the limb is not so typically neglected. This hypothesis would therefore suggest that unilateral motor neglect is no more a specific sign of disease of the subordinate parietal lobe than is, for example, unilateral visual or tactile inattention.

The second question concerns neglect of one half of external space. Again, this phenomenon is more often found in the clinic involving the left half of space, for it shows itself more particularly as a manifestation of disease of the minor or subordinate hemisphere. This may be so, but certainly spatial neglect to the right of the midline can now and then be demonstrated in patients with left parietal lesions, and who are not left-handed subjects. Until the clinical problem is clarified thoroughly, it will perhaps be more satisfactory to include this sign among the manifestations of unilateral parietal disease, irrespective of sidedness.

The final issue concerns constructional apraxia. Again, some would associate this symptom more closely with lesions of the subordinate parietal lobe. It is probably more accurate to say that constructional apraxia may occur with lesions of either hemisphere : that it is seen in its most florid style with bilateral lesions, and least clearly with lesions of the dominant side of the brain. In the last-named conditions, other types of apraxia may complicate the clinical picture.

In Table 2, parietal syndromes appear in their severest form, as if any compensatory role played by the unaffected hemisphere in cases of unilateral parietal disease had ceased to be operative.

Table 2

BILATERAL SYNDROMES

Visual disorders
    Central blindness with Anton's syndrome
    Visual disorientation
    Visual object " agnosia "
Constructional apraxia (severe)
Universal somatagnosia and aschematia
Stupor
Loss of re-visualization (?)

As with the pseudobulbar syndrome, the clinical picture is something more than a mere arithmetical compound of two unilateral parietal defects, a two-sided parietal syndrome. This shows itself particularly in the case of so-called visual object agnosia (with bilateral occipitoparietal lesions) and better still in certain peculiar stuporose states. The latter is especially well illustrated in the following case previously recorded by Gooddy (1949).

Female, aged 53, whose brain at autopsy proved to show marked bi-parietal atrophy, was admitted to hospital with a three-month history of periodic attacks of unconsciousness. On her recovery from each attack, she would be confused, and for some hours would lie in bed moving her legs rhythmically from side to side with her hip joints flexed. Between whiles, she appeared fairly normal. She was admitted to hospital with the sequelae of the fourth of these attacks. She was wasted and dehydrated, lying in bed with her eyes open, silent and unresponsive to her surroundings. She blinked her eyelids normally, and also when menaced. She grimaced at painful stimulation. Swallowing of fluids was possible, but only in sips. No voluntary movements took place. She was doubly incontinent. Her eyes were fixed upon the ceiling. The limbs were hypotonic. All tendon reflexes were present ; abdominal responses were not obtained, and plantar stimulation produced an extensor movement of the big toe on each side. She appeared to sense only very strong painful stimuli. Blood pressure measured 200/110. Blood urea 176 per cent.

Some days later, her condition improved a little. Although still not speaking, she would occasionally follow with her eyes the nurses as they walked round the ward. Occasionally, she would feebly and slowly obey commands such as shutting the eyelids, protruding the tongue. She would move the right limbs but never the left. Response to painful stimuli could be obtained from the right side only. It appeared as though she were ignoring the left side of her body, and also the left half of extrapersonal space.

Later still, she was able to chew and swallow more easily. Occasionally, on being asked how she was, she would smile wanly and perhaps murmur that she was " better ".

Five weeks after admission, she had a series of epileptic fits, after which her condition markedly deteriorated. She died 90 days after her entry to hospital. (Case No. 12900.)

The most doubtful item upon the list of alleged biparietal (or parieto-occipital) phenomena is loss of revisualization. Not enough clinical evidence is yet to hand to enable one to say with confidence how often this symptom appears after focal lesions of the brain, and whether or not it can follow unilateral disease. Table 3 shows the symptoms which are claimed to be the hallmarks of disease of the parietal lobe of the dominant hemisphere. Some, or even all, of them may be expected to be demonstrable in addition to the items contained in Table 1.

Table 3

LEFT HEMISPHERE IN RIGHT-HANDED SUBJECTS

Additional phenomena
Disorders of language (especially dyslexia)
Dyscalculia
Bilateral apraxia of ideomotor type
Gerstmann's syndrome
" Pain asymboly "
Anaestho-agnosia
Bimanual astereognosis (tactile agnosia)
Loss of topographical memory (?)

General
Loss of abstract attitude (?)
Deterioration in attentiveness (?)
Global impairment of memory (?)

Most items in Table 3 have already been discussed in earlier chapters, and offer no particular difficulties. One or two, however, are debatable. Loss of topographical memory has been alleged to be a specific manifestation of left parietal disease (in dextrad subjects), as opposed to a loss of topographical " sense " claimed to be a specific symptom of right parietal lesions. So far, the evidence, whether clinical or theoretical, does not yet warrant such a dichotomy, though, of course, in the fullness of time, a better case might be made out to support this contention. At present, however, it would be going too far.

Still graver doubts attach themselves to the alleged equation of general psychological defects with lesions of the dominant hemisphere in a specific fashion. Particularly dubious is the notion that a deterioration of thought from a conceptual to a categorical level is a feature of left-brained lesions, rather than of cerebral disease any-where, and on either side. The evidence so far adduced is not con-vincing, as has already been mentioned. It is very questionable whether a change in total behaviour, such as loss of abstract attitude, can be adequately revealed by the ordinary routine sorting-tests and verbal abstractions. Particularly is this true when recourse is had merely to Weigl's test. The ability to employ two or more systems of sorting in Weigl's test is not an adequate index of loss of conceptual thinking. The inadequacies of such a test are further increased when the patients' performance is arbitrarily marked with a " o " or a " 3 ". No numerical system of evaluation is good enough : a complete verbal description of the speed and manner of the patient's performance is essential and cannot be replaced by a simple mark.

Goldstein's claim that a loss of abstract attitude develops with cerebral lesions, irrespective of questions of sidedness and location within the hemisphere, is not yet contradicted by the available evidence to the contrary. Time may eventually show that this change really is an expression of disease of the dominant hemisphere, but the arguments are still not yet adequate to justify that claim.

The idea that the dominant hemisphere (both the parietal and the frontal lobes) plays a special role in the genesis of defects of memory and of attention, derives chiefly from Pfeifer (1928). Confirmation of this idea is, however, still awaited. In many ways, it is the opposite contention to that made by Hughlings Jackson, Bastian and Rosenthal. Each of these writers believed that the posterior parts of the brain are more concerned with intellectual functions that the anterior, and that lesions there produced psychical disturbances. Jackson specified the right side in particular . . . " I am convinced that disease of the *right* cerebral hemisphere is more likely to cause mental defect (other than affection of speech) than is disease of the left ; and, again, that mental defect is more likely to result the further back in the hemisphere the damage is." Lloyd Anderson (1951) observed changes which were more qualitative than quantitative when lesions of the two sides of the brain were compared. Using the Wechsler-Bellevue indices of deterioration, he found that the functions of the non-dominant and the dominant hemispheres were comparable with disorders of a front office (executive) and a warehouse (storage) respectively. The patient with damage to the dominant half of the brain forgets *what* to do, while the patient with a lesion of the non-dominant hemisphere forgets *how* to do it.

In Table 4 are set out the chief clinical phenomena which have been looked upon as specific manifestations of disease of the minor parietal lobe. As already stated, objection may perhaps be taken first to the relegation of unilateral spatial neglect to disease of the minor hemisphere alone, and secondly to the inclusion here of constructional apraxia. Less debatable is the status of disorders of the body-image [1] (anosognosia ; somatoparaphrenia), and of spatial agnosia in the widest sense of the term in the realm of affections of the subordinate hemisphere.

Table 4

Right Hemisphere in Right-handed Subjects

Additional phenomena
Anosognosia
Denial of hemiplegia
Somatoparaphrenia
Neglect of external space to the left (?)
Spatial agnosia
Constructional apraxia (?)

Some of the early anatomists described a greater development of the posterior parts of the brain on the right side (Gratiolet ; Barkow ; Broca). Jackson (1874) regarded this region of the brain as the chief seat of the revival of images in the *recognition* of objects, places and persons. In a minor degree, such a person would have difficulty in

[1] In their valuable paper, Denny-Brown, Meyer and Horenstein (1952) have doubted the propriety of ascribing the integrity of the body-image to the right hemisphere : indeed, they were tempted—in so far as it represents a symbolic conception—to associate it more particularly with the left or dominant hemisphere. Ignoral of the left side and anosognosia are regarded more as distortions of behaviour, and the authors rather assume that the body-image is intact in such cases.

recognizing things, in relating what had occurred, not from lack of words, but from a prior inability to revive images of persons, objects and places.   In severer cases, the condition would be one of imbecility ; for " if all visual ideas were cleared out of a man's mind, he would be practically mindless " (1897).   Jackson's original description of an agnosic disability—which he called " imperception ", without, however, defining the condition—dates from 1875.   This patient would lose herself in familiar places : she could not dress herself properly ; she would put sugar in her tea two or three times over.   She mistook the identity of people.   Occasionally, she would misname coins, though the error was not a gross one.   She had difficulty in reading, and could not trace the lines in the correct direction.   At this time, she had a left hemiplegia, and probably a left hemianopia.   Gowers, who examined the brain after death, found a large gliomatous tumour in the right temporoparieto-occipital region, together with two other and smaller tumours nearby.

The problem of the left-handed subject with parietal disease now arises.   A steady accumulation of clinico-pathological data has accrued to show that, in sinistrality, there does not necessarily occur a mere mirror-reversal of cerebral dominance.   The right hemisphere may not constitute simply the left hemisphere in reverse, in regard to its functional significance.   So long as the causation and the essential meaning of handedness remain obscure, we are not likely to understand or to be able to predict the clinical phenomena due to unilateral parietal disease.

The relationship of handedness to cerebral dominance is still not fully understood ; which phenomenon is causal, and how the one entails the other.   Nor is the relation of handedness to sidedness (eyedness, footedness) as yet established, and the difficult and interesting cases where dissociation occurs have not yet been studied.

Even the term " left handedness " has been used with such imprecision as to invalidate much of the published work upon the problem of cerebral disease in sinistrals.   The 5–10 per cent of the community regarded as being left-handed is probably made up of a very heterogeneous set of cases, which may differ widely in their behaviour when cerebral disease appears.   Thus, the loosely applied term " left-handedness " may happen to include :

(1) Cases of genetically determined left-handed preference.   Not only is the favoured hand the left one, but the left eye and left foot are also dominant ; the right hemisphere is the major one, and is more bound up with the faculty of symbolic thought than is the left.   This is the purest type of sinistrality.

(2) Cases of pure genetically determined sinistrality, where the behavioural pattern has been complicated by the artificial insistence upon the

employment of the right hand in an unnatural fashion in the act of writing. In such individuals, it is probable that a clear-cut cerebral dominance in respect of language functions does not obtain. The effects of parietal disease may be quite different here than in the case of (1).

(3) Cases of genetically determined right-handedness (as in the majority), where disease of the right arm (whether peripherally determined, or resulting from affection of the left brain) at a very early age, leads to a left-sided manual preference. In such cases, there may be a dissociation between handedness and eyedness. The left cerebral hemisphere may or may not be the dominant one. Superficially, however, the patient seems to be a left-hander, and he may proclaim himself as such. The effects of parietal disease in cases like these cannot be confidently predicted.

(4) Cases of true left-handedness occurring in a family where right-handedness is the rule : and conversely, right-handed members of a left-handed family. Here the problem of stock-brainedness enters (Foster Kennedy, 1916), and here again, the results of unilateral parietal disease are unpredictable.

(5) Cases of alleged ambidexterity : or, where both hands are equally inexpert, " ambilevity ". Here, various type of dissociation may occur between haphazard use of the hands, and preferred use of one eye over the other, or one foot in particular. One hand may be favoured in the act of writing. Whether one hemisphere is dominant in respect of language is uncertain.

In taking a census of handedness (as in a survey of brain-injured patients, for example), any of the foregoing five sets of circumstances may lead the subject to proclaim himself, in good faith, a sinistral ; and for his statement to be accepted at face value. And yet, the five sets of circumstances are very different. Until more data is afforded as to the nature and type of manual preference, too much credence cannot be paid to descriptive studies of cerebral disorder in left-handed subjects.

Quite apart from this matter of whether an individual is a true sinistral or not, is the problem of the totally illiterate. This factor arises when speech disorder is being considered in relation to disease of one or other hemisphere, or of both.

The contributions made by Chesher (1936), Nielsen (1937, 1938, 1940), Russell Brain (1941, 1945), and others, have contributed to the realization that the problem of handedness and cerebral dominance, and especially of sinistrality, is much more complicated than once imagined. Conrad (1949) studied a series of 808 patients with unilateral disease of the brain, of which 47 (5·8 per cent) were regarded as being left-handed. Aphasia occurred in about a fourth of the right-handed patients, and in over a third of the left-handed patients. This observation was interpreted as showing that left-handed individuals had a greater susceptibility to aphasia. Nevertheless, the aphasia in the left-handed was on the whole less severe than in the right-handed, and less enduring. When Conrad came to correlate the side of the brain-injured with the factor of handedness and the presence of aphasia, he found that most of the aphasic left-handed patients were victims of damage to the left half of the brain. (The total number of cases, however, is disappointingly small, being only ten.) This is the phenomenon originally described by Bramwell (1899) as " crossed aphasia " (see also Marinesco, Grigoresco and Axente, 1938). One patient had sustained injury to both hemispheres. Seven had right brain disease. Conrad thereupon concluded that, though right-handedness implies left cerebral dominance, the contrary does not follow, and left-handedness does not necessarily indicate right cerebral dominance. Rather does it imply the expression of a less specialized transition stage between a bilateral controlling mechanism and a unilateral dominance. In other words, the left-handed subject possesses a sort of " bi-cerebrality " (*Beidhirnigkeit*). Subirana (1952), in his thoughtful studies of right-handedness in relation to unilateral cerebral disease, was inclined to support Conrad, and his electro-encephalographic researches, in association with Corominas and Oller-Daurella, suggested a certain cerebral immaturity in sinistrals.[1] We must seriously take into account the conclusions upon handedness which Subirana cautiously put forward. He pointed out that right-handedness and left-handedness are not mirror-opposite phenomena. Much more notice should be taken of the numerous intermediate forms between pure right-handedness and pure left-handedness.

Humphrey and Zangwill (1952) in the main supported Conrad's views. Their series comprised ten cases of unilateral brain disease in naturally left-handed subjects ; five had injuries to the left and five to the right half of the brain. Dysphasia was present in all cases of left-sided lesion, and in all but one of the right-sided lesions. The dysphasic symptoms were more severe in the former, and disorders of calculation in the latter. This last observation recalls an important conclusion made by Nielsen (1939, 1946) on the basis of a considerable morbid anatomical experience of aphasic patients, to the effect that different aspects of speech may be located in opposite hemispheres. Or, in paraphrasis, exclusively unilateral lesions do not necessarily ablate all the various aspects of symbolic thought, even when the

[1] Subirana, Corominas and Oller-Daurella studied a series of young children with distinct manual preferences. They found : (1) diminution in the percentage of alpha waves and increase in the slow frequency waves in left-handed subjects ; and (2) increased sensitivity to the effects of hyperpnoea in the case of left-handed children. They were not able to confirm the findings of Cornil and Gastaut (1947, *a* and *b*), as to the identification of the major and minor hemispheres.

lesion is widespread ; bilaterally situated disease would be needed to produce a permanent and global ablation of language.

With these observations in mind, it will be interesting to investigate parietal disease in left-handed subjects. In tabulating the syndromes, it would obviously be unwise to employ the expressions " subordinate " and " dominant " hemispheres (or even the terms " minor " and " major ") in this connection. It would be safer merely to speak of left parietal and right parietal lesions in left-handed subjects. Because of the imprecision of the conception of sinistrality, and because of the transition forms, a uniform clinical picture can scarcely be expected. Despite the variability, the schemata displayed in Tables 5 and 6 may be of interest.

Table 5

LEFT HEMISPHERE IN LEFT-HANDED SUBJECTS

Additional phenomena
Language disorders (severe and protracted)

We do not yet know whether we should add to this table other syndromes which ordinarily are ascribed to the minor or subordinate hemisphere (e.g. disorders of the body-image ; unilateral spatial imperception ; spatial agnosia ; constructional apraxia). Time alone will solve these problems, although it can be surmised first that the pattern may well be inconsistent, and secondly that, on the whole, the criteria of the right parietal lobe in dextrad subjects probably will not be found consistently in sinistrals with left parietal disease.

In Table 6 we see a most interesting state of affairs, whereby a combination of phenomena may occur.

This table is based upon an important case-report made by Humphrey and Zangwill (1952) of a left-handed man who sustained an injury to the right side of the head. The result was a mixed parieto-occipital syndrome. Other comparable cases are those published by Herrmann and Pötzl (1926), and by Russell Brain (1941). The Humphrey-Zangwill case concerned a left-handed soldier who sustained a compound fracture of the skull from a mortar bomb, in the right occipito-parietal region. He developed a left homonymous hemianopia, left-sided sensory disturbances, motor disabilities (partly dyspraxic in nature), and a mixed type of dysphasia. During the ensuing two months the patient improved, so as to leave a left visual inattention with disorientation in the left lower quadrants ; gross neglect of the left half of visual space and perhaps of the left half

Table 6

RIGHT HEMISPHERE IN LEFT-HANDED SUBJECTS

" *Dual* " *phenomena*

Major :
Transient dysphasia, dyslexia ; dysgraphia (slight)
    depending upon the hand ordinarily used for writing
Dyscalculia
Dyspraxia
Right-left disorientation
Impaired verbal intelligence tests (transient)

Minor :
Unilateral spatial agnosia (?)
Left motor neglect (autotopamnesia) (?)
Dressing dyspraxia (?)
Visual-constructive defects (?)

---

of the body, dressing dyspraxia, right-left confusion, visual constructive loss, and some disturbance of spatial orientation. There was
no visual object agnosia, and no finger-agnosia. Writing was impaired
only in a paragrammatic fashion. A serious dyscalculia persisted
after the speech had improved. Intelligence testing showed a
moderate impairment in both verbal and non-verbal spheres. Six
and a half years after the wound, there remained a very slight dyslexia,
moderate dyscalculia, some unilateral spatial agnosia and visual constructive loss, mild topographical disabilities and slight weakness of
concentration and memory. Hand-preference had shifted to the
right for most purposes.

The authors regarded this case as showing a medley of " major "
and " minor " parietal signs, and they rightly pointed out that the
picture was not identical with a biparietal syndrome, the disabilities
being far less severe. They suggested that " in addition to the
principle of unilateral representation and cerebral dominance, there
is a ' biparietal integrative function ', disturbances of which lead to
symptoms very much more severe and long-lasting than those
produced by lesions of the major hemisphere alone, in whichever
side it may be."

Interesting cases of this sort are highly important and suggestive.
The evidence of other comparable cases is very much needed, because
the weakness of the conception of duality or mixed major and minor
parietal signs lies in the doubt first as to the correctness of regarding
the minor signs as such, and secondly, to what type of sinistrality
the patient belonged. Dressing dyspraxia certainly cannot of necessity be a minor parietal sign, despite the opinion of Hécaen and

Ajuriaguerra. Right-handed patients with left parietal lesions may also show much difficulty in dressing. In the Humphrey-Zangwill case, the only details about this particular impairment were to the effect that there was " no residual dressing disability, though the patient confessed that he would get into a ' most appalling tangle ' with his clothes in the first six months after injury ". As thus described, this symptom could well be an index of dysfunction of the dominant hemisphere. The other alleged " minor " parietal signs in this case comprised unilateral spatial agnosia, left-sided motor neglect and visual constructive defects. As already mentioned, not one of these signs can really be regarded as pathognomic of minor as opposed to major parietal defect.

Until more certitude exists as to the nature and specificity of signs of disease of the minor parietal lobe, the interesting conception of " dualism " in lesions of the right hemisphere in sinistrals must be taken as non-proven.

Localization within the Parietal Lobe

The temptation to associate conspicuous clinical phenomena with small and circumscribed lesions within the parietal lobe is one to be resisted rather than encouraged. There have been, however, one or two attempts in the literature to trace certain " syndromes " which really belong to the domain of parietal symptomatology, irrespective of sidedness. In the first place, an *anterior parietal syndrome* has been distinguished from a *posterior parietal syndrome*, though the distinction is largely an artificial one.

Of more particular interest is what has been called the *inter-parietal syndrome*. This, in practice, refers to the clinical con-comitant of a lesion involving the midpart of the parietal lobe behind the postcentral gyrus and extending equally above and below the interparietal sulcus. More specifically, however, the syndrome has been associated with a lesion of the visuosensory band of Elliot Smith. This syndrome, coupled with the names of Pötzl (1924–25), Foerster, Hoff and Kamin (1930), Friant, Pero, Lhermitte and Trelles, Gurewicz (1932), Bychowski, Olsen and Ruby and others, is said to be characterized by vertiginous symptoms and disorders of the body-image. In the two cases recorded by Hoff and Kamin, a trephination gap over the interparietal sulcus permitted the authors to excite the cortex by alternate cold and hot stimuli. This procedure resulted in various visual symptoms whereby objects would seem to be dis-placed to the opposite side, colours could not be recognized, and the environment appeared cloudy.

The advantages of this type of clinico-anatomical correlation are

very limited, and are indeed liable to abuse.   Parcellation of the lobe
into smaller zones, with attempts to associate limited lesions thereof
with certain clinical states, has, of course, been practised and this
trend will no doubt continue for a while.   There comes a time,
however, when broader and more dynamic conceptions of cerebral
function can no longer be resisted especially when the somewhat
elusive psychosensory and psychomotor activities are under consideration.   Parietal symptomatology is in this respect on a par with
the problem of aphasia.

   The same critical attitude is necessary towards what might be dubbed
" cerebral localization in reverse ".   That is to say, a tendency to trace a
causal association between some particularly well-evolved aptitude and a
condition of localized convolutional complexity or hypertrophy.   From time
to time, reports have appeared as to the morphology of the brain in cases of
scientists, musicians, mathematicians, and so on, particularly at the hands of
Russian investigators.   In the case of the parietal lobe, for example, we read
that the supramarginal gyrus in both hemispheres (as well as the superior
temporal gyri) were of excessive size in the case of two musicians (Somogyi,
1930).   Santha (1932) found a complexity of the right angular gyrus in the
case of a *Rechenskunstler* or arithmetical prodigy.   We are told that the
brain of Ernst Haeckel showed well-developed angular gyri (Maurer, 1924) ;
that Klose (1920) found *inter alia* an elaborate supramarginal gyrus in the
case of the pianist Sockeland ; and that Riese and Goldstein (1950) found
considerable asymmetry between the hemispheres of the left-handed
anatomist, Ludwig Edinger, including the parietal lobes.   How to interpret
these data can scarcely as yet be expressed dogmatically.

   The tendency to speak of gradients of localization has far greater
advantages, and accords better with modern views as to cerebral
function and the consequences of disease.   This is well illustrated
by Teuber's study of the performance level of brain-injured veterans
(1952) (in conjunction with Bender), who found it convenient to
divide their patients into three groups according to the situation of
the entry wound.   Their division was : (1) *anterior penetrations*
(frontal and frontotemporal) ;   (2) *posterior penetrations* (occipital,
occipitoparietal) ;   and (3) *intermediate penetrations* (temporal, parietal).
Groups (2) and (3) are of more particular interest in this connection,
but the important result of the investigation was not that there was an
ability or inability to execute the various performance-tests, but that
the quality of achievement varied according to the site of penetration.
Thus, Teuber found a number of deficits which appeared, not
uniquely, but maximally, with lesions in the posterior lobe substance,
in particular the parieto-occipital convexity.   These impairments
could not fully be explained in terms of primary sensory deficits.
" Frontal lobe tests " were found not to be specific for frontal lobe

lesions . . . and indeed, they could be demonstrated readily with posterior penetrating lesions.

General symptoms and signs

Brief mention should be made of certain " general " symptoms which at different times have been associated with parietal lesions. The statements have resulted less from statistical analysis of case series than from a clinical impression. Thus, generalized epileptic convulsions (i.e. fits without focal phenomena) have been said to occur more often with tumours of the parietal lobe than elsewhere. Whether this belief can be substantiated is doubtful. The evidence available rather suggests that the highest incidence of symptomatic epilepsy occurs when the tumours involve the " central " region of the hemispheres. This area of course includes the postcentral gyrus. With tumours located within the parietal lobe, but behind the sensory cortex, there is a fall in the frequency with which convulsions occur. The incidence quoted by different authors is so wide in its range as to suggest an inherent inaccuracy in these surveys. Thus, the figures extend from 11·4 per cent (Gliddon), to 23·7 per cent (Steinthal); 33·3 per cent (Ascroft); 54·2 per cent (Lund); 66 per cent (Kirstein); and 68 per cent (Penfield *et al.*). In the series of post-traumatic cases analysed by Ritchie Russell and Whitty (1952), fits were associated with 65 per cent of the cases where the parietal lobes were injured, confirming Baumm's figure of 67·7 per cent. The technical fallacies in such a type of study are, however, serious.

Baruk (1926) was impressed by the high incidence of melancholia in his cases of parietal tumour. His series was, however, a small one for it numbered only 55 cases of brain tumour in all situations. The clinical impression gleaned from a very much larger series does not suggest at all that depression is relatively common in cases of parietal tumour.

Relative incidence of parietal disease

There are no statistics available as yet to show exactly how often parietal lesions occur in the general incidence of brain pathological disorder. This is particularly true of vascular disease. The fact that the middle cerebral artery is the largest arterial channel within the cranium would imply that lesions here would probably make up the bulk of cases.

In the case of brain tumours, there are already some statistical data available. Cowie analysed a series of cases of brain tumour, according to their situation and histological nature. Her results are displayed in the following table.

Cowie found that the tumours within the parietal lobe significantly exceeded the percentage values regarding area and weight of this lobe. ". . . When the group of tumours is considered, omitting secondary carcinomata, the percentage of tumour-incidence falls in the parietal lobe, rising slightly in other lobes, which may be an

Table 7

Lobe	Percentage area of whole cerebral cortex (Donaldson)	Percentage area of whole cerebral cortex (Wagner)	Percentage weight of whole cerebral cortex (Meynert)	Percentage of total number of tumours occurring within the confines of the lobe	Ditto, omitting secondary carcinomata
Frontal	38·33	41·2	41·5	40·3	40·81
Parietal	52·47	{20·9	23·4	31·4	29·9
Temporal		{20·7}		{25·2	25·9
Occipital	9·2	17·2}	35·1	{ 3·1	3·4

(After Cowie, 1953.)

indication that the parietal lobe is favoured by metastases." Of the cases of parietal metastatic carcinomata, five involved the left side and nineteen the right.

Another subject not without interest is the relative involvement of the parietal lobe by senile plaques in various conditions, including extreme old age, senile dementia and Alzheimer's disease (Critchley, 1929). According to Simchowicz, in normal senility plaques are to be found in greatest profusion in the most forward regions of the cerebral cortex. In cases of senile dementia, the plaques though still present chiefly in the frontal region are also to be found in the parietal, temporal and occipital regions. But in Alzheimer's disease, the posterior distribution of senile plaques increases and overshadows the frontal lobe incidence. Thus, the " senile index ", I.F./I.Occ., is important, according to Simchowicz, in distinguishing senile from pre-senile dissolution (where I = incidence of plaques ; F = frontal lobe ; and Occ. = parieto-occipital region).

CHAPTER XIV

A SUMMING-UP

I have said it before, but a teacher who hesitates to repeat, shrinks from his most important duty, and a learner who dislikes to hear the same thing twice over lacks his most essential acquisition.

WILLIAM GOWERS.

The men of experiment are like the ant ; they only collect and use. The reasoners resemble spiders, who make cob-webs out of their own substance. But the bee takes a middle course ; it gathers its material from the flowers of the garden and of the field, but transforms and digests it by a power of its own. Not unlike this is the true business of philosophy.

FRANCIS BACON.

The opinion was ventured in the introductory paragraphs that, while this monograph possibly constitutes the first one to be devoted to the subject of the parietal lobes, it may well also be the last. While the clinical concomitants of parietal disease form an important and rapidly expanding chapter in current neurology, the idea of restricting discussion of cerebral function to a limited compartment of the brain is stultifying and wholly artificial. It has repeatedly been emphasized that the parietal lobe is neither an anatomical nor a physiological unit, but merely that part of the convex surface of the cerebral hemispheres which happens to be covered by the parietal bone. A neurological study confined to the topic of parietal disease is likely to be rewarding only to a limited extent. Subsequent monographs will no doubt broach the subject from the aspect of various faculties and aptitudes, e.g. disorders of calculation, of disintegration or de-differentiation, of tactile or visual dysfunction and so on.

Chapter I recapitulated the traditional points in anatomical teaching. At the meeting-point of anatomy and physiology, certain interesting conceptions have developed which, however stimulating, need to be examined critically. The doctrine of discrete, cyto-architectonic areas, specific, identifiable and variegated, each with its private functional role, has appealed to many as being plausible and significant. We recall the Vogts' belief in the existence of two hundred or so distinct cortical organs. But the cogent arguments against the specificity of these areas, and against the belief in a sharp demarcation one from another, have attracted less attention. The use of cyto-architectonic numerals to connote this area or that is of questionable propriety ; the common practice of resorting now to the terminology of Brodmann, and now to that of Economo, or of Vogt, is inexcusable.

Physiological neuronophagy has supported the contention of many clinicians to the effect that one cortical area is coupled to another by intimate corticocortical connections. This fact detracts even further from doctrines of architectonic autonomy, and it emphasizes that any claim to subdivide the cortex on the basis of cellular arrangement exclusively, ignores the all-important factor of axonal and dendritic connections. If, then, each and every small area of cortex is admitted to be tightly linked with other areas, contiguous or remote, ipsilateral or contralateral, rigid attempts to demonstrate a strict localization of cortical function become still more unconvincing, and the dangers of associating a particular symptom with a small cortical lesion become even more apparent.

The fallacy of confusing localization of sign-producing lesions with localization of function still needs reiteration. This error of thinking was first pointed out by Lange ; it was emphasized over and over again by Hughlings Jackson, and has been repeated later by Monakow, Pick, Riese, Walshe and others. Many writers pay a preliminary lip-service to this axiom and then ignore it. It would be a wise discipline to avoid as far as possible the term " localization " and to speak of " specialization " of function and to recall that it is open to explanation along the lines of gradients. In the case of the parietal lobe, we therefore should not be astonished or dismayed when we find that some of the more characteristic " parietal " phenomena at times follow a lesion which is quite remote from this situation. After leucotomy, or in the case of frontal, temporal or occipital tumours, examples of spatial agnosia, of tactile inattention, or sensory or visual disturbances have not infrequently been noted. In other words, the so-called parietal signs are only too often release phenomena and represent the activity of some region of the nervous system other than the parietal lobe. That they might also be released by a lesion at some quite different site should not be difficult to conceive.

The second chapter dealt in a descriptive fashion with physiology from the aspect of experimentation. Conclusions as to the functional role of the human parietal region are less readily drawn. One of the weaknesses of the experimental method concerns the essentially artificial nature of so many of the techniques, e.g. electrical stimulation, strychninization. Horsley declared in quite unequivocal terms that an electrical stimulus is a crude method of exciting the nerve centres; that a threshold stimulus merely "samples the point" and does not reveal its full physiological possibilities. Another disadvantage is bound up with the fact that the co-operation of an intelligent, conscious and articulate subject is often not feasible, except in the case of cortical excitation on the operating table. Walshe has spoken of the fact that science is formed by the meeting of the two orders of experience—operational and conceptual—and that the former can be interpreted only in terms of the latter. By now, a vast amount of physiological as well as clinical facts have been amassed. The second and more difficult stage in scientific method is less adequately accounted for, and there is much need for reflective consideration of the data, and for the logical discernment of generalizations. There is a tendency to assume a strict and almost point-to-point localization within the somaesthetic cortex. This doctrine possesses the attractiveness of dogmatism, but fails to meet the objections of Leyton and Sherrington, Graham Brown, Liddell and Phillips, and Walshe, who have all emphasized the flexible nature of cortical function. The rigid patterning of cortical sensory centres probably indicates that at a particular moment in time, and in certain circumstances, a current of known constancy causes a certain response to take place. In so far as each different method, many of them very diverse, leads to almost the same results, an approximate somatotopy must be admitted. But the approximate nature should not be forgotten. In the case of the human postcentral cortex, the role of the so-called hand-and-finger area needs special mention. This hand area is conspicuous by reason of its large size, and its low threshold of excitability, so that sensory phenomena referred to the hand are easily fired off by weak electrical excitations. In disease states, Jackson's " double plan " of studying both discharging and destructive lesions can be followed. Where a discharging lesion is concerned, the hand area is the chief " leading part ", as Jackson put it, and focal sensory convulsive attacks are " physiological fulminates ", being most readily initiated by phenomena which are referred to the hand. This is followed by a compound sequence of spread, that is one which shows a gradual increase both in distribution and severity. Again, in destructive lesions of the postcentral cortex, the hand is most often the seat of sensory defect, even though the defect is rarely complete in intensity or extensity, and rarely permanent in time. The cortex shows itself to be " tolerant " of destroying lesions. These observations suggest strongly that the postcentral hand area is not an exclusive territory for the cortical representation of sensation within that limb, any more than the motor hand area is the sole domain of manual and digital movement. As Walshe said, the hand area is more a " macula " of the field of hand movements. This opinion derives directly from the foresight of Hughlings Jackson, who declared quite explicitly that the " arm centre " was for him a centre representing movements of all parts of the body, but movements of the arm very much more than any others.

It is important to be clear as to the precise meaning of the word " representation ". We may quote Walshe's definition : " The word

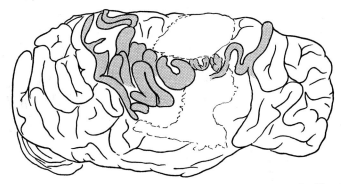

Fig. 138. Outer aspect of right hemisphere, showing the enormously dilated veins and thickened dura.

' representation ' . . . is a general term for all those processes in the cortex by which these visible results are brought about, and this method of direct observation does not concern itself with the analysis of these processes, e.g. conduction in the neurone and across synaptic

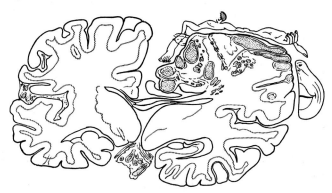

Fig. 139. Vertical coronal section, showing distribution of the veins on inner aspect of right hemisphere. Penfield's " sensory homunculus " is inserted (after Worster-Drought and Carnegie Dickson).

junctions, the physical basis of facilitation, excitation, etc., and the term ' representation ' as thus employed subsumes all these processes."

A single clinicopathological illustration may be given, taken from a paper by Worster-Drought and Carnegie Dickson (1927). Their patient died after a clinical history of convulsive attacks ; at autopsy, there was found a large venous angeioma on the cortex of the right hemisphere (see Fig. 138).

The relationship of the mass in respect of the " sensory homunculus " has been sketched in Fig. 139. Although there would seem to be no good reason why the " leading part " of the sensory focal attacks might well have been the foot, leg, face or hand, as a matter of fact, during life, each one of the patient's seizures had started with subjective tingling in the left side of the face and tongue. It is possible that the lowermost part of the sensory cortex was the site of a discharging lesion rather than a destructive one, being just outside the confines of the tumour itself. This raises interesting considerations in any attempt to relate clinical phenomena with the anatomical site of a new-growth.

Flexibility, plasticity and resilience of cortical functioning with high-grade powers of compensation mediated through firm inter-cortical connections, can alone explain the clinical phenomena of transiency, incompleteness of defect, as well as the paradoxical nature of a disability, when cortical sensory changes are concerned. No hard and fast point-to-point deficit can readily account for the incon-sistency of response, slowness of performance and tactile illusions so often met with in testing patients with sensory loss from parietal disease.

To seek to establish a formula of normal parietal function is largely a vain and meaningless pursuit, however attractive. It is probable that, without falling into the error of morcellating the lobe into areas subserving different functions, one might, nonetheless, isolate an important tactual role among others. Even here, one cannot assume an identity of the parietal lobe with the sensory sphere. The central sulcus does not definitively separate a purely motor domain from one which is mainly sensory. Neither on histological grounds, nor on the basis of electrical stimulation can one make too sharp a contrast between the pre- and postcentral gyri, for giant motor cells can be detected here and there posterior to the central sulcus, and sensory responses can be obtained from stimulation anteriorly. These facts lend colour to the older ideas as to the sensorimotor nature of the cortex, that all sensation embraces movement, and that co-ordinated movement depends upon sensory integrity. Jackson regarded the highest level sensory centres as only *chiefly* sensory (and the highest motor centres only *chiefly* motor).

The sensory cortex is therefore not synonymous with the parietal cortex. Nevertheless, the two regions are very comparable, for they overlap to a considerable degree. The role of the cortex in the world of touch is mainly discriminative ; objects are localized and compared ; minor differences are realized ; judgments are made as to physical properties and identification is effected. Simple notions of a thermal or painful quality are less the concern of the cortex. Indeed, per-ception of simple pain sense data would largely interfere with dis-criminative activities. It is not surprising therefore that postcentral topectomies are not of consistent or permanent value in the treatment of painful phantom limbs.

That the parietal cortex represents the highest level mechanism for tactile percepts is the conclusion to which every available line of research leads. The evidence of comparative morphology reveals how a parietal sensory cortex originates from the oral sense (i.e. combined tactual, olfactory and gustatory) of the primitive mammal. To this are added, in the case of the terrestrial mammals, the cortical centres mediating the motile and sensitive palpatory organs. Clinical evidence from both destructive and discharging lesions points to the parietal cortex, especially in its forward portions, as being intimately concerned with sensory equipment, of the most highly evolved organs in the biological sense.

Cortical sensation is very much a question of the appreciation of a change of state, a change which can be brought about either by a moving stimulus object passing over adjacent skin segments, or by palpatory movements feeling a stationary object. In this way, we again see the operation of motor components in a sensory act— Monakow's kinetic melody. We furthermore witness the operation of a temporal factor, whereby one stimulus, by succeeding another, forms a meaningful pattern. This is Monakow's chronogenic factor in sensation.

Comparative morphology indicates that the parietal lobe forms an expansion which crowds the motor, auditory and visual cortices forwards, downwards and backwards respectively. This particular location suggests that cortical tactual discriminative processes may in certain circumstances entail auditory and visual components. The peculiar role of the parietal lobe—or lobes—in the building-up of the postural schema of the body leads to an important association with corporeal awareness, imagery and memory. Hence the appearance of unusual disorders of the body-image with parietal disease. Spatial manipulations and ideas are of themselves essentially bound up with parietal integrity, and in so far as they entail tactile and visual perceptions, they may be concerned with their three-dimensional qualities.[1]

---

[1] This idea ties up with the conception of " morphosynthesis ", recently expounded by Denny-Brown, Meyer and Horenstein, as the function of the parietal cortex. By this term is meant the spatial summation of sense data leading to perception and recognition. In the first place, this conception applies to the tactual sphere and may perhaps explain the phenomenon of extinction, suppression or inattention when perceptual rivalry are concerned, whereby poorly differentiated features are eliminated in favour of those better perceived. " Morphosynthesis " also includes visual components, loss of which would help explain unawareness of part of extrapersonal space as well as unawareness of self.

Probably, temporal qualities also combine with the three-dimensional spatial factors.

The interaction of vision and motility in the manipulation of one, two or three-dimensional data is witnessed in certain acts of construction and designing. Though unjustifiable to regard such activities as part of the normal physiology of the parietal lobe, it can be said that destructive lesions of the parietal lobe, especially when bilateral, may be associated clinically with considerable difficulties in drawing, copying and constructing of two or three-dimensional patterns according to a model. Again, it can be said that, when the parietal lobe is diseased, more especially on the right side in dextrad subjects, there may be grave difficulties in route-finding, in topographical memorizing and orientation, in map-reading and map-making. It would still be illogical to conclude that in some way these activities are part of the normal function of the parietal lobe. These rather complex mental tasks should be looked upon as mediated by the cerebral hemispheres in a diffuse fashion, entailing the harmonious integration of manifold impulses, afferent as well as efferent. Topographical disorders may therefore result from lesions in various parts of the brain. Parietal disease is the most significant in this connection, the topographical faculty being apparently vulnerable at a parietal level, which represents nodal point in the mechanism of differentiation.

The problem of insight into bodily functions also arises here. Particularly are we concerned with a patient's insight into his bodily dysfunction or sickness. In certain circumstances, unawareness of disease may pass over into denial of disease, which in turn will necessitate a confabulatory explaining-away of the objective evidences of disease. As already discussed, these phenomena are often conspicuous in patients with parietal lesions, especially when the right side of the brain is at fault. It would be rash, however, to try to equate in a specific fashion the right parietal lobe with the normal process of awareness of bodily function and dysfunction. Such is more probably an activity of the brain as a whole, one which is inherent in the personality, and which cannot logically be localized to this or that region of the brain. Disease anywhere within the brain may at times determine states in which insight is impaired, or the very existence of a malady denied. The type of premorbid personality may prove to be more significant than the site of the lesion. Nonetheless, it can scarcely be denied that the parietal lobe constitutes an area of regional vulnerability in this respect, in that disease here is so often followed by symptoms of disavowal or denial.

Language disorder occupies a comparable role in the problem of parietal function. Both arrest and arousal of vocalization in the case

Plate 10

CONSTANTIN VON MONAKOW

of a conscious human subject can be produced by appropriate stimulations of the cortex of either hemisphere (Penfield *et al.*). Few would choose to align these phenomena with anything more than the instrumentalities of spoken speech. In the ordinary educated adult person, the left hemisphere obviously has a greater importance in symbolic thinking and expression than the right. This unilateral predominance is not an exclusivism, however, and can be modified if necessary, the two hemispheres being flexible in this respect. In so far as it is an aspect of mentation, the faculty of language cannot logically be localized to any one part of the brain, or even strictly lateralized to one hemisphere or the other. This must be so, even though clinical experience at present teaches that one hemisphere, when diseased, is ordinarily more liable to be followed by speech disorders than the other. Moreover, of the more vulnerable hemisphere, the middle third, which includes the parietal lobe, is more likely to be followed, when diseased, by disorders of language. Also within this significant middle third of the cerebrum, there seems to be a certain specialization, in that lesions in the hinder part are apt to be followed by difficulties in the understanding of verbal symbols presented visually. Beyond this, it would be unwise to elaborate the role of the left parietal lobe in the domain of speech.

Another variety of symbolic thought entails calculation. This too is sensitive to lesions situated almost anywhere within the cerebral hemispheres, even more so than speech. Parietal lesions, like those in the frontal, temporal and occipital lobes, are apt to be followed by dyscalculia, though its clinical manifestations may differ according to the site of disease.

The diversity of clinical consequences of parietal disease now known to us contrasts strongly with the conception held up to fifty or sixty years ago of the parietal lobes as a " silent area ". Thus, in Oppenheim's text-book, the whole problem was dismissed in a single paragraph. . . . " Tumours arising from the parietal lobes may produce symptoms of motor irritation and inhibition (from compression of the motor zone). Disturbances of sensibility, especially of the sense of position and of stereognostic perception, and ataxia have been found in tumours of this region . . . (the so-called mind-paralysis being less common). Alexia and optic aphasia may be symptoms of growths arising from the left inferior parietal lobe. If the tumour penetrates deep into the substance of the inferior parietal lobe, it may give rise to hemianopsia."

Nowadays, our ideas are less simple. Within the brain, no territory surpasses the parietal lobe in the rich variegation of clinical phenomena which follows disease states. The basal ganglia are perhaps the nearest approximation in this respect. Despite the lush variety of the signs, they require special techniques for their elicitation, if they are not to pass unnoticed. This point has already been made several times, but can scarcely be emphasized too often. Not only are there shortcomings to the ordinary routine neurological examination, but the conventional psychological testing also fails to do justice to the nature of parietal disorders. No simple system of marking can possibly replace the full and faithful recording in a descriptive fashion of exactly what the patient says and does under performance. Qualitative changes in behaviour can only in this way be given their true value.

The manifold symptoms and signs of parietal and parieto-occipital disease at the present time attract considerable attention and debate. Of all these, visual disorders are provoking the most significant discussions. The post-war German literature has contained subject-matter of the utmost importance, the main burden of which concerns the status of visual object-agnosia. Much of the evidence for and against the alleged unmasking of agnosia has been given in Chapter IX. The views of Best (1952) and of Duensing (1952) could not be included, however, and may be mentioned here.

It can be said that there are at present three main attitudes towards the problem of visual agnosia :

(1) It may be put down to a local lesion, unilateral or bilateral, within the posterior regions of the brain, in front of the striate cortex, involving hypothetical gnosic centres by which visual percepts are related to the recollection of previous visual experiences. This might be called the traditional *specific hypothesis* which is held in most neurological centres. Dejerine's definition of visual agnosia may be quoted in illustration : " L'agnosie est un trouble de la reconnaissance. La reconnaissance est ce phénomène psychologique qui nous permet, par l'usage de l'un ou l'autre de nos sens, d'indentifier un objet que nous observons actuellement, avec un objet anterieurement observé et dont nous avons enregistré le souvenir sous forme d'image mentale."

(2) It may be ascribed to a deficit in the formation of Gestalten, either at the preliminary (*Vorgestaltung*) stage or at the final point. Questions of localization, though not excluded, are of minor interest. This is the *configurational hypothesis* ; and lastly,

(3) It may be attributed to a combination of perceptual visual defects (either gross and quantitative, or else elusive, subtle and

qualitative), with an added impairment of general intelligence (consciousness, vigilance, awareness). This theory, which presupposes widespread but ill-defined lesions in the posterior parts of both hemispheres, may be spoken of as the *nihilistic* or *rational hypothesis*. Shorn of its holism, this hypothesis reminds one of Pavlov's criticisms of Munk's mind-blindness. To Pavlov, there was no mystery about the matter. A dog whose posterior regions of the brain had been ablated could make coarse analyses such as between light and dark. Finer distinction, i.e. between combinations of light and shade, were impossible. When the dog was no longer able to recognize its master, it was not a question of not being able to " understand ", but because of damage to the visual analysers, it had lost the capacity to form conditional reflexes on the more delicate and complex visual stimuli.

The recent article by Best describing two case-reports is an important one, for it retails the use of the battery of visual tests advocated by Bay. His second patient (also recorded earlier by Kleist) was an outstanding example of severe visual disorientation with inability to perceive two objects simultaneously, due to a through and through G.S.W. of the back of the head. The first patient with an injury to the right side of the skull was a case of left hemianopia, coupled with many other visual defects, e.g. difficulty in recognizing small objects and in surveying the whole of large objects; impaired visual acuity when tested in poor illumination ; reduced stereoscopic vision ; poverty of three-dimensional (plastic) visual imagery ; poor topographical sense ; inability to state which eye was stimulated when the beam of a torch was directed on to the closed eyelids ; disordered colour sense ; possibly visual perseveration ; and great difficulty in recognizing drawings and pictures as well as human faces (including his own reflection in a mirror). Writing and drawing were done very slowly and proved most exhausting. There was an illusory acceleration of the passage of time. Other features included an inability to count several articles of a kind, and difficulty in putting on his trousers. Best's conclusions conformed chiefly with the conventional hypothesis of visual agnosia as a specific focal symptom. He concluded that a visual space agnosia may occur associated with a bilateral field defect in the lower quadrants, while a visual object agnosia can accompany an upper quadrantic defect (a state of affairs which is actually much rarer).

Duensing based his views upon the study of a single case, but the contribution is a valuable one, for his patient was co-operative and intelligent. As the result of partial occlusion of both posterior cerebral arteries, there developed a visual object-agnosia, which Duensing did not think could be explained adequately by sense-physiological disturbances. The author blamed in particular a marked inability to conjure up visual images. This was shown, for example, by his replies when confronted with a cabbage butterfly. He called it a butterfly, but could not say what kind it was, although he could describe the markings accurately. He also listed all the morphological differences between the leaves of a spray of roses and of lilac, but he could not identify either of them. There was particular difficulty in the identification of faces, while the understanding of facial expression

E E

was less severely involved. Affective concomitants of visual perception, including aesthetic appreciation, were in abeyance. The patient showed a gross inability to draw from memory. According to Duensing, one can distinguish three stages : (1) of Gestalt-seeing (*Gestaltwahrnehmung*) ; (2) of Gestalt-recognition (*Gestalterkennung*) ; and (3) of object-comprehension (*Dingauffassung*). He believed that in visual agnosia, the non-recognition of the object-gestalt would of necessity cause disturbance in object-comprehension. Visual agnosia is not a disturbance of gestalt-perception, but of the process of recognition. (*Optische Agnosie ist nicht ein Störung der Gestaltwahrnehmung, sondern des Erkennungsvorganges.*)

It is very obvious that no firm expression of opinion is really yet justifiable. The question of visual agnosia has become a spearhead of the problem of cortical localization, but the clinical evidence is not yet adequate to warrant dogmatism. There is need for further studies of these rare cases at the hands of competent and informed neurologists who will include in their investigative armamentarium all the special tests of qualitative visual disorders. No more promising topic in present day neurology exists than an evaluation of the nature of the agnosias.

These rare and difficult cases of central affection of vision, ordinarily described as visual agnosia, lend themselves to study in a natural setting. The alterations in total behaviour, the reductions in performance, are less well suited for observation within the artificial environment of the clinic or consulting-room than in the home. Progressive and more especially retrogressive syndromes need to be studied longitudinally, for investigation—however elaborate—during a sojourn in a hospital merely affords a static representation of a moving picture. The Goldstein-Gelb case is an outstanding contribution to the literature, not only because of its thoroughness, but also by virtue of the novel principles which it formulated. Adler's patient, although less intimately studied, was followed up over a period of years, so that the gradual improvement and the adaptation of the personality to the residual defect could be witnessed in the natural surroundings. She was investigated in her capacities as a housewife, a mother and shop-assistant. This case-report is in its way a model for future researchers. Wilbrand's patient, although recorded sixty years ago, was also remarkable for its ecological value.

The danger of erecting a top-heavy structure of hypothesis upon the foundations of an elaborately studied but solitary case needs emphasis. By so doing, conceptual thinking is apt to overtake operational experience, and the opposite error of scientific method is the result. Consequently, there is much need for many further similar studies, with experienced neurologists co-operating with social workers, observing the reaction of the agnosic patient towards his environment and towards society. Such field-work might well follow the examples afforded by Rylander in the case of frontal lobectomy, and Partridge, in his follow-up of leucotomized patients. The dynamic or mobile character of the clinical phenomena in parietal disease is constantly obtruding, and needs to be reckoned with in our diagnostic judgments. Very abrupt lesions (e.g. traumata, vascular accidents) provoke shock affects of various sorts which gradually alter with time. Progressive lesions (neoplasms) produce progressive disabilities ; and in the case of metastatic growths, the picture may become hopelessly complicated. With stationary lesions (old softenings, scarring), the organism may in time utilize *détours*, by-passes and trick accomplishments so successfully as to bring about an astonishing degree of compensation. All these secondary chronogenic factors play a most important part, though too often imperfectly understood and neglected.

Quite apart from these secondary factors, there is another matter which needs consideration, although often difficult to assess in retrospect, namely, the problem of premorbid personality. As already emphasized, some of the phenomena which are lightly regarded as localizing focal signs may in reality be the outcome of the personality reacting in its own way to the handicap of a brain lesion. This is an important subject wherein the evidence is still incomplete, and much more clinical information is needed.

Until the last two decades, the growth of knowledge as to cerebral function largely proceeded along the lines of isolating various faculties, functions and aptitudes, with a special bias towards the correlation of ablated function with focal disease of the brain. The intriguing idea of a sort of phylogenetic stratification of function was popular, culminating in the bald statement that " the day will come when we shall be able to estimate the functional value of every convolution of the brain " (Keith, 1925). Such a materialistic attitude would nowadays appeal to few. The conception is growing up among neurologists that cerebral activity is something more than a simple summation of a number of discrete faculties—e.g. speech, memory, imagery, consciousness, praxis, gnosis, perception, and so on. In other words, the conventional association psychology is no longer proving adequate or satisfying. The stage has therefore been set for a different orientation in neurology. A more holistic conception seemed to answer better some of the problems encountered at the bedside. An increasing sympathy with the ideas expressed by configurational or Gestalt psychology has developed in many centres, as it gave promise of explaining more satisfactorily the common paradoxes and inconsistencies of clinical performance. Being a dynamic attitude of mind, configurationism is interested in the adaptive behaviour of the organism with its adjustments and compensation after chronic cerebral lesions. It does not need to gloss over the erratic and unexpected performance of the neurological patient ; nor the occasional lack of correspondence between clinical data and anatomical finding. The phenomena of unawareness, neglect, denial ; the *Funktionswandel* in both visual and tactile spheres are more readily explained. Disorders of perception (and especially of visual perception) fit most easily in the cadre of configurational psychology. No artificial distinction between lower and higher visual function is deemed advisable or indeed possible.

For these reasons, parietal symptomatology promises to be illuminated by this kind of research. The configurational approach is not without certain drawbacks, however. Its philosophy is somewhat intolerant (or more accurately, some of the exponents have been so), and is perhaps too reluctant to acknowledge the valuable spadework which has been done by traditional methods in neurology. Its terminology is difficult ; and it has been said that, when not platitudinous, it is obscure. This latter criticism would apply particularly to the extension of Gestaltism into vector psychology. Yet another drawback of some of the applications of Gestaltism to neurology is the paucity of scientific method in the presentation of the facts. This again is a fault of some of the exponents of Gestaltism, rather than of the subject itself. There is no inherent reason why disciplined study and thought should not accompany a configurational approach.

Some writers have claimed that no compromise whatsoever is possible between the two schools of thought, organismic and associational, as they represent opposite poles in ideology. This is going too far. It is submitted that some give-and-take is not only feasible, but is highly desirable. The traditional method has led us far along the road towards understanding cerebral function, and it can continue to be of guidance. But a configurational—or at any rate—a holistic attitude is likely to animate and amplify one's conception of nervous disease in a manner which gives promise of great developments.

Jackson, Pick, Monakow and Head would probably have found a great appeal in the neurological implications of the Gestalt school. Special mention in this connection should be made of Monakow, whose penetrating writings have still not received the attention they merit, for, like Hughlings Jackson, his thinking was far ahead of his time. To read Monakow is to find what is actually a stimulating compromise between holistic and associational conceptions of cerebral function. For example, Monakow declared that no " visual sphere " can be demonstrated on the basis of a single or common psychological, physiological and anatomical principle. He believed that other factors, not yet understood, besides the anatomical component, participated in the aetiology of cortical visual defects. The physiological visual sphere was to him extensive and varied. One should distinguish between " looking at " and " seeing ". Vision represents —he taught—much more than the sum of the collective activity of the representational areas of movements of the eye, trunk and limbs, the vestibular apparatus, and the various visual reflexes. Monakow looked upon, and defined, the visual sphere as a cortical area (with a specialized type of layering), with no clear-cut boundaries, where visual reflexes have their finer anatomical bases according to the location and origin of the retinal stimuli giving rise to them, and in the sense of optical local signs ; and where originate, furthermore, the earliest assimilation of degrees of illumination and physiological perception of colour, and perhaps also the earliest stages of the assimilation of visual components for the perception of form. *The transformation of these elementary factors into optical perception and later into imagination, takes place in the whole cortex,* although naturally not in a homogeneously diffuse manner. (Die Umwandlung dieser Elementarfaktoren in optische " Wahrnehmung " (Erkennen) und später in " Vorstellungen ", subj. vorwiegend visuellen Inhalts, vollzieht sich, wie bereits bemerkt wurde, in der ganzen Rinde, wenn auch selbstverständlich nicht in gleichmässig diffuser Weise.)

SELECTIVE BIBLIOGRAPHY

CHAPTER I

1. ARNOLD, F. (1838) Bemerkungen über den Bau des Hirns und Rückenmarks, Zürich, S. Höhr.
   ARIËNS KAPPERS, C. U. (see KAPPERS, No. 76).
2. BAILEY, P. (1948) Concerning the organization of the cerebral cortex, *Texas Rep. Biol. Med.*, **6**, 34–56.
3. —— (1949) Concerning the functions of the cerebral cortex, *J. nerv. ment. Dis.*, **110**, 369–378.
4. —— (1950) Considérations sur l'organization et les functions du cortex cérébral, *Rev. neurol.*, **82**, 1, 3–20.
5. BAILEY, P., and von BONIN, G. (1946) Concerning cytoarchitectonics, *Trans. Amer. neurol. Ass.*, **71**, 89–93.
6. —— —— (1951) The Isocortex of Man, Urbana, Univ. Ill. Press.
7. BAILEY, P., von BONIN, G., and McCULLOCH, W. S. (1950) The Isocortex of the Chimpanzee, Urbana, Univ. Ill. Press.
8. BAILLARGER, J. C. F. (1838–1840) Recherches sur la structure de la couche corticale des circonvolutions du cerveau, *Mém. Acad. roy. Méd.*, **7–8**, part 2, 149–183.
9. —— (1845) De l'étendue de la surface du cerveau et de ses rapports avec le developpement de l'intelligence, *Gaz. Hôp.*, **18**, 179.
10. —— (1872) Recherches sur l'anatomie, la physiologie et le pathologie du système nerveux, Paris, Masson.
11. BECK, E. (1950) Nachweis vom unterschiedlichen Bau in der linken und nachten hinteren Zentralwindung und die Frage der Rechts- und Linkshirnigkeit, *Dtsch. Z. Nervenheilk.*, **163**, 214–244.
12. BERITOFF, J. S. (1924) On the fundamental processes in the cortex of the cerebral hemispheres, *Brain*, **47**, 358–376.
13. BERRY, R. J. A. (1932) Brain structure in relation to mind, *J. Neurol. Psychopath.*, **13**, 97–117.
14. BETZ, V. (1881) Quelques mots sur la structure de l'écorce cérébrale, *Rev. Anthrop.*, 2e series, **4**, 426–438.
15. BIEMOND, A. (1930) Experimentell-anatomische Untersuchungen über die corticofugalen optischer Verbindungen bei Kaninchen und Affen, *Z. ges. Neurol. Psychiat.*, **129**, 65–127.
16. BOLTON, J. Shaw (1910) A contribution to the localization of cerebral function based on the clinico-pathological study of mental disease, *Brain*, **33**, 26–148.
17. von BONIN, G. (1938) The cerebral cortex of the cebus monkey, *J. comp. Neurol.*, **69**, 181–227.
18. —— (1941) On Encephalometry ; a preliminary study of the brain of man, chimpanzee and macaque, *ibid.*, **75**, 287–314.
19. —— (1942) The striate area of primates, *ibid.*, **77**, 405–429.
20. —— (1948) The frontal lobe of primates ; cytoarchitectural studies, *Res. Publ. Ass. nerv. ment. Dis.*, **27**, 67–83.
21. —— (1949) The cytoarchitecture of the precentral motor cortex, Chap. III in The Precentral Motor Cortex, 2nd ed. edited by P. C. Bucy, *Illinois Monographs in Med. Sci.*, *IV*, Urbana, Univ. Ill. Press.
22. —— (1950) Essay on the cerebral cortex, *American Lecture Series*, *No. 59*, Springfield, Thomas.

23. von BONIN, G., and BAILEY, P. (1947) The neocortex of Macaca Mulatta, Urbana, Univ. Ill. Press.

24. von BONIN, G., GAROL, H., and McCULLOCH, W. B. (1942) The functional organization of the occipital lobe, *Visual Mechanisms*, ed. H. Klüver, *Biological Symposium*, **7**, 165–192.

25. BROCA, P. (1888) Mémoire sur le cerveau de l'homme et des Primates, *Mémoires d'Anthropologie*, **5**. Poni, Paris.

26. BRODAL, A. (1948) Neurological anatomy in relation to clinical medicine, Oxford, Clarendon Press.

27. BRODMANN, K. (1908) Die Cortexgliederung des Menschen, *J. Psychol. Neurol.*, **10**, 231–287.

28. —— (1925) Vergleichende Lokalisationslehre der Grosshirnrinde, Leipzig, Barth.

29. BROUWER, B. (1936) Chiasma, Tractus opticus, Sehstrahlung und Sehrinde : Handbuch der Neurologie, ed. O. Bumke and O. Foerster, **6**, 449–532. Berlin, Springer.

30. CAMPBELL, A. W. (1905) Histological studies on the localization of cerebral function, Cambridge Univ. Press.

31. CHOW, K. L. (1950) A retrograde cell degeneration study of the cortical projection field of the pulvinar in the monkey, *J. comp. Neurol.*, **93**, 313–340.

32. CLAES, E. (1939) Contribution à l'étude physiologique de la fonction visuelle, *Arch. intern. Physiol.*, **48**, 238–261.

33. CLARK, W. E. Le Gros (1948) The connexions of the frontal lobes of the brain, *Lancet*, **1**, 353–356.

34. —— (1948) African fossil primates discovered during 1947, *Nature*, **161**, 667–669.

35. —— (1952) A note on cortical cytoarchitectonics, *Brain*, **75**, 96–104.

36. CLARK, W. E. Le Gros, and BOGGON, R. H. (1935) The thalamic connections of the parietal and frontal lobes of the brain in the monkey, *Phil. Trans.*, **224B**, 313–359.

37. CLARK, W. E. Le Gros, and MEYER, M. (1950) Anatomical relationships between the cerebral cortex and the hypothalamus, *Brit. med. Bull.*, **6**, 341–344.

38. COHN, H. A., and PAPEZ, J. W. (1930) Comparative study of visuosensory or striate area in two hemispheres of human brain, *Amer. J. phys. Anthrop.*, **14**, 405–415.

39. CONNOLLY, C. J. (1950) The external morphology of the primate brain, Springfield, Thomas.

40. CUNNINGHAM, D. J. (1890) The intraparietal sulcus of the brain, *J. Anat., Lond.*, **24**, 135–155.

41. —— (1890–1) The development of the gyri and the sulci in the surface of the island of Reil of the human brain, *Trans. R. Acad. Med. Ire.*, **9**, 469–480.

42. —— (1892) Contributions to the surface anatomy of the cerebral hemispheres with a chapter upon craniocerebral topography by Victor Horsley, *Roy. Irish Acad.* " Cunningham Mem.", **7**, 1–358, 8 pl., Dublin, Academy House.

43. DEJERINE, J. (1901) Séméiologie du système nerveux, Paris, Masson.

44. DEJERINE, J., and DEJERINE-KLUMPKE (Mme.) (1895) Anatomie des centres nerveux, 2 vols., Paris, J. Rueff.

45. DIXON, A. G. (1918) Why are the cerebral motor and sensory cortical areas arranged in an inverted order ? *Dublin J. med. Sci.*, **145**, 154–160.

46. DURET, H. (1874) Recherches anatomiques sur la circulation de l'encéphale, *Arch. Physiol. norm. path.*, 2nd series, **1**, 60–91, 316–353, 664–693, 919–957.

47. ECKER, A. (1873) The convolutions of the human brain, London, Smith Elder. \

48. von ECONOMO, C. (1927) Zellaufbau der Grosshirnrinde des Menschen, Berlin, Springer.

49. —— (1929) The cytoarchitectonics of the human cerebral cortex, London, Oxford Univ. Press.

50. —— (1929) Wie sollen wir Elitegehirne verarbeiten ? Berlin, Springer.

51. —— (1930) Zur Frage des Vorkommens der Affenspalte beim Menschen im Lichte der Cytoarchitektonik, Z. ges. Neurol. Psychiat., 130, 419–531.

52. von ECONOMO, C., and KOSKINAS, G. W. (1925) Die Cytoarchitektonik der Hirnrinde des erwachsenen Menschen, Berlin, Springer.

53. FILIMONOFF, I. N. (1932) Regio occipitalis beim erwachsenen Menschen, J. Psychol. Neurol., 44, 1–96.

54. —— (1947) A rational subdivision of the cerebral cortex, Arch. Neurol. Psychiat., 58, 296–311.

55. FISHGOLD, H. (1949) L'organization fonctionnelle du cortex cerebral, Rev. neurol., 81, 487–501.

56. FLECHSIG, P. (1920) Anatomie des menschlichen Gehirns und Rückenmarks auf myelogenetischer Grundlage, Leipzig, Thieme.

57. FOIX, Ch., and LÉVY, M. (1927) Les ramollissements sylviens. Syndromes des lésions en foyer du territoire de l'artère sylvienne et de ses branches, Rev. neurol., 2, 1–51.

58. FOVILLE, A. L. (1844) Traité complêt de l'anatomie, de la physiologie et de la pathologie du système nerveux cérébro-spinal, Paris, Fortin, Masson.

59. GEREBTZOFF, M. A. (1937) Le pédoncule cérébelleux supérieur et les terminasions réelles de la voie cérébello-thalamique ; étude anatamo-expérimentalle, Mém. Acad. roy. Méd. Belg., 25, 1–58.

60. —— (1940) Les connexions thalamostriées, le noyau parafasciculaire et le centre médian, J. belge Neurol., 40, 407–416.

61. HAMMARBERG, C.—cited by Campbell : see No. 30.

62. HASSLER, R. (1949) Ueber die afferenten Bahnen und Thalamuskerne des motorischen Systems des Grosshirns ; Bindearm und Fasciculus thalamicus, Arch. Psychiat. Nervenkr., 182, 759–785.

63. —— (1949) Ueber die afferenten Bahnen und Thalamuskerne des motorischen Systems des Grosshirns ; weitere Bahnen aus Pallidum, Ruber, vestibulärem System zum Thalamus ; Uebersicht und Besprechung der Ergebnisse, ibid., 182, 786–818.

64. HÉCAEN, H., DAVID, M., and TALAIRACH, J. (1947) L'aire " suppressive " du cortex prémoteur chez l'homme, Rev. neurol., 79, 726–732.

65. HENLE, J. (1855–1868) Handbuch des Gefässlehre des Menschen, 3, of Handbuch der Systematischen Anatomie des Menschen, 3 vols., Braunschweig, Friedrich und Sohn.

66. HERRICK, C. J. (1921) A sketch of the origin of the cerebral hemispheres, J. comp. Neurol., 32, 429–454.

67. —— (1933) The functions of the olfactory parts of the cerebral cortex, Proc. nat. Acad. Sci. Wash., 19, 7–14.

68. HILTON, J. (1880) Lectures on Rest and Pain, London, Bell (2nd ed.).

69. HIS, W. (1892) Zur Allgemeine Morphologie des Gehirns, Arch. Anat. Physiol., Anat. Abt., 346–383.

70. —— (1892) Die Entwickelung der Menschl. und Thier Physiognomen, ibid., 384–424.

71. HIS, W. (1892)   Zur Nomenclatur des Gehirnes und Rückenmarkes, *ibid.*, 425–428.

72. INGALLS, N. W. (1914)   The parietal region in the primate brain, *J. comp. Neurol.*, **24**, 291–341.

73. JEFFERSON, G. (1913)   The morphology of the sulcus interparietalis, *J. Anat. Lond.*, **47**, 365–380.

74. —— (1914)   The parietal Area, *Rev. Neurol. Psychiat.*, **12**, 54–58.

75. JONES, F. Wood, and PORTEUS, S. D. (1929)   Matrix of the Mind, London, Arnold.

76. KAPPERS, C. U. Ariëns (1920–1921)   Die vergleichende Anatomie des Nervensystems der Wirbeltiere und des Menschen, 2 vols., Haarlem, Bohn.

77. KAPPERS, C. U. Ariens, HUBER, G. C., and CROSBY, E. C. (1936)   The comparative anatomy of the nervous system of Vertebrates including man, 2 vols.   New York, Macmillan.

78. KATZENSTEIN, E. (1929)   Der Fasciculus centroparietalis (von Monakow), *Schweiz. Arch. Neurol. Psychiat.*, **25**, 3–55.

79. KEITH, A. (1895)   The growth of the brain in men and monkeys, with a short criticism of the usual method of stating brain ratios, *J. Anat. Lond.*, **29**, 282–303.

80. —— (1925)   Antiquity of man, 2nd edit., 2 vols., Chap. 32, London, Williams & Norgate.

81. —— (1931)   New discoveries relating to the antiquity of man, London, Williams & Norgate.

82. —— (1948)   Human embryology and Morphology, 6th ed., London, Arnold.

83. KOTZ, D. A., and CLARK, G. (1950)   Attempt at graphic cytoarchitectonic description, *J. comp. Neurol.*, **92**, 215–225.

84. KRAUS, W. (1933)   Le principe qui préside à l'évolution du cortex cérébral chez l'homme, *Encéphale*, **28**, 465–468.

85. LASHLEY, K. S. (1929)   Brain mechanism and intelligence, Chicago, Univ. Ill. Press.

86. —— (1941)   Thalamo-cortical connections of the rat's brain, *J. comp. Neurol.*, **75**, 67–121.

87. LASHLEY, K. S., and CLARK, G. (1946)   The cytoarchitexture of the cerebral cortex in Ateles, *J. comp. Neurol.*, **85**, 223–305.

88. LEWIS, A. Bevan (1879)   On the comparative structure of the cortex cerebri, *Brain*, **1**, 79–100.

89. LÉVY, M. (1927)   Les Ramollissements Sylviens, Paris, Doin.

90. LOWREY, L. G. (1920)   A note on a certain anomaly of gyration in brains of the insane, *Amer. J. Insan.*, **77**, 87–90.

91. McCULLOCH, W. S. (1944)   Corticocortical connections, Chap. 8 in Precentral Motor Cortex, 211–243, Chicago, Univ. Ill. Press.

92. MARTIN, J. Purdon (1937)   A dissection of the lower half of the optic radiation, *Trans. ophthal. Soc. U.K.*, **57**, 141–146.

93. von MAYENDORFF, Niessl (1925)   Zur Lokalizationsfrage der kutanen Sensibilität an der Hirnrinde, *Dtsch. Z. Nervenh.*, **86**, 220–236.

94. METTLER, F. A. (1935)   Corticofugal fiber connections of the cortex of macaca mulatta.   The frontal region, *J. comp. Neurol.*, **62**, 263–291.

95. MEYNERT, T. (1877)   Die Windungen der convexen Oberfläche des Vorderhirnes bei Menschen, Affen und Raubthieren, *Arch. Psychiat. Nervenkr.*, **7**, 257–286.

96. —— (1884)   Psychiatrie.   Klinik der Erkrankungen des Vorderhirns, Wien, Braumüller.

97. —— (1892)   Ueber die Gefühle.   Samml. v. populär-wissenschaftl. Vortr, über den Bau u. d. Leistungen des Gehirns, p. 43, Wien.

98. MILLS, C. K. (1904) The physiological areas and centres of the cerebral cortex of man with new diagrammatic schemes, *Univ. Pa. med. Bull.*, **17**, 90–98.

99. MINKOWSKI, M. (1923) Étude sur les connexions anatomiques des circonvolutions rolandiques, pariétales et frontales, *Schweiz Arch. Neurol. Psychiat.*, **12**, 71–227, 227–268.

100. —— (1924) *ibid.*, **14**, 255–278.

101. —— (1924) *ibid.*, **15**, 97–132.

102. —— (1949) Sur les connexions du thalamus avec les circonvolutions pariétales, rolandiques et frontales, en particulier chez le singe Macacus rhesus, *C.R. IVth int. Congr. Neurol.*, **3**, 164–175, Paris, Masson, 1951.

103. MOFFIE, D. (1949) The parietal lobe. A survey of its anatomy and functions, *Folia psychiat. neerl.*, **52**, 418–444.

104. von MONAKOW, C. (1882) Ueber einige durch Exstirpation in circumscripter Hirnrindenregionen bedingte Entwickelungshemmungen des Kaninchengehirns, *Arch. Psychiat. Nervenkr.*, **12**, 141–156.

105. —— (1882) Weitere Mittheilungen über durch Exstirpation circumscripter Hirnrindenregion bedingte Entwickelungshemmungen des Kaninchengehirns, *ibid.*, **12**, 535–549.

106. —— (1883) Experimentelle und pathologisch-anatomische Untersuchungen über die Beziehungen der sogenannten Sehsphäre zu den infracorticalen Opticuscentren und zum Ni opticus, *ibid.*, **14**, 669–751.

107. —— (1885) *ibid.*, **16**, 151–199, 317–352.

108. —— (1915) Zur Anatomie und Physiologie der Pyramidenbahn und der Armregion, nebst Bemerkungen über die sekundäre Degeneration des Fasciculus centroparietalis, *Neurol. Zbl.*, **34**, 217–224.

109. MOTT, F. W. (1907) The progressive evolution of the structure and functions of the visual cortex in mammalia, Bowman lecture, 4.11.1904 ; *Trans. ophthal. Soc. U.K.*, 1905, **25**, liii–cv ; *Arch. Neurol.* (ed. F. W. Mott), **3**, 1–123.

110. MUNK, H. (1890) Ueber die Funktionen der Grosshirnrinde ; Gesammelte Mitteilungen mit Anmerkungen, 2 Aufl., Berlin, Hirschwald.

111. NIEMER, W. T., and JIMENEZ-CASTELLANOS, J. (1950) Cortico-thalamic connections in the cat as revealed by " physiological neuronography ", *J. comp. Neurol.*, **93**, 101–123.

112. O'CONNELL, J. E. A. (1934) Some observations on the cerebral veins, *Brain*, **57**, 484–503.

113. PAPEZ, James W. (1929) Comparative Neurology, New York, Crowell.

114. PEELE, T. L. (1942) Cytoarchitecture of individual parietal areas in the monkey (macaca mulatta) and the distribution of the efferent fibers, *J. comp. Neurol.*, **77**, 693–723.

115. PENFIELD, W. (1938) The cerebral cortex in man, *Arch. Neurol. Psychiat.*, **40**, 417–442.

116. PFEIFFER, R. A. (1928) Die Angioarchitektonik der Grosshirnrinde, Berlin, Springer.

117. PITRES, A., and TESTUT, L. (1925) Les nerfs en schemas. Anatomie et Physiopathologie, Paris, Doin.

118. QUAIN'S ELEMENTS OF ANATOMY (1908) Edit. by E. A. Schäfer, J. Symington and T. H. Bryce. 11th edit., Vol. III, Neurology, Part I, by E. A. Schäfer and J. Symington, London, Longmans, Green.

428   SELECTIVE BIBLIOGRAPHY

119. RETZIUS, G. (1896) Das Menschenhirn, Stockholm, Kgl. Buch-
      druckerei, P. A. Norstedt, 2 vols.
120. —— (1902) Zur Morphologie der insula Reilii, Biol. Untersuch.,
      10, 15–20.
121. RIESE, W., and GOLDSTEIN, K. (1950) The brain of Ludwig Edinger.
      An enquiry into the cerebral morphology of mental ability and left-
      handedness, J. comp. Neurol., 92, 133–168.
122. ROSETT, J. (1933) Intercortical systems of the human cerebrum,
      mapped by means of new anatomic methods, New York, Columbia
      Univ. Press.
123. SAKUMA, S. (1937) Ueber die Faserbeziehungen der Areae 7a und 7b.
      Unter besonderer Berücksichtigung der corticalen extrapyramidalen
      Bahnen beim Affen, Z. mikr.-anat. Forsch., 42, 70–80.
124. SCHEPERS, G. W. H. (1948) Evolution of the Fore Brain, Cape Town,
      Masken Miller.
125. SHELLSHEAR, J. L. (1927) A contribution to our knowledge of the
      Arterial supply of the cerebral cortex in man, Brain, 50, 236–253.
126. SMITH, G. Elliot (1902) On the homologies of the cerebral sulci,
      J. Anat., Lond., 36, 309–319.
127. —— (1904) The fossa parieto-occipitalis, ibid., 38, 164–169.
128. —— (1907) A new topographical survey of the human cerebral
      cortex, ibid., 41, 237–254.
129. —— (1908) The localization of the human cerebral cortex, Rep. Brit.
      Ass., 78, 876 only.
130. —— (1910) Arris and Gale Lectures. Some problems relating to
      the Evolution of the Brain, Lancet, 1, 1–6 ; 147–153 ; 220–227.
131. —— (1930) The Evolution of Man, 2nd ed. Oxford, Oxford Univ.
      Press.
132. —— (1930) Human History, London, Jonathan Cape.
133. —— (1931) Search for Man's Ancestors, London, Watts.
134. SPITZKA, E. A. (1903) The postorbital limbus, a formation occasion-
      ally met with at the base of the human brain, Philad. med. J., 11,
      646–648.
135. —— (1907) A study of the brains of six eminent scientists and
      scholars belonging to the American Anthropometric Society together
      with a description of the skull of Prof. E. D. Cope, Trans. Amer.
      phil. Soc., 21, 175–308.
136. STOFFELS, J. (1939) La projection des noyaux antérieurs du thalamus
      sur l'écorce interhémispherique ; étude anatome-expérimentale,
      Mém. Acad. roy. Méd. Belg., 1, 1–59.
137. —— (1939) Organisation du thalamus et du cortex cérébral chez
      le lapin ; synthésie finale, J. belge Neurol., 39, 557–575.
138. STRASSBURGER, E. H. (1937) Der Faserbau des Stirnhirns beim
      Schimpansen, J. Psychol. Neurol., Lpz., 47, 565–580.
139. SUGAR, O., PETR, R., AMADOR, L. V., and GRIPONISSIOTIS, B. (1950)
      Cortico-cortical connections of the cortex buried in the intraparietal
      and principal sulci of the monkey (macaca mulatta), J. Neuropath.,
      9, 430–437.
140. SUNDERLAND, S. (1940) The projection of the cerebral cortex on the
      pons and cerebellum in the macaque monkey, J. Anat., Lond., 74,
      201–226.
      TESTUT, L.—See PITRES, A., and TESTUT, L. (See No. 115.)
141. TILNEY, F. (1927) The brain of prehistoric man. A study of the
      psychologic foundations of human progress, Arch. Neurol. Psychiat.,
      17, 723–769.
142. TILNEY, F., and RILEY, H. A. (1938) Form and Functions of the
      Central Nervous System, 3rd Edit., New York, Hoeber.

143. TURNER, O. A. (1948) Growth and development of the cerebral cortical pattern in man, *Arch. Neurol. Psychiat.*, **59**, 1–12.
144. TURNER, W. (1866) The convolutions of the human cerebrum topographically considered, *Edinb. med. J.*, **12**, 1105–1122.
145. —— (1891) The convolutions of the brain ; a study in comparative anatomy, *J. Anat., Lond.*, **25**, 105–153.
146. UESUGI, M. (1937) Ueber die corticalen extrapyramidal Fasern aus den sog. sensiblen Rindenfeldern (Areae 1 und 27) beim Affen, *Anat. Anz.*, **84**, 179–197.
147. VOGT, C., and VOGT, O. (1919) Allgemeinere Ergebnisse unserer Hirnforschung, Leipzig, Barth.
148. VOGT, O. (1903) Zur anatomischen Gliederung des Cortex cerebri, *J. Psychol. Neurol., Lpz.*, **2**, 160–180.
149. WAGNER, R. (1864) Massbestimmungen der Oberfläche des grossen Gehirns, Wigand, Cassel u. Gottingen.
150. WALKER, A. Earl (1934) The thalamic projection to the central gyri in macacus rhesus, *J. comp. Neurol.*, **60**, 161–184.
151. —— (1938) The primate thalamus, Chicago, Ill., Univ. of Chicago Press.
151a. WALKER, A. Earl (1938) The Thalamus of the Chimpanzee, *J. Anat., Lond.*, **73**, 37–92.
152. WERNICKE, C. (1876) Das Urwindungssystem des menschlichen Gehirns, *Arch. Psychiat. Nervenkr.*, **6**, 298–326.
153. WINKLER, C. (1918–1933) Anatomie du Système nerveux, 5 vols. Haarlem, Bohn.
154. ZUCKERKANDL, E. (1904) Ueber die Collateralfürche, *Arb. neurol. Inst.* (Inst. Anat. Physiol. ZentNerv.), Univ. Wien, **11**, 407–442.

CHAPTER II

155. ADRIAN, E. D. (1941) Afferent discharges to the cerebral cortex from peripheral sense organs, *J. Physiol.*, **100**, 159–191.
156. —— (1943) Afferent areas in the brain of ungulates, *Brain*, **66**, 89–103.
157. —— (1946) The somatic receiving area in the brain of the Shetland pony, *ibid.*, **69**, 1–8.
158. BARD, P. (1938) Cortical representation of somatic sensibility, *Bull. N.Y. Acad. Med.*, **14**, 585–607.
159. de BARENNE, J. G. Dusser (1916) Experimental researches on sensory localizations in the cerebral cortex, *Quart. J. exp. Physiol.*, **9**, 355–390.
160. —— (1924) Experimental researches on sensory localization in the cerebral cortex of the monkey (Macacus), *Proc. roy. Soc.*, **96B**, 272–291.
161. —— (1934) Some aspects of the problem of " corticalization " of function and of functional localization in the cerebral cortex, *Res. Publ. Ass. nerv. ment. Dis.*, **13**, 85–106.
162. —— (1935) A word of criticism on the designation " localization " of function in the cerebral cortex, *Arch. Neurol. Psychiat.*, **33**, 108.
163. de BARENNE, J. G. Dusser, and McCULLOCH, W. S. (1938) Functional organization in the sensory cortex of the monkey (Macaca Mulatta), *J. Neurophysiol.*, **1**, 68–85.
164. BARTHOLOW, R. (1874) Experimental investigations into the functions of the human brain, *Amer. J. med. Sci.*, **67**, 305–313.
165. BASTIAN, H. C. (1909) The functions of the kinaesthetic area of the brain, *Brain*, **32**, 327–341.

430 SELECTIVE BIBLIOGRAPHY

166. BIELCHOWSKY, M. (1917) Ueber Mikrogyrie, *J. Psychol. Neurol.*, **22**, 1–46.
BOLTON, J. Shaw (1910) (see No. 16).
167. BROWN, T. Graham, and SHERRINGTON, C. S. (1912) On the instability of a cortical point, *Proc. roy. Soc.*, **85B**, 250–277.
168. CAJAL, S. Ramón y (1903) Las fibras nerviosas de origen cerebral del tuberculo cuadrigemino anterior y talamo optico, *Trab. Lab. Invest. biol. Univ. Madr.*, **2**, 5–21.
169. CHANG, Hsiang-Tung (1950) The repetitive discharges of cortico-thalamic reverberating circuit, *J. Neurophysiol.*, **13**, 235–258.
170. —— (1951) An observation on the effect of strychnine on local cortical potentials, *ibid.*, **14**, 23–28.
171. CUSHING, H. (1909) A note upon the faradic stimulation of the post-central gyrus in conscious patients, *Brain*, **32**, 44–53.
172. DAWSON, G. D. (1950) Cerebral responses to nerve stimulation, *Brit. med. Bull.*, **6**, 326–329.
173. DRUCKMAN, R. (1952) A critique of " suppression " with additional observations in the cat, *Brain*, **75**, 226–243.
DUSSER de BARENNE, J. G. (see de Barenne, J. G. Dusser).
174. FERRIER, D. (1886) The Functions of the Brain, 2nd ed., London, Smith Elder.
175. FERRIER, D., and YEO, G. F. (1884) A record of experiments of the effects of lesion of different regions of cerebral hemispheres, *Phil. Trans.*, **175**, 479–564.
176. FLECHSIG, P. (1876) Die Leitungsbahnen im Gehirn und Rücken-mark des Menschen auf Grund entwickelungsgeschichtlicher Unter-suchungen, Leipzig, Engelmann.
177. —— (1896) Ueber die Lokalization der geistigen Vorgänge insbe-sondere der Sinnesempfindungen des Menschen, Leipzig, Veit.
—— (1920) (see No. 56).
178. FOERSTER, O. (1936) Hughlings Jackson Lecture. The motor cortex in man in the light of Hughlings Jackson's doctrines, *Brain*, **59**, 135–159.
179. FRITSCH, G., and HITZIG, E. (1870) Ueber die elektrische Erregbar-keit des Grosshirns, *Arch. Anat. Physiol. Wiss. med.*, **37**, 300–332.
180. FULTON, J. F. (1949) Physiology of the Nervous System, 3rd ed., New York, Oxford Univ. Press.
181. GAY, J. R., and GELLHORN, E. (1949) Cortical Projection of Proprio-ception in the cat and monkey, *Proc. Soc. exp. biol. Med.*, **70**, 711–718.
182. GOLTZ, F. (1869) Beiträge zur Lehre von der Funktionen der Nerven-centren des Frosches, Berlin (Tract).
183. GRÜNBAUM, A. S. F., and SHERRINGTON, C. S. (1901) Observations on the physiology of the cerebral cortex of some of the higher apes, *Proc. roy. Soc.*, **69**, 206–209.
184. —— —— (1903) Observation on the physiology of the cerebral cortex of the anthropoid apes, *ibid.*, **72**, 152–155.
185. van't HOOG, E. G. (1920) On deep-localization in the cerebral cortex, *J. nerv. ment. Dis.*, **51**, 313–329.
186. HORSLEY, V., and SCHÄFER, E. A. (1888) A record of experiments upon the functions of the cerebral cortex, *Philos. Trans.*, **179B**, 1–45.
187. JEFFERSON, G. (1950) Localization of function in the cerebral cortex, *Brit. med. Bull.*, **6**, 333–340.
188. KAPPERS, C. U. Ariëns (1909) The phylogenesis of the palaeocortex and archicortex compared with the evolution of the visual neocortex, *Arch. Neurol. Psychiat., Lond.*, **4**, 161–173.
189. LEYTON, A. S. F., and SHERRINGTON, C. S. (1917) Observations on

the excitable cortex of the chimpanzee, orang-utan and gorilla, *Quart J. exp. Physiol.*, **11**, 135–222.

190. LIDDELL, E. G. T., and PHILLIPS, C. G. (1950) Threshold of cortical representation, *Brain*, **73**, 125–140.

McCULLOCH, W. S. (1944) (see No. 91).

191. McCULLOCH, W. S., and PITTS, W. (1949) How nervous structures have ideas, *Trans. Amer. neurol. Ass.*, **74**, 10–16.

192. MARSHALL, W. R., TALBOT, S. A., and ADES, H. W. (1942) Cortical response of the anaesthetized cat to gross photic and electrical afferent stimulation, *J. Neurophysiol.*, **6**, 1–15.

193. MARSHALL, W. R., WOOLSEY, C. N., and BARD, P. (1937) Cortical representation of tactile sensibility as indicated by cortical potentials, *Science*, **85**, 388–390.

194. —— —— —— (1941) Observations on cortical somatic sensory mechanisms of cat and monkey, *J. Neurophysiol.*, **4**, 1–24.

195. MUNK, H. (1892) Ueber die Fühlsphären der Grosshirnrinde, Erste Mitteilung, Sit. Ber. Akad. Wissen. 679–723, reprinted in Ueber die Funktionen von Hirn und Rückenmark, Gesamelte Mitteilungen, pp. 11–55, Berlin, Hirschwald, 1909.

196. NIEUWENHUIJSE, P. (1913) Zur Kenntnis der Mickrogyrie, *Psychiat. neurol. Bl., Amst.*, **17**, 9–53.

197. PEELE, T. L. (1944) Acute and chronic parietal lobe ablations in monkeys, *J. Neurophysiol.*, **7**, 269–286.

198. PENFIELD, W. (1947) Some observations on the cerebral cortex of man, *Proc. roy. Soc.*, **134B**, 329–347.

199. —— (1949) A secondary somatic sensory area in the cerebral cortex of man, *Trans. Amer. neurol. Ass.*, **74**, 184–186.

200. PENFIELD, W., and BOLDREY, E. (1937) Somatic motor and sensory representation in the cerebral cortex of man as studied by electrical stimulation, *Brain*, **60**, 389–443.

RAMÓN Y CAJAL (see CAJAL, S. Ramón y).

201. RANSOM, W. B. (1892) A case illustrating kinaesthesis, *Brain*, **15**, 437–442.

202. RASMUSSEN, A. T., and PENFIELD, W. (1947) Further studies of sensory and motor cerebral cortex of man, *Fed. Proc.*, **6**, 452–460.

203. —— —— (1950) The Cerebral Cortex of Man. A clinical study of localization of function, New York, Macmillan.

204. RUCH, T. C., FULTON, J. F., and GERMAN, W. J. (1938) Sensory discrimination in monkey, chimpanzee and man after lesions of the parietal lobe, *Arch. Neurol. Psychiat.*, **39**, 919–938.

205. SCHAEFER, E. A. (1898) On the alleged sensory functions of the motor cortex cerebri, *J. Physiol.*, **23**, 310–314.

206. SUGAR, O., AMADOR, L. V., and GRIPONISSIOTIS, B. (1950) Cortico-connections of the walls of the superior temporal sulcus in one monkey (macaca mulatta), *J. Neuropath. exp. Neurol.*, **9**, 179–185.

SUGAR, O., PETR, R., AMADOR, L. V., and GRIPONISSIOTIS, B. (1950) (see No. 139).

207. TALBOT, S. A., and MARSHALL, W. H. (1941) Physiological studies on neural mechanisms of visual localization and discrimination, *Amer. J. Ophthal.*, **24**, 1255–1264.

208. van VALKENBURG, C. T. (1914) Zur fokalen Lokalisation der Sensibilität in der Grosshirnrinde des Menschen, *Z. ges. Neurol. Psychiat.*, **24**, 294–312.

van't HOOG, E. G. (see HOOG, No. 185).

209. WALSHE, F. M. R. (1947) 1946 Victor Horsley Memorial Lecture, " On the contribution of clinical study to the physiology of the cerebral motor cortex ", Edinburgh, Livingstone.

210. WOOLSEY, C. N. (1947)   The somatic functions of the central nervous system, *Ann. Rev. Physiol.*, **9**, 525–552.
211. —— (1947)   Patterns of sensory representation in the cerebral cortex, *Fed. Proc.*, **6**, 437–441.
212. WOOLSEY, C. N., and BARD, P. (1936)   Cortical control of placing and hopping reactions in macaca mulatta, *Amer. J. Physiol.*, **116**, 165–166.
213. WOOLSEY, C. N., CHANG, H. T., and BARD, P. (1947)   Distribution of cerebral potentials evoked by electrical stimulation of dorsal roots in macaca mulatta, *Fed. Proc.*, **6**, 230 only.
214. WOOLSEY, C. N., and ERICKSON, T. C. (1950)   Study of the post-central gyrus of man by the evoked potential technique. *Trans. Amer. neurol. Ass.*, **75**, 50–52.
215. WOOLSEY, C. N., and FAIRMAN, D. (1946)   Contralateral, Ipsilateral and Bilateral representation of cutaneous receptors in somatic areas I and II of the cerebral cortex of pig, sheep and other mammals, *Surgery*, **19**, 684–702.
216. WOOLSEY, C. N., MARSHALL, W. H., and BARD, P. (1942)   Representation of cutaneous tactile sensibility in the cerebral cortex of the monkey as indicated by evoked potentials, *Bull. Johns Hopkins Hosp.*, **70**, 399–441.

CHAPTER III

217. BAY, E., and CIBIS, P. (1950)   Funktionswandel und Gesichtsfeld bei Sehhirnverletzten, *Dtsch. Z. Nervenheilk*, **163**, 577–628.
218. BENDER, M. B., and TEUBER, H.-L. (1949)   " Psychopathology of Vision " from Progress in Neurology and Psychiatry, New York, Greene and Stratton.
219. BENTON, A. L. (1952)   La signification des tests de rétention visuelle dans le diagnostic clinique, *Rev. Psychol. appl.*, **2**, 151–179.
220. BRAIN, W. R. (1945)   Speech and handedness (Bradshaw Lecture), *Lancet*, **2**, 837–841.
221. CIBIS, P., and MUELLER, H. (1948)   Lokaladaptometrische Untersuchungen am Projectionsperimeter nach Maggiore, *Graefe's Arch.*, **148**, 468–489.
222. CRITCHLEY, M. (1951)   The parietal lobe, *Proc. roy. Soc. Med.*, **44**, 337–341.
223. GOLDSTEIN, K. (1936)   The modifications of behaviour consequent to cerebral disease, *Psychiat. Quart.*, **10**, 586–610.
224. JACKSON, J. Hughlings (1894)   The factors of insanities, *Med. Press and Circular*, **2**, 615 ; also Selected Writings of, **2**, 411–421, Ed. J. Taylor, London, Hodder and Stoughton.
225. KOHS, S. C. (1927)   Intelligence Measurement, New York, Macmillan.
226. McFIE, J., and PIERCY, M. F. (1952)   The relation of laterality of lesion to performance on Weigl's sorting test, *J. ment. Sci.*, **98**, 299–305.
227. NIELSEN, J. M. (1946)   Agnosia, Apraxia, Aphasia. Their value in cerebral localization, 2nd ed., New York, Hoeber.
     PFEIFFER, R. A. (1928) (see No. 116).
228. REINHOLD, M. (1951)   Some clinical aspects of human cortical function, *Brain*, **74**, 399–431.
229. RIESE, W. (1950)   Principles of neurology in the light of history and their present use, *No. 80, Nerv. ment. Dis. Monograph Ser.*, New York, Coolidge Foundation.

230. TEUBER, H.-L., BATTERSBY, W. E., and BENDER, M. B. (1951) Performance of complex visual tasks after cerebral lesions, *J. nerv. ment. Dis.*, **114**, 413–429.
WALSHE, F. M. R. (1947) (see No. 209).

CHAPTER IV

231. ALAJOUANINE, Th., and AKERMAN, A. (1931) Attitude de la main dans une poussée monobrachiale astéréognostique de la sclérose en plaques, *Rev. neurol.*, **1**, 318–322.
232. ALAJOUANINE, Th., THUREL, R., and BRUNELLI (1934) Syndrome sensitif cortical avec troubles de la sensibilité profonde à topographie pseudo-radiculaire. Instabilité et astéréognosie limites aux trois derniers doigts, *Rev. neurol.*, **1**, 560–564.
233. ALLEN, I. M. (1928) Unusual sensory phenomena following removal of a tumour of the sensory cortex, *J. Neurol. Psychopath.*, **9**, 133–145.
234. ANDRÉ-THOMAS and CEILLIER, H. (1917) Hémianesthésie cérébrale par blessure de guerre, *Rev. neurol.*, **1**, 34–38.
235. ANDRÉ-THOMAS and COURJON, J. (1917) Hémianesthésie par lésion du lobe pariétal, *Rev. neurol.*, **2**, 269–273.
236. ANDRÉ-THOMAS and Mme. LONG-LANDRY (1914) Monoplégie pure du membre supérieur, motrice et sensitive, dissociée. Distribution pseudo-radiculaire des troubles de la sensibilité, *Rev. neurol.*, **1**, 307–310.
237. de BARENNE, J. G. Dusser, and McCULLOCH, W. S. (1934) An " extinction " phenomenon on stimulation of the cerebral cortex, *Proc. Soc. exp. Biol. Med.*, **32**, 524–527.
238. BARRÉ, J., MORIN, L., and KAISER (1923) Étude clinique d'un nouveau cas d'Anosognosie de Babinski, *Rev. neurol.*, **1**, 500–504.
239. BAY, E. (1944) Zum Problem der taktilen Agnosie, *Dtsch. Z. Nervenheilk.*, **156**, 64–96.
240. BENDER, M. B. (1945) Extinction and precipitation of cutaneous sensations, *Arch. Neurol. Psychiat.*, **54**, 1–9.
241. —— (1946) Changes in sensory adaptation in time and aftersensation with lesions of parietal lobe, *ibid.*, **55**, 299–329.
242. —— (1948) The advantages of the method of simultaneous stimulation in the neurological examination, *Med. Clin. N. Amer.*, **32**, 755–758.
243. —— (1952) Disorders in Perception, Springfield, Ill., Thomas.
244. BENDER, M. B., and FELDMAN, D. S. (1952) Extinction of taste sensation on double simultaneous stimulation, *Neurology*, **2**, 195–202.
245. BENDER, M. B., FINK, M., and GREEN, M. (1950) Patterns in perception on simultaneous tests of face and hand, *Trans. Amer. neurol. Ass.*, **75**, 250–252.
246. BENDER, M. B., and SHAPIRO, M. F. (1949) Sensory interrelationships illustrated by double simultaneous stimulation, *C.R. IVth int. Congr. Neurol.*, **2**, 75, Paris, Masson (1951).
247. BENDER, M. B., SHAPIRO, M. F., and SCHAPPEL, A. W. (1949) Extinction phenomenon in Hemiplegia, *Arch. Neurol. Psychiat.*, **62**, 717–724.
248. BENDER, M. B., TEUBER, H.-L., and BATTERSBY, W. S. (1950) Discriminations of weights by man with penetrating lesions of parietal lobes, *Trans. Amer. neurol. Ass.*, **75**, 252–255.
249. BÉNISTY, Mme (*née* Athanasio) (1918) Les lésions de la zone rolandique (zone motrice et zone sensitive) par blessures de guerre, Thèse de Paris, Vigot.

250. BIEMOND, A. (1949) Discussions sur la pathologie du thalamus, *C.R., IVth int. Congr. Neurol.*, **3**, 116–117, Paris, Masson (1951).
251. BIANCHI, L. (1910) La sindrome parietale, *Ann. Nevrol.*, **28**, 137–178.
252. BING, R. (1925) Allgemeine Symptomatologie der Gehirnkrankheiten, Handbuch der Inneren Medizin, **1**, 1–146.
253. BING, R., and SCHWARZ, L. (1919) Contribution à la localisation de la stéréoagnosie, *Schweiz Arch. Neurol. Psychiat.*, **4**, 187–198.
254. BONNIER, Pierre (1894) La pariétale ascendante, *C.R. Soc. de Biol., Paris*, **10**, 533–536.
255. —— (1900) L'orientation, Paris, Carré et Naud.
256. —— (1902) Les sens des attitudes, *C.R. Soc. de Biol., Paris*, **54**, 362–365 ; *Nouv. Icon. Salpêt.*, **15**, 146–184.
257. —— (1904) Les Sens des Attitudes, Paris, Naud.
258. BOSC, F. J. (1892) De l'allochirie sensorielle ; sa place dans la symptomatologie des maladies du système nerveu, *Rev. Méd.*, **12**, 841–866.
259. BUERKLEN, K. (1924) Blindenpsychologie, Leipzig, Barth.
260. BURR, C. W. (1897) A case of tactile amnesia and mind-blindness, *J. nerv. ment. Dis.*, **24**, 259–262.
261. —— (1898) A case of pyschic anesthesia, *ibid.*, **25**, 37–38.
262. BYCHOWSKY, G., and EIDINOW, M. (1934) Doppelseitige Sensibilitätsstörungen bei einseitigen Gehirnherden, *Nervenarzt*, **7**, 498–506.
263. CALLIGARIS, G. (1910) Disturbi della sensibilità di origine cerebrale a tipo radicolare, *Riv. Patol. nerv. ment.*, **10**, 402–415.
264. —— (1920) L'anesthésie cérébrale de type longitudinal, *Rev. neurol.*, **2**, 1073–1083.
265. CHRÉTIEN, R. (1902) De la perception stéréognostique, Thèse de Paris.
266. CLAPARÈDE, E. (1898) La perception stéréognostique, *Intermed. Biol. Paris*, **1**, 432–437.
267. —— (1906) Agnosie et asymbolie, à propos d'un soi-disant cas d'aphasie tactile, *Rev. neurol.*, **14**, 803–805.
268. COHN, R. (1951) On certain aspects of the sensory organization of the human brain, *J. nerv. ment. Dis.*, **113**, 471–484.
269. COHN, R., and RAINES, G. N. (1949) On certain aspects of the sensory organization of the human brain. A study in rostral dominance as determined by ipsilateral simultaneous stimulation, *Trans. Amer. neurol. Ass.*, **74**, 162–167.
270. CRITCHLEY, M. (1949) Observations on tactile, visual and auditory alloesthesia, *C.R. IVth int. Congr. Neurol.*, **2**, 105 ; *ibid.*, **2**, 389 ; Paris, Masson (1951).
271. —— (1949) Phenomenon of tactile inattention with special reference to parietal lesions, *Brain*, **72**, 538–561.
CUSHING, H. (1909) (see No. 171).
272. DEJERINE, J. (1906) Considérations sur la soi-disant " aphasie tactile", *Rev. neurol.*, **14**, 597–601.
273. —— (1907) À propos de l'agnosie tactile, *ibid.*, **15**, 781–784.
274. —— (1914) Séméiologie des affections du système nerveux, Paris, Masson.
275. DEJERINE, J., and MOUZON, J. (1914–1915). Deux cas de syndrome sensitif cortical, *Rev. neurol.*, **28**, 388–392.
276. —— —— (1914–1915) Un nouveau type de syndrome sensitif cortical observé dans un cas de monoplégie corticale dissociée, *ibid.*, **28**, 1265–1273.
277. DEJERINE, J., and ROUSSY, G. (1906) Le syndrome thalamique, *Rev. neurol.*, **14**, 521–532.

278. DELAY, J.-P. L. (1935) Les Astéréognosies, Pathologie du Toucher, Paris, Masson.
279. DERCUM, F. X. (1900) Studies in astereognosis, *J. nerv. ment. Dis.*, **27**, 569–579.
280. DILLER, T. (1901) Two cases of astereognosis, *Brain*, **24**, 649–655.
281. DUBBERS (1897) Ein Fall von Tastlähmung, *Neurol. Zbl.*, **16**, 61–65.
    DUSSER de BARENNE. See de BARENNE, J. G. Dusser.
282. EVANS, J. P. (1935) A study of the sensory defects resulting from excision of cerebral substance in humans, *Res. Publ. Ass. nerv. ment. Dis.*, **15**, 331–370.
283. FINK, M., GREEN, M., and BENDER, M. B. (1952) The face and hand test as a diagnostic sign of organic mental syndrome, *Neurology*, **2**, 46–58.
284. FINKELNBURG (1870), cited by J.-P. L. DELAY, No. 278.
285. FISCHER, B. (1923) Ueber corticale Sensibilitätsstörungen, *Z. ges. Neurol. Psychiat.*, **87**, 490–493.
286. FISCHER, B., and POETZL, O. (1924) Zur Symptomatologie der Sensibilitätsstörungen von cerebralem Typus; I. Eine noch nicht bekannte cutan Sensibilitätsstörung von zentralem Typus, *Z. ges. Neurol. Psychiat.*, **88**, 58–76.
287. FOERSTER, O. (1916) Die Topik der Sensibilitätsstörungen bei Unterbrechung der sensiblen Leitungsbahnen, *Neurol. Zbl.*, **35**, 807–810.
288. —— (1936) Sensible corticale Felder, Handbuch der Neurologie, ed. Bumke and Foerster, **6**, 358–448, Berlin, Springer.
289. FOIX, Ch. (1922) Sur une variété de troubles bilatéraux de la sensibilité par lésion unilatérale du cerveau. Anesthésie par agnosie (anesthéso-agnosie) avec prédominance des troubles de la notion de position (atopognosie) constituant par leur association à une hémiplégie et une aphasie d'intensités variables et à l'apraxie idéo-motrice, un syndrome caractéristique des lésions profondes du lobe pariétal, *Rev. neurol.*, **1**, 322–331.
290. FOIX, Ch., CHAVANY, J.-A., and LÉVY, Maurice (1927) Syndrome pseudo-thalamique d'origine pariétale. Lésion de l'artère du sillon interpariétal (Pa P_1 P_2 antérieures, petit territoire insulo-capsulaire), *Rev. neurol.*, **1**, 68–76.
291. FOX, J. C., and KLEMPERER, W. W. (1942) Vibratory Sensibility; a quantitative study of its thresholds in nervous disorders, *Arch. Neurol. Psychiat.*, **48**, 622–645.
292. von FREY, M. (1896) (also cited by PIÉRON, H., No. 349) Untersuchungen über die Sinnesfunktionen der menschlichen Haut; Druckempfindung und Schmerz, *Abh. math.-phys. Kgl. sächs. Gesellsch. Wissensch.*, **23**, 169–266.
293. FUCHS, A. (1908) Neurologische Kasuistik : Eigentümliche Sensibilitätsstörung (Tastlähmung) bei Polyneuritis, *Wien. Klin. Wschr.*, **21**, 1180–1183.
294. GAMPER, E. (1918) Zur Klinik der Sensibilitätsstörungen bei Rindenläsionen, *Mschr. Psychiat. Neurol.*, **43**, 21–36.
295. GERSTMANN, J. (1915) Ein weiterer Beitrag zur Kenntnis kortikaler Sensibilitätsstörungen von spino-segmentalem Typus, *Wien. med. Wschr.*, **65**, 1748–1750.
296. —— (1930) Zur Symptomatologie der Herderkrankungen in der Uebergangsregion der unteren Parietal- und mittleren Okzipitalhirnwindung, *Dtsch. Z. Nervenheilk.*, **116**, 46–49.
297. GOLDSTEIN, K. (1914) Ein Beitrag zur Lehre von der Bedeutung der Insel für die Sprache und der linken Hemisphäre für das linksseitige Tasten, *Arch. Psychiat. Nervenkr.*, **55**, 158–173.

298. GOLDSTEIN, K. (1916) Ueber kortikale Sensibilitätsstörungen, *Z. ges. Neurol. Psychiat.*, **33**, 494–517 ; *Neurol. Zbl.*, **35**, 825–827.

299. GOLDSTEIN, K., and REICHMANN, Frieda (1919–1920) Ueber corticale Sensibilitätsstörungen, besonders am Kopfe, *Z. ges. Neurol. Psychiat.*, **53**, 49–79 ; *Arch. Psychiat. Nervenkr.*, **56**, 466–521.

300. GUILLAIN, G., ALAJOUANINE, Th., and GARCIN, R. (1925) Un cas d'apraxie idéo-motrice bilatérale coincidant avec une aphasie et une hémiparésie gauche chez une gauchère. Troubles bilatéraux de la sensibilité profonde, *Rev. neurol.*, **2**, 116–124.

301. HALPERN, L. (1939) Monoplegie der Finger und taktile Agnosie. Zur Klinik eines cerebralen Gefässyndroms, *Schweiz. Arch. Neurol. Psychiat.*, **44**, 35–42.

302. —— (1945) Macrostereognosis, *J. nerv. ment. Dis.*, **102**, 260–264.

303. —— (1948) Troubles de l'appréciation stéréognostique des dimensions, *Presse méd.*, **56**, 607–608.

304. —— (1949) Disturbances of dermatokinesthesis in cerebral and spinal diseases, *J. nerv. ment. Dis.*, **109**, 1–8.

305. HEAD, H., and HOLMES, G. (1911–1912) Sensory disturbances from cerebral lesions, *Brain*, **34**, 102–254.

306. HEAD, H., and RIVERS, W. H. R. (1908) A human experiment in nerve division, *Brain*, **31**, 323–450.

307. HÉCAEN, H., and de AJURIAGUERRA, J. (1950) Asymbolie à la douleur. Étude anatomo-clinique, *Rev. neurol.*, **83**, 300–302.

308. HELLER, Th. (1904) Studien zur Blindenpsychologie, Leipzig, Engelmann.

309. —— (1905) Ueber einen Fall von sensorischer Aphasie, *Mitt. Ges. inn. Med. Kinderheilk. Wien*, **4**, 150.

310. HEYMANNS—cited by Foerster, No. 288.

311. HIPPIUS, R. (1934) Erkennendes Tasten, *N. psychol. Stud.*, **12**, 83–98.

312. HOFF, H. (1932) Beitrag zur Beziehung funktioneller und organischer Symptome, *Nervenarzt*, **5**, 293–294.

313. HOFFMANN, H. (1885) Stereognostische Versuche, angestellt zur Ermitelung der Elemente des Gefühlssinnes, aus denen die Vorstellungen der Körper im Raume gebildet werden, *Dtsch. Arch. klin. Med.*, **36**, 398–426.

314. HOLMES, Gordon (1927) Disorders of sensation produced by cortical lesions, *Brain*, **50**, 413–427.

315. JAFFÉ, J., and BENDER, M. B. (1951) Perceptual patterns during recovery from general anesthesia, *J. Neurol. Neurosurg. Psychiat.*, **14**, 316–321.

316. JANOTA, O. (1928) Pózuchy Citlivosti z poškození temenních laloků mozkových a jejich lokalisačné diagnostický význam, *Sborn. Lekar.*, **30–35**, 1–84.

317. —— (1928) Des troubles de la sensibilité dus aux lésions des lobes pariétaux et de leur valeur pour le diagnostic topique, *Rev. neurol.*, **2**, 797–798.

318. JONES, E. (1907) The precise diagnostic value of Allochiria, *Brain*, **30**, 490–532.

319. —— (1907) The clinical significance of Allochiria, *Lancet*, **2**, 830–832.

320. JUMENTIÉ (1922) (cited by Delay) (see No. 278).
KAPPERS, C. U. Ariëns, HUBER, G. C., and CROSBY, E. C. (1936) (see No. 77).

321. KATO, T. (1911) Ueber die Bedeutung der Tastlähmung für die topische Hirndiagnostik, *Dtsch. Z. Nervenheilk.*, **42**, 128–154.

322. KATZ, D. (1925) Der Aufbau der Tastwelt, *Z. Psychol. Physiol. Sinnesorg.*, **11**, 1–270.

323. Kolb, L. G. (1950) Observations on the somatic sensory extinction phenomenon and the body schema after unilateral resection of the posterior central gyrus, *Trans. Amer. neurol. Ass.*, **75**, 138–141.

324. Kramer, F. (1916) Demonstration zweier Fälle von segmentalen Sensibilitätsstörungen bei kortikalen Läsionen, *Neurol. Zbl.*, **35**, 478–479.

325. —— (1917) Sensibilitätsstörung im Gesicht bei kortikaler Läsion durch Schussverletzung, *ibid.*, **36**, 329–331.

326. Krestnikoff (1923) Beitrag zur Lehre von der Astereognosie (Tastsinnagnosie), *Z. ges. Neurol. Psychiat.*, **83**, 527–537.

327. Kroll, M. (1910) Beiträge zum Studium der Apraxie, *Z. ges. Neurol. Psychiat.*, **2**, 315–345.

328. —— (1929) Die neurologischen Symptomenkomplexe, Berlin, Springer.

329. Lhermitte, J. (1909) De la valeur séméiologique des troubles de la sensibilité à disposition radiculaire dans les lésions de l'encéphale, *Sem. méd.*, **24**, 277–279.

330. Lhermitte, J., and de Ajuriaguerra, J. (1935) Syndrome hémialgique fruste par ramollissement pariétal, *Rev. neurol.*, **64**, 204–210.

331. —— —— (1942) Psychopathologie de la vision, Paris, Masson.

332. Liepmann, H. (1909) Agnostische Störungen. Taktile Agnosie (Tastlähmung), p. 486 in H. Curschmann's Lehrbuch der Nervenkrankheiten, Berlin, Springer.

333. Marie, André P. (1924) Étude comparée des troubles sensitifs d'origine cérébrale, Thèse de Paris.

334. Marie, P. (1916) Monoplégies corticales, *Rev. neurol.*, **2**, 617.

335. Marie, P., and Bouttier, H. (1922) Études cliniques sur les modalités des dissociations de la sensibilité dans les lésions encéphaliques, *Rev. neurol.*, **1**, 1–22 et 144–160.

336. —— —— (1922) L'hyperesthésie douloureuse au froid dans les syndromes thalamiques dissociés, *ibid.*, **2**, 985–990.

337. Marie, P., Bouttier, H., and van Bogaert, L. (1924) Sur un cas de tumeur préfrontale droite. Troubles de l'orientation dans l'espace, *Rev. neurol.*, **2**, 209–221.

338. Marie, P., and Chatelin, Ch. (1916) Les troubles visuels consécutifs aux blessures des voies optiques centrales et de la sphère visuelle corticale : Hémianopsies en quadrant supérieur ; Hémiachromatopsies, *Rev. neurol.*, **1**, 138–140.

339. Markova, K. (1900) Contribution à l'étude de la perception stéréognostique, Thèse de Genève.

340. McDougall, W. (1903) The nature of inhibitory processes within the nervous system, *Brain*, **26**, 153–191.

341. Marshall, J. (1951) Sensory disturbances in cortical wounds with special reference to pain, *J. Neurol. Psychiat.*, **14**, 187–204.

342. Minkowski, M. (1917) Étude sur la physiologie des circonvolutions rolandique et pariétale, *Schweiz. Arch. Neurol. Psychiat.*, **1**, 389–459.

343. —— (1923, 1924) (see Nos. 99, 100, 101).

344. von Monakow, C. (1897) Gehirnpathologie, Wien, Nothnagel.

345. —— (1914) Die Lokalisation im Grosshirn, Wiesbaden, Bergmann.

345. Mouzon, J., and Paulian (1915) Hémiplégie spinale droite avec syndrome de Brown-Séquard et paralysie radiculaire droite C³, C⁴, par balle de shrapnell ayant pénétré par la racine du nez et logée à la partie droite du corps de la IIIᵉ vertèbre cervicale, *Rev. neurol.*, **1**, 411–414.

Munk, H. (1890) (see No. 110).

346. Nathan, P. W. (1946) On simultaneous bilateral stimulation of the body in a lesion of the parietal lobe, *Brain*, **69**, 325–334.

347. NOTHNAGEL (1867) Beiträge zur Physiologie und Pathologie des Temperatursinns, *Dtsch. Arch. klin. Med.*, **2**, 284–299.

348. OPPENHEIM, H. (1885) Ueber eine durch eine klinisch bisher nicht verwertete Untersuchungsmethode ermittelte Form der Sensibilitätsstörung bei einseitigen Erkrankungen des Grosshirns, *Neurol. Zbl.*, **4**, 529–532.

349. PIÉRON, H. (1934) Le Toucher, *Traite de Physiologie nerveuse*, **10**, 1055–1228, Paris, Masson.

350. PINÉAS, H. (1931) Ein Fall von räumlicher Orientierungsstörung mit Dyschirie, *Z. ges. Neurol. Psychiat.*, **133**, 180–195.

351. POETZL, O., and STENGEL, E. (1936) Ueber das Syndrom Leitungsaphasie - Schmerzasymbolie, *J. Psychiat. Neurol.*, **53**, 174–207.

352. POGGIO, E. (1908) Die kortikale Lokalisation der Asymbolie, *Neurol. Zbl.*, **27**, 817–818.

353. PUCHELT, F. (1844) Ueber partielle Empfindungslähmung, *Heidelberg Med. Annalen*, **10**, 485.

354. RAYMOND, F. (1896–1903) Clinique des maladies du système nerveux, 6 vols., **1**, 15 ; **2**, 268 ; **3**, 298. Paris, Doin.

355. RAYMOND, F., and EGGER, M. (1906) Un cas d'aphasie tactile, *Rev. neurol.*, **14**, 371–375.

356. REDLICH, E. (1928) Zur Topographie der Sensibilitätsstörungen am Rumpfe bei der zerebralen Hemianästhesia, *Mschr. Psychiat. Neurol.*, **68**, 453–469.

357. REGNARD, M. (1913) Contribution à l'étude anatomo-clinique des monoplégies d'origine corticale, Thèse de Paris.

358. REIDER, N. (1946) Phenomena of sensory suppression, *Arch. Neurol. Psychiat.*, **55**, 583–590.

359. REINHARD, C. (1887) Zur Frage der Hirnlocalisation mit besonderer Berücksichtigung der cerebralen Sehstörungen, *Arch. Psychiat. Nervenkr.*, **18**, 240–258.

360. RÉVÉSZ, G. (1928) Ueber taktile Agnosie ; psychologische Analyse der Störungen in der Tastwahrnehmung (Tract), Haarlem.

361. —— (1950) Psychology and art of the blind, London, New York, Toronto ; Longmans, Green.

362. ROGER, H. (1927) Du syndrome thalamique au syndrome pariétal. Diagnostic différentiel des syndromes sensitifs corticaux, *Sud méd. chir.*, 926.

363. ROUQUÈS, L. (cited by SCHWOB, R. A. (1933)) (see No. 380). Case of parietal tumour with loss of sensation, pp. 145–150 in Schwob, R. A., " Les syndromes pariétaux ".

364. ROUSSY, G., and BRANCHE, J. (1918) Deux cas de syndrome sensitif cortical par blessure de guerre, *Rev. neurol.*, **2**, 221–225.

365. ROUSSY, G., and LEVY, G. (1926) Troubles sensitivo-moteurs d'aspect radiculaire et troubles d'aspect cérébelleux par lésion corticale, *Rev. neurol.*, **2**, 376–389.

366. RUBINS, J. L., and FRIEDMAN, E. D. (1948) Asymboly for pain, *Arch. Neurol. Psychiat.*, **60**, 554–573.

367. RUCH, T. C., FULTON, J., and GERMAN, W. J. (1938) Sensory discrimination in monkey, chimpanzee and man after lesions of the parietal lobe, *Arch. Neurol. Psychiat.*, **39**, 919–938.

368. RUEMKE, H. C. (1925) (cited by DELAY) (see No. 278) Over " Astereognosie " tengevolge van een letsel in de middenhersenen, *Ned. Tijdschr. Geneesk.*, **69**, 2310.

369. RUSSEL, C. K., and HORSLEY, V. (1906) Note on apparent re-representation in the cerebral cortex of the type of sensory representation as it exists in the spinal cord, *Brain*, **29**, 137–151.

370. RUSSELL, E. R. (1945) Transient disturbances following gunshot wounds of the head, *Brain*, **68**, 79–97.

371. SAILER, J. (1899) A contribution to the knowledge of the stereognostic sense, *J. nerv. ment. Dis.*, **26**, 161–170.

372. SCHILDER, P. (1925) Das Körperschema, Berlin, Springer.

373. SCHILDER, P., and STENGEL, E. (1928) Schmerzasymbolie, *Z. ges. Neurol. Psychiat.*, **113**, 143–158.

374. —— —— (1930) Das Krankheitsbild der Schmerzasymbolie, *ibid.*, **129**, 250–279.

375. —— —— (1931) Asymbolie for pain, *Arch. Neurol. Psychiat.*, **25**, 598–600.

376. SCHITTENHELM, A. (1905–6) Untersuchungen über das Lokalisationsvermögen und das stereognostische Erkennen, *Dtsch. Arch. klin. Med.*, **85**, 562–577.

377. SCHUSTER, P. (1909) Beitrag zur Kenntnis der Alexie und verwandter Störungen, *Mschr. Psychiat. Neurol.*, **25**, 349–424.

378. —— (1917) Beitrag zur Lehre von den sensiblen Zentren der Grosshirnrinde, *Neurol. Zbl.*, **36**, 331–336.

379. —— (1931) Verlust der Bilateralitätsvorstellung (Demonstration), *Zbl. ges. Neurol. Psychiat.*, **59**, 524–525.

380. SCHWOB, R. A. (1933) Les syndromes pariétaux, Paris, Arnette.

381. SHERRINGTON, C. S. (1900) Cutaneous sensations, Textbook of Physiology, ed. E. A. Schäfer, **2**, 920–1001, Edinburgh, London ; Pentland.

382. SILVERSTEIN, A. (1931) Tumor of the parietal lobe, *Arch. Neurol. Psychiat.*, **26**, 1342–1348.

383. SITTIG, O. (1914) (cited by DELAY) (see No. 278). Klinische Beiträge zur Lehre von den sensiblen Rindenzentren, *Prag. med. Wschr.*, **39**, 548.

384. —— (1916) Ueber einen eigenartigen flächenhaft lokalisierten Destruktionsprozess der Hirnrinde bei einem Falle von Hirntuberkel, *Z. ges. Neurol. Psychiat.*, **33**, 301–313.

385. —— (1922) Weiteres über kortikale Sensibilitätsstörungen, *ibid.*, **76**, 265–274.

386. ŠPRINČOVÁ, M. (1926) Případ Fokálního typu poruchy citlivosti po haemorrhagii s hemianopsií korového původu téže aetiologie, *Čas. čes. Lék.*, číslo 16.

387. von STAUFFENBERG, W. (1918) Klinische und anatomische Beiträge zur Kenntniss der aphasischen, agnostischen und apraktischen Symptome, *Z. ges. Neurol. Psychiat.*, **39**, 71–212.

388. STEIN, H. (1924) Nachempfindungen bei Sensibilitätsstörungen, als Folge gestörter Umstimmung (Adaptation), *Dtsch. Z. Nervenheilk.*, **80**, 218–233.

389. STEIN, H., and von WEIZSÄCKER, V. (1926) Ueber klinische Sensibilitätsprüfungen, *Dtsch. Arch. klin. Med.*, **151**, 230–253.

390. —— —— (1927) Der Abbau der sensiblen Funktionen, Eine sinnesphysiologische Analyse der Hypästhesie, *Dtsch. Z. Nervenheilk.*, **99**, 1–30.

391. STENVERS, H. W. (1949) Anosognosie. Localisation par l'image, *C.R. IVth int. Congr. Neurol.*, **2**, 27 ; **3**, 207 ; 386, Paris, Masson (1951).

392. STEWART, T. Grainger (1894) On a case of perverted localization of sensation or allachaesthesia, *Brit. med. J.*, **1**, 1–4.

393. von STRUEMPELL, A. (1918) Die Stereognose durch den Tastsinn und ihre Störungen, *Dtsch. Z. Nervenheilk.*, **60**, 154–168.

394. TATERKA, H. (1926) Beitrag zur Symptomatologie und Lokalisation der Sensibilitätsstörungen von cerebralem Typus, *Dtsch. Z. Nervenheilk.*, **90**, 193–200.

395. TSCHLENOW, L. G. (1928) Sur la cinesthésie cutanée, *Rev. neurol.*, 2, 506–508.

396. VERCELLI, G. (1947) Interesse e significato del fenomeno della eclissi della sensibilità in una metà del corpo al doppio stimolo simultaneo e simmetrico in determinate sindromi da lesione dell'emisfero cerebrale opposto, *Riv. Neurol.*, 17, 243–252.

397. VERGER, H. (1900) Sur les troubles de la sensibilité générale consecutifs aux lésions des hémisphères cérébraux chez l'homme, *Arch. gén. de Méd.*, 6, 641–713.

398. —— (1902) Sur la valeur séméiologique de la stéréo-agnosie, *Rev. neurol.*, 2, 1201–1205.

399. VILLARET, M., and FAURE-BEAULIEU, M. (1916) Les anesthésies corticales à topographie atypique dans les traumatismes craniens, *Paris méd.*, 1, 514–518.

400. VILLEY, P. (1930) The world of the blind (a psychological study), London, Duckworth.

401. van VLEUTEN, C. F. (1907) Linksseitige motorische Apraxie, ein Beitrag zur Physiologie des Balkens, *Allg. Z. Psychiat.*, 64, 203–239.

402. VOUTERS, L. (1909) Sur l'agnosie tactile, Thèse de Paris.

403. WALTON, G. L., and PAUL, W. E. (1901) The clinical value of astereognosis and its bearing upon cerebral localization, *J. nerv. ment. Dis.*, 28, 191–213.

404. WEBER (1835) Ueber den Tastsinn, *Arch. Anat. Physiol.*, 152–160.

405. WERNICKE, C. (1895) Zwei Fälle von Rindenläsion, *Arb. psychiat. Klin. Breslau*, 2, 35.

406. WERTHEIM-SALOMONSON, J. (1888) Stereognosis, Leiden.

407. WILLIAMSON, R. T. (1897) On " Touch Paralysis " or the inability to recognize the nature of objects by tactile impressions, *Brit. med. J.*, 2, 787–788.

408. WUNDT, W. (1910) Grundzüge der Physiologischen Psychologie, II, 6th ed., Leipzig, Engelmann.

409. ZIEGLER, D. K. (1952) Extinction phenomenon in patients with verified cerebral tumours, *Neurology*, 2, 501–508.

CHAPTER V

410. ALAJOUANINE, Th., and LEMAIRE, A. (1925) Tumeur de la région paracentrale postérieure avec symptômes " pseudo-cérébelleux ", *Rev. neurol.*, 1, 71–75.

411. ANDRÉ-THOMAS (1918) Étude sur les blessures du cervelet, Paris, Vigot.

412. ANTON, G. (1893) Beiträge zur klinischen Beurtheilung und Localisation der Muskelsinnstörungen im Grosshirne, *Z. Heilk.*, 14, 313–348.

413. BARRÉ, J. A., and MORIN, P. (1925) Syndrome de sclérose latérale amyotrophique unilatérale, expression d'une tumeur Rolandique, *Ann. Méd.*, 17, 478–483.

414. BECHTEREW, W. V. (1894) Unaufhaltsames Lachen und Weinen bei Hirnaffectionen, *Arch. Psychiat. Nervenkr.*, 26, 791–817.

BÉNISTY, Mme. (*née* Athanasio) (1918) (see No. 249).

415. BESTA, C. (1922) Sulla funzione della regione parietale dell' Uomo, *Riv. Pat. nerv. ment.*, 27, 531–538.

416. van BOGAERT, L. (1933) L'amyotrophie précoce dans les tumeurs du lobe pariétal, *Paris méd.*, 2, 261–264.

417. —— (1935) Sur la signification de certains mouvements forcés complexes, *Encéphale*, 30, 453–508.

418. BORCHERINI, A. (1890) Ueber einen Fall frühzeitiger Muskelatrophie cerebralen Ursprungs, Neurol. Zbl., 9, 545–556.

419. BREMER, F. (1921) Global aphasia and bilateral apraxia due to an endothelioma compressing the gyrus supramarginalis, Arch. Neurol. Psychiat., 5, 663–669.

420. BREMER, L., and CARSON, N. B. (1895) Cylindroma endotheliosis of the dura mater causing localizing symptoms and early muscular atrophy, Amer. J. med. Sci., 109, 120–137.

421. BRISSAUD, E. (1879) De l'atrophie musculaire dans l'hémiplégie, Rev. Méd., 3, 616–642.

422. BURR, C. W., and TAYLOR, W. J. (1902) A case of Jacksonian Epilepsy caused by a tumor of the brain relieved by operation ; hemiplegia and muscular atrophy. Death in ten months, Amer. J. med. Sci., 124, 34–43.

423. CHATIN, P. (1900) Troubles trophiques et troubles de la sensibilité chez les hémiplégiques, Rev. Méd., 20, 781–811.

424. CHARCOT, J. M. (1879) Lectures on diseases of the nervous system, translated by G. Sigerson, Philadelphia, Lea.

425. CLAUDE, H., and LHERMITTE, J. (1916) Les paraplégies cérébello-spasmodiques et ataxo-cérébello-spasmodiques consécutives aux lésions bilatérales des lobules paracentraux par projectiles de guerre, Bull. Soc. méd. hôp. Paris, 40, 796–804.

426. CLAUDE, H., and LOYEZ, M. (1913) Étude anatomique d'un cas d'apraxie avec hémiplégie droite et cécité verbale, Encéphale, 8 ii, 289–307.

427. COHN, R. (1948) The Babinski sign. Extinction during bilateral simultaneous cutaneous stimulation, J. Neurophysiol., 11, 193–197.

428. CRISTINI, Renato (1937) Tumore del lobo parietale sinistro con amiotrofia controlaterale, Riv. Neurol., 10, 456–475.

429. DARKSCHEWITSCH, L. (1891) Ein Fall von frühzeitiger Muskel-atrophie bei einem Hemiplegiker, Neurol. Zbl., 10, 622–630.

430. DAVID, M., HÉCAEN, H., and SAUGUET, H. (1944) Épilepsie gyratoire par traumatisme pariéto-occipital gauche, Rev. neurol., 77, 299–300.

431. —— —— —— (1945) Sur une modalité de " mouvements forcés complexes " à type d'enroulement et de gyration, ibid., 77, 333–336.

432. DEJERINE, J. (1889) De la névrite périphérique dans l'atrophie musculaire des hémiplégiques, C.R. Soc. de Biol., Paris (9's), 1, 523–530.

433. EISENLOHR, C. (1893) Beiträge zur Hirnlocalisation, Dtsch. Z. Nervenheilk., 3, 260–279.

434. FEARNSIDES, E. G. (1915) A case of motor dyspraxia and paraphasia : autopsy : tumour in supramarginal convolution, Brain, 37, 418–432.

435. FOIX, Ch. (1916) Contribution à l'étude de l'apraxie idéo-motrice, de son anatomie pathologique et de ses rapports avec les syndromes qui ordinairement l'accompagnent, Rev. neurol., 1, 283–298.

FOIX, Ch., CHAVANY, J.-A., and LÉVY, Maurice (1927) (See No. 290).

436. FOIX, Ch., and THÉVENARD, A. (1922) Symptômes pseudo-cérébelleux d'origine cérébrale, tubercule de la région paracentrale postérieure, Rev. neurol., 29, 1502–1504.

437. GEREBTZOFF, M. A. (1938) Le problème de la localisation et des ataxies corticales comme conclusion à des recherches anatomc-expérimentales, J. belge Neurol. Psychiat., 38, 108–132.

GILLES DE LA TOURETTE (see TOURETTE) (see No. 486).

438. GOLDSCHEIDER, A. (1894) Zur allgemeinen Pathologie des Nerven-systems, Berl. klin. Wschr., 31, 421–425.

439. GORDON, A. (1927) Segmental trophic edema of cerebral origin, *J. nerv. ment. Dis.*, **66**, 381–389.

440. GOWERS, W. R. (1885) Lectures on the diagnosis of diseases of the brain, London, Churchill.

441. GUILLAIN, G., PETIT-DUTAILLIS, D., and ROUQUÈS, L. (1932) Gliome kystique du lobe pariétal opéré et guéri. Valeur sémiologique de l'atrophie musculaire dans les lésions pariétales, *Rev. neurol.*, **1**, 485–490.

442. HALL, Marshall (1841) On the diseases and derangements of the nervous system, London, Baillière.

443. HEAD, Henry (1920) Studies in Neurology, **2**, 786, London, Oxford Univ. Press.

444. HERRMANN, G. (1928) Zur Pathologie der temporo-parietalen Krampfanfälle, *Z. ges. Neurol. Psychiat.*, **114**, 173–184.

445. HOWDEN, J. C. (1875) Case of atrophy of right hemisphere of cerebrum and left side of cerebellum, with atrophy of left side of body, *J. Anat., Lond.*, **9**, 288–296.

446. JOFFROY, A., and ACHARD, Ch. (1891) Contribution à l'étude de l'atrophie musculaire chez les hémiplégiques, *Arch. Méd. exp.*, **3**, 780–795.

447. KIRCHHOFF, V. (1897) Ueber trophische Hirncentren und über den Verlauf trophischer und schmerzleitender sowie einiger Fasersysteme im Gehirn von unsicherer Function, *Arch. Psychiat. Nervenkr.*, **29**, 888–932.

448. KISS, J. (1929) Ueber die cerebrale Muskelatrophie, *Arch. Psychiat. Nervenkr.*, **88**, 411–424.

449. KLEIST, K. (1934) Gehirnpathologie, Leipzig, Barth.

450. KRAMER, L. (1891) Beitrag zur Lehre von der Jackson'schen Epilepsie und der cerebral bedingten Muskelatrophie, *Jb. Psychiat.*, **10**, 91–104.

451. KRAUS, W. M., and PERKINS, O. C. (1926) A syndrome of the cerebral origins of the visceral nervous system, *Trans. Amer. neurol. Ass.*, **52**, 503–516.

KROLL, M. (1910) (see No. 327).

452. LAIGNEL-LAVASTINE, and LÉVY-VALENSI, J. (1914) Gliome du corps calleux et du lobe pariétal gauche. Apraxie bilatérale. Mort par ponction lombaire, *Encéphale*, **9 i**, 411–424.

453. LIEPMANN, H. (1900) Das Krankheitsbild der Apraxie (" motorische Asymbolie "), auf Grund eine Falles von einseitiger Apraxie, *Mschr. Psychiat. Neurol.*, **8**, 182–197.

454. LUNTZ, M. A. (1896) Hemiatrophia totalis cruciata, *Neurol. Zbl.*, **15**, 1045–1046.

455. LUZZATO, A. M. (1903) Ueber vasomotorische Muskelatrophie, *Dtsch. Z. Nervenheilk.*, **23**, 482–498.

456. MARINESCO, G. (1898) Recherches sur l'atrophie musculaire et la contracture dans l'hémiplégie organique, *Sem. méd.*, **18**, 465–470.

457. MEYER, E. (1910) Totale Hemiatrophie, *Neurol. Zbl.*, **29**, 450–459.

458. MILLS, C. K., KEEN, W. W., and SPILLER, W. G. (1900) Tumour of the superior parietal convolution, accurately localised and removed by operation, *J. nerv. ment. Dis.*, **27**, 244–264.

von MONAKOW, C. (see Nos. 343 and 344).

459. MORLAAS, J. (1928) Contribution à l'étude de l'apraxie, Thèse de Paris.

460. de MORSIER, G. (1938) Le syndrome vestibulo-visuel pariétal d'origine traumatique. Contribution à l'étude des centres vestibulaires corticaux et des hallucinations lilliputiennes, *Encéphale*, **33**, 57–72.

461. de MORSIER, G. and, BROCCARD, R. (1937) Syndrome pariétal avec mouvements forcés complexes et hallucinations visuelles, Contribution a l'étude de l' " automatose " et de la " grande attaque hystérique ", *Schweiz. Arch. Neurol. Psychiat.*, **40**, 164–172, 362–371.

462. OPPENHEIM, H. (1911) Zur Lehre der neurovaskulären Erkrankungen, *Dtsch. Z. Nervenheilk*, **41**, 376–405.

463. ORBISON, T. J. (1908) Trophic Hemiatrophy : complete ; a trophoneurosis, *J. nerv. ment. Dis.*, **35**, 695–701.

464. PACKARD, F. A. (1896) A case of endothelioma of the cerebral membranes with Jacksonian epilepsy and wasting of the paralysed muscles, *Arch. Pediat.*, **13**, 666–677.

465. PATELLA, V. (1886) Delle atrofie muscolari secondarie a malattie nervose, a malattie generali ed infettive, loro patogenesi e diagnosi, e diagnosi differenziale, Padova, Prosperini.

466. PELIZAEUS, H. (1897) Ueber einen ungewöhnlichen Fall von progressiver Hemiatrophie, Myosclerose, Sclerodermie und Atrophie der Knochen und Gelenke, *Neurol. Zbl.*, **16**, 530–537.

467. PENFIELD, W., and ROBERTSON, J. S. M. (1943) Growth asymmetry due to lesions of the post-central cerebral cortex, *Arch. Neurol. Psychiat.*, **50**, 405–430.

PINÉAS, H. (1931) (see No. 350).

468. PITHA, M. V. (1936) Les atrophies musculaires au cours des lésions du lobe pariétal, *Rev. neurol.*, **1**, 756–765.

469. PITRES, A. (1876) Sur un cas d'atrophie musculaire, consécutive à une sclérose latérale secondaire de la moelle épinière, *Arch. Physiol. norm. path.*, 2nd series, **3**, 657–663.

470. PRINCE, Morton (1906) Limited area of anesthesia, epileptiform attacks of hemialgesia and early muscular atrophy in a case of brain tumor, *J. nerv. ment. Dis.*, **33**, 698–703.

471. QUINCKE, H. (1893) Ueber cerebrale Muskelatrophie, *Dtsch. Z. Nervenheilk.*, **4**, 299–311.

472. RHEIN, J. H. W. (1917) Central atrophy, *J. nerv. ment. Dis.*, **46**, 251–259.

473. ROTHFELD, J. (1932) Der " Beugereflex der Beine " als lokaldiagnostisches Symptom cerebraler Herde, *Nervenarzt*, **5**, 528–532.

474. ROTT, V. K., and MOURATOFF, V. A. (1891) Contribution à l'étude de la pathologie des hémisphères cérébraux, Moscow, 1890. Review and summary by Roubinovitch in *Arch. Neurol.* par Charcot, **21**, 296–300.

ROUSSY, G., and LEVY, G. (1926) (see No. 365).

475. SCHAFFER, K. (1897) Zur Lehre der cerebralen Muskelatrophie nebst Beitrag zur Trophik der Neuronen, *Mschr. Psychiat. Neurol.*, **2**, 30–52.

SCHWOB, R. A. (1933) (see No. 380).

476. SILVERSTEIN, A. (1931) Atrophy of the limbs as a sign in involvement of the parietal lobe, *Philadelphia Neurol. Soc.*, **19**, xii (1930) ; *Arch. Neurol. Psychiat.*, **26**, 237–240.

477. —— (1931) Cerebral muscular atrophy as a significant sign of tumor of the parietal lobe with presentation of cases, *ibid.*, **26**, 670–674.

478. —— (1933) Tumor of the parietal lobe showing Jacksonian sensory seizures involving the tongue, face, thumb and index fingers with advanced premature atrophy of the affected parts, *J. nerv. ment. Dis.*, **77**, 371–384.

479. von STAUFFENBERG, W. (1911) Beitrag zur Lokalisation der Apraxie, *Z. ges. Neurol. Psychiat.*, **5**, 434–444.

480. STALKER, A. M. (1894) Muscular atrophy of cerebral origin, *Edinb. Hosp. Rep.*, **2**, 411–419.

481. STEINER, A. (1893) Ueber die Muskelatrophie bei cerebraler Hemiplegie, *Dtsch. Z. Nervenheilk.*, **3**, 280–299.

482. STEINERT, H. (1903) Cerebrale Muskelatrophie. Nebst einem Beitrag zur Casuistik der Balkentumoren, *Dtsch. Z. Nervenheilk.*, **24**, 1–59.

483. STEWART, P. (1908) A case of disease of the post-central gyrus, associated with astereognosis, *Rev. Neurol. Psychiat.*, **6**, 379–390.

484. STROHMAYER, W. (1903) Ueber " subkortikale Alexie " mit Agraphie und Apraxie, *Dtsch. Z. Nervenheilk.*, **24**, 372–380.

485. TAYLOR, F. (1878) Unilateral atrophy with muscular spasm, *Lancet*, **1**, 387–389.

486. de la TOURETTE, Gilles (1897) Pathogénie et prophylaxie de l'atrophie musculaire et des douleurs des hémiplégiques, *Bull. Soc. méd. hôp. Paris*, **14**, 499–513. Discussion : *Sem. méd.*, **17**, 130–131.

487. WEISENBERG, T. H. (1905) A clinical study of hemiplegia in the adult, *J. Amer. Med. Ass.*, **44**, 603–608.

488. WINKELMAN, N. W., and SILVERSTEIN, A. (1934) Trophic disturbance of the limbs in retro-rolandic lesions, *Res. Publ. Ass. nerv. ment. Dis.*, **13**, 485–528.

489. —— —— (1935) Unilateral amyotrophy ; its diagnostic importance for cerebral localization, *Amer. J. Syph.*, **19**, 58–76.

490. ZINGERLE, H. (1926) Klinische Studie über Haltungs- und Stellreflexe sowie andere automatische Körperbewegungen beim Menschen, *Z. ges. Neurol. Psychiat.*, **105**, 548–598.

CHAPTER VI

491. de AJURIAGUERRA, J., ZAZZO, R., and GRANJON, N. (1949) Le phénomène d'accolement au modèle (*closing-in*) dans un syndrome d'apraxie oxycarbonée, *Encéphale*, **38**, 1–20.

492. BÁLINT, R. (1909) Seelenlähmung des Schauens, optische Ataxie, räumliche Störung der Aufmerksamkeit, *Mschr. Psychiat. Neurol.*, **25**, 51–81.

493. BENDER, B., and TEUBER, H. L. (1947) Spatial organization of visual perception following injury to the brain, *Arch. Neurol. Psychiat.*, **58**, 721–739.

494. —— —— (1948) *ibid.*, **59**, 39–62.

495. CRITCHLEY, M. (1951) Types of visual perseveration ; " paliopsia " and illusory visual spread, *Brain*, **74**, 267–299.

496. EHRENWALD, H. (1931) Störung der Zeitauffassung, der räumlichen Orientierung, des Zeichnens und des Rechnens bei einem Hirnverletzten, *Z. ges. Neurol. Psychiat.*, **132**, 518–569 ; *Zbl. ges. Neurol. Psychiat.*, **60**, 681, abstract.

497. FEUCHTWANGER, E. (1934) Ueber optisch-konstructive Agnosie (Zugleich ein Beitrag zur Pathologie der optischen Vorstellungstätigkeit), *Z. ges. Neurol. Psychiat.*, **151**, 469–496.

498. GOLDSTEIN, K. (1928) Beobachtungen über die Veränderungen des Gesamtverhaltens bei Gehirnschädigung, *Mschr. Psychiat. Neurol.*, **68**, 217–242.

499. —— (1934) Der Aufbau des Organismus. Einführung in die Biologie unter besonderer Berücksichtigung der Erfahrungen am kranken Menschen, Haag, Martinus Nijhoff. *Zbl. ges. Neurol. Psychiat.*, **76**, 268 (abstract).

500. GRÜNBAUM, A. A. (1930) Ueber Apraxie (mit Filmvorführungen), *Zbl. ges. Neurol. Psychiat.*, **55**, 788–792.

501. GYÁRFAS, K. (1939) Disturbances of drawing in hypoglycemia, *Confin. Neurol.*, **2**, 148–160.
502. HAMILTON, A. M. (1884) A case of word-blindness, with impairment of the faculty of space association, *Med. News Philad.*, **44**, 92–95.
503. HÉCAEN, H., de AJURIAGUERRA, J., and MASSONET, J. (1951) Les troubles visuo-constructifs par lésion pariéto-occipitale droite. Rôle des pertubations vestibulaires, *Encéphale*, **40**, 122–179.
504. HOLMES, G., and HORRAX, G. (1919) Disturbances of spatial orientation and visual attention with loss of stereoscopic vision, *Arch. Neurol. Psychiat.*, **1**, 385–407.
505. van der HORST, L. (1932) The psychology of constructive apraxia, psychological views on conception of space, *Psychiat. en neurol. bl.*, **36**, 661–677.
506. —— (1934) Constructive apraxia. Psychological views on the conception of space, *J. nerv. ment. Dis.*, **80**, 645–650.
507. KAMMERER, Th., and SINGER, L. (1951) Troubles praxiques et gnosiques à prédominance optico-spatiale, résultants d'un processus d'atrophie cérébrale progressive, *Cahiers de Psychiatrie (Strasbourg)*, **1**, 49–58.
508. KLEIST, K. (1906) Ueber Apraxie, *Mschr. Psychiat. Neurol.*, **19**, 269–290.
509. —— (1912) Der Gang und der gegenwärtige Stand der Apraxieforschung, *Ergebn. Neurol. Psychiat.*, **1**, 342–452.
—— (1934) (see No. 449).
510. KRAPF, E., and COURTIS, Baudilio (1937) Sindrome optico-espacia por lesion parietal, *Rev. Neurol. B. Aires*, **1**, 280–291.
KROLL, M. B. (1910) (see No. 327).
511. KROLL, M. B., and STOLBUN, D. (1933) Was ist konstruktive Apraxie? *Z. ges. Neurol. Psychiat.*, **148**, 142–158.
LAIGNEL-LAVASTINE and LÉVY-VALENSI, J. (1914) (see No. 452).
512. LANGE, J. (1930) Fingeragnosie und Agraphie (eine psychopathologische Studie), *Mschr. Psychiat. Neurol.*, **76**, 129–188.
513. LEONHARD, K. (1952) Reine Agraphie und konstruktive Apraxie als Ausdruck einer Leitungsstörung, *Arch. Psychiat. Nervenkr.*, **188**, 471–503.
514. LHERMITTE, J., LEVY, G., and KYRIACO, N. (1925) Les perturbations de la représentation spatiale chez les apraxiques.—A propos de deux cas cliniques d'apraxie, *Rev. neurol.*, **2**, 586–600.
515. LHERMITTE, J., de MASSARY, J., and KYRIACO, N. (1928) Le rôle de la pensée spatiale dans l'apraxie, *Rev. neurol.*, **2**, 895–903.
516. LHERMITTE, J., and TRELLES, J. O. (1933) Sur l'apraxie pure constructive. Les troubles de la pensée spatiale et de la somatognosie dans l'apraxie, *Encéphale*, **28**, 413–444.
517. LIEPMANN, H. (1912) Anatomische Befunde bei Aphasischen und Apraktischen, *Neurol. Zbl.*, **31**, 1524–1528.
518. LYMAN, R. S., KWAN, S. T., and CHAO, W. H. (1938) Left occipitoparietal brain tumor. Observations on alexia and agraphia in Chinese and in English, *Chinese med. J.*, **54**, 491–516.
519. McFIE, J., PIERCY, M. F., and ZANGWILL, O. L. (1950) Visualspatial agnosia associated with lesions of the right cerebral hemisphere, *Brain*, **73**, 167–190.
520. MARIE, P., BOUTTIER, H., and BAILEY, P. (1922) La planotopokinésie. Étude sur les erreurs d'exécution de certains mouvements dans leurs rapports avec la représentation spatiale, *Rev. neurol.*, **1**, 505–512.
521. MAYER-GROSS, W. (1935) Some observations on apraxia, *Proc. roy. Soc. Med.*, **28**, 1203–1212.

446 SELECTIVE BIBLIOGRAPHY

522. MAYER-GROSS, W. (1935)   Spatial anomalies of higher motor activity, *Proc. Physiol. Soc.*, in *J. Physiol.*, **85,** 9P–10P.
523. —— (1936)   Further observations on apraxia, *J. ment. Sci.*, **82,** 744–762.
524. —— (1936)   The question of visual impairment in constructional apraxia, *Proc. roy. Soc. Med.*, **29,** 1396–1400.
525. MUNCIE, W. (1938)   Concrete model and abstract copy : a psychological interpretation of the " closing-in " symptom of Mayer-Gross, *J. nerv. ment. Dis.*, **88,** 1–11.
526. NIELSEN, J. M. (1938)   Gerstmann Syndrome ; finger agnosia, agraphia, confusion of right and left and acalculia ; comparison of this syndrome with disturbances of body scheme resulting from lesions of right side of brain, *Arch. Neurol. Psychiat.*, **39,** 536–560. —— (1946) (see No. 227).
527. PATERSON, A., and ZANGWILL, O. L. (1944)   Disorders of visual space perception associated with lesions of right cerebral hemisphere, *Brain*, **67,** 331–358.
528. PINÉAS, H. (1924)   Ein Fall von linksseitiger motorischer Apraxie nach Balkenerweichung, *Mschr. Psychiat. Neurol.*, **56,** 43–46.
529. POPPELREUTER, W. (1917)   Die psychischen Schädigungen durch Kopfschuss im Kriege 1914/16. Band 1. Die Störungen der niederen und höheren Sehleistungen durch Verletzungen des Okzipitalhirns, Leipzig, Voss.
530. POETZL, O. (1937)   Zum Apraxieproblem, *Jb. Psychiat. Neurol.*, **54,** 133–149.
531. REICHARDT, M. (1918)   Allgemeine und spezielle Psychiatrie, II, 2nd ed., p. 45, Jena, Fischer.
532. RIEGER, C. (1909)   Ueber Apparate in dem Hirn, *Arb. psychiat. Klin. Würzburg*, Heft 5, Leipzig.
533. ROTH, M. (1949)   Disorders of the body image caused by lesions of the right parietal lobe, *Brain*, **72,** 89–111.
534. SCHELLER, H., and SEIDEMANN, H. (1931–32)   Zur Frage der optisch-räumlichen Agnosie—(Zugleich ein Beitrag zur Dyslexie), *Mschr. Psychiat. Neurol.*, **81,** 97–188.
    SCHILDER, P. (1925) (see No. 372).
535. —— (1931)   Fingeragnosie, Fingerapraxie, Fingeraphasie, *Nervenarzt*, **4,** 625–629.
536. SCHLESINGER, B. (1928)   Zur Auffassung der optischen und konstruktiven Apraxie, *Z. ges. Neurol. Psychiat.*, **117,** 649–697. ·
537. SEELERT, H. (1920)   Beitrag zur Kenntnis der Rückbildung von Apraxie, *Mschr. Psychiat. Neurol.*, **48,** 125–149.
538. SOLOMON, A. P. (1932)   Acalculia, other agnosias and multiple neuritis following carbon monoxide poisoning, *Med. Clin. N. Amer.*, **16,** 531–538.
539. STEELE, G. D. F., and HEGARTY, A. B. (1950)   Parieto-occipital syndrome following carbon monoxide poisoning, *J. ment. Sci.*, **96,** 1015–1023.
540. STENGEL, E. (1944)   Loss of spatial orientation, constructional apraxia and Gerstmann's syndrome, *J. ment. Sci.*, **90,** 753–760.
541. STRAUSS, H. (1924)   Ueber konstruktive Apraxie, *Mschr. Psychiat. Neurol.*, **56,** 65–124.
542. ZUTT, J. (1932)   Rechts-Linksstörung, konstruktive Apraxie und reine Agraphie. Darstellung eines Falles. Ein Beitrag zur Pathologie der Handlung, *Mschr. Psychiat. Neurol.*, **82,** 253–305, 355–396.

CHAPTER VII

543. von ANGYÁL, L. (1936) Beiträge zur Symptomatologie, Lokalisation und hirnpathologischen Auffassung des Gerstmannschen Syndroms, *Z. ges. Neurol. Psychiat.*, **156**, 245–264.

544. —— (1941) Thumb-mouth Agnosia : A special form of Gerstmann's Syndrome, *Confin. Neurol.*, **3**, 245–252.

545. ANTON, G. (1898) Ueber Herderkrankungen des Gehirns, die vom Patienten selbst nicht wahrgenommen werden, *Wien. med. Wschr.*, **48**, 1282–1283 ; *Mitth. d. Ver. d. Aerzte in Steierm*, 20.12.1897.

546. —— (1899) Ueber die Selbstwahrnehmungen der Herderkrankungen des Gehirns durch den Kranken bei Rindenblindheit und Rindentaubheit, *Arch. Psychiat. Nervenkr.*, **32**, 86–127.

547. ARBUSE, D. I. (1947) The Gerstmann Syndrome. Case report and review of the literature, *J. nerv. ment. Dis.*, **105**, 359–371.

548. BENDER, M. B., and FURLOW, L. T. (1945) Phenomenon of visual extinction in homonymous fields and psychologic principles involved, *Arch. Neurol. Psychiat.*, **53**, 29–33.

549. BENTON, A. L., and ABRAMSON, Leonard S. (1952) Gerstmann symptoms following electroshock treatment, *Arch. Neurol. Psychiat.*, **68**, 248–257.

550. BENTON, A. L., HUTCHEON, J. F., and SEYMOUR, E. (1951) Arithmetic ability. Finger-localization capacity and right-left discrimination in normal and defective children, *Amer. J. Orthopsychiat.*, **21**, 756–766.

551. BONHOEFFER, K. (1922) Demonstration des anatomischen Befundes bei einem Fall von Rechts-Links-Störung und Agrammatismus, *Berl. Ges. Psychiat. Nervenkrank.*, **13**, 11 ; *Neurol. Zbl.*, **28**, 376.

552. —— (1923) Zur Klinik und Lokalisation des Agrammatismus und der Rechts-Links-Disorientierung, *Mschr. Psychiat. Neurol.*, **54**, 11–42.

553. CONRAD, K. (1947–48) (i) Strukturanalysen hirnpathologischer Fälle über Struktur- und Gestaltwandel, *Dtsch. Z. Nervenheilk.*, **158**, 344–371 ; (ii) Ueber Gestalt- und Funktionswandel bei einem Fall von transcorticaler motorischer Aphasie, *ibid.*, **158**, 372–434.

554. CRITCHLEY, M. (1939) The Language of Gesture, London, Arnold.

555. —— (1942) Aphasic disorders of signalling (constitutional and acquired) occurring in naval signalmen, *J. Mount Sinai Hosp.*, **9**, 363–375.

556. EHRENWALD, H. (1930) Verändertes Erleben des Körperbildes mit konsekutiver Wahnbildung bei linksseitiger Hemiplegie, *Mschr. Psychiat. Neurol.*, **75**, 89–97.
—— (1931) (see No. 496).

557. ENGERTH, G. (1933) Zeichenstörungen bei Patientin mit Autotopagnosie, *Z. ges. Neurol. Psychiat.*, **143**, 381–402.

558. GERSTMANN, J. (1924) Fingeragnosie : Eine umschriebene Störung der Orientierung am eigenen Körper, *Wien. klin. Wschr.*, **37**, 1010–1012.

559. —— (1927) Fingeragnosie und isolierte Agraphie, ein neues Syndrom, *Z. ges. Neurol. Psychiat.*, **108**, 152–177.

560. —— (1930) Zur Symptomatologie der Hirnläsionen im Uebergangsgebiet der unteren Parietal- und mittleren Occipitalwindung. (Das Syndrom : Fingeragnosie, Rechts-Links-Störung, Agraphie, Akalkulie), *Nervenarzt*, **3**, 691–695 ; (1931) *Zbl. ges. Neurol. Psychiat.*, **59**, 220.

561. —— (1940) Syndrome of Finger Agnosia ; disorientation for

right and left, agraphia and acalculia, *Arch. Neurol. Psychiat.*, **44,** 398–408.

GRÜNBAUM, A. A. (1930) (see No. 500).

562. GUTTMANN, E. (1936) Congenital arithmetic disability and acalculia, (Henschen), *Brit. J. med. Psychol.*, **16,** 16–35.

563. HARTMANN, F. (1902) Die Orientierung, Leipzig, Vogel.

564. HERRMANN, G. (1928) Beiträge zur Lehre von den Störungen des Rechnens bei Herderkrankungen des Okzipitallappens (Akalkulie Henschen), *Mschr. Psychiat. Neurol.*, **70,** 193–278.

565. HERRMANN, G., and KERSCHENER (1926) Der eine Fall ist der oben vielfach zitierte Agraphiefalle der zweite ein vor kurzem aus der Pötzlschen Klinik im Prager ärztlichen Verein demonstrierter Fall, *Sitzungsber. in der Med. Klinik 1926*, Nr. 46 (cited by Gertstmann, J. (1927)).

566. HERRMANN, G., and POETZL, O. (1926) Ueber die Agraphie und ihre lokaldiagnostischen Beziehungen, Berlin, Karger.

567. ISAKOWER, O., and SCHILDER, P. (1928) Optisch-räumliche Agnosie und Agraphie, *Z. ges. Neurol. Psychiat.*, **113,** 102–142.

568. JACKSON, C. V., and ZANGWILL, O. L. (1952) Experimental finger dyspraxia, *Quart. J. exp. Psychol.*, **4,** 1–10.

569. JUBA, A. (1948) Ueber nach Elektroschock auftretende kortikale Funktionsstörungen (Gerstmann'sches Syndrom, Gesichts- und Raumagnosien), *Schweiz. Arch. Neurol. Psychiat.*, **61,** 217–226.

570. —— (1949) Beitrag zur Struktur der ein- und doppelseitigen Körperschemastörungen. Fingeragnosie, atypische Anosognosien, *Mschr. Psychiat. Neurol.*, **118,** 11–29.

KAMMERER, Th., and SINGER, L. (1951) (see No. 507).

571. KAO, C. C., and LI, M. Y. (1939) Tests of Finger Orientation ; Neuropsychiatry in China, ed. R. S. Lyman, V. Maker, P. Liang, pp. 315–339.

572. KLEIN, R. (1931) Zur Symptomatologie des Parietallappens, *Z. ges. Neurol. Psychiat.*, **135,** 589–608.

573. —— (1933) Ueber die Funktionen des Parietallappens, *Nervenarzt*, **6,** 1–7, 67–74.

574. KLEIN, R., and MALLIE, P. P. (1945) A syndrome associated with left-hand paralysis of central origin, *J. ment. Sci.*, **91,** 518–522.

KROLL, M. B. (1929) (see No. 328).

LANGE, J. (1930) (see No. 512).

575. —— (1933) Problem der Fingeragnosie, *Z. ges. Neurol. Psychiat.*, **147,** 594–610.

576. —— (1936) Agnosien und Apraxien ; Bumke, O., and Foerster, O. : Handbuch der Neurologie, **6,** 807–960, Berlin, Springer.

577. LAUBENTHAL, F. (1933) Zur psychologischen Analyse von Kranken mit einem Syndrom der linken Parieto-Occipitalgegend, *Arch. Psychiat. Nervenkr.*, **99,** 633–682.

LYMAN, R. S., KWAN, S. T., and CHAO, W. H. (1938) (see No. 518).

578. MARBURG, O. (1931) Scheitellappenerweichung unter dem Bilde eines Pseudotumor cerebri (Zugleich ein Beitrag zur Frage der Fingeragnosie ohne Agraphie), *Arb. neurol. Inst. Wien. Univ.*, **33,** 1–13.

MAYER-GROSS, W. (1935) (see No. 521).

MAYER-GROSS, W. (1936) (see No. 524).

579. MUNCIE, W. (1935) Fingeragnosia (Gerstmann), *Bull. Johns Hopk. Hosp.*, **57,** 330–342.

580. MUSSIO-FOURNIER, J. C., and RAWAK, F. (1934) Glioblastome de l'hémisphère gauche avec syndrome de Gerstmann. Réaction mélanophorotrope sur la grenouille par l'urine de la malade, *Rev. neurol.*, **2,** 681–685.

NIELSEN, J. M. (1938) (see No. 526).
581. OLSEN, C. W., and RUBY, C. (1941) Anosognosia and autotopagnosia, *Arch. Neurol. Psychiat.*, **46**, 340–345.
582. PEDERSEN, A. L. (1946) A case of Gerstmann's syndrome, *Acta psychiat. Kbh.*, **21**, 643–654.
583. POLLAK, Franz (1938) Zur Pathologie und Klinik der Orientierung (Isolierte Orientierungsstörung im Raum infolge übergrossen, linksseitigen Stirnhirntumors), *Schweiz. Arch. Neurol. Psychiat.*, **42**, 141–164.
POETZL, O. (1937) (see No. 530).
584. von RAD, C. (1930) Kasuistischer Beitrag zur Symptomatologie der Herderkrankungen in der Uebergangsregion des Parietal- und des Occipitallappens, *Z. ges. Neurol. Psychiat.*, **131**, 273–288.
ROTH, M. (1949) (see No. 533).
585. RUBENSTEIN, L. H. (1941) Imperception for the position of the eyelids on one side, *J. Neurol. Psychiat.*, **4**, 191–205.
RUBINS, J. L., and FRIEDMAN, E. D. (1948) (see No. 366).
586. RUEMKE, H. C. (1950) Over afkeer van de eigen neus. Overwegingen over de mens en zijn lichaam en over de grenzen van plastische en cosmetische chirurgie, *Ned. Tijdschr. Geneesk.*, **3/37**, 2654–2664.
587. SCHELLER, H. (1936) Demonstration eines Falles mit dem Syndrom der Parieto-Occipitalgegend und symptomatischer Epilepsie nach Kohlenoxydvergiftung, *Zbl. ges. Neurol. Psychiat.*, **81**, 109–110.
SCHILDER, P. (1931) (see No. 535).
588. —— (1932) Localization of the Body Image (Postural model of the body). Localization of function in the cerebral cortex, *Res. Publ. Ass. nerv. ment. Dis.*, **13**, 466–484 (1934).
589. SCHLESINGER, B. (1941–42) A study on dissociation and reorganization of cerebral function, *Confin. Neurol.*, **4**, 14–31.
590. SELETSKY, V. V. (1936) Ueber Fingeragnosie und Akalkulie, *Sovet. Psich.*, **12**, 82–87 and *Zbl. ges. Neurol. Psychiat.*, **86**, 392–393.
591. SPILLANE, J. D. (1942) Disturbances of the Body Scheme, Anosognosia, and Fingeragnosia, *Lancet*, **1**, 42–44.
STENGEL, E. (1944) (see No. 540).
592. von STOCKERT, F. G. (1934) Das Gerstmannsche Syndrom der Fingeragnosie, mit besonderer Berücksichtigung der Sprach- und Schreib- Störung, *Mschr. Psychiat. Neurol.*, **88**, 121–151.
593. STRAUSS, A., and WERNER, H. (1938) Deficiency in the finger schema in relation to arithmetic disability (fingeragnosia and acalculia), *Amer. J. Orthopsychiat.*, **8**, 719–725.
594. —— —— (1939) Fingeragnosia in children, *Amer. J. Psychiat.*, **95**, 1215–1225.
595. —— —— (1942) Experimental analysis of clinical symptom " perseveration" in mentally retarded children, *Amer. J. ment. Defic.*, **47**, 185–188.
596. TEICHER, J. (1947) Disorientation of body image, *J. nerv. ment. Dis.*, **105**, 619–636.
597. VLAVIANOS, G. (1933) Zur Symptomatologie des Parieto-Occipitalhirnes, *Wien. med. Wschr.*, **83**, 502–505.
598. WAGNER, G. (1932) Ueber Raumstörung, *Mschr. Psychiat. Neurol.*, **84**, 281–307.
599. WERNER, H., and STRAUSS, A. (1939) Problems and methods of functional analysis in mentally deficient children, *J. abnorm. soc. Psychol.*, **34**, 37–62.
600. van WOERKOM, W. (1919) Sur la notion de l'espace (le sens géometrique). Sur la notion du temps et du nombre. Une

démonstration de l'influence du trouble de l'acte psychique de l'évocation sur la vie intellectuelle, *Rev. neurol.*, **1**, 113–119.

601. —— (1931) Psychopathologische Beobachtungen bei Stirnhirngeschädigten und bei Patienten mit Aphasien. Eine zusammenfassende Darstellung, *Mschr. Psychiat. Neurol.*, **80**, 274–331.

602. ZEH, W. (1950) Störung des Ausdruckserkennens beim Gerstmannschen Syndrom, *Arch. Psychiat. Nervenkr.*, **185**, 193–210.

ZUTT, J. (1932) (see No. 542).

CHAPTER VIII

603. de AJURIAGUERRA, J., and HÉCAEN, H. (1949) Le cortex cérébral. Étude neuro-psycho-pathologique, Paris, Masson.

604. ALAJOUANINE, Th., THUREL, R., and OMBREDANE, A. (1934) Somatoagnosie et apraxie du membre supérieur gauche, *Rev. neurol.*, **1**, 695–703.

605. ANGYAL, A. (1936) The experience of the body-self in schizophrenia, *Arch. Neurol. Psychiat.*, **35**, 1029–1053.

606. von ANGYÁL, L., and FRICK, F. (1941) Beiträge zur Anosognosie und zu der Regression des Phantomgliedes, *Z. ges. Neurol. Psychiat.*, **173**, 440–447.

607. ANTON (1896) Blindheit nach beiderseitiger Gehirnerkrankung mit Verlust der Orientierung im Raume, *Mitt. des Vereines der Aerzte in Steiermark*, No. 3.

—— (1898) (see No. 545).

—— (1899) (see No. 546).

608. BABINSKI, J. (1914) Contribution à l'étude des troubles mentaux dans l'hémiplegie organique cérébrale, *Rev. neurol.*, **1**, 845–848.

609. —— (1918) Anosognosie, *ibid.*, **1**, 365–367.

610. BABINSKI, J., and JOLTRAIN, E. (1924) Un nouveau cas d'anosognosie, *Rev. neurol.*, **2**, 638–640.

611. BARKMAN, A. (1925) De l'anosognosie dans l'hémiplégie cérébrale : Contribution clinique à l'étude de ce symptome, *Acta med. scand.*, **62**, 235–254.

BARRÉ, J. A., MORIN, L., and KAISER (1923) (see No. 238).

612. BENDER, L. (1934) Psychoses associated with somatic diseases that distort the body structure, *Arch. Neurol. Psychiat.*, **32**, 1000–1029.

613. BENDER, M. B., WORTIS, S. B., and GORDON, Gustave-G. (1949) Disorders in body image : anosognosia, *C.R. IVth int. Congr. Neurol.*, **2**, 112. Paris, Masson (1951).

614. BENEDEK, L., and von ANGYÁL, L. (1939) Ueber Körperschemastörungen bei Psychosen teils unter experimentellen Bedingungen, *Mschr. Psychiat. Neurol.*, **101**, 26–84.

615. BIRKMAYER, W. (1949) Double-image of the right hand after lesion of the left parietal lobe, Pötzl-Festschrift, pp. 123–131, Innsbruck, Innrain.

616. van BOGAERT, L. (1934) Sur la pathologie de l'image de soi, *Ann. méd.-psychol.*, **92**, 2/4, 419–555 ; 2/5, 744–759.

617. BONNIER, P. (1905) L'Aschématie, *Rev. neurol.*, **13**, 605–609.

618. BROUWER, B. (1930–31) Ueber Anosognosie, Niederländ Vereinig. Psychiat. Neurol. Amsterdam, Sitzg. v. 19 IV (1930), *Zbl. ges. Neurol. Psychiat.*, **60**, 184 (1931).

619. BRUNS, L. (1897) (cited by Rubenstein, L. H., No. 585) Die Geschwülste des Nervensystems, Berlin, Karger.

620. BYCHOWSKI, G. (1943) Disorders in the body-image, *J. nerv. ment. Dis.*, **97**, 310–355.
621. CHARCOT, J. M. (1889) Physiologie et pathologie du moignon, Leçons du Mardi à la Salpêtrière, Paris, Delahaye & Lecrosnier.
622. CRITCHLEY, M. (1952) A phantom supernumerary limb after a cervical root lesion, *Arch. Neuropsic. S. Paulo*, **10**, 269–275.
623. DATTNER, B. (1950) Body image disturbances with lesions of the dominant hemisphere, *Trans. Amer. neurol. Ass.*, **75**, 141–143.
624. DAVIDSON, G. M. (1941) The syndrome of Capgras, *Psychiat. Quart.*, **15**, 513–521.
625. DEJERINE (1914) Discussion (see No. 608).
626. DENY, G., and CAMUS, P. (1905) Sur une forme d'hypochondrie aberrante due à la perte de la conscience du corps, *Rev. neurol.*, **13**, 461–467.
    EHRENWALD, H. (1930) (see No. 556).
627. —— (1931) Anosognosie und Depersonalisation, *Nervenarzt*, **4**, 681–688.
628. EHRENWALD, H., and KOENIGSTERN, H. (1929) Klinische und experimentelle Untersuchungen über das Juckgefühl; vorläufige Mitteilung, *Wien. klin. Wschr.*, **42**, 1397–1398.
629. ENGERTH, G., and HOFF, H. (1929) Ein Fall von Halluzinationen im hemianopischen Gesichtsfeld. Beitrag zur Genese der optischen Halluzinationen, *Mschr. Psychiat. Neurol.*, **74**, 246–256.
630. FURTADO, D. (1945) Asomatognosia. Estudo da regressão do fenómeno, *Impr. Med. S. Paulo.*, **12**, 93–99.
631. GARCIN, R., VARAY, A., and DIMO, H. (1938) Document pour servir à l'étude des troubles du schéma corporel (sur quelques phénomènes moteurs, gnosiques et quelques troubles de l'utilisation des membres du côté gauche au cours d'un syndrome temporo-pariétal par tumeur, envisagés dans leurs rapports avec l'anosognosie et les troubles du schéma corporel), *Rev. neurol.*, **69**, 498–510.
632. GERSTMANN, J. (1942) Problem of imperception of disease and of impaired body territories with organic lesions, *Arch. Neurol. Psychiat.*, **48**, 890–913.
633. GILLIATT, R. W., and PRATT, R. T. C. (1952) Disorders of perception and performance in a case of right-sided cerebral thrombosis, *J. Neurol. Neurosurg. Psychiat.*, **15**, 264–271.
634. GUREWITSCH, M. (1932) Ueber das interparietale Syndrom bei Geisteskrankheiten, *Z. ges. Neurol. Psychiat.*, **140**, 593–603.
635. GUTTMANN, E. (1931) Klinische Demonstrationen. Parietalanfälle mit flüchtiger Entfremdung einer Extremität, *Zbl. ges. Neurol. Psychiat.*, **60**, 396.
636. von HAGEN, K., and IVES, E. R. (1937) Anosognosie (Babinski), Imperfection of hemiplegia. Report of 6 cases, one with autopsy, *Bull. Los Angeles neurol. Soc.*, **2**, 95–103.
637. —— —— (1939) Two autopsied cases of anosognosia, *ibid.*, **4**, 41–44.
638. HALLORAN, P. M. (1946) Delusion of body scheme due to subdural haematoma, *Bull. Los Angeles neurol. Soc.*, **11**, 88–89.
639. HASENJÄGER, Th., and POETZL, O. (1941) Phantomarm bei Plexuslähmung, *Dtsch. Z. Nervenheilk.*, **152**, 112–132.
640. HAUPTMANN (1927) Die Bedeutung der linken Hemisphäre für das Bewusstsein vom eigenen Körper, Vers. südwestdtsch. Neurol. u. Irrenärzte Baden-Baden Sitzg. v. 11. bis 13. VI, *Zbl. ges. Neurol. Psychiat.*, **48**, 282 (1928).
    HEAD, H., and HOLMES, G. (1911–1912) (see No. 305).
641. HÉCAEN, H., and de AJURIAGUERRA, J. (1952) Méconnaissances et hallucinations corporelles, Paris, Masson.

642. HÉCAEN, H., and DAVID, M. (1945) Syndrome pariétal traumatique. Asymbolie tactile et hémiasomatognosie paroxystique et douloureuse, *Rev. neurol.*, **77**, 113–124.

643. HÉCAEN, H., DAVID, M., and FRANQUET, R. (1942) Hémiasomatognosie associée à des troubles de la dénervation par tumeur pariétale droite, *Rev. neurol.*, **74**, 310–311.

644. HEMPHILL, R. E. (1948) Misinterpretation of mirror image of self in pre-senile atrophy, *J. ment. Sci.*, **94**, 603–610.

645. HEMPHILL, R. E., and KLEIN, R. (1948) Contribution to the dressing disability as a focal sign and to the imperception phenomena, *J. ment. Sci.*, **94**, 611–622.

646. HENSCHEN, S. E. (1920) Klinische und anatomische Beiträge zur Pathologie des Gehirns, *Fünfter Teil*. Ueber Aphasie, Amusie, und Akalkulie, Stockholm, Nordiska Bokhandeln.

647. —— (1920) Klinische und anatomische Beiträge zur Pathologie des Gehirns. *Sechster Teil*. Ueber sensorische Aphasie, Stockholm, Nordiska Bokhandeln.

648. HOFF, H., and KAMIN, M. (1930) Reizversuche im linken Sulcus interparietalis beim Menschen, *Z. ges. Neurol. Psychiat.*, **125**, 693–699.

649. HOFF, H., and POETZL, O. (1931) Experimentelle Nachbildung von Anosognosie, *Z. ges. Neurol. Psychiat.*, **137**, 722–734.

650. —— —— (1935) Ueber eine neues parieto-occipitales Syndrom. Störungen des Körperschema, *Jb. Psychiat. Neurol.*, **52**, 173–218.

651. —— —— (1937) Ueber Transformationen zwischen Körperbild und Aussenwelt, *Wien klin Wschr.*, **1**, 247–251 ; *Zbl. ges. Neurol. Psychiat.*, **86**, 257–258.

652. IVES, E. R., and NIELSEN, J. M. (1937) Disturbance of Body Scheme : delusion of the absence of part of body in two cases with autopsy verification of lesion, *Bull. Los Angeles neurol. Soc.*, **2**, 120–125.

JUBA, A. (1949) (see No. 570).

653. KATZ, D. (1930) Phantomglied. Die sogen. Illusionen der Amputierten, Handwörterbuch der med. Psychologie, Leipzig, Thieme.

654. KLEIN, R., and SCHILDER, P. (1929) The Japanese illusion and the postural model of the body, *J. nerv. ment. Dis.*, **70**, 241–263.

655. KRAMER, F. (1917) Bulbärapoplexie (Verschluss der Arteria cerebelli posterior inferior) mit Alloästhesie, *Z. ges. Neurol. Psychiat.* (Ref.), **14**, 58–60.

656. KROLL, M. (1936) Personal communication.

LANGE, J. (1930) (see No. 512).

657. LHERMITTE, J. (1939) L'image de notre corps, Paris, Nouvelle Revue Critique.

658. —— (1948) De l'image corporelle et de se déformations pathologiques, *Folia Psychiat. Neurol. Neurochir. neerl.*, **51**, 374–384.

659. —— (1951) Visual hallucination of the Self, *Brit. med. J.*, **1**, 431–434.

660. LISSAUER, H. (1890) Ein Fall von Seelenblindheit nebst einem Beitrage zur Theorie derselben, *Arch. Psychiat. Nervenkr.*, **21**, 222–270.

661. MAYER-GROSS, W. (1929) Ein Fall von Phantomarm nach Plexuszerreissung, mit einigen Bemerkungen zum Problem des Phantomgliedes überhaupt, *Nervenarzt*, **2**, 65–72.

662. —— (1935) On depersonalization, *Brit. J. med. Psychol.*, **15**, 103–126.

663. MUELLER, F. (1892) Ein Beitrag zur Kenntnis der Seelenblindheit, *Arch. Psychiat. Nervenkr.*, **24**, 655–692.

664. —— (1905) Ueber Störungen der Sensibilität bei Erkrankungen des Gehirns, in Volkmann : Sammlung klinischer Vorträge, Leipzig, Breitkopf & Härtel, Ser. 14, 394–395.

665. MUENZ, L., and LOEWENFELD, V. (1934) Plastische Arbeiten Blinder, Brünn, Verlag. Rohrer.
666. NATHANSON, M., BERGMAN, P. S., and GORDON, G. G. (1952) Denial of illness. Its occurrence in one hundred consecutive cases of hemiplegia, *Arch. Neurol. Psychiat.*, **68**, 380–387.
667. NIELSEN, J. M. (1938) Disturbances of the body scheme ; their physiological mechanism, *Bull. Los Angeles neurol. Soc.*, **3**, 127–135.
668. —— (1940) The unsolved problems of aphasia, III Amnesic Aphasia, *ibid.*, **5**, 78–84.
669. —— (1941) The unsolved problems of apraxia and some solutions, *ibid.*, **6**, 1–20.
—— (1946) (see No. 227).
670. NIELSEN, J. M., and FITZGIBBON, J. F. (1936) Agnosia, Apraxia, Aphasia ; their value in cerebral localization. Los Angeles, Cal., Baltimore, Md. Waverly Press Inc.
671. NIELSEN, J. M., and von HAGEN, K. O. (1936) Three cases of mind blindness (visual agnosia) : one due to softening in the occipital lobes (autopsy), one due to anterior poliomyelitis (non-fatal), one due to drugs (transient), *J. nerv. ment. Dis.*, **84**, 386–398.
OLSEN, C. W., and RUBY, C. (1941) (see No. 581).
672. OPPENHEIM, H. (1911) Text book of Nervous Diseases, 2 vols. (translated by A. Bruce), London, Foulis.
673. —— (1913) (cited by Rubenstein, L. H.) (see [No. 585). Lehrbuch Nervenkrankh, 6th ed., p. 889, Berlin, Karger.
674. PICK, A. (1898) Beiträge zur Pathologie und pathologischen Anatomie des Centralnervensystems, Berlin, Karger.
675. —— (1908) Ueber Störungen der Orientierung am eigenen Körper, *in Arbeiten aus der psychiatrischen Klinik in Prag.*, *I*, Berlin, Karger.
676. —— (1922) Störung der Orientierung am eigenen Körper, *Psychol. Forsch.*, **1**, 303–318.
677. PINÉAS, H. (1926) Der Mangel an Krankheitsbewusstein und seine Variationen als Symptom organischer Erkrankungen, *Verhandl. d. Gesell. deutsch. Nervenärzte*, **16**, 238–248.
—— (1931) (see No. 350).
678. —— (1932) Ein Fall von phantomähnlichen Erscheinungen (" Phantomarm ") bei hemiplegischer Lähmung, *Nervenarzt*, **5**, 233–236.
679. POETZL, O. (1923) Ueber die Herderscheinungen bei Läsionen des linken unteren Scheitelläppchens, Enfahrungen an einem palliativ trepanierten Hirntumor, *Med. Klin. Berl.*, **19**, 7–11.
680. —— (1924) Ueber Störungen der Selbstwahrnehmung bei linksseitiger Hemiplegie, *Z. ges. Neurol. Psychiat.*, **93**, 117–168.
681. —— (1924–1925) Ueber die Bedeutung der interparietalen Region im menschlichen Grosshirn. Rückbildung einer Apraxie nach Operation eines interparietal gelegenen Tumors, *ibid.*, **95**, 659–700.
682. RANEY, R. B., and NIELSEN, J. M. (1940) Spatial disorientation. Diagnostic differentiation between frontal and occipital lesions, *Bull. Los Angeles neurol. Soc.*, **5**, 73–77.
683. REDLICH, E., and BONVICINI, G. (1908) Ueber das Fehlen der Wahrnehmung der eigenen Blindheit bei Hirnkrankheiten, *Jb. Psychiat. (etc.) Leipz. u. Wien.*, **29**, 1–133.
684. —— —— (1911) Weitere klinische und anatomische Mitteilungen über das Fehlen der Wahrnehmung der eigenen Blindheit bei Hirnkrankheiten, *Dtsch. Z. Nervenheilk.*, **41**, 121–123.
685. RIDDOCH, G. (1941) Phantom limbs and body shape, *Brain*, **64**, 197–222.
686. RIESE, W. (1928) Ueber die sogenannte Phantomhand der Amputierten, *Dtsch. Z. Nervenheilk.*, **101**, 270–281.

454   SELECTIVE BIBLIOGRAPHY

687. ROHEIM, G. (1921)   Das Selbst, *Imago*, **7**, 453–514.
688. ROSENBAUM, M. (1948) " Pentothal Sodium " as an adjunct in therapy of anxiety hysteria : report of a case, *Arch. Neurol. Psychiat.*, **60**, 70–76.
    ROTH, M. (1949) (see No. 533).
    RUBENSTEIN, L. H. (1941) (see No. 585).
689. SANDIFER, P. H. (1946)   Anosognosia and disorders of body scheme, *Brain*, **69**, 122–137.
690. SCHILDER, P. (1919)   Projektion eigener Defekte in Trugwahrnehmungen, *Neurol. Zbl.*, **38**, 300–302.
691. —— (1923)   Seele und Leben, Berlin, Springer.
    —— (1925) (see No. 372).
692. —— (1931)   Brain and Personality. Studies in the Psychological aspects of cerebral neuropathology and the neuropsychiatric aspects of the motility of schizophrenia, *Nerv. & Ment. Dis. Monograph Ser.* No. 53, New York, Nerv. Ment. Dis. Pub. Co.
    —— (1932) (see No. 588).
693. —— (1935)   The image and appearance of the human body, London, Kegan Paul, Trench, Trubner.
694. SCHILDER, P., and HARTMANN (1926)   Körperinneres und Körperschema, *Z. ges. Neurol. Psychiat.*, **109**, 666–675.
695. SCHUSTER, P. (1931)   Verlust der Bilateralitätsvorstellung (Demonstration Berliner Gesellschaft für Psychiat. u. Nervenkr. 12.1.31), *Zbl. ges. Neurol. Psychiat.*, **59**, 524–525.
696. STEIN, W. N. (1936)   Anozofnosja i zaburzenia schematu ciala w przypadku porażenia polowiczego, wywolanego przez guz mózgu, *Neurol. polska*, **19**, 131–144, 187–188 ; *Zbl. ges. Neurol. Psychiat.*, **85**, 293 (1937).
697. von STOCKERT, F. G. (1934)   Lokalisation und klinische Differenzierung des Symptoms der Nichtwahrnehmung einer Körperhälfte, *Dtsch. Z. Nervenheilk*, **134**, 1–13.
    STRAUSS, A., and WERNER, H. (1938) (see No. 593).
698. TEITELBAUM, H. A. (1941)   Psychogenic body image disturbances associated with psychogenic aphasia and agnosia, *J. nerv. ment. Dis.*, **93**, 581–612.
699. —— (1943)   An analysis of the disturbances of the higher cortical functions, agnosia, apraxia and aphasia, *ibid.*, **97**, 44–51.
700. TOURNAY, A. (1922)   État transitoire d'agnosie de ses membres chez l'enfant en bas âge. Observation d'une différence chronologique dans la régression de cet état à droite et à gauche, suivie d'une différence similaire dans la disparition du signe de Babinski, *Rev. neurol.*, **1**, 581–583.
701. WEBER, F. Parkes (1942)   Agnosia of hemiplegia and of blindness after cerebral embolism, *Lancet*, **1**, 44.
702. WEINSTEIN, E. A., and KAHN, R. L. (1950)   The syndrome of anosognosia, *Arch. Neurol. Psychiat.*, **64**, 772–791.
703. WORTIS, H., and DATTNER, B. (1942)   Analysis of somatic delusion ; case report, *Psychosom. Med.*, **4**, 319–323.
704. ZILLIG, G. (1940)   Beobachtungen bei einer Kranken mit rechtsseitiger Hemiplegie, motorischer Aphasie, Agraphie, Anosognosie und Phantomerlebnissen im gelähmten Arm unter besonderer Berücksichtigung der Rückbildung dieser Störungen, *Arch. Psychiat. Nervenkr.*, **112**, 110–135.
705. ZINGERLE, H. (1913)   Ueber Störungen der Wahrnehmung des eigenen Körpers bei organischen Gehirnerkrankungen, *Mschr. Psychiat. Neurol.*, **34**, 13–36.

CHAPTER IX

706. ADLER, A. (1944) A case of visual agnosia, *Trans. Amer. neurol. Ass.*, **70**, 168.

707. —— (1944) Disintegration and restoration of optic recognition in visual agnosia ; analysis of a case, *Arch. Neurol. Psychiat.*, **51**, 243–259.

708. —— (1950) Course and outcome of visual agnosia, *J. nerv. ment. Dis.*, **3**, 41–51.

709. ALLEN, I. M. (1948) Unilateral visual inattention, *N.Z. med. J.*, **47**, 605–617.

710. ANDRÉ-THOMAS (1943) Sur un cas de dysgnosie visuelle, *Rev. neurol.*, **75**, 76–78.

711. von ANGYÁL, L. (1949) Beiträge zur hirnphysiologischen Struktur parietaler Aphasie, Festschrift zum 70. Geburtstag von Prof. Dr. Otto Pötzl, pp. 55–65 ; Innsbruck, Wagner.

von ANGYÁL, L., and FRICK, F. (1941) (see No. 606).

ANTON, G. (1899) (see No. 546).

ARBUSE, D. (1947) (see No. 547).

712. AXENFELD, Th. (1915) Hemianopische Gesichtsfeldstörungen nach Schädelschüssen, *Klin. Mbl. Augenheilk.*, **55**, 126–143.

BÁLINT, R. (1909) (see No. 492).

713. BÁRÁNY, R. (1921) Zur Klinik und Theorie des Eisenbahn-Nystagmus, *Arch. Augenheilk.*, **87**, 139–142.

714. BAY, E. (1947) Eine Methode zur Lokalisation von Hirnverletzungen, *Nervenarzt*, **18**, 17–21.

715. —— (1950) Agnosie und Funktionswandel, *Monogr. Gesamtgeb. Neurol. Psychiat.*, **73**, 1–194, Berlin, Springer.

716. —— (1951) Ueber den Begriff der Agnosie, *Nervenarzt*, **22**, 179–187.

717. —— (1951) Schlussbemerkung zur Agnosiediskussion, *ibid.*, **22**, 309–310.

718. —— (1952) Analyse eines Falles von Seelenblindheit. Ein kasuistischer Beitrag zum Agnosieproblem, *Dtsch. Z. Nervenheilk.*, **168**, 1–23.

719. BAY, E., and LAUENSTEIN, O. (1948) Zum Problem der optischen Agnosie, *Dtsch. Z. Nervenheilk.*, **158**, 107–210.

720. BAY, E., LAUENSTEIN, O., and CIBIS, P. (1949) Ein Beitrag zur Frage der Seelenblindheit, *Psychiat. Neurol. med. Psychol.*, **1**, 73–91.

721. BELZ (1950) Au sujet des hémianopsies absolues et relatives. Lecture verticale, *Bull. Soc. Ophtal. France*, **3**, 121–122.

722. BENARY, W. (1922) Studien zur Untersuchung der Intelligenz bei einem Fall von Seelenblindheit ; No. 8 in Goldstein, K., and Gelb, A. Psychologische Analysen hirnpathologischer Fälle, *Psychol. Forsch.*, **2**, 209–297.

723. BENDER, M. B. (1945) Polyopia and monocular diplopia of cerebral origin, *Arch. Neurol. Psychiat.*, **54**, 627–658.

BENDER, M. B., and FURLOW, L. T. (1945) (see No. 548).

724. —— —— (1945) Visual disturbances produced by bilateral lesions of the occipital lobes with central scotomas, *Arch. Neurol. Psychiat.*, **53**, 165–170.

725. BENDER, M. B., FURLOW, L. T., and TEUBER, H.-L. (1949) Alterations in behaviour after massive cerebral trauma (intraventricular foreign body), *Confin. neurol.*, **9**, 140–157.

726. BENDER, M. B., and JUNG, R. (1948) Abweichungen der subjektiven optischen Vertikalen und Horizontalen bei Gesunden und Hirnverletzten, *Arch. Psychiat. Nervenkr.*, **181**, 193–212.

456   SELECTIVE BIBLIOGRAPHY

727. BENDER, M. B., and KANZER, M. G. (1939) Dynamics of homonymous hemianopias and preservation of central vision, *Brain*, **62**, 404–421.

728. BENDER, M. B., and KRIEGER, H. P. (1951) Visual function in perimetrically blind fields, *Arch. Neurol. Psychiat.*, **65**, 72–79.

729. BENDER, M. B., and STRAUSS, I. (1937) Defects in visual field of one eye only in patients with a lesion of one optic radiation, *Arch. Ophthal. Chicago*, **17**, 765–787.

730. BENDER, M. B., and TEUBER, H.-L. (1946) Disturbances in the visual perception of space after brain injury, *Trans. Amer. neurol. Ass.*, **71**, 159–161.

731. —— —— (1946) Phenomena of fluctuation, extinction and completion in visual perception, *Arch. Neurol. Psychiat.*, **55**, 627–658.

732. —— —— (1946) Ring scotoma and tubular fields, *ibid.*, **56**, 300–326.
    —— —— (1947) (see No. 493).
    —— —— (1948) (see No. 494).

733. —— —— (1948) Flicker perimeter, *Trans. Amer. neurol. Ass.*, **73**, 174–175.

734. —— —— (1948) Disorders in the visual perception of motion, *ibid.*, **73**, 191–193.

735. —— —— (1949) Disturbances in visual perception following cerebral lesions, *J. Psychol.*, **28**, 223–233.

736. BERINGER, K., and STEIN, J. (1930) Analyse eines Falles reiner Alexie, *Zbl. ges. Neurol. Psychiat.*, **56**, 475–476.

737. BERRY, G. A. (1918) Remarks suggested by Dr. Gordon Holmes's papers " Disturbances of visual orientation ", *Brit. J. Ophthal.*, **2**, 597–607.

738. BERTHA, H. (1942) Die Spiegelschrift der linken Hand. Eine hirnpathologische Studie zur Frage der Leistung der rechten Grosshirnhemisphäre, *Z. ges. Neurol. Psychiat.*, **175**, 68–96.

739. BEST, F. (1917) Hemianopsie und Seelenblindheit bei Hirnverletzungen, *Arch. Ophthal.*, **93**, 49–150.

740. —— (1950) Ueber optische Agnosie, *Klin. Mbl. Augenheilk*, **116**, 14–18.

741. BIANCHI, L. (1925) Le syndrome pariétal. Contribution à l'étude d'une variété d'aphasie optique, *Acta oto-laryng.*, **8**, 353–363.

742. BIRKMAYER, W. (1951) Hirnverletzungen, Wien, Springer-Verlag.

743. BODAMER, J. (1947) Die Prosop-Agnosie (Die Agnosie des Physiognomieerkennens), *Arch. Psychiat. Nervenkr.*, **179**, 6–53.

744. van BOGAERT, L. (1934, 1936) Sur les changements métriques et formels de l'image visuelle dans les affections cérébrales, *J. belge Neurol. Psychiat.*, **34**, 717–725 ; *Arch. Neurol. Psychiat.*, **36**, 193 (abstract).

745. BRAIN, W. Russell (1941) Visual object agnosia with special reference to the Gestalt theory, *Brain*, **64**, 43–62.

746. —— (1947) Some observations in visual hallucinations and cerebral metamorphopsia, *Acta psychiat. Kbh.* suppl. 46, 28–40.

747. BRAMWELL, B. (1915) Clinical Studies. VI. Lesions of the occipital lobe and affection of vision, *Edinb. med. J.*, N.S. **15**, 165–185.
    BRICKNER, cited by No. 603.

748. BROADBENT, W. H. (1872) On the cerebral mechanism of speech and thought, *Med.-chir. Trans. London*, **55**, 145–194.

749. —— (1879) A case of peculiar affection of speech with commentary, *Brain*, **1**, 484–503.

750. BRUNNER, H. (1922) Zur klinischen Bedeutung des optischen Drehnystagmus, *Klin. Mbl. Augenheilk.*, **68**, 783–784.

751. BUCY, P. C., and KLÜVER, H. (1940) Anatomic changes secondary to temporal lobectomy, *Arch. Neurol. Psychiat.*, **44**, 1142–1146.

751a. BUTZMANN (cited by BIRKMAYER, W.) (see No. 742).

752. CHARCOT, J. M. (1883) Un cas de suppression brusque et isolée de la vision mentale des signes et des objets (formes et couleurs), *Progrès méd.*, **11**, 568–571.

753. —— (1890) Sur un cas de suppression brusque et isolée de la vision mentale des signes et des objets (formes et couleurs), Œuvres complètes, Vol. III, Leçon XIII, 178–192, Paris, Lecrosnier et Babé.

754. CIBIS, P. (1947) I. Zur Pathologie der Lokaladaptation, *Arch. Ophthal.*, **148**, 1–92.

755. —— (1948) II. *ibid.*, **148**, 216–257.

756. CIBIS, P., and BAY, E. (1950) Funktionswandel und Gesichtsfeld bei Sehhirnverletzten, *Dtsch. Z. Nervenheilk.*, **163**, 577–628.

757. CONRAD, K. (1947) Ueber den Begriff der Vorgestalt und seine Bedeutung für die Hirnpathologie, *Nervenarzt*, **18**, 289–298.

—— (1947/48) (see No. 553).

—— (1947/48) (see No. 554).

758. —— (1949) Beitrag zum Problem der parietalen Alexie, *Arch. Psychiat. Nervenkr.*, **181**, 393–420.

759. —— (1951) Diskussionsbemerkung zu der Arbeit von Bay : Ueber den Begriff der Agnosie, *Nervenarzt*, **22**, 191–192.

760. —— (1951) Aphasie, Agnosie, Apraxie, *Fortschr. Neurol. Psychiat.*, **19**, 291–325.

761. CORDS, R. (1925) Die Bedeutung des optomotorischen Nystagmus für die neurologische Diagnostik, *Dtsch. Z. Nervenheilk.*, **84**, 152–155.

762. COUCH, F. H., and FOX, J. C. (1934) Photographic study of ocular movements in mental science, *Arch. Neurol. Psychiat.*, **31**, 556–578.

763. CRITCHLEY, M. (1949/50) The problem of awareness or non-awareness of hemianopic field defects, *Trans. ophthal. Soc. U.K.*, **69**, 95–109.

764. —— (1949/50) Metamorphopsia of central origin, *ibid.*, **69**, 111–121.

765. —— (1950) Visual perseveration, *ibid.*, **70**, 91–96.

—— (1951) (see No. 495).

766. DELAY, J., NEVEU, P., and DESCLAUX, P. (1944) La forme pariéto-occipitale de la maladie de Pick. Étude de l'agnosie visuelle, *Rev. neurol.*, **76**, 264–265.

767. DIDE, M., and BOTCAZO (1902) Amnésie continue, cécité verbale pure, perte du sens topographique, ramollissement double du lobe lingual, *Rev. neurol.*, **10**, 676–680.

768. DODGE, R., and FOX, J. C. (1928) Optic Nystagmus ; I. Technical introduction with observations in a case with central scotoma in the right eye and external rectus palsy in the left eye, *Arch. Neurol. Psychiat.*, **20**, 812–823.

769. DODGE, R., TRAVIS, R. C., and FOX, J. C. (1930) Optic Nystagmus ; III. Characteristics of the slow phase, *ibid.*, **24**, 21–34.

770. DUFOUR, M. (1889) Sur la vision nulle dans l'hémianopsie, *Rev. méd. Suisse rom.*, **9**, 445–451.

771. DUKE-ELDER, W. S. (1949) The Neurology of Vision, motor and optical anomalies, Text-book of Ophthalmology, Vol. IV, London, Kimpton.

772. ENGERTH, G. (1933/34) Ueber isolierte Störungen in der Verwendung der blauen Farbe bei parietalen Herderkrankungen, *Z. ges. Neurol. Psychiat.*, **149**, 723–736.

773. FAUST, C. (1947) Ueber Gestaltzerfall als Symptom des parieto-occipitalen Uebergangsgebietes bei doppelseitiger Verletzung nach Hirnschuss, *Nervenarzt*, **18**, 103–115.

774. FAUST, C. (1949)   Ein Beitrag zur Diagnostik der optischen Agnosie, Pötzl Festschrift, pp. 198–206, Innsbruck, Innrain.
775. ——(1951)   Entwicklung und Abbau optisch-gnostischer Störungen nach traumatischer Hirnschädigung, *Nervenarzt*, **22**, 176–179.
     FERRIER, D. (1886) (see No. 174).
     FINKELNBURG (1870) (cited by No. 743).
776. FLORRIS, V., and AGOSTINI, L. (1950)   Afasia amnesica da lesione del II giroparietale, *Riv. neurol.*, **20**, 145–156.
     FOIX, Ch. (1922) (see No. 289).
     FOIX, Ch., CHAVANY, J.-.A., LÉVY, M. (1927) (see No. 290).
777. FOX, J. C. (1932)   Disorders of optic nystagmus due to cerebral tumors, *Arch. Neurol. Psychiat.*, **28**, 1007–1029.
778. FOX, J. C., and COUCH, F. H. (1936)   Spontaneous nystagmus—A study in neural rivalry and competition, *Psychol. Monographs*, **47**, 250–267.
779. FOX, J. C., COUCH, F. H., and DODGE, R. (1931)   Optic Nystagmus ; IV. Psychologic conditions, *Arch. Neurol. Psychiat.*, **26**, 23–35.
780. FOX, J. C., and DODGE, R. (1929)   Optic Nystagmus ; II. Variations in nystagmographic records of eye movement, *Arch. Neurol. Psychiat.*, **22**, 55–74.
781. FOX, J. C., and GERMAN, Wm. J. (1936)   Macular vision following cerebral resection, *Arch. Neurol. Psychiat.*, **35**, 808–826.
782. FOX, J. C. and HOLMES, G. (1926)   Optic nystagmus and its value in the localization of cerebral lesions, *Brain*, **49**, 333–371.
783. FUCHS, W. (1920)   Untersuchungen über das Sehen der Hemianopiker und Hemiamblyopiker ; Gelb-Goldstein Psychol. Analysen hirnpathologischer Fälle, 251–419, Leipzig, Barth.
784. GARNER, H. H., and BERLIN, L. (1951)   Blindness on the basis of inattention. Report of a case, *Arch. Neurol. Psychiat.*, **66**, 388–389.
785. GOGOL (1873) (cited by No. 743), Beitrag zur Lehre der Aphasie, Breslau, Diss.
786. GOLDSTEIN, K. (1943)   Some remarks on Russel (sic) Brain's article concerning visual object-agnosia, *J. nerv. ment. Dis.*, **98**, 148–153.
787. GOLDSTEIN, K., and GELB, A. (1918)   Psychologische Analysen hirnpathologischer Fälle auf Grund von Untersuchungen Hirnverletzter, *Z. ges. Neurol. Psychiat.*, **41**, 1–142.
788. GOLDSTEIN, K., and STEINFELD, J. I. (1942)   The conditioning of sexual behavior by visual agnosia, *Bull. Forest Sanit.*, **I**, 37–45.
     GONZALO, J. (cited by No. 603).
789. GOWERS, W. (1887)   Lectures on the Diagnosis of Diseases of the Brain, London, Churchill.
790. GRUNSTEIN, A. (1924)   Grosshirnrinde und Corpus striatum, *Z. ges. Neurol. Psychiat.*, **90**, 260–262.
791. GUILLAIN, G., LEREBOULLET, J., and BRISSET, Ch. (1947)   Sur un cas d'agnosie visuelle, avec agnosie spatiale, syndrome de Gerstmann et syndrome de Parinaud, *Rev. neurol.*, **79**, 510–515.
     GUTTMANN (cited by No. 603).
     HALPERN, L. (1948) (see No. 303).
     HAMILTON, A. M. (1884) (see No. 502).
792. HASSLER, R. (1951)   Diskussionsbemerkung zu Bay's Agnosiekritik, *Nervenarzt*, **22**, 308–309.
     HEAD, H., and HOLMES, G. (1911) (see No. 305).
793. HÉCAEN, H., de AJURIAGUERRA, J., ROUQUÈS, L., DAVID, M., and DELL, M. B. (1950)   Paralysie psychique du regard de Bálint au cours de l'évolution d'une leucocencéphalite type Balo, *Rev. neurol.*, **83**, 81–104.

794. HEIDENHAIN, A. (1927) Beitrag zur Kenntnis der Seelenblindheit, *Mschr. Psychiat. Neurol.*, **66**, 61–116.
HEMPHILL, R. E. (1948) (see No. 644).
795. HENDERSON, J. W., and CROSBY, E. C. (1952) An experimental study of optokinetic responses, *Arch. Ophthal. Chicago*, **42**, 43–54.
796. HENSCHEN, S. E. (1910) Zentrale Sehstörungen, Lewandowsky's Handbuch der Neurologie, **1**, ii, 891–918.
797. HERRMANN, G., and POETZL, O. (1928) Die optische Allaesthesie, Berlin, Karger.
798. HINE, M. L. (1918) The recovery of fields of vision in concussion injuries of the occipital cortex, *Brit. J. Ophthal.*, **2**, 12–25.
799. HOCHHEIMER, W. (1932) Analyse eines " Seelenblinden " von der Sprache aus, *Psychol. Forschung.*, **16**, 1–69.
HOFF, H., and POETZL, O. (1935) (see No. 650).
800. —— —— (1937) Ueber ein eigenartiges Syndrom bei einem Tumor im Mittelhirn. (Optische Simultanagnosie, in Schlafsucht übergehend), *Jb. Psychiat. Neurol.*, **54**, 13–54.
801. —— —— (1937) Reine Wortblindheit bei Hirntumor, *Nervenarzt*, **10**, 385–394.
802. —— —— (1937) Ueber Polyopie und gerichtete hemianopische Halluzinationen, *Jb. Psychiat. Neurol.*, **54**, 55–88.
803. —— —— (1937) Ueber eine optisch-agnostische Störung des " Physiognomie-Gedächtnisses ". (Beziehungen zur Rückbildung einer Wortblindheit), *Z. ges. Neurol. Psychiat.*, **159**, 367–395.
804. —— —— (1938) Anisotropie des Sehraums bei occipitaler Herderkrankung, *Dtsch. Z. Nervenheilk.*, **145**, 179–217.
805. HOLMES, G. (1918) Disturbances of vision by cerebral lesions, *Brit. J. Ophthal.*, **2**, 353–384.
806. —— (1918) Disturbances of visual orientation, *ibid.*, **2**, 449–468, 506–516.
807. —— (1931) A contribution to the cortical representation of vision, *Brain*, **54**, 470–479.
808. —— (1938) Cerebral integration of ocular movements, *Brit. med. J.*, **2**, 107–112.
809. —— (1945) Ferrier Lecture : The organization of the visual cortex in man, *Proc. roy. Soc.*, B, **132**, 348–361.
810. —— (1950) Pure word blindness, *Folia psychiat. neerl.*, **53**, 279–288.
HOLMES, G., and HORRAX, G. (1919) (see No. 504).
811. HUMPHREY, M. E., and ZANGWILL, O. L. (1951) Cessation of dreaming after brain injury, *J. Neurol. Psychiat.*, **14**, 322–325.
812. INGHAM, S. D., and NIELSEN, J. M. (1937) Interpretation dissociated from recognition of visual verbal symbols illustrated by case of complete major (left) temporal lobectomy, *Bull. Los Angeles neurol. Soc.*, **2**, 1–4.
813. JACOB, H. (1951) Diskussionsbemerkung zu Bay : Ueber den Begriff der Agnosie, *Nervenarzt*, **22**, 306–308.
814. JAMES, William (1950) A selection from his writings on psychology, edited with a commentary by Margaret Knight, Penguin Books, Harmondsworth, Mx.
815. JOSSMANN, P. (1929) Zur Psychopathologie der optisch-agnostischen Störungen, *Mschr. Psychiat. Neurol.*, **77**, 81–149.
816. JUNG, R. (1949) Ueber eine Nachuntersuchung des Falles Schn . . . von Goldstein and Gelb, *Psychiat. Neurol. med. Psychol.*, **1**, 353–362.
817. —— (1951) Bemerkungen zu Bay's Agnosiearbeiten, *Nervenarzt*, **22**, 192–193.
818. KLEIN, R., and ATTLEE, J. H. (1948) The syndrome of alexia and

amnesic aphasia. Subarachnoidal haemorrhage with symptom of partial occlusion of the spinal subarachnoidal space, *J. ment. Sci.*, **94**, 59–69.

819. KLEIST, K. (1922) Handbuch der ärztlichen Erfahrungen im Weltkriege, **4**, 343.

820. KLOPP, H. W. (1951) Ueber Umgekehrt- und Verkehrtsehen, *Dtsch. Z. Nervenheilk.*, **165**, 231–260.

821. KLÜVER, H. (1936) An analysis of the effects of the removal of the occipital lobes in monkeys, *J. Psychol.*, **2**, 49–61.

822. —— (1952) Brain mechanisms and behaviour, with special reference to the Rhinencephalon, *Journal-Lancet*, **72**, 567–577.

823. KLÜVER, H., and BUCY, P. C. (1937) " Psychic blindness " and other symptoms following temporal lobectomy in Rhesus monkeys, *Amer. J. Physiol.*, **119**, 352–353.

824. —— (1938) An analysis of certain effects of bilateral temporal lobectomy in the rhesus monkey, with special reference to " psychic blindness ", *J. Psychol.*, **5**, 33–54.

825. —— —— (1939) Preliminary analysis of functions of the temporal lobes in monkeys, *Arch. Neurol. Psychiat.*, **42**, 979–1000.

826. von KRIES (cited by No. 603).

827. KUSSMAUL, A. (1877) (cited by No. 831).

LANGE, J. (1936) (see No. 576).

828. LASHLEY, K. S. (1939) Mechanism of vision. XVI ; the functioning of small remnants of the visual cortex, *J. comp. Neurol.*, **70**, 45–67.

829. LENZ, H. (1949) Ueber zentral bedingte Störungen des Grössensehens, *Poetzl Festschrift*, pp. 316–323, Innsbruck, Wagner.

830. LEWANDOWSKY, M. (1908) Ueber Abspaltung des Farbensinnes, *Mschr. Psychiat. Neurol.*, **23**, 488–510.

831. LHERMITTE, J., and de AJURIAGUERRA, J. (1942) Psychopathologie de la Vision, Paris, Masson.

LISSAUER, H. (1890) (see No. 660).

832. LISTER, W. T., and HOLMES, G. (1916) Disturbances of vision from cerebral lesions, with special reference to the cortical representation of the macula, *Proc. roy. Soc. Med.*, **9**/3 Ophthal. Sec., 57–96.

833. LORDAT (1843–44) Analyse de la parole pour servir à la théorie de divers cas d'alalie et de paralalie, *J. Soc. Pr. Montpellier*, **7** and **8**, Paris, Baillière.

834. LOTMAR, F. (1938) Zur Kenntnis der herdanatomischen Grundlagen leichterer optisch-agnostischer Störungen, *Schweiz. Arch. Neurol. Psychiat.*, **42**, 299–322.

LYMAN, R. S., KWAN, S. T., and CHAO, W. H. (1938) (see No. 518).

835. MÄKI, N. (1928) Psychologische Analysen hirnpathologischer Fälle von Gelb und Goldstein. Natürliche Bewegungstendenzen der rechten und der linken Hand und ihr Einfluss auf das Zeichnen und der Erkennungsvorgang, *Psychol. Forschung*, **10**, 1–19.

MARIE, P., and CHATELIN, Ch. (1916) (see No. 338).

836. MARTIN, I. H. (1952) Cortical neurology : visual disturbances and the optic part of the body image, *Med. J. Aust.*, **i**, 211–220.

837. MEYER, O. (1900) Ein- und doppelseitige homonyme Hemianopsie mit Orientierungsstörungen, *Mschr. Psychiat. Neurol.*, **8**, 440–456.

838. MILES, P. W. (1951) Flicker fusion fields. IV, neuro-ophthalmic lesions, *Amer. J. Ophthal.*, **34**, 51–56.

839. —— (1951) Testing visual fields by flicker fusion, *Arch. Neurol. Psychiat.*, **65**, 39–47.

840. MOLLARET, P., BÉNARD, R., and PLUVINAGE, R. (1941) Déficits optico-gnosiques, optico-praxiques et optico-psychiques par ramol-

lissement étendu de l'artère cérébrale postérieure gauche, *Rev. neurol.*, **73**, 356–360.

von MONAKOW, C. (1885) (see No. 107).

841. MOORE, A. Eisdell (1915) Temporary blindness from a penetrating bullet wound of the occipital lobe, *Lancet*, **2**, 383–386.

MUELLER, F. (1892) (see No. 663).

842. MUNK, H. (1877) Erfahrungen zu gunsten der Localisation, *Verh. Physiol. Ges. Berl.*, No. 16, 30.3.77 ; *Dtsch. med. Wschr.*, No. 13, 31.3.77.

—— (1890) [see No. 110 (pp. 9–14)].

NIELSEN, J. M. (1946) (see No. 227).

843. NIELSEN, J. M., and OLSEN, C. W. (1936) Mindblindness. Optical disorientation in space and simultanagnosia. Two slightly dissimilar cases, one verified by autopsy, *Bull. Los Angeles neurol. Soc.*, **1**, 73–81.

844. NIELSEN, J. M., and SANBORN, A. L. (1942) Agnosia for animate objects, *Bull. Los Angeles neurol. Soc.*, **7**, 102–104.

845. OHM, J. (1926) Der optische Drehnystagmus bei Halbblindheit, *Z. ges. Neurol. Psychiat.*, **102**, 444–463.

846. OLSEN, C. W. (1942) Mindblindness : clinical and pneumencephalographic study of a case of infarction of the brain, *Bull. Los Angeles neurol. Soc.*, **7**, 43–47.

847. OPPENHEIM, H. (1923) Lehrbuch der Nervenkrankheiten für Ärzte und Studierende, 2 vols., 7th ed., Berlin, Karger.

848. PARSONS, J. H. (1927) An introduction to the Theory of Perception, Cambridge Univ. Press.

849. PATERSON, M. T., and STENGEL, E. (1943) Apperceptive blindness in Lissauer's dementia paralytica, *J. Neurol. Psychiat.*, **6**, 83–86.

850. PENTA, P. (1949) Due casi di visione capovolte, *Cervello*, **25**, 377–389.

851. PÉRON, N., DRIGUET, P., and GRANIER (1947) Agnosie visuelle avec perte élective de la reconnaissance topographique ; hémianopsie homonyme gauche, *Rev. neurol.*, **78**, 596–597.

852. PÉRON, N., and GOUTNER, V. (1944) Alexie pure, sans hémianopsie, *Rev. neurol.*, **76**, 81–82.

853. PETIT-DUTAILLIS, D., CHAVANY, J. A., and FÉNÉLON, F. (1949) Disparition des phénomènes agnosiques après amputation du lobe occipital gauche chez un droitier opéré d'un méningiome du pressoir, *Rev. neurol.*, **81**, 424–427.

854. PICHLER, E. (1943) Ueber Störungen des Raum- und Zeiterlebens bei Verletzungen des Hinterhauptlappens, *Z. ges. Neurol. Psychiat.*, **176**, 434–464.

855. PICK, A. (1915) Zur Lokalisation in den Sehbahnen mit einem Beitrage zur Lehre von den Störungen der Orientierung im Raum, *Prag. med. Wschr.*, **40**, No. 8, 81–82.

856. POETZL, O. (1928) Die optisch-agnostischen Störungen, Leipzig, Deuticke.

857. —— (1933) Polyopie und gnostische Störung. Ein Beitrag zur Pathophysiologie der cerebralen Sehstörungen, *Jb. Psychiat. Neurol.*, **50**, 57–77.

858. —— (1937) Zur Pathologie der optischen Agnosien mit verhältnismässig geringer Lesestörung, *Z. ges. Neurol. Psychiat.*, **160**, 255–296.

859. —— (1937) Optische Simultanagnosie eines Rechtshänders bei rechtshirnigen Herden, *Wien. med. Wschr.*, **1**, 269–274.

860. —— (1949) Ueber einige zentrale Probleme des Farbensehens, *Wien. klin. Wschr.*, **61**, 706–709.

861. POPPELREUTER, W. (1917/18) Die psychischen Schädigungen durch Kopfschuss im Kriege, 1914–1917, 2 vols., Leipzig, Voss.

862. —— (1923) Zur Psychologie und Pathologie der optischen Wahrnehmung, *Z. ges. Neurol. Psychiat.*, **83**, 26–152.

863. PROBST, M. (1901) Ueber einen Fall vollständiger Rindenblindheit und vollständiger Amusie, *Mschr. Psychiat. Neurol.*, **9**, 5–21.

864. QUENSEL, F. (1927) Ein Fall von rechtsseitiger Hemianopsie mit Alexie und zentral bedingtem monokulärem Doppeltschen, *Mschr. Psychiat. Neurol.*, **65**, 173–207.

865. —— (1931) Alexie (in Kurzes Handbuch der Ophthalmologie, VI) ; Die Erkrankungen der höheren Zentren (in Kurzes Handbuch der Ophthalmologie, von Schieck and Brickner), Berlin, Springer.

866. RADEMAKER, G. G. J., and GARCIN, R. (1934) Le réflexe de cligne-ment à la menace. Étude physiologique et clinique. La valeur séméiologique de son abolition dans les lésions corticales rolandiques et occipito-rolandiques des hémisphères cérébraux, en l'absence de toute hémianopsie, *Encéphale*, **29**, 1–17.

867. RANEY, A. A., and NIELSEN, J. M. (1942) Denial of Blindness (Anton's Symptom). Two clinical cases, *Bull. Los Angeles neurol. Soc.*, **7**, 150–151.

868. RANSCHBURG, P., and SCHILL, E. (1932) Ueber Alexie und Agnosie, *Z. ges. Neurol. Psychiat.*, **139**, 192–240.

869. RAYMOND, F., LEJONNE, P., and GALEZOWSKI, J. (1906) Cécité corticale par double hémianopsie, *Rev. neurol.*, **14**, 680–683.

870. REDLICH, E., and BONVICINI, G. (1907) Ueber mangelnde Wahrneh-mung (Autoanästhesie) der Blindheit bei cerebralen Erkrankungen, *Neurol. Zbl.*, **26**, 945–951.

—— —— (1908) (see No. 683).

871. REINHARD, C. (1886) Zur Frage der Hirnlocalisation mit besonderer Berücksichtigung der cerebralen Sehstörungen, *Arch. Psychiat. Nervenkr.*, **17**, 717–756.

—— (1887) (see No. 359).

872. RIDDOCH, G. (1917) On the relative perceptions of movement and a stationary object in certain visual disturbances due to occipital injuries, *Proc. roy. Soc. Med.*, **10**, 13–31.

873. —— (1917) Disorders of visual perceptions due to occipital injuries with especial reference to appreciation of movement, *Brain*, **40**, 15–57.

874. —— (1935) Visual disorientation in homonymous half-fields, *Brain*, **58**, 376–382.

875. RIESE, W. (1949) Gliome étendu aux lobes frontal et pariétal gauches. Hallucinations visuelles. Note suivi d'un essai de théorie des hallucinations, survenant chez des malades atteints de lésions du système nerveux central, *Rev. neurol.*, **81**, 785–787.

876. ROBINSON, P. K., and WATTS, A. C. (1947) Hallucinations of re-membered scenes as an epileptic aura, *Brain*, **70**, 440–448.

877. ROUDINESCO, T., and TRÉLAT, J. (1950) Note sur la dyslexie, *Bull. Soc. méd. hôp. Paris*, **66**, 1451–1458.

878. RÜSSEL, A. (1937) Zur Psychologie der optischen Agnosien. (Neue psychol. Stud. Hrsg. v. Felix Krueger u. Arnulf Rüssel, Bd. 13, H. 1), München, Becksche Verlagsbuchhandl.

879. SANDER, F. (1928) Experimentelle Ergebnisse der Gestaltpsycho-logie, *Berl. Kongr. exp. Psychol.*, **10**, 23–88.

880. SCHELLER, H. (1951) Ueber das Wesen und die Abgrenzung optisch-agnostischer Störungen, *Nervenarzt*, **22**, 187–190.

881. SCHUSTER, P., and TATERKA, H. (1928) Zur Klinik der Seelen-blindheit, *Dtsch. Z. Nervenheilk.*, **102**, 112–117.

882. SIEMERLING (1890) Ein Fall von sogenannter Seelenblindheit nebst anderweitigen cerebralen Symptomen, *Arch. Psychiat.*, **21**, 284–299.

883. SITTIG, O. (see No. 603).
884. SPALDING, J. M. K., and ZANGWILL, O. L. (1950) Disturbances of number-form in a case of brain injury, *J. Neurol. Psychiat.*, **13**, 24-29.
885. SOLMS, A. (1936) Zur Frage der Alexie und ihrer anatomischen Lokalisation, Inaugr. Dissert., Basel.
886. STADLIN, W. (1949) Hémianopsie et nystagmus optocinétique, *Ophthalmologica*, **118**, 383-388.
887. von STAUFFENBERG, W. (1914) Ueber Seelenblindheit. *Arb. hirnanatom. Institut Zürich*, Wiesbaden, **8**, 1-212.
888. STEIN, W. N. (1936) Anozofnosja i zaburzenia schemata ciala w przypadku porażenia polowiczego, wywolanego przez guz mósgu, *Neurol. polska*, **19**, 131-144.
889. STENGEL, E. (1948) The syndrome of visual alexia with colour agnosia, *J. ment. Sci.*, **94**, 46-58.
890. STENVERS, H. W. (1924) Ueber die klinische Bedeutung des optischen Nystagmus für die zerebrale Diagnostik, *Schweiz Arch. Neurol. Psychiat.*, **14**, 279-288.
891. —— (1925) Over den Optischen Nystagmus, *Psychiat. neurol. Bl.*, *Amst.*, **29**, 137-153.
892. —— (1925) On the optic (opto-kinetic, opto-motorial) nystagmus, *Acta oto-laryng.*, **8**, 545-562.
893. —— (1945) Contribution to the diagnostics of defects and disorders in the brain by means of the examination in the fields of vision and the fields of conjugate movements to the right and to the left, *Verh. k. med. Akad. Weten.*, Afd. natur., **42**, 1-46.
     —— (1949) (see No. 391).
894. —— (1951) Localisation directe et localisation par image dans les champs visuels périphériques, *Rev. Oto-neuro-ophtal.*, **23**, 6-14.
895. von STOCKERT, F. G. (1952) Störungen der Darstellungsfunktion bei Sinnesdefekt. Gleichzeitig ein Beitrag zum Agnosie-Problem, *Nervenarzt*, **23**, 121-126.
896. STOLLREITER-BUTZON, L. (1950) Zur Frage der Prosopagnosie, *Arch. Psychiat. Nervenkr.*, **184**, 1-27.
897. STRAUSS, H. (1925) Die diagnostische Bedeutung des optomotorischen (Eisenbahn-) Nystagmus für die Neurologie, *Z. ges. Neurol. Psychiat.*, **98**, 93-101.
898. STUMPFL, F. (1930) Ein Fall von Anton's Symptom (Nichtwahrnehmung der eigenen Blindheit), *Mschr. Psychiat. Neurol.*, **76**, 58-79.
899. SZATMARI, A. (1938) Ueber optische Sinnestäuschungen als epileptisches Aequivalent bei traumatischer Schädigung des Hinterhauptlappens, *Arch. Psychiat.*, **107**, 290-299.
900. TEITELBAUM, H. A. (1943) An analysis of the disturbances of higher cortical functions, agnosia, apraxia and aphasia, *J. nerv. ment. Dis.*, **97**, 44-61.
     TEUBER, H.-L., BATTERSBY, W. G., and BENDER, M. B. (1951) (see No. 230).
901. TEUBER, H.-L., and BENDER, M. B. (1948) Critical flicker frequency in defective fields of vision, *Fed. Proc.*, **7**, 123-124.
902. —— —— (1949) Alterations in pattern vision following trauma of occipital lobes in man, *J. gen. Psychol.*, **40**, 37-57.
903. —— —— (1951) Neuro-ophthalmology. The oculomotor system, *Progr. Neurol. Psychiat.*, **6**, 148-178.
904. THIÉBAUT, F., and GUILLAUMAT, L. (1945) Hémianopsie relative, *Rev. neurol.*, **77**, 129-130.
905. TOURNAY, A. (1942) Sur un trouble déréglant la fixation attentive du regard, *Rev. neurol.*, **74**, 325-329.

906. URECHIA, C. J., CREMENE, V., and POPESCU, P. (1948) Hémianopsie avec chromo-agnosie (agnosie des couleurs), *Rev. Neurol.*, **80**, 70–72.
907. VERHOEFF, F. H. (1900) The cause of a special form of monocular diplopia, *Arch. Ophthal*, **29**, 565–572.
908. VITZOU, A. N. (1893) Effets de l'ablation totale des lobes occipitaux sur la vision chez le chien, *Arch. physiol. norm. path.*, **5**, 688–698.
909. VOGEL, P. (1951) Diskussion zum Thema Agnosie, *Nervenarzt*, **22**, 190–191.
910. VORSTER (1893) Ueber einen Fall von doppelseitiger Hemianopsie mit Seelenblindheit, Photopsien und Gesichtstäuschungen, *Allgem. Z. Psychiat.*, **49**, 227–249.
911. WERNICKE, C. (1881) (cited by No. 743).
912. —— (1885–1886) Nervenheilkunde. Die neueren Arbeiten über Aphasie, besprochen von C. Wernicke, *Fortschr. Med.*, **3**, 824–830 ; *ibid.*, **4**, 371–377 ; *ibid.*, **4**, 463–482.
913. WILBRAND, H. (1887) Die Seelenblindheit als Herderscheinung, Wiesbaden, Bergmann.
914. —— (1892) Ein Fall von Seelenblindheit und Hemianopsie mit Sectionsbefund, *Dtsch. Z. Nervenheilk*, **2**, 361–387.
915. WILBRAND, H., and SAENGER, A. (1921) Pathologie der Bahnen und Centren der Augenmuskeln, Vol. 8 of " Neurologie des Auges ", München, Bergmann.
916. WILDER, J. (1928) Ueber Schief- und Verkehrtsehen, *Dtsch. Z. Nervenheilk.*, **104**, 222–256.
917. WILSON, I. G. H. (1925) A case of bilateral cortical blindness, *J. Neurol. Psychiat.*, **6**, 42–45.
918. WILSON, S. A. KINNIER (1917) Concussion injuries of the visual apparatus in warfare of central origin, *Lancet*, **2**, 1–5.
919. WOLPERT, I. (1924) Die Simultanagnosie-Störung der Gesamtauffassung, *Z. ges. Neurol. Psychiat.*, **93**, 397–415.
920. —— (1930) Ueber das Wesen der literalen Alexie. Beitrag zur Aphasielehre, *Mschr. Psychiat. Neurol.*, **75**, 207–266.
921. ZANGWILL, O. L. (1946) Qualitative observations on verbal memory in cases of cerebral lesions, *Brit. J. Psychol.*, **37**, 8–19.
ZEH, W. (1950) (see No. 602).

CHAPTER X

922. ANGYAL, A. (1930) Die Lagebeharrung der optisch vorgestellten räumlichen Umgebung, *Neue psychol. Stud.*, **6**, 291–309 ; (1931) *Zbl. ges. Neurol. Psychiat.*, **60**, 37.
BENDER, M. B., and TEUBER, H.-L. (1946) (see No. 729).
—— —— (1947–1948) (see Nos. 493 and 494).
923. —— —— (1949) 1948 Year Book Neurol. Psychiat. Neurosurgery, Chicago, Year Book Publishers, p. 334.
924. BENEDEK, L., and von ANGYÁL, L. (1941) Ueber einen Fall von operiertem rechtsseitigem occipitalem Tuberkel mit transitorischer Raumwahrnehmung- und Zeitstörung, wie auch mit atypischer Ventrikelveränderung, *Dtsch. Z. Nervenheilk.*, **153**, 29–39.
925. —— —— (1945) Sur un cas de tubercule occipital droit opéré, avec troubles de la perception de l'espace et du temps, ainsi qu'avec des modifications ventriculaires atypiques, *Rev. neurol.*, **77**, 159 (abstract).
BIRKMAYER, W. (1951) (see No. 742).
926. BOUMAN, L., and GRÜNBAUM, A. A. (1929) Eine Störung der Chrono-

gnosie und ihre Bedeutung im betreffenden Symptomenbild, *Mschr. Psychiat. Neurol.*, **73**, 1–39.

927. BRUSH, E. N. (1930) Observations on the temporal judgment during sleep, *Amer. J. Psychol.*, **42**, 408–411.

928. CAMIS, M. (1930) The Physiology of the Vestibular Apparatus, (translated by R. S. Creed), Oxford, Clarendon Press.

929. von CYON, E. (1908) Das Ohrlabyrinth als Organ der mathematischen Sinne für Raum und Zeit, Berlin, Springer.

930. DAVIDSON, G. M. (1941) A syndrome of time-agnosia, *J. nerv. ment. Dis.*, **94**, 336–343.

931. DIDE, M. (1938) Diagnostic anatomo-clinique de désorientations temporo-spatiales, *Rev. neurol.*, **69**, 720–725.

EHRENWALD, Hans (1931) (see No. 496).

932. FERRARO, A. (1921) Ricerche sul valore della prova " P. Marie-Béhague ", diretta a svelare i disturbi dell' orientamento fine, *Riv. Patol. nerv. ment.*, **26**, 74–78 ; *J. Neurol. Psychopath.*, **3**, 366 (abstract).

933. FISCHER, M. H. (1932) Die Orientierung im Raume bei Wirbeltieren und beim Menschen, *Zbl. ges. Neurol. Psychiat.*, **63**, 746.

934. FRANTZ, E. E. (1950) Amnesia for left limbs and loss of interest and attention in left fields of vision, *J. nerv. ment. Dis.*, **112**, 240–244.

935. GELB, A. (1925) Disturbances in space perception, *J. Amer. med. Ass.*, **85**, 532 ; (1929) *J. nerv. ment. Dis.*, **70**, 339 (abstract).

GERSTMANN, J. (1930) (see No. 560).

936. —— (1937) Ueber ein neuartiges hirnpathologisches Phänomen, *Wien. klin. Wschr.*, **1**, 294–296 ; (1938) *Zbl. ges. Neurol. Psychiat.*, **90**, 331.

937. GIBSON, J. J. (1950) The Perception of the Visual World, Boston, Houghton Mifflin.

938. GOODDY, W., and REINHOLD, M. (1952) Some aspects of human orientation in space, *Brain*, **75**, 472–509.

GYÁRFAS, K. (1939) (see No. 501).

939. HALL, W. W. (1927) Time-sense, *J. ment. Sci.*, **73**, 421–428.

940. HERMANN, I. (1951). Rapports spatiaux de quelques phénomènes psychiques, *Acta psychol.*, **7**, 225–246.

van der HORST, L. (1934) (see No. 506).

941. JONES, A. O. (1930) Is there a " time " sense ? *Psyche*, **11**, 82–85.

942. KAHN, E. (1951) Erwägungen über Raum- und Zeiterleben, *Mschr. Psychiat. Neurol.*, **122**, 1–31.

943. KOHLMANN, Th. (1950) Das psychologische Problem der Zeitschätzung und der experimentelle Nachweis seiner diagnostischen Anwendbarkeit bei senilen Demenzen, Hirntumoren sowie traumatischen Hirnschädigungen, *Wien. Z. Nervenheilk.*, **3**, 241–260.

KROLL, M. B., and STOLBUN, D. (1933) (see No. 492).

944. el KOUSSY, A. A. H. (1935) The Visual Perception of Space, London, Cambridge Univ. Press.

945. LAIGNEL-LAVASTINE et VALENCE (1926) Grande aphasie de Wernicke avec deficit particulièrement marqué de la représentation spatiale, *Bull. Soc. méd. hôp. Paris*, **42**, 270–272. *Zbl. ges Neurol. Psychiat.*, **43**, 855.

946. LEOPOLD, S. (1936) Orientation of time in psychotic, neurotic and delinquent persons, *Arch. Neurol. Psychiat.*, **36**, 223–226.

947. LHERMITTE, J., de AJURIAGUERRA, J., and HÉCAEN, H. (1949) Le syndrome thalamique. Troubles de la somatognosie, *C.R. IVth int. Congr. Neurol.*, **1**, Rapports, 78–79. Paris, Masson (1951).

LHERMITTE, J., de MASSARY, J., and KYRIACO (1928) (see No. 515).

LHERMITTE, J., and TRELLES, J. O. (1933) (See No. 516).

McFIE, J., PIERCY, M. F., and ZANGWILL, O. L. (1950) (see No. 519).

948. MALAMUD, W., and NYGARD, W. J. (1930) Rôle played by the cutaneous senses in spatial perceptions, *J. nerv. ment. Dis.*, **73,** 465–477.

949. MARIE, P., and BÉHAGUE, B. (1919) Syndrome de désorientation dans l'espace consécutif aux plaies profondes du lobe frontal, *Rev. neurol.*, **26,** 1–14.

950. MATSUDA, A. (1930) Untersuchungen zur optischen Raumwahrnehmung, *Z. Sinnesphysiol.*, **61,** 225–246 ; *Zbl. ges. Neurol. Psychiat.*, **60,** 28.

MAYER-GROSS, W. (1935) (see No. 522).

951. MEERLOO, A. M. (1935) Development and disturbances of time sense, *Ned. Tijdschr. Geneesk.*, **79,** 1570–1577.

952. —— (1935) Ueber Entwicklung und Störung des Zeitsinns, *Z. ges. Neurol. Psychiat.*, **153,** 231–241.

OLSEN, C. W., and RUBY, C. (1941) (see No. 581).

PATERSON, A., and ZANGWILL, O. L. (1944) (see No. 527).

PINÉAS, H. (1931) (see No. 350).

953. RÉVÉSZ, G. (1937) The problems of space with particular emphasis on specific sensory spaces, *Amer. J. Psychol.*, **50,** 429–444 ; *Zbl. ges. Neurol. Psychiat.*, **90,** 136.

SCHELLER, H., and SEIDEMANN, H. (1931–32) (see No. 534).

954. SCHILDER, P. (1935) Psychopathology of time, *Arch. Neurol. Psychiat.*, **34,** 1099–1105.

955. SHAPIRO, M. F., FINK, M., and BENDER, M. A. (1952) Exosomesthesia, or displacement of cutaneous sensation into extrapersonal space, *Arch. Neurol. Psychiat.*, **68,** 481–490.

956. VICKER, J. (1930) Ein eigenartiger Fall von Störung der räumlichen Orientierung, *Trudy tomask. med. Inst.*, **1,** 158–162 ; (1932) *Zbl. ges. Neurol. Psychiat.*, **61,** 799.

957. —— (1936) Ueber Störung der Orientierung in der Raumrichtung, *Sovet. psisch.*, **12,** 34–41 ; (1937) *Zbl. ges. Neurol. Psychiat.*, **85,** 295–296.

958. VILATO GOMEZ, J. (1947) La orientacion en el espacio y psicopatologia de la orientacion, *An. Med. Cirug.*, **22/30,** 373–382.

959. WAGNER, W. (1932) Ueber Raumstörung, *Mschr. Psychiat. Neurol.*, **84,** 281–307.

960. von WEIZSÄCKER, V. (1929) Space orientation disturbance, *J. nerv. ment. Dis.*, **70,** 338 (abstract).

961. WICKER, I. (1930) Ein eigenartiger Fall von räumlicher Orientierungsstörung, *Mschr. Psychiat. Neurol.*, **77,** 310–317 ; (1931) *Zbl. ges. Neurol. Psychiat.*, **60,** 63.

962. WILLIAMS, M., and ZANGWILL, O. L. (1950) Disorders of temporal judgment associated with amnesic states, *J. ment. Sci.*, **96,** 484–493.

van WOERKOM, W. (1919) (see No. 600).

963. ZUTT, J. (1931) Demonstration eines Dämmerzustandes mit optischen apraktischagraphischen Ausfällen und schwerer Raumorientierungsstörung, *Zbl. ges. Neurol. Psychiat.*, **59,** 267.

CHAPTER XI

964. ALAJOUANINE, Th. (1948) Aphasia and artistic realization, *Brain*, **71,** 299–241.

965. ALFORD, L. B. (1937) Defects of intelligence from focal lesions within the central part of the left cerebral hemisphere, *Amer. J. Psychiat.*, **94,** 615–633.

966. ALLISON, R. S. (1950) Symptomatologie des Sauerstoffmangels im Gehirn und verwandter Zustände, *Schweiz. Arch. Neurol. Psychiat.*, **66**, 1–22.

967. von ANGYÁL, L., and LORAND, B. (1938) Beiträge zu den Zeichnenstörungen autopagnostischaphatischer Kranker, *Arch. Psychiat. Nervenkr.*, **108**, 493–516.

968. AUSTREGESILO, A. (1952) Afasia del lobulo parietal izquierdo, *Folia clin. int.*, **2**, 47–51.

969. BAILEY, P. (1924) A contribution to the study of aphasia and apraxia, *Arch. Neurol. Psychiat.*, **2**, 501–529.

970. BATEMAN, F. (1890) On Aphasia or Loss of Speech, and the Localization of the Faculty of Articulate Language, London, Churchill.

971. BERLIN, R. (1887) Eine besondere Art der Wortblindheit (Dyslexie) ; Tract ; Wiesbaden.

BERLIN and BRUNS (cited by No. 831).

BIANCHI, L. (1925) (see No. 741).

BREMER, F. (1921) (see No. 419).

972. BRUGIA, R. (1929) Révision de la Doctrine des Localisations Cérébrales. Unité Segmentaire des Réflexes. Préface du Prof. Pierre Marie, Paris, Masson.

973. BRUN, R. (1921) Klinische und anatomische Studienr übe Apraxie, *Schweiz. Arch. Neurol. Psychiat.*, **9**, 29–64, 194–226 ; *ibid.*, **10**, 48–79.

974. BURR, C. W. (1905) Loss of the sign language in a deaf-mute, from cerebral tumour and softening, *N.Y. med. J.*, **81**, 1106–1108.

CONRAD, K. (1951) (see No. 760).

975. CRITCHLEY, M. (1938) " Aphasia " in a partial deaf-mute, *Brain*, **61**, 163–169.

—— (1939) (see No. 554).

—— (1942) (see No. 555).

976. —— (1953) Tactile thought, with special reference to the blind, *Brain*, **76**, 19–35.

von ENGERTH, G. (1933) (see No. 557).

977. FALRET, J. P. J. (1864) Des troubles du language et de la mémoire des mots dans les affections cérébrales (aphémie, aphasie, alalie, amnésie verbale), Paris, Asselin. Reprint from *Arch. gén. méd.*, **6**, 3, Paris, 1864.

FEARNSIDES, E. G. (1915) (see No. 434).

978. FOIX, Ch. (1925) L'aphasie temporo-pariétale dite aphasie de Wernicke, *Presse méd.*, **33**, 1457–1459.

979. GOLDSTEIN, K. (1948) Language and Language Disturbances, New York, Grune and Stratton.

980. GRASSET, J. (1896) Aphasie de la main droite chez un sourd-muet, *Progr. méd.*, 3s, T. iv, No. 44, 281.

981. GREWEL, F. (1952) Acalculia, *Brain*, **75**, 397–407.

GRÜNBAUM, A. A. (1930) (see No. 500).

982. HEAD, H. (1923) Speech and cerebral localization, *Brain*, **46**, 355–528.

HENSCHEN, S. E. (1920) (see Nos. 646 and 647).

983. HILPERT, J. (1931) Aphatische Störungen bei Prozessen im Bereich des linken Gyrus supramarginalis, *Arch. Psychiat. Nervenkr.*, **95**, 743–747 ; *Zbl. ges. Neurol. Psychiat.*, **61**, 273–275.

984. HUMPHREY, M. E., and ZANGWILL, O. L. (1952) Effects of a right-sided occipito-parietal brain injury in a left-handed man, *Brain*, **75**, 312–324.

985. IVES, E. R. (1937) Case illustrating capacity for use of symbols after destruction of the major (left) language area, *Bull. Los Angeles neurol. Soc.*, **2**, 36–40.

468 SELECTIVE BIBLIOGRAPHY

968. KENNEDY, F., and WOLF, A. (1936) The relationship of intellect to speech defect in aphasic patients, with illustrative cases, *J. nerv. ment. Dis.*, **84**, 125–311.
KLEIST, K. (1934) (see No. 449).
KOHS, S. C. (1927) (see No. 225).
987. KRAPF, E. (1937) Ueber Akalkulie, *Schweiz. Arch. Neurol. Psychiat.*, **39**, 330–334.
988. KRAUSE, G., and ZÜLCH, K. J. (1951) Ueber die Häufigkeit der Hirntumorarten in den verschiedenen Regionen, *Zbl. Neurochir.*, **11**, 222–230.
KROLL, M., and STOLBUN, D. (1933) (see No. 511).
LANGE, J. (1936) (see No. 576).
989. LEISCHNER, A. (1943) Die " Aphasie " der Taubstummen. Ein Beitrag zur Lehre von der Asymbolie, *Arch. Psychiat. Nervenkr.*, **115**, 469–548.
LEONARD, K. (1952) (see No. 513).
990. —— (1952) Rechen- und zeitliche Orientierungsstörung bei Agraphie und konstruktive Apraxie, *Arch. Psychiat. Nervenkr.*, **188**, 504–510.
991. LEWIN, W., and PHILLIPS, C. G. (1952) Observations on partial removal of the post-central gyrus for pain, *J. Neurol. Psychiat.*, **15**, 143–147.
LORDAT (1825), published (1843) (see No. 833).
992. LUND, M. (1952) Epilepsy in association with intracranial tumour, *Acta psychiat., Kbh.*, Suppl. 81, p. 149.
993. MARIE, P., and FOIX, Ch. (1917) Les aphasies de guerre, *Rev. neurol.*, **1**, 3–87.
994. OGDEN, C. K., and RICHARD, I. A. (1923) The Meaning of Meaning, London, Kegan Paul, Trench, Trubner.
995. OMBREDANE, A. (1943) Études de psychologie médicale. (1) Perception et Langage, Rio de Janeiro, Atlantica Editoria.
996. PETRIE, A. (1949) Preliminary report of changes after prefrontal leucotomy, *J. ment. Sci.*, **95**, 449–455.
997. RANEY, A. A., FRIEDMAN, A. P., and NIELSEN, J. M. (1942) Aphasia after major temporal lobectomy, *Bull. Los Angeles neurol. Soc.*, **7**, 154–156.
998. RANEY, R. P. (1937) Aphasic disturbances in cerebral trauma, *Bull. Los Angeles neurol. Soc.*, **2**, 30–33.
999. RIESE, W. (1949) Aphasia in brain tumors ; its appearance in relation to the natural history of the lesion, *Confinia Neurol.*, **9**, 64–79.
1000. SCHILLER, F. (1947) Aphasia studied in patients with missile wounds, *J. Neurol. Psychiat.*, **10**, 183–197.
1001. SINGER, H. D., and LOW, A. A. (1933) Acalculia (Henschen). *Arch. Neurol. Psychiat.*, **29**, 467–498.
1002. SUBIRANA, A. (1952) La droiterie, *Schweiz. Arch. Neurol. Psychiat.*, **69**, 1–40.
1003. TUREEN, L. L., SMOLIK, E. A., and TRITT, J. H. (1951) Aphasia in a deaf mute, *Neurology*, **1**, 237–244.
1004. VIGOTSKY, L. S. (1939) Thought and speech, *Psychiatry*, **2**, 29–54.
WAGNER, W. (1932) (see No. 959).
1005. WINSLOW, Forbes (1861) Obscure Diseases of the Brain and Disorders of the Mind, 2nd ed., London, Davies.
1006. WOLPERT, I. (1930) Ueber das Wesen der literalen Alexie. Beitrag zur Aphasielehre, *Mschr. Psychiat. Neurol.*, **75**, 207–266.

CHAPTER XII

1007. GOLDSTEIN, K. (1936)   The modifications of behaviour consequent to cerebral lesions, *Psychiat. Quart.*, **10**, 586–610.

1008. —— (1939)   The Organism ; a Holistic Approach to Biology derived from Pathological Data in Man, New York, American Book Co.

1009. McFIE, J., and PIERCY, M. F. (1952)   Intellectual impairment with localized cerebral lesions, *Brain*, **75**, 292–311.

1010. MAYER-GROSS, W. (1938)   Discussion on the presenile dementias ; symptomatology, pathology and differential diagnosis, *Proc. roy. Soc. Med.*, **31**, 1443–1454.
REINHOLD, M. (1951) (see No. 228).

1011. —— (1952–3)   Reactions to organic cerebral disease, *J. ment. Sci.*, **99**, 130–135.

1012. ROTH, M. (1952)   Discussion on the differential diagnosis of early dementia, *Proc. roy. Soc. Med.*, **45**, 369–372.

1013. ZANGWILL, O. L. (1952)   Discussion on the role of the psychologist in psychiatric practice, *Proc. roy. Soc. Med.*, **45**, 445–447.

CHAPTER XIII

ALLISON, R. S. (1950) (see No. 966).

1014. ANDERSEN, A. L. (1950)   The effect of laterality localization of brain damage on Wechsler-Bellevue indices of deterioration, *J. clin. Psychol.*, **6**, 191–194.

1015. —— (1951)   The effect of laterality localization of focal brain lesions on the Wechsler-Bellevue subtests, *J. clin. Psychol.*, **7**, 149–153.

1016. ANDERSON, E. W. (1942)   Abnormal mental states in survivors with special reference to collective hallucinations, *J. R. Nav. med. Serv.*, **28**, 361–377.

1017. ASCROFT, P. B. (1941)   Traumatic epilepsy after gunshot wounds of the head, *Brit. med. J.*, **1**, 739–744.

1018. BARUK, H. (1926)   Les troubles mentaux dans les tumeurs cérébrales, Paris, Doin ; (1927)   *Arch. Neurol. Psychiat.*, **17**, 422–424 (review).

1019. BAUMM, H. (1930)   Erfahrungen über Epilepsie bei Hirnverletzten, *Z. ges. Neurol. Psychiat.*, **127**, 279–311.

1020. BLAU, A. (1946)   The Master Hand, New York, Amer. Orthopsychiat. Ass.

1021. BRAIN, W. R. (1941)   Visual disorientation with special reference to lesions of the right cerebral hemisphere, *Brain*, **64**, 244–272.
—— (1945) (see No. 220).

1022. BRAMWELL, B. (1899)   On " crossed " aphasia and the factors which go to determine whether the " leading " or " driving " speech-centres shall be located in the left or in the right hemisphere of the brain, *Lancet*, **1**, 1473–1479.

1023. BYCHOWSKI, G. (1936)   Les syndromes frontaux et les syndromes pariéto-occipitaux, *Neurol. polska*, **19**, 3–35.

1024. COWIE, V. (1953)   personal communication.

1025. CHESHER, E. C. (1936)   Some observations concerning the relation of handedness to the language mechanism, *Bull. neurol. Inst. N.Y.*, **4**, 556–562.

1026. CLAUDE, H., and SCHAEFFER, H. (1921)   Un nouveau cas d'hémiplégie gauche avec aphasie chez un droitier, *Rev. neurol.*, **1**, 170–175.

1027. CONRAD, K. (1949) Ueber aphatische Sprachstörungen bei hirnverletzten Linkshändelr, *Nervenarzt*, **20**, 148–154.

1028. CORNIL, L., and GASTAUT, H. (1947) Étude électro-encéphalographique de la dominance sensorielle d'un hémisphère cérébral, *Presse méd.*, **55**, 421–422.

CRITCHLEY, M. (1951) (see No. 222).

1029. CREDNER, L. (1930) Klinische und soziale Auswirkungen von Hirnschädigungen. *Z. ges. Neurol. Psychiat.*, **126**, 721–757.

1030. DENNY-BROWN, D., MEYER, S., and HORENSTEIN, S. (1952) The significance of perceptual rivalry, resulting from parietal lesion, *Brain*, **75**, 433–471.

1031. GIANNULI, F. (1918) Amnesia globale delle parole e paralisi omolaterale da emorragia del lobo temporale, *Riv. Patol. nerv. ment.*, **23**, 73–89 ; *J. nerv. ment. Dis.*, **51**, 585 (abstract).

1032. GLIDDON, W. O. (1943) Gunshot wounds of head (review of after effects in 500 Canadian pensioners from Great War, 1914–1918), *Canad. med. Ass. J.*, **49**, 373–377.

1033. GOODDY, W. (1949) Sensation and volition, *Brain*, **72**, 312–339.

1034. GREWEL, F. (1950) De pathologie van de lobulus parietalis inferior, *Ned. Tijdschr. Geneesk.*, **94**, 3634–3643.

GUREWITSCH, M. (1932) (see No. 634).

1035. HENSCHEN, S. E. (1926) On the function of the right hemisphere of the brain in relation to the left in speech, music and calculation, *Brain*, **49**, 110–123.

HERRMANN, G., and POETZL, O. (1926) (see No. 566).

HOFF, H., and KAMIN, M. (1930) (see No. 648).

1036. HUMPHREY, M. E., and ZANGWILL, O. L. (1952) Dysphasia in left-handed patients with unilateral brain lesions, *J. Neurol. Psychiat.*, **15**, 184–193.

—— —— (1952) (see No. 984).

1037. KENNEDY, Foster (1916) Stock-brainedness, the causative factor in the so-called " crossed aphasias ", *Amer. J. med. Sci.*, **152**, 849–859.

1038. KUTTNER, H. (1930) Ueber die Beteiligung der rechten Hirnhälfte an der Sprachfunktion. Kasuistische Mitteilung zum Aphasie-Problem, *Arch. Psychiat. Nervenkr.*, **91**, 691–693.

1039. KLOSE, R. (1920) Das Gehirn eines Wunderkindes (des Pianisten Goswin Sökeland), *Mschr. Psychiat. Neurol.*, **48**, 63–102.

1040. LARRIVÉ, E., and JASIENSKI, H.-J. (1931) L'illusion des sosies. Une nouvelle observation du syndrome de Capgras, *Ann. méd.-psychol.*, **89**, 501–507.

1041. LIEBERS, M. (1933) Alzheimersche Krankheit mit Pickscher Atrophie der Parieto-Occipitallappen, *Arch. Psychiat. Nervenkr.*, **100**, 100–110.

LUND, M. (1952) (see No. 992).

1042. MAAS, O. (1920) Ueber Agrammatismus und die Bedeutung der rechten Hemisphäre für die Sprache, *Neurol. Zbl.*, **39**, 465–488 ; 506–511.

McFIE, J., and PIERCY, M. F. (1952) (see No. 226).

MARBURG, O. (1931) (see No. 578).

1043. MARINESCO, G., GRIGORESCO, D., and AXENTE, S. (1938) Considérations sur l'aphasie croisée, *Encéphale*, **23**, 27–46.

1044. MARTIN, J. P. (1949) Consciousness and its disturbances, *Lancet*, **1**, 1–6 ; 48–52.

1045. MAURER, F. (1924) Das Gehirn Ernst Haeckels, Jena, Fischer.

MOFFIE, D. (1949) (see No. 103).

de MORSIER, G. (1938) (see No. 460).

de MORSIER, G., and BROCCARD, R. (1937) (see No. 461).

1046. NIELSEN, J. M. (1937) Cerebral thrombosis causing deletion of artificial writing center in left cerebral hemisphere of left-handed man, *Bull. Los Angeles neurol. Soc.*, **2**, 176–179.

1047. —— (1938) Function of the minor (usually right) cerebral hemisphere in language, *ibid.*, **3**, 67–75.
—— (1940) (see No. 668).
—— (1946) (see No. 227).

1048. OJEMANN, R. H. (1931) Studies in handedness. III. Relation of handedness to speech, *J. educat. Psychol.*, **22**, 120–126.

1049. PFEIFER, B. (1923) Die Bedeutung psychologischer Leistungs- und Arbeitsprüfungen für die Topik der Grosshirnrinde, *Dtsch. Z. Nervenheilk.*, **77**, 139–142; (1929) *J. nerv. ment. Dis.*, **70**, 431 (abstract).
POETZL, O. (1924–25) (see No. 681).
RIESE, W., and GOLDSTEIN, K. (1950) (see No. 121).

1050. ROTHSCHILD, K. (1931) The relation of Broca's center to left-handedness, *Amer. J. med. Sci.*, **182**, 116–118.

1051. RUSSELL, W. R. (1947) The anatomy of traumatic epilepsy, *Brain*, **70**, 225–233.

1052. RUSSELL, W. R., and WHITTY, C. W. M. (1952) Studies in traumatic epilepsy. I. Factors influencing the incidence of epilepsy after brain wounds, *J. Neurol. Psychiat.*, **15**, 93–98.

1053. von SÁNTHA, K. (1932) Ueber das hirnanatomische Substrat des Rechentalentes, *Arch. Psychiat. Nervenkr.*, **98**, 313–338.
SCHWOB, R. A. (1933) (see No. 380).

1054. SMITH, G. Elliot (1925) Right and left handedness in primitive man, *Brit. med. J.*, **2**, 1107–1108.

1055. SOMOGYI, I. (1930) Localization of musical rhythm, *Orvosi hetil.*, **74**, 779–782.

1056. —— (1930) Beiträge zur Gehirnlokalisation der musikalischen Begabung, *Verh. ungar. ärztl. Ges.*, **2**, 33–35.

1057. —— (1930) Ueber das morphologische Korrelat der musikalischen Fähigkeiten, *Arch. Psychiat. Nervenkr.*, **98**, 313–338.

1058. STEELE, G. D. F., and HEGARTY, A. B. (1950) Parieto-occipital syndrome following carbon monoxide poisoning, *J. ment. Sci.*, **96**, 1015–1023.

1059. STEINTHAL (cited by LUND, M., p. 91, No. 992).
SUBIRANA, A. (1952) (see No. 1002).

1060. SUBIRANA, A., COROMINAS, J., and OLLER-DAURELLA, L. (1950) Las afasias congénitas infantiles ; estudio clinico y electroencefalografico de tres casos personales, *Actas luso-esp. Neurol. Psiquiat.*, **9**, 14–25.

1061. TEUBER, H.-L. (1952) Some observations on the organization of higher functions after penetrating brain injury in man ; Millbank symposium : Biology of mental health and disease, New York, Hoeber.

1062. YAHN, M., PIMENTA, A. M., and SETTE, A. (1948) Leucotomia parietal, resultados em 22 pacientes, *Arquiv. Neuro-psiquiat.*, **6**, 225–233.

CHAPTER XIV

1063. BAY, E. (1953) Disturbances of visual perception and their examination, *Brain*, **76** (in press).

1064. BEST, F. (1952) Zur Frage der Seelenblindheit, *Arch. Psychiat. Nervenkr.*, **188**, 511–543.

1065. BRAIN, W. R. (1951) Mind, Perception and Science, Oxford, Blackwall Scientific Publications.

BROWN, T. G., and SHERRINGTON, C. S. (1912) (see No. 167).

1066. COHEN, H. (1952) The status of brain in the concept of mind (Manson Lecture), *Philosophy*, **27**, 195–210.

DENNY-BROWN, D., MEYER, J. S., and HORENSTEIN, S. (1952) (see No. 1030).

1067. DUENSING, F. (1952) Beitrag zur Frage der optischen Agnosie, *Arch. Psychiat. Nervenkr.*, **188**, 131–161.

1068. FLUGEL, J. C. (1945) A Hundred Years of Psychology, 5th imp., London, Duckworth.

1069. GERSTMANN, J. (1940) The phenomenon of body rotation in frontal lobe lesions, *J. nerv. ment. Dis.*, **92**, 36–40.

1070. GOLDSTEIN, K. (1923) Zur Frage der Restitution nach umschriebenem Hirndefekt, *Schweiz. Arch. Neurol. Psychiat.*, **13**, 283–296.
—— (1939) (see No. 1008).

1071. —— (1952) The effect of brain damage on the personality, *Psychiat.*, **15**, 245–260.

1072. HORSLEY, V. (1909) The Linacre Lecture. The function of the so-called motor area of the brain, *Brit. med. J.*, **2**, 125–132.

1073. JACKSON, J. HUGHLINGS (1874) On the nature of the duality of the brain. Reprinted (1915) in *Brain*, **38**, 80–103.

1074. —— (1876) Case of large cerebral tumour without optic neuritis and with left hemiplegia and imperception, 1932, Selected Writings, **2**, 146–152, London, Hodder & Stoughton.

1075. —— (1887) Remarks on evolution and dissolution of the nervous system, (1932), Selected Writings, **2**, 92–118.

1076. KATZ, D. (1951) Gestalt Psychology (translated by R. Tyson), London, Methuen.

KEITH, A. (1925) (see No. 80).

KLEIST, K. (1934) (see No. 449).

1077. KOEHLER, W. (1947) Gestalt Psychology, New York, Liveright.

LEYTON, O., and SHERRINGTON, C. (1917) (see No. 189).

1078. LIDDELL, E. G. T., and PHILLIPS, C. G. (1951) Overlapping areas in the motor cortex of the baboon, *J. Physiol.*, **112**, 392–399.

1079. MALIS, L. I., PRIBRAM, K. H., and KRUGER, L. (1952). Action potentials of motor cortex evoked by peripheral nerve stimulation, *Fed. Proc.*, **11**, 99–100.

1080. MILES, W. R. (1939) Visual-tactual illusions from a crystal ball, *Amer. J. Psychol.*, **52**, 449–452.

1081. MILLS, C. K., and FRAZIER, C. H. (1908–9) A brain tumour localized and completely removed, with some discussion of the symptomatology of lesions variously distributed in the parietal lobes, *Penn. med. Bull., Pa.*, **21**, 186–194.

von MONAKOW, C. (1914) (see No. 330).

MUNK, H. (1890) (see No. 110).

1082. PAVLOV, I. P. (1928) Lectures on conditioned reflexes, translated from the Russian by W. H. Gantt, London, Lawrence.

PENFIELD, W., and BOLDREY, E. (1937) (see No. 200).

RASMUSSEN, T., and PENFIELD, W. (1950) (see No. 203).

RIESE, W. (1950) (see No. 223).

1083. RIESE, W., and HOFF, E. C. (1950) A history of the doctrine of cerebral localization. I. Sources, anticipations and basic reasoning, *J. Hist. Med.*, **5**, 50–71.

1084. —— —— (1950) II. Methods and main results, *ibid.*, **6**, 439–470.

1085. RUSSELL, W. R. (1951) Parietal lobe syndromes, *Proc. roy. Soc. Med.*, **44**, 341–343.

1086. SEITELBERGER, F. (1952) Ein anatomisch untersuchter Fall von akustischer Allästhesie, *Wien Z. Nervenheilk.*, **4**, 411–423.

1087. SOURY, J. (1899) Rapports du lobe pariétal avec le développement de l'intelligence, *Le système nerveux central*, **2**, 1002, Paris, Carré et Naud.

1088. WALSHE, F. M. R. (1943) On the mode of representation of movements in the motor cortex with special reference to " convulsions beginning unilaterally " (Jackson), *Brain*, **66**, 104–139.

—— (1947) (see No. 205).

1089. —— (1948) Critical Studies in Neurology, Edinburgh, Livingstone.

1090. —— (1951) Lloyd Roberts Lecture : The arts of medicine and their future, *Lancet*, **2**, 895–899.

1091. WECHSLER, I. S. (1924) On the difficulty of utilizing aphasic symptoms in the localization of brain tumors : with a report of 4 cases, *J. nerv. ment. Dis.*, **59**, 31–38.

1092. WORSTER-DROUGHT, C., and CARNEGIE DICKSON, W. E. (1927) Venous angioma of the cerebrum, *J. Neurol. Psychopath.*, **8**, 19–22.

1093. YOUNG, J. Z. (1951) 1950 B.B.C. Reith Lectures. Doubt and Certainty in Science, Oxford, Clarendon Press.

INDEX

Date Due